ODORS
Physiology and Control

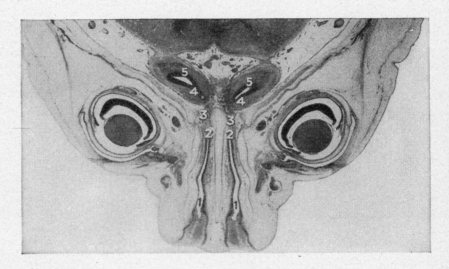

FRONTISPIECE. Vertical section presenting developing olfactory areas (crown—rump length 39 mm. Menstrual age, 10½ weeks). Human being.

1. Nasal passages.
2. Region of olfactory mucosa.
3. Indicates total length of olfactory nerve.
4. Olfactory bulb.
5. Ventricle of olfactory bulb which does not persist into adult life in human beings.

(Courtesy of Dr. George L. Streeter.)

ODORS
Physiology and Control

by

CAREY P. MCCORD

*The Industrial Health Conservancy
Laboratories, Detroit*

and

WILLIAM N. WITHERIDGE

*Ventilation Consultant
General Motors Corporation
Detroit*

FIRST EDITION

McGRAW-HILL BOOK COMPANY, INC.

NEW YORK   LONDON   TORONTO

1949

ODORS: PHYSIOLOGY AND CONTROL

PREFACE

THE AUTHORS have attempted in this book a summary of the latest knowledge of the perception, measurement, classification, control, and elimination of odors, and an appraisal of the significance of odors in relation to health, emotional life, economics, and related legal problems. It is believed that the present work is the first full-length technical book to appear in the United States that deals completely with the subject of odors, particularly those odors which are classified as offensive.

The material here offered will, it is hoped, provide those interested with a working knowledge of olfactory physiology and anatomy, the hedonics of odors, the relationship between health and odors, the control and abatement of odor nuisances, and the legal statutes pertaining to such control, together with a broad survey of the extant literature of the field. It has been the authors' intention also to provide opportunity for the upgrading of such knowledge in the numerous scientific fields in which odors now present special difficulties. Specifically, the book advances a new theory of odor stimulation, provides extensive information on a wide variety of measures for the elimination of odors from factories, homes, public buildings, and the person, and includes what is thought to be the first substantially complete odor bibliography in the English language.

Quite understandably, the search for odor knowledge has hitherto been chiefly directed to the perfumes and other pleasant aromas. Proportionately little, however, has been achieved in revealing the intricacies of odor physiology or the abatement of noisome odors. The filling in of this gap has been the primary purpose of the present work. Starting with the common ground of odor physiology, emphasis is early shifted to the significance and control of offensive odors. The authors have drawn freely, and not always with adequate credit, upon the investigations of many diligent early workers in the field of olfaction. They have profited by the counsel, guidance, or services of the following persons to whom they acknowledge with gratitude their indebtedness: Drs. George L. Streeter, C. Judson Herrick, Normand L. Hoerr, and Harold C. Voris for photographic material relative to the olfactory brain; to Dr. Elizabeth Crosby for continuing guidance on olfactory brain anatomy; to Dr. Bradley M. Patten for photographic material relative to sudoriparous and allied glands; to Dr. Clayton R. Lewis and James Lunan for guidance in the concepts of the olfactory apparatus as electrical systems; to Arthur R. Youtz and his associates of Florida Chemical Research, Inc., for the major portion of the bibliographic material; to the U.S. Bureau of Mines for various materials, including illustrations not subject to copyright; to Mrs. Edward Dart for library research and preliminary preparation of certain chapters; to Sue Biethan, medical librarian of the University of Michigan, for library services; to Dr. W. L. Shields for historic items; to *Punch* for permission to use historical cartoons; to Dr. R. W. Moncrieff and his publishers, Leonard Hill, Ltd., for permission to incorporate extensive quotations from "The Chemical Senses"; to David Ronald, formerly chief engineer, Department of Health, Scotland, and his publisher, William Hodge and Company, Ltd., London, for authority to introduce extensive quotations; to the publishers of *Consumers' Research Bulletin* and the director of research, E. J. Schlink, for the use of a great many data concerned with the properties of commercial body deodorants.

They are especially indebted to F. H. Munkelt, of the W. B. Connor Engineering Corporation, for generous advice and consultation in the field of odor adsorption; to John P. Harris, of the Industrial Chemical Sales Division, West Virginia Paper and Pulp Company, for extensive material on the adsorption of odors in potable water supplies; to A. E. Griffin of the Wallace and Tiernan Company for valuable assistance on the problems of chlorination for odor control; and to H. S. Winnicki of the Westvaco Chlorine Products Corporation for practical guidance on engineering problems in industrial odor control.

Further thanks are due Claude B. Schneible of the C. B. Schneible Company of Detroit for advice on the subject of gas and vapor retention by scrubbers and washers and to the Schutte-Koerting Company of Philadelphia for material on the scrubbing and condensing of obnoxious odors in many industrial applications.

Grateful acknowledgment is made to William C. Hoad, emeritus professor, Prof. Earnest Boyce, and H. E. Miller of the University of Michigan for criticisms and suggestions; to Louis Dodson of the National Sanitation Foundation, Ann Arbor, for important information on the use of sanitary land fills for industrial and community odor control in relation to difficult problems of waste disposal; to A. C. Funke of the West Disinfecting Company for helpful material on the control of odors in sanitary facilities of industrial and commercial buildings; to Dr. W. G. Fredrick of the Detroit Department of Health for consultation on the chemical destruction of odorous substances; to H. C. Murphy of the American Air Filter Company for reference materials on odor control in air conditioning; to F. A. Patty of General Motors Corporation for information on the use of odorous warning agents in flammable and toxic gaseous materials; and to A. R. Behnke of the Naval Medical Research Institute for reports of studies of odor control.

Debts of appreciation are due various other authors and their publishers for authority to make quotations and duplicate illustrations. In the main, credit is extended directly in connection with the quotations or illustrations as they appear in the text.

CAREY P. McCORD
WILLIAM N. WITHERIDGE

Detroit, Mich.
January, 1949

CONTENTS

Introduction

PRESENT-DAY man lives in a world harboring a greater number of odoriferous materials than ever before. At the same time, the total number of downright stenches has lessened. All the old unpleasant odors may be encountered in some places, but no longer are they an inescapable commonplace of daily life. The bathtub, the water carriage of body wastes, refrigeration, and disinfectants have mitigated the olfactory load, but the percentage of persons still lacking these refinements is distressingly high even in the United States.

In urban life for every disagreeable odor that has been brought under substantial control as a community objective, there probably have appeared two newer ones, although these are likely to be of less intensity, and only rarely are entire communities involved. These newer odors are chiefly related to industry or the products of industry. On a single morning the urbanite might encounter 25 different nasal offenders that were wholly unknown to his great-grandfathers: leaky gas from the kitchen, motor exhaust in his garage, the patient with a treatment with iodoform on the streetcar, the scrubwoman and her cresolic washing compounds, a passage by the egg dehydration plant, gases from an oil-burning furnace, odors from a near-by foundry, and odors from ozone machines installed to combat other odors.

The colonial American had his own industries, few in number, simple in nature, but frequently exasperatingly productive of odors. The operations aboard a New England whaler after a catch must have fully taxed the endurance of all noses aboard and robbed other odors of their significance. Slaughterhouses, tan yards, candlemaking, fisheries, and other early industries are credited with a share in the disturbances of the peace of mind of the country's forefathers. In fine regard for the neighborhood, the majority of the operators of offensive trades built their plants apart from the community proper—this to their credit. More often than not, residences have been brought to proximity of offensive industries rather than the reverse.

Man's perception of odors perhaps never was equal to that of some of the lower animals. Such a statement must be safeguarded, since among contemporary little-civilized groups some entire tribes are credited with ability to follow scents with all the facility of bloodhounds. Among more highly developed persons, a few individuals have retained or acquired exquisite skill in the detection of slight variations in odors, such, for example, as differentiate types of tobaccos. In a household with several children, the mother may associ-

1

ate with each child or other family member a constant distinctive odor regardless of similar habits of bathing, eating, sleeping, and the use of drugs or perfumes. Confronted with so many instances of acute capacity for odor detection and designation, no insistence is here introduced that for man the olfactory sense is a degenerating one. Rather, emphasis is directed to the scant use in modern life of the olfactory sense to many useful ends.

That we live in a world teeming with odoriferous substances is daily dramatized by every dog in the community. Man's inequality in this regard still leaves him with the fact that more than half the endless variety of things that surround him possess some odor, albeit the majority are indifferent ones. Little attention is attracted by other than highly pleasing or highly offensive ones.

The thousands of materials that lead to the sensation of odor are termed "osmyls." "Osmics" is an acceptable term that embraces the field of science concerned with smell. Rightly applied, osmics is the science of the stimuli, organs, and sense of smell. Precisely applied, the term "odor" perhaps should be limited to the sensation of odor perception and not be extended to the chemical that induces the sensation. So widespread is the dual usage of such terms as "odors," "scents," "smells" that no attempt will here be made regularly to segregate application to any restricted meaning.

For these highly numerous osmyls, a generous language provides wide choice in overlapping terms. The greater number indicate that the odor is pleasant or, instead, disagreeable. Thus for pleasant odors we find such designations as "fragrance," "aroma," "perfume," "redolence," "bouquet," for foul odors, "stinks," "stenches," "fetor," "fetidness," "mephitis," "nidor," "putrescence." Within these categories, this book is foremostly concerned with the latter group.

Just what is an offensive odor is well individualized. The most exotic of perfumes becomes offensive if it reaches into the subconscious or the conscious past and ignites unpleasant associations. No claim may be made that an odor is offensive only if disturbing to all exposed persons. Always a few persons are unaware of offense from such odors as throw the majority into a protesting uproar. Some odors portending cleanliness may disturb because of their chief applications. Thus pine oil, in itself scarcely offensive, is by some so closely associated with the cleaning of toilets as to acquire all the onus connected with the toilets themselves.

Circumstances usually determine the degree of disaffection occasioned by malodors. It may be doubted that the handful of men and women on Noah's Ark, traditionally representing as they did the sole survivors of the human race, with their own existence moment by moment threatened and altogether with little assurance of security, complained of animal odors about the place. There were other things to occupy the mind. If in fact all the persons claimed to have reached this country on the Mayflower were aboard, body odors in the absence of tubs, showers, and adequate water must have been considerable. However, this group appears to have been more concerned with its immediate and early security than with odors. Contrariwise, more than one fashionable home wedding has been rated a social catastrophe because kitchen servants, excited and temporarily neglectful, permitted the wedding-feast toast to burn at the moment of the wedding march. The shade of offense from odors is measured by time, place, occasion, and inurement.

Granting endless opportunities for disagreement, for the objectives of this book an offensive odor is one that, from its own properties, chemical and physical, is disturbing to the majority of healthy persons exposed to its olfactory action.

Without, on the one hand, condoning all the disturbances attributed to offensive odors or, on the other, rejecting all significance of offensive odors, this book has been devised to make available, in objective fashion, personal and accumulated experience related to odors in general but chiefly to the offensive ones, their control, and their import in the human communality.

Chapter I

The Anatomy of the Olfactory System

THROUGHOUT the earth, many substances—animal, vegetable, and mineral—possess properties that are disclosed to animal life forms as odors. These odors are significant in the procurement of food, in the detection and repelling of enemies, in the pursuit of sex functions, in the rejection of the unsuitable, and in special orientation. So significant is this olfactory faculty that, in many species, specialized tissues and mechanisms have been set apart for the prehension and translation into consciousness of these properties identified as odors.

Behind the physiology of odor perception stand four anatomic arrangements, namely: (1) the tissues concerned in the odor stimulus perception; (2) the vomeronasal nerve and Jacobson's organ; (3) the tissues involved in the translation into awareness or consciousness; and (4) the trigeminal nerve. In introducing descriptions of these structures, the desire is to present the human olfactory apparatus; but, unfortunately, man is microsmatic and in adult human life, some structures are entirely absent or are present only as vestigia. Consequently, recourse must be had to some extent to the macrosmatic species. In some macrosmatics, such as the opossum, more than one-third of the entire brain is dedicated to olfaction (Figs. 1–3).

THE TISSUES CONCERNED IN THE ODOR STIMULUS PERCEPTION

Terminal Receptors.—The end organs for odor perception are peculiar in that they are associated with the only sense in which the primary neuron (of the cranial nerve) itself is the receptor or is closely identified with the receptor. This perceptive apparatus is bilaterally located high in the nasal vault immediately beneath the cribriform plate of the ethmoid bone and spreading over a small portion of the topmost part of the nasal septum and the adjacent turbinate tissue as well. The ordinary mucous membrane of the nasal area is not involved in odor perception. In the area mentioned (Figs. 4, 5), a specialized mucous membrane representing not more than 500 sq. mm. is distinguishable from ordinary nasal mucous membrane by its yellow or brownish yellow color, which is due to a pigment content, presumably a modified melanin. This area contains at least three and possibly four types of cells. The commonest cell is a high columnar type of

5

epithelium, which provides the bed or support for the more important olfactory nerve terminals shortly to be mentioned. Proximally, these supporting cells taper sharply and ultimately some may undergo ramification (Fig.
6). A second group of cells, the basal cells, appear to represent partially
developed supporting cells and apparently are held in reserve as spares
against injury to the more highly developed ones. Cells of the third type,
the bipolar nerve cells, are the true olfactory sense prehenders (Fig. 7).
They are relatively few in number and are well embedded in the supporting
and basal cells. The dendrite is remarkably long, being as much as 200
microns in some species, and is known to have a high lipin content. This
hairlike organ is believed to be essential to odor prehension. The distal end,
which projects beyond the mucosal surface, expands slightly to form an
olfactory tuft or a vesicle or both. While proof is lacking, it may be true
that a vesicle exists that is equipped with six or eight projections or possibly
a fimbria and that within this vesicle are located numerous free-moving
granules of functional import.

The numbers of these granular bipolar cells are undetermined, but from
the axon content of the olfactory nerve fila it may appear that the figures
300 to 800 encompass the number of bipolar cells.

The possibility of a fourth type of cell in the olfactory mucous membrane
was mentioned. This represents a modified epithelium within one layer of
the mucous membrane, which constitutes glands—the glands of Bowman.
The secreted serous fluid possibly acts as a solvent for odoriferous substances
and thus may constitute an essential in the several steps of odor perception.

From the proximal end of the bipolar cells run the axons in olfactory
nerve fila. These nerve fiber bundles, about 20 on each side, pass in un-
myelinated state through foramina of the cribriform plate to the olfactory
bulb, there synapsing with the second olfactory neuron. It would thus appear
that this single first neuron constitutes the entire course of the olfactory
nerve and thus by far is the shortest of all cranial nerves. Considering the
entire olfactory apparatus as an electrical communication system, or comparable thereto, these bipolar receptor cells represent the antennae.

The Olfactory Bulb.—An essence of the difference in olfactory capacity
between the microsmatic and macrosmatic animals may be due to the variations in size and functional activity of the olfactory bulb (Fig. 8). This
portion of the brain lies just above the cribriform plate, on either side, is
roughly date-shaped in man, but smaller, and in adult man is without a
ventricle. It is connected with other portions of the rhinencephalon by the
olfactory tract.

Before discussion of the detailed structure of the olfactory bulb, it is
noted that this organ, without well-defined demarcation, is segmented in two
planes. The arrangement is both like the interior of an orange and of an

Fig. 1.—Brain of opossum, *Didelphis virginiana*. Lateral aspect. 1, olfactory fila (exaggerated) ; 2, olfactory bulb; 3, olfactory tract; 4, tubercle olfactorium; 5, optic nerve; 6, pituitary; 7, pyriform lobe cortex; 8, nonolfactory cortex; 9, rhinal fissure; 10, orbital fissure; 12 to 16, cranial nerves; 17, cerebellum. (*From Streeter model, courtesy of Voris and Hoerr.*)

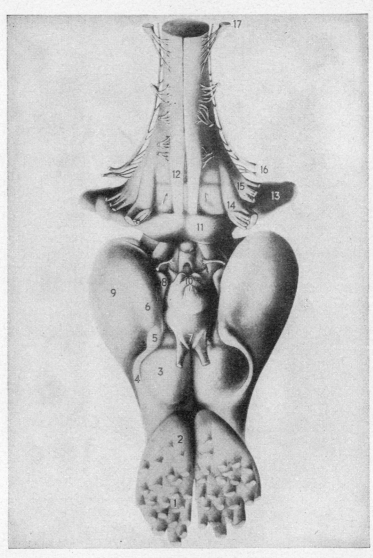

FIG. 2.—Brain of opossum, *Didelphis virginiana*. Ventral aspect. 1, olfactory fila; 2, olfactory bulb; 3, tubercle olfactorium; 4, lateral olfactory tract; 5, nucleus of lateral olfactory tract; 6, amygdala; 7, optic chiasm; 8, uncus; 9, pyriform lobe; 10, region of hypophysis; 11, pons; 12, pyramid; 13, paraflocculus; 14 to 17, cranial and spinal nerves. (*From Streeter model, courtesy of Voris and Hoerr.*)

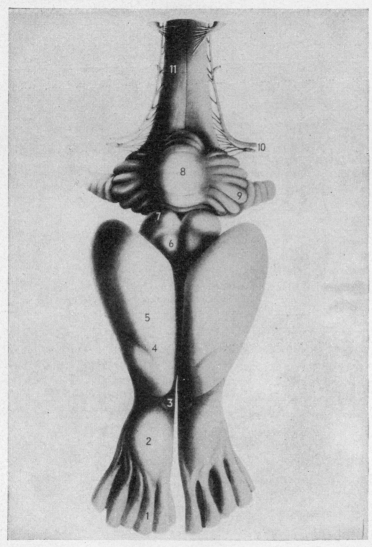

Fig. 3.—Brain of opossum, *Didelphis virginiana*. Dorsal aspect. 1, olfactory fila; 2, olfactory bulb; 3, accessory olfactory bulb; 4, 5, nonolfactory cortex; 6, superior colliculus; 7, inferior colliculus; 8, cerebellum; 9, region of paraflocculus; 10, cranial nerve; 11, medulla. (*From Streeter model, courtesy of Voris and Hoerr.*)

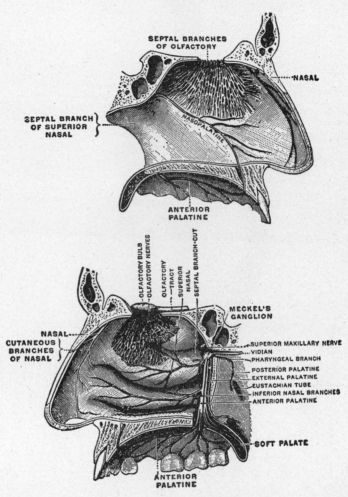

SEPTAL BRANCHES
OF OLFACTORY

NASAL

SEPTAL BRANCH
OF SUPERIOR
NASAL

NASOPALATINE

ANTERIOR
PALATINE

OLFACTORY BULB
OLFACTORY NERVES
OLFACTORY
TRACT
SUPERIOR
NASAL
SEPTAL BRANCH-CUT

MECKEL'S
GANGLION

NASAL
CUTANEOUS
BRANCHES
OF NASAL

SUPERIOR MAXILLARY NERVE
VIDIAN
PHARYNGEAL BRANCH
POSTERIOR PALATINE
EXTERNAL PALATINE
EUSTACHIAN TUBE
INFERIOR NASAL BRANCHES
ANTERIOR PALATINE

SOFT PALATE

ANTERIOR
PALATINE

Figs. 4 and 5.—Schematic drawing indicating site of olfactory mucosa. (*Millard and King,* "*Human Anatomy and Physiology*," *W. B. Saunders Company, from Testut.*)

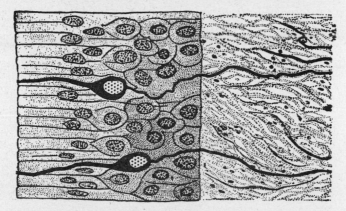

FIG. 6.—Vertical section of the olfactory mucous membrane prepared by silver technique. The olfactory cells with axons and dendrites are in heavy black. Mucosal surface at left. (*Schaeffer, "Morris' Human Anatomy," P. Blakiston's Son & Co.*)

The nerves below are the only ones actually exposed to the outside of the body skin or mucous membrane. These

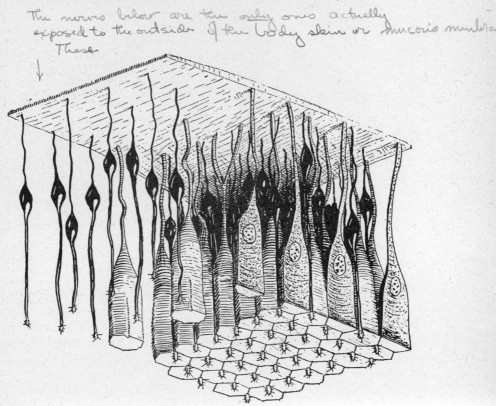

FIG. 7.—Stereogram of olfactory epithelium. Olfactory cells, black, supporting cells, light. (*Krieg, "Functional Neuro-anatomy," P. Blakiston's Son & Co.*)

onion. In the orangelike clefting it is octofid. In the onionlike segmentation there exist five concentric areas or zones. In the concept of the olfactory brain as an electrical system, the olfactory bulb is the intensifier or amplifier and the relay. The subsequent description of the intimate arrangements of the bulb rather closely adheres to that of Krieg:[1] The bulb is divided into five conventional layers (Fig. 9). The periphery of the bulb is covered by a matting of primary olfactory fibers, which, grouped into minute bundles, pass to the second or glomerular layer to terminate in compact globular tangles, the olfactory glomeruli. The termination of each fiber is fairly simple, but the unusual grouping of a number of endings into one mass accounts for the complexity (Fig. 10).

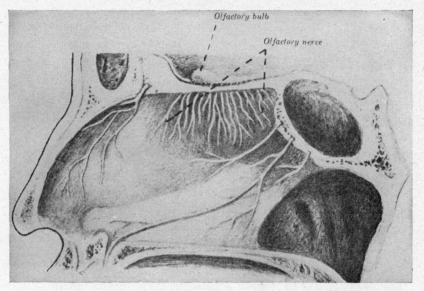

Fig. 8.—Location of olfactory bulb, with cribriform plate and olfactory nerve fila beneath. (*Kuntz, "Neuro-anatomy," Lea & Febiger.*)

From each glomerulus emerges the dendrite of the secondary olfactory fiber. Its ramification within the glomerulus is different in character from that of the primary axon, being radially disposed. Each secondary ramification gathers into a single large dendrite, which enters a pyramidal cell body called the "mitral cell" from its resemblance to a bishop's miter. These cells are arranged in a distinct layer. Each mitral cell receives several such dendrites, which ramify in the cell-scant layer outside the mitral cell zone but do not take part in the formation of glomeruli. The axons of the mitral

[1] KRIEG, "Functional Neuro-anatomy," The Blakiston Company, Philadelphia, 1942.

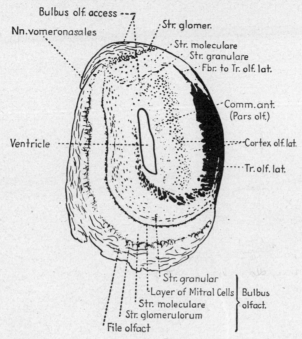

Bulbus olf. access
Nn. vomeronasales
Str. glomer.
Str. moleculare
Str. granulare
Fbr. to Tr. olf. lat.
Comm. ant. (Pars olf.)
Ventricle
Cortex olf. lat.
Tr. olf. lat.
Str. granular
Layer of Mitral Cells
Str. moleculare
Str. glomerulorum
File olfact
Bulbus olfact.

Fig. 9.—Zones within olfactory bulb of opossum as found in transverse section through caudal portion. (*Courtesy of McCotter and The Anatomical Record.*)

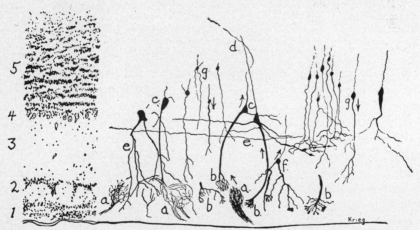

Fig. 10.—Structure of olfactory bulb. Adult rat. Left: Nissl section; right: details from Golgi preparations. 1, olfactory nerve; 2, glomeruli; 3, outer plexiform layer; 4, mitral cells; 5, granule cells; (*a*), olfactory glomeruli; (*b*), tufts of mitral dendrites; (*c*), mitral cell body; (*d*), mitral cell axon—to olfactory tracts; (*e*), mitral cell collaterals—to plexiform layer; (*f*), small tufted cells; (*g*), granule cells. (*Krieg, "Functional Neuro-anatomy," P. Blakiston's Son & Co.*)

cells plunge deep into the olfactory bulb, forming cumulatively a fibrous core, which is the olfactory projection tract. In the deeper layers the axons send off collaterals that ramify within the bulb (Fig. 11).

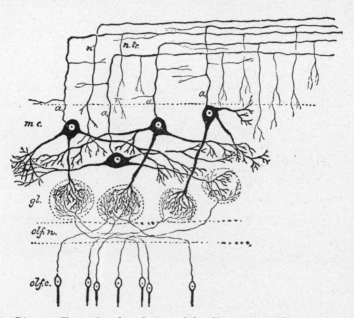

Fig. 11.—Diagram illustrating the relations of the olfactory nerve fibers to the neurons of the second order in the olfactory bulb. olf.c., olfactory nerve cells in the olfactory epithelium; olf.n., olfactory nerve; mc., mitral cells; gl. olfactory glomeruli; n.tr., olfactory tract. (*Schäfer, "Organs of the Senses," Longmans, Green & Co., Inc.*)

Similar to the mitral cells, but smaller, are the tufted cells whose axons, finer in caliber, cross to the opposite olfactory bulb through the anterior component of the anterior commissure, ramifying freely in the deeper layers of the bulb at their termination.

The above arrangement is the basic plan for relay of olfactory impulses; but the olfactory bulb apparently also has an elaborate mechanism for intensifying the olfactory impulses, which certainly must be of a very low intensity, considering the infinitesimal amounts of odoriferous substances required to incite a sensation. This intensification is effected by the numerous granule cells. Granular cells of one type, the less numerous one, are situated in the glomerular layer. Impulses from their dendritic endings, distributed among several adjacent glomeruli, are accumulated in the axon, which discharges into mitral dendrites on deeper granule cells. The deeper granule cells, numerous and arranged in little groups, form a thick layer; they receive dendrites from the deeper plexiform layers and synapse with axons from mitral cells. The granular-cell axons run toward the surface of the bulb and synapse with the extra dendrites of the mitral cells described above. Thus, a circular or reverberating conducting system is formed: from the mitral cell collaterals, through the granule cells, where it is stepped up, and thus augmented returns to the mitral cells. The fact that olfactory impulses are not localized makes this mechanism feasible. Such an arrangement in the cochlea, for example, would be destructive of all distinction between tones.

The Olfactory Tract.—In the conventional description of the olfactory tract, it is customary to indicate that it is (in the human) merely a slender bundle of afferent and efferent fibers, between the olfactory bulb and the lowermost of the higher brain centers, dividing in its course into three striae, the lateral, medial, and intermediate, with some variations as to terminals and some communication to the tract of the opposite side.

It is possible that the odor stimulus as it reaches the primary neuron may represent a specific signal or, instead, that by the time the signal reaches the second neuron provision has been made for identity or selection. The olfactory bulb clearly is structurally, unadapted to selection, so that, if odor selection on a unit basis does not derive from the primary neuron, on the basis of anatomic economy it probably occurs in the area represented by the proximal portion of the bulb, the olfactory tract, and its primary connections, such as the tubercle olfactorious. However, proof for this is lacking.

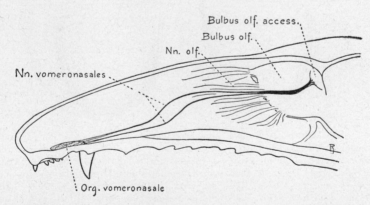

Fig. 12.—Median section of the head of an opossum with the mandible and nasal septum removed to show the course and connections of the vomeronasal nerves. Natural size. (*Courtesy of McCotter and The Anatomical Record.*)

THE VOMERONASAL NERVE AND JACOBSON'S ORGAN

In the human embryo, but not in the human adult, and in certain macrosmatic species, there exists an auxiliary olfactory mechanism apart from the true olfactory one. This is well developed, for example, in the opossum, as has been described by McCotter.[1] This investigator states that the fibers arising from the vomeronasal organ (Jacobson's organ) and the fibers connected with the accessory olfactory bulb are for the opossum one and the same and that the vomeronasal nerves represent the combined filaments from the vomeronasal organ and are the only fibers received in the accessory olfactory bulb. This Jacobson's organ is believed to be located further forward and downward along the wall of the nasal septum. In brief, this represents an accessory olfactory apparatus, the special function of which is unknown (Fig. 12).

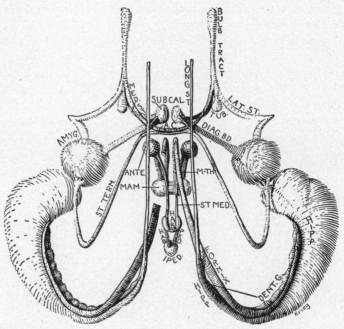

Fig. 13.—Reconstruction of human rhinencephalon as seen from above. Amyg., amygdala; Ante. Comm., A.C., anterior commissure; Ante., anterior nucleus of thalamus; Bulb, olfactory bulb; Comm. Hipp., hippocampal commissure; Dent.G., dentate gyrus; Diag. Bd., diagonal band; Hab., habenula; Hab. ped., habenulopeduncular tract; Hipp., hippo-campus; Iped., interpeduncular nucleus; Lat. St., lateral olfactory stria; Long. St., longitudinal stria; Mam., mammillary body; Med. St., medial olfactory stria; M.F.B., medial forebrain bundle; M.-th., mammillothalamic tract; St.Med., stria medullaris; St. Term, stria terminalis; Subcal., subcallosal gyrus; Tract., olfactory tract; Tub., olfactory tubercle. (*Krieg, "Functional Neuro-anatomy," P. Blakiston's Son & Co.*)

TISSUES INVOLVED IN ODOR TRANSLATION INTO AWARENESS OR CONSCIOUSNESS

Thus far, the anatomic forms mentioned are chiefly concerned with odor registration, intensification, and selection. Beyond the tubercle olfactorious

[1] McCotter, R. E., The Connection of the Vomeronasal Nerves with the Accessory Olfactory Bulb in the Opossum and Other Mammals, *Anat. Record*, **6**, 299 (1912).

and possibly including that facility, the remaining portions of the rhinencephalon are dedicated to translation into consciousness. Ample provision is made through commissures for connections with the opposite side, so that usually olfaction is a birhinal matter. This interpretative area of the rhinencephalon consists of a complex series of brain nuclei. High ranking among these nuclei are the amygdaloid and pyriform areas. Here the overlapping sensations of odor, taste, and touch are appraised. Other units entering into odor discrimination, along with intricate connective ramifications, are the subcallosal gyrus, the hippocampus, the uncus, the dentate nucleus, the fornix, and the mammillary body (Figs. 13, 14). Ultimately the rhinencephalon is in communication with all other portions of brain and nervous system; for example, ovarian dysfunction through reflex action may modify odor per-

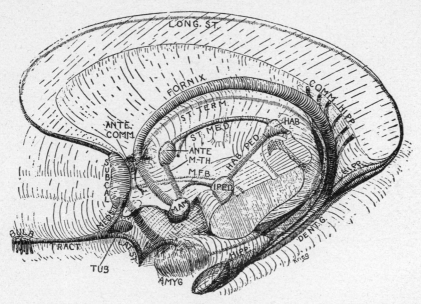

Fɪɢ. 14.—Reconstruction of human rhinencephalon, as seen in a ventromedial view of the right cerebrum. (*Krieg, "Functional Neuro-anatomy," P. Blakiston's Son & Co.*)

ception. Adhering to the concept of the rhinencephalon as an electrical system, it may be observed that primary olfactory stimulation excites characteristic action potentials in the hippocampus.

INTERRELATION WITH TRIGEMINAL NERVE

For a long while confusion prevailed because of the belief that the trigeminal nerve is concerned with odor perception. Indeed, branches of the trigeminal nerve pervade various portions of the nasal mucous membrane

* *su: Ann. Otol. Rhinol. & Laryngol. 69 398-409 (June 1960)*
L. M. Beidler reports that trigeminal nerves are stimulated even by mild odors

and possibly Jacobson's organ. It is probable that the trigeminal receives stimuli, on a common chemical sense basis, related to odors but not precisely representing odors. These qualities are suggested in the term "cooling, irritating, acrid, pungent" and may be associated, for example, with such substances as ammonia, chlorine, or pepper. The desire is to separate these irritant sensations from true odors and to relegate their perception to the trigeminal nerve. It thus becomes obvious that such a substance as peppermint, along with a myriad of others, might provoke sensations of both the trigeminal and the olfactory nerve.

Through design, this presentation of the anatomic features of the olfactory brain is of far lower order than the highly detailed descriptions of the neuro-anatomist. A need for minutiae may be met through readily accessible publications exclusively dedicated to brain anatomy.

Chapter II

The Physiology of the Olfactory Sense

THE MECHANISM through which a tiny area within the nasal fossae is able to receive an unlimited number of dissimilar odor stimuli, sometimes from remote distances and sometimes in dilutions as weak as one part in billions of air, constitutes a prime biologic mystery. In the case of the eye and ear, the perceiving apparatus is confronted only with a limited and precise range of vibration. Exactness attends these two sensations. For taste only four primary stimuli are involved. Not so for odors. The varieties of odor stimuli requiring appraisal and identification are to be reckoned by the tens of thousands, and possibly the capacity even in humans reaches to hundreds of thousands. In species more macrosmatic than man, the reach of the olfactory function is imponderable. Day by day new odors are appearing, all of which are immediately accepted within the seemingly unlimited categories of the olfactory brain.

Moncrieff has assembled 21 theories sponsored by divers investigators during relatively modern years. A few are nearly fantastic; a few are impressive; none is adequate to real understanding of the complex ramifications of olfaction. Any acceptable theory, according to Moncrieff, must stand in relation to certain basic facts established for human olfaction. They are:

1. All normal people can smell.
2. People suffering from brain lesions, injured olfactory nerve or obstructed nasal passages may be anosmic.
3. Cases of preferential anosmia, *i.e.*, ability to sense certain smells and not others, are not well established. Such cases occur, but little is known of them.
4. Some substances are odorous, others are not.
5. We can smell at a distance. If we smell the roses in a garden we do not ordinarily consider part of the roses as being in contact with the nose (although corpuscles may in fact be so).
6. Substances of different chemical constitution may have similar odours.
7. Substances of similar constitution usually have similar odours, *e.g.*, in a homologous series. Nevertheless, isomers and even stereoisomers may have different odours.
8. Substances of high molecular weight are usually inodorous and often non-volatile and insoluble.
9. The quality as well as the strength of odour may change on dilution.
10. The sense of smell is rapidly fatigued.

19

11. Fatigue for one odour will not affect the perception of other dissimilar odours, but will interfere with the perception of similar odours.

12. Two or more odorous substances may cancel each other out. This compensation will mean that two odorous substances smelt together will be inodorous.

13. Odour travels down-wind.

14. Many animals have a keener sense of olfaction than man. Insects have such extraordinary keenness of smell that it may be a different modality of the chemical sense from that known to us.

All the substantial theories advanced to explain the nature of olfaction fall into two categories—the physical and the chemical. A mosaic of proof and opinion is now presented for each group.

THE PHYSICAL THEORY

According to the physical theory (Heyninx), odorous substances emit radiations of high frequency that directly transmit their energy or vibration to pigment granules in the olfactory receptors. The energy involved in olfactory stimulation in this theory is the characteristic molecular vibration of each specific odorous substance, and differences in odor are dependent upon differences in the wave lengths of the radiation emitted.

In support of this hypothesis, its sponsors have demonstrated that certain odorous substances in the gaseous state have absorption bands in the ultraviolet region of the spectrum (0.20 to 0.36 microns), while the absorption bands of the nonodorous substances tested fall outside this range. Some test substances in hyperconcentration presented complete absorption of ultraviolet rays with no separate bands, a finding that might be proffered in explanation of the fact that some perfumes in strong concentrations yield an indefinite, unrecognizable odor. In advocacy of the "radiation" theory, early investigators noted the apparent lack of diminution in mass of some strongly odorous substances. Musk, for instance, gives off an odor for years without appreciable loss in weight. Later, measurements in enclosed spaces under highly controlled conditions demonstrated the starkly minute quantities necessary for odor stimulation and thus apparently invalidated this support. If the hypothesis of olfactory resonance is to be admitted, the grains of olfactory pigment, or at least some particulate content of the cell, should possess diameters or some vibratory response comparable to the wave lengths of the exciting radiations. According to Heyninx, this is the case, and variation in particle size is sufficient to support the theory that specific granules respond to specific wave lengths (Fig. 1). That the olfactory pigment is involved in some manner is suggested by the common knowledge that some albinos are congenitally hyposmatic or even anosmatic. A report has been made of the case of a Negro who became leucodermic and at the same time lost the sense of smell.

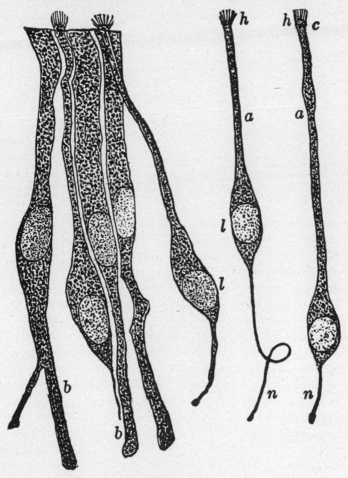

FIG. 1.—The multisized granules of olfactory bipolar cells are believed to be of functional import. *a,a*, olfactory cells; *b,b*, epithelial cells; *n,n*, central process prolonged as an olfactory nerve fibril; *l,l*, nucleus; *c*, knob-like clear termination of peripheral process; *h,h*, bunch of olfactory hairs. (*Howell, "Textbook of Physiology," W. B. Saunders Company.*)

THE CHEMICAL THEORY

According to the chemical or corpuscular theory of the mechanism of olfactory stimulation, it is claimed that odoriferous substances regularly emit chemical units (earlier referred to by its sponsors as *particles*), which as a rule are in gaseous form. These particles are conveyed to the olfactory epithelium by convection, diffusion, or both and directly or indirectly induce chemical changes in the olfactory receptors. The supporters of the chemical theory emphasize that odors are present only in the direction of air currents, and thus the implication is that this nullifies the radiation concept, since radiation may be expected to disperse in all directions, as does light. In still air, within a small, confined space, the rate of diffusion, though it varies widely, is roughly inverse to the molecular weight. These facts are held out in support of a gaseous or vaporous state as requisite to olfactory stimulation. The acceptor of the chemical theory faces, among other disputed points, this one: Does the stimulating substance act in the gaseous state when it reaches the olfactory area, or must it first dissolve in the serous fluid, which is always present about the supporting tissues? The early and sometimes current belief in stimulation only by a gas or vapor was somewhat shaken by the experiments of Aronsohn, who reported that solutions of odorous substances introduced directly into the nasal cavity induced weak odor signals usual for these respective substances. The ease with which gases leave solutions and the fact that only minute quantities are requisite to odor stimulation at once introduce question into the conclusion made. A worker after the time of Aronsohn, Zwaardemaker, claimed that these results were obtained by faulty procedures, namely, that air pockets were allowed to remain in the upper portion of the nasal cavities. Still another worker, Veres, sought to eliminate the air pockets and did in fact elicit some odor responses, but these were far below the level produced by gases or vapors per se. A fundamental protest has been made that few valid conclusions may be reached from the immersion of the nasal olfactory area in various fluids, since this may upset the normal functioning of a highly specific fluid there present for the solution of odorous materials.

There is no warrant for the full acceptance of either of these old theories. It is not known that either has been reexplored in the light of new developments in physics and chemistry. It would be convenient indeed to have established an odor spectrum in terms of chemical energy similar to the light spectrum generated by fluorescent and phosphorescent crystals, in turn excited by electron or ultraviolet rays. As Kahn states, "Light and sound are related to the energy spectrum. Why not odor as well?" It is possible that not enough attention has been paid to the apparent fact that all odorous substances are capable of reducing surface tensions, albeit not all surface-tension reducers are odorous. The possible degrees in surface-tension modification are scarcely sufficient to encompass the range of specific odors.

AN ELECTROCHEMICAL THEORY OF ODOR STIMULATION

Only on the basis of frankly labeled speculation are some new concepts presented, although behind every item mentioned are some established facts, chiefly as sponsored by Pauling.

The energy of the precise stimulus of odor receptors probably derives electrochemically from the odorous substance. The electron pattern within the molecule varies even for such kindred substances as O_2 (nonodorous) and O_3 (odorous). The available energy of the molecule is in part linked with the shared interatomic electrons. For all molecules with three or more atoms, the electron arrangement is conceived to exist as angles—bonding angles between the atoms. The total potential number of such angles is one less than the number of atoms within the molecule. Modification of the bonding angles at the moment of solution is believed to be associated with the rearrangement of the electrons with adjustments or alterations in potential or vibrational energy. Pauling thus epitomizes the general situation[1]:

The answers to many of the basic problems of biology—the nature of the process of growth, the mechanism of duplication of viruses, genes, and cells, the basis for the highly specific interactions of these structural constituents, the mode of action of enzymes, the mechanism of physiological activity of drugs, hormones, vitamins, and other chemical substances, the structure and action of nerve and brain tissue—the answers to all these problems are hiding in the remaining unknown region of the dimensional forest, mostly in the strip between 10 and 100 A., 10^{-7} and 10^{-6} cm.; and it is only by penetrating into this region that we can track them down.

And again:

Even the senses of taste and odor are based upon molecular configuration rather than upon ordinary chemical properties—a molecule which has the same shape as a camphor molecule will smell like camphor even though it may be quite unrelated to camphor chemically.[2]

Only for conceptional purposes may bonding angle shifts be regarded as analogous to the varying number of degrees marked by shifts in the legs of calipers. The electrical charge of the individual electron is constant and approximates one 2,300,000,000,000,000,000 $[1/(23\times10^{17})]$ part of the quantity of electricity utilized by a standard 40-watt 110-volt lamp per second. On the solution of an odorous substance on the olfactory mucosa, it is believed that the electrostatic fields are so altered or unbalanced as to provide a potential difference affecting the olfactory receptors there present for that very purpose. Since bonding angles are susceptible to infinite degrees of change, the energy modifications are likewise infinitely variable and somewhat specific for the individual molecule. If not specific those yielding the same energy alteration will stimulate the same odor sensation from highly dissimilar chemical substances.

In a single molecule many bonding angles may exist, but in the impact upon receptors the energy charges involved therein at the solution moment may be believed to act not individually but on a net basis. Thus the bonding

---

[1] Molecular Architecture and Biological Reactions, *Chem. Eng. News*, **24**, 1375 (May 25, 1946),

[2] *Chem. Eng. News*, **24**, 1065 (1946).

angle energy of some single radical within the molecule may constitute the sole trigger providing the signal to the receptor area. Notwithstanding all the negative implications (later to appear in the chapter devoted to chemical constitution and odors), chemical structure as it influences bonding angle energy readjustment within the molecule at the solution moment may be the determinant of odor.

Without any denial that bonding angle energy may be modified under circumstances other than solution, it may be observed that, in the olfactory train of actions, solution on or within the olfactory mucosal bed is an

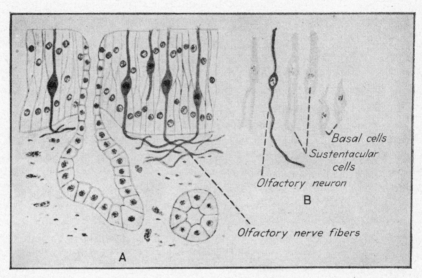

Fig. 2.—The solution function of olfactory mucosa is suggested in schematic drawing derived from Hardesty. (*Kuntz, "Neuro-anatomy," Lea & Febiger.*)

essential (Fig. 2). Likewise, the immediate nearness of the receptors to the wet mucosal bed appears essential. In delegating to the molecule specificity as to olfactory signal, some degree of selectivity may be accorded the pigmented granules of the bipolar cells, primary or secondary, being conditional upon the possession by the olfactory tubercles of selective rather than universal responsiveness to the bonding angle energy.

It follows that a nonodorous substance is (*a*) one with no bonding angle(s); (*b*) one insusceptible of solution in the mucosal fluids and at the olfactory receptor face; (*c*) one rejected by the higher rhinencephalon on the basis of habituation; (*d*) one that has an energy potential of a character for which there is no corresponding receptor; or (*e*) one in which the molecular concentration is so high as to glut the receptor to functional incapacity.

These concepts, insofar as acceptable, at once remove some of the enigmas of olfaction:

Odors are derivable only from gases and vapors because of the functional necessity of a high degree of molecular dispersion.

Solids and liquids in truth may be soluble at the bipolar face, but the density of molecules disrupts the mechanism.

Multiple substances of unrelated chemical nature may provoke the same odor because the bonding angle energy is of the same order.

Two or more odorous substances in mixture may produce odor cancellation and absence of all odor impaction. This results from intermolecular satisfaction and adjustment of energy potentials without availability to the receptor.

High concentrations of gases and vapors strongly odorous in diffuse molecular state may be inodorous for the same reason that dissolved solids and liquids are inodorous.

Loss of odor perception in the presence of some types of rhinitis issues from the edematous submersion of the receptors.

Multiplicity of odor perceptions apart from a dominant odor is reasonable, since every unit of impurity or admixture in gaseous or vaporous state may thrust its own bonding angle energy upon appropriate receptors.

Monatomic substances are inodorous since they possess no bonding angle.

This theory provides no ready explanation[1] for the common experience that some substances in low concentrations provoke one sensation while for higher levels the odor may be indubitably different. For taste a similar paradox may arise. For example, a little saccharin may induce the taste of pronounced sweetness while somewhat more leads to equally definite bitterness.

Manifestly, the power of the primary signal is weak. The architecture of the olfactory bulb with its further neurons at once suggests amplification, intensification, and quantitation. This implicates no violation of the law of conservation of energy, since additional energy requirements are supplied through other circuits. However, odor quantitation in part resides in higher centers as a volitional facility (Fig. 3).

Granting the absence of fundamental exactness, many special features connected with the physiology of olfaction are well established and some are herewith set forth.

ODOR FOCUSING AND SELECTION

Few substances possess a single odor. Usually one is outstanding and the others commonly overlooked. By some process of selection other than focusing in an optical sense, it is possible to fix attention upon any one of

[1] A possibility exists that several odor-producing energy potentials having different threshold levels may arise from the same molecule.

several odors within a group to the exclusion of others. The highly skilled odor analyst is able to shift odor perception rapidly from one to another stimulus in a mixture. Rather than implying any special mechanism in the process, it appears sufficient to make comparison with the ability of the musician to pick out the music of any one instrument in an orchestra with the rejection of others.

INTERRELATION OF ODOR TO TASTE SENSE

Kahn states, "Taste and smell are sisters. Taste is the smelling of liquids and smell is the tasting of gases." It is not remarkable that any substance

Fig. 3.—Apparatus for measuring electrical impulse on olfactory nerve of rat, in connection with investigation of mechanics of odor perception. Impulses are registered on cathode-ray screen on an oscilloscope shown at far right. (*Florida Chemical Research, Inc.*)

in a form that may stimulate both odor and taste receptors may occasion confusion in sensation. In view of the minute quantities sufficient to induce olfaction, it becomes a somewhat regular process that smelling accompanies tasting, provided, as just stated, gaseous or vaporous emanations be produced by the substance stimulating the taste bud. However, it is probably true that much of the overlapping between these two senses takes place in the higher brain centers in connection with volitional appraisal.

NASAL AIR FLOW AND ODOR STIMULATION

The ordinary passage of air through the nose does not provide ready contact with the olfactory area. In order to smell, it is common practice to "sniff," thus upsetting the common course of air through the nasal passages. No less, it is common experience that odors are perceived without "sniffing," and this is due to slow diffusion of odor-bearing air upward and onto the olfactory mucous membrane. In the presence of a foul odor that one hopes to escape, resort is at once made to gentle breathing through the nose or mouth—breathing in order to avoid the air turbulence that would involve olfaction. Even animals may be observed, when in the presence of odors that are apparently offensive to them, to engage in little activity, remaining so quiet as to diminish visibly the volume of respiration. In the occasional odor panics that upset groups of persons such as factory workers, the running around and screaming manifestly increase the opportunity for nasal air current disturbances. Lastly, it is here observed that odor stimulation may be provoked by air with its odor-stimulating content entering the nasal cavities from the pharynx as well as from the nares.

OLFACTORY ADAPTATION AND FATIGUE

Odor-generating substances in weak concentrations sometimes provoke greater odor sensations than the same materials in higher concentrations. Hydrogen sulfide gas, a highly odorous material, is most disturbing in high dilutions; after momentary stimulation, high concentrations no longer excite odor distress; in time, even weak concentrations fail to induce odor sensations. Such happenings are commonly associated with "fatigue." If in truth this represents "fatigue," the nonresponse is on a highly specific basis. Other odorous stimulants reaching the olfactory receptors are promptly and accurately perceived. There is thus no extensive "paralysis" of the olfactory response. It is perhaps preferable that the term "odor adaptation" or "odor adjustment" be applied. The body odors, oral odors, and respiratory tract odors of individuals are only infrequently recognized by their creators. The use of excessive amounts of perfume to the point of offense to others may leave the offender wholly unaware of the affront. Elsberg contends that odor rejection is central rather than peripheral—a temporary abeyance of performance in the brain instead of an impaired state of the receptors. It has been already mentioned that odor stultification may possibly be associated with excessive molecular concentration.

CENTRAL ODOR STIMULATION

Not all odor sensations originate in the peripheral mechanism. In the presence of tumors and possibly of some inflammatory process involving the higher brain centers, definite odor sensations may be excited, and unfortunately these are usually offensive rather than pleasant. To a limited extent, this phenomenon may be utilized in localization of tumors. The term "uncinate fits" is associated with some of these occurrences of centrally created odors. In these instances, the odors are genuine in that they are to be distinguished from odor hallucinations, which may have origin on no organic basis.

HEDONICS AND ODORS

The term "hedonics" represents the branch of psychology concerned with pleasantness versus unpleasantness. The hedonics of odors is highly variable. No two persons will be in full agreement as to pleasant odors and disagreeable odors. The majority of persons do agree that the odor of burning, putrescent material stands near the top of disagreeableness. Likewise, the majority of persons accords the natural odors of most fruits a high position on the scale of pleasantness. However, apart from the instinct of self-preservation and protection there is no known physiologic mechanism that arbitrarily partitions the pleasant from the unpleasant. Beebe-Center quotes Henning on the relation of hedonic tone to odors. Among other items, he notes that racial preferences influence hedonic tone. Orientals enjoy the odor of valerian, which is detested by most occidentals. The Japanese revel in the odors of camphor and borneol, while the Phoenicians are credited with delight from the sensation imparted by pepper in their perfumes. In some primitive groups in which butter is the favored hair oil, rancid lots are chosen because of the pleasureableness of their odors.

Odor hedonics decidedly have changed throughout the centuries. At the time of Louis XIV, the delectable odors derived from spice, resins, and incenselike aromatics. At the present time, favor is for mild flower scents and little-recognizable exotic blends. The possibility exists that if the ladies of the court of Louis XIV had had available perfumes of the present the choice rapidly might have been altered. A captivatingly perfumed lady of the sixteenth century possibly, at the present time, might be banished as a social outcast. A reversal of the situation is likewise conceivable.

Such matters so invade the realm of emotions and habituation that further delineation must be delegated to the psychologists.

THRESHOLDS OF ODOR STIMULATION

Already several statements indicate that fantastically small quantities of odoriferous material are in some instances sufficient to set in action the chains of odor mechanism. When one reckons the potential energy content of the small number of molecules apparently sufficient to provoke odors, it will be recognized that the quantity of energy is exceedingly low. This is reflected in the M.I.O. (minimum identifiable odor) or the olfactory co-efficient of the substances now presented:

Substance	M.I.O., Mg. per L. of Air
Artificial musk	0.00004
Natural musk	0.000005
Mercaptans (some)	0.00000004
Butyric acid	0.009
Iodoform	0.018
Pyridine	0.032
Rosemary	0.0008

On a different scale of quantitation, the following may be considered:

Substance	M.I.O., P.P.M.
Phosgene	5.6
Chlorine	3.5
Sulfur dioxide	3.0
Ammonia	53.0

It may be noted that in the first listing of figures values are expressed in milligrams per liter of air, but the quantity of air involved in a "sniff" is not a liter but some quantity approximating 50 cc. From the foregoing, the astonishing conclusion appears to be tenable that 0.000000002 mg. of mercaptan serves as an adequate odor stimulus. This degree of sensitivity challenges the threshold responses of almost any physical instrument.

It might be inferred that regularly these minute quantities of chemicals will induce odor sensation at all times and for all persons. Repeated testing on different days is likely to disclose a varying capacity for odor detection in the same individual. Thus, the figures cited possibly are to be accepted as the lowest extreme for highly experienced individuals.

ODOR PERCEPTION AND LIFE SPAN PERIODS

There are reasons to believe that the olfactory capacity is present in normal persons in some degree from birth to death. Newborn infants indicate responsiveness to odor stimuli, and in fact odors may play some role in the early feeding reactions of infants. Apparently, in the average population, odor acuity reaches its highest point in children at about the age of puberty and then slightly wanes. In advanced years, just as hearing and vision become impaired, so the acuity of odor detection may diminish. In a group of persons with an average age of seventy-eight, Vaschide determined that 36 per cent were anosmatic in contrast to 5 per cent in another group with an average age of twenty-six.

On an individual basis, everyone probably possesses a physiologic limit to olfactory acuity. Education probably will not expand this limit. However, ability to associate, recall, and classify olfactory impressions probably may be cultivated. A few persons claim an odor memory storehouse of as many as 4,000 odors, which, if true, still fails to preëmpt the total number of odors, although the total number is unknown and unknowable, since the number increases daily. Persons deprived of some sense faculties, such as sight or hearing, may come to utilize the olfactory capacity to a greater degree than average normal persons.

MONORHINAL VS. BIRHINAL OLFACTION

Some interest has developed as to possible variations in odor acuity when, under experimental conditions, the stimulant is introduced into only one side of the nose and when it is simultaneously introduced into the two sides. The results, as might have been anticipated, reveal a higher acuity for birhinal stimulation. This indicates central summation of the impulses from the two olfactory membranes, mediated perhaps by synapsis of two or more olfactory tract fibers with a single mitral cell.

PRIMITIVE RACES AND ODOR ACUITY

Conceding to some lower animals an unquestioned olfactory superiority over man, it might follow that those races of man least civilized might possess higher olfactory capacities. It is widely believed and frequently stated that such is the case. Lumholtz recorded that certain tribes of Queensland hunted boars by smell, and Humboldt attributed to the Indians of Peru the ability to follow human trails by the same sense. Darwin disagreed, concluding that close visual observation was the more likely basis of the well-recognized ability to track the quarry. Rivers, by careful measurement, established that the odor acuity of the Todas, a primitive group living in the Nilgri Hills of southern India, was somewhat inferior to that of a group of Englishmen serving as controls. The investigation of a Cambridge anthropological expedition to the Torres Straits established a slightly greater olfactory acuity among the natives of Murray Island. Under still other circumstances, frequent claims have been made that various human groups utilized the smell sense to ends quite beyond the capacities of the observers. The present-day appraisal of these observations appears to yield the conclusion that primitive people use their faculties, particularly vision, to better advantage, rather than profiting by any natural endowment such as a superior olfactory mechanism. Somewhat related to the immediate topic under discussion is the belief and possibly the fact that, regardless of race, persons with lowered mentality—the feeble-minded, the criminal type—may possess less well-developed odor perception. It may be pertinent to raise the question as to equal capacity to cooperate in determining thresholds between these inferior persons and their superior controls.

The intent that has governed this presentation of the physiology of the olfactory sense has been to emphasize obvious need for the reexploration of all the mechanisms of odor perception to the end that the content of knowledge of the odor sense may come to equal that of hearing and vision.

Chapter III

Chemical Constitution and Odors

IT HAS long been the hope of chemists that a fixed relationship between chemical structure and odors might be so well established that at will any desired odor might be provided through proper synthesis. This hope has not been realized. Complexity rather than simplicity has derived from all investigations. This complexity begins at the lowest level of chemical architecture. Atomic oxygen (O_1) is not available for odor perception. Molecular oxygen (O_2) is odorless. Ozone (O_3) possesses a definite odor and at the same time stimulates the trigeminal nerve, leading to irritation. It might be inferred that increasing atomicity is the key to odor stimulation. At once this breaks down from the knowledge that phosphorus in its yellow form (P_4) is odorous, while in the red form with increased atomicity ($P_4 + n$) it is odorless.

Further disturbing in this situation, among other items, are the following: (1) Failure in odor detection of such gases as oxygen (O_2) and nitrogen (N_2) may result from refusal of the odor receptors to register an odor present in the atmosphere from birth to death. Habituation to water may, on a subjective basis, deprive the olfactory sense in man of a potential odor. It is possible that perception of an odor of water is preserved in some lower animals. (2) Many substances rated as nonodorous may be so only through lack of receptor capacity in the olfactory mucous membrane. (3) Most work with odors has dealt solely with dominant odors for any substance and has failed to recognize that most substances have from two to eight odors when appraised by highly skilled odor analysts. (4) By odor counteraction many odors may be eliminated by the presence of other odors to the end that no odor at all is present or detectable. It becomes possible that many substances labeled as nonodorous are continually subject to odor autocounteraction. (5) Many substances of highly dissimilar chemical nature provide identical or similar fundamental odors. (6) Isomers of the same substance, thus chemically nearly identical, may provoke widely dissimilar odors. (7) In high dilution, some substances may excite one type of odor, and the same substance in greater concentration may excite an entirely different odor.

CHEMICAL ELEMENTS AND ODORS

Some of the 96 elements may exist or be produced in atomic state, but none is known to be odor stimulating in that state. This negation is commonly made categorically. The possibility is here accepted that some metals, such as silicon and magnesium, may be odoriferous, although equally granted are the uncertainties of the atomic state and the complete disassociation from impurities and contaminants. A few elements, notably the halides, in the molecular state are odoriferous. Odors from the halides are similar but not identical. All are grouped as "haloid." Arsenic and phosphorus may yield odors under some circumstances that are likewise similar but not identical. These are commonly catalogued as "alliaceous." The difficulties that attend the quest for basic odors to serve as keys to classification are exemplified in the fact that the five halides, while all possessing the haloid odor, no less exhibit specific odor differences.

The monatomic gases He, Ne, A, Kr, Xe, and Rn are odorless. In our concepts the absence of a bonding angle assumes significance. Chiefly the diatomic gases, such as H_2, N_2, O_2, CO, and NO (although the last as such does not exist in the air), are odorless. Therefore, the nature of the bonding angle may be noteworthy (see Chap. II).

Niccolini (1934) pointed out that the elements occurring in odorous substances lie above a diagonal line drawn from upper left to lower right of Mendeleef's table. In this area lie the elements possessing high volatility and great affinity for oxygen. These elements he classified as "olfacto-positive" and subdivided into odorous (in the elementary state) and nonodorous. The remaining elements, the "olfacto-negative," never form part of an odorous molecule and therefore, by inference, are considered to possess the power of suppressing organoleptic properties. Elements that, according to Niccolini's classification, possess odor in the elementary state are fluorine, chlorine, bromine, iodine, phosphorus, and arsenic.

The nonodorous olfacto-positive elements may be subdivided into those which acquire odor in combination with nonodorous elements (H, B, C, N, O, Si, S, Ti, Mn, Se, Zn, Ru, Sn, Sb, Te, and Os) and those which acquire odor only in combination with one of the seven odorous elements (Ga and Ge). Certain elements, notably sulfur, selenium, and tellurium, impart a vile odor to their simpler compounds; compounds of phosphorus, bismuth, and arsenic often have an alliaceous odor. However, these influences are completely lost in large molecules or when these elements occur as members of rings.

The elements most active in suppressing odor, especially in binary compounds, are high in the electropositive series (lithium, sodium, potassium, rubidium, cesium, copper, silver, gold, beryllium, magnesium, calcium, strontium, barium, zinc, cadmium, mercury, and radium) (Niccolini 1937).

Compounds in which an element functions at a valency lower than its maximum usually have offensive odors, *e.g.*, the carbylamines (C), the mercaptans and hydrogen sulfide (S), and the amines (trivalent nitrogen). Even this influence toward offensive odor is subordinated by great molecular size and by ring structure. Thiophen

$$\begin{pmatrix} CH\!-\!CH \\ | \quad\quad | \\ CH \quad CH \\ \diagdown\diagup \\ S \end{pmatrix}$$

containing divalent sulfur has only a faint, not unpleasant smell, and Bogert and Stull (1925) have pointed out that several of the substituted benzothiazoles and some of the analogous benzoselenazoles, in spite of their ordinarily malodorous elements, have a tearose or geranium odor.

INORGANIC CHEMICAL COMPOUNDS AND ODORS

The odors of inorganic compounds generally are not associated with metallic salts, though some salts possess odor properties vaguely grouped as "chemical odors."

As a class, odors from inorganic compounds are cacosmic and frequently are associated with irritation and toxicity. Obvious examples are found in hydrogen sulfide, sulfur dioxide, hydrogen selenide, etc. The demarcation between inorganic and organic compounds is not sharply drawn. If thiophosgene ($CSCl_2$) is accepted as inorganic, it will be recognized that the introduction of chlorine and sulfur in a carbon compound paves the way for a highly disturbing odor. Combinations of carbon and oxygen and of hydrogen and oxygen are usually odorless; thus carbon monoxide and carbon dioxide are odorless, as are hydrogen peroxide and water. Not all the simple halogen compounds are odorless. Some are highly irritating and many are toxic. It is noteworthy that all the many compounds liberating chlorine excite the same odor, although calcium bleaching powder containing chlorine imparts an odor somewhat deviating from chlorine, which may be attributable to chlorine monoxide. HCN, which may be accepted as inorganic, will be recognized to possess the highly characteristic odor of bitter almonds, which is carried over into several indubitably organic compounds with chemical kinship. Some of the compounds of silica, tin, titanium, antimony, and bismuth are odoriferous, but many of this group are better known for pungent properties. Phosphine (PH_3) stands apart in that its odor resembles that of trimethylamine and other substances linked with putrefaction.

From this recital there emerges no common denominator of chemical structure and odors.

ODORS FROM ORGANIC COMPOUNDS

The odors from inorganic compounds are predominantly offensive. However, the most offensive odors are associated with organic compounds, although preponderantly these compounds provide pleasing odors. The odors of perfumes, fruits, and flowers obviously represent complex organic structures.

At the lowest level of organic compounds stand the simple hydrocarbons containing only the two elements, carbon and hydrogen. The lowest series is the methane group, within which odor properties vary enormously. Some members of this series are:

Methane, CH_4 ....Odorless
Ethane, C_2H_6 ....Practically odorless
Propane, C_3H_8 ⎫
Butane, C_4H_{10} ⎬.........................Practically odorless in concentrations below flammable limits
Pentane, C_5H_{12} ....Indistinct
Hexane, C_6H_{14} ....Easily noticeable
Heptane, C_7H_{16} ....Easily noticeable
Octane, C_8H_{18} ....Powerful petrol odor
Nonane, C_9H_{20} ....Powerful petrol odor
Decane, $C_{10}H_{22}$ ....Powerful petrol odor

At once it might appear that accretions in this homologous series are responsible for odor prominence and intensity. This concept fails since, in the case of the members near the top of the series (not mentioned), volatility becomes so diminished that odor properties are impaired.

In like manner, odor exploration might be extended to all other organic series embracing the aromatic hydrocarbons, alcohols, phenols, ethers, organic acids, aldehydes, amines, ketones, ketals, halogen compounds, nitrogen compounds, sulfur compounds, paraffins, esters, etc. Such exploration would involve saturation and unsaturation, open chains and closed chains, straight chains and branched chains, chemical radicals commonly called "odorphores," isomerism, odor carriers, and odor extenders. At the end of any such pursuit, the outstanding fact established would be that no single pattern of chemical structure serves to maintain even a trend of odor properties. Moncrieff, the latest provider of a comprehensive investigation, having reached this conclusion, promulgated a long series of principles relative to odors and chemical structure. Those principles so far as directed to organic compounds are here presented but in an arrangement dissimilar to his original.

1. Compounds of different constitutions may have similar odours, *e.g.*, camphor, silicononyl alcohol, durene.
2. Compounds of very similar constitution may have different odours. If, however, the constitutional differences are slight, odour differences are generally correspondingly slight.

3. Polymerisation reduces or destroys odour whether in elements (*e.g.*, red phosphorus) or in compounds (*e.g.*, glycols).

4. Unsaturation enhances odour but does not initiate it. (The paraffins are odorous.)

5. In the paraffins, straight and branched-chain isomers have similar odours, and the position of the double bond (if any) is unimportant.

6. In a homologous series the odour will rise to a maximum as we ascend the series and will then fall off owing to decreased volatility.

7. Unsaturation often introduces an irritant note to the odour, particularly if close to a polar group—*e.g.*, aliphatic aldehydes and acids.

8. A tertiary carbon atom will frequently induce a camphoraceous odour.

9. The osmophoric influence of the phenyl group is strong. It overcomes that of alkyl ether groups and also of the amino group.

10. The introduction of a hydroxyl group frequently depresses or abolishes odour—*e.g.*, aliphatic acids.

11. Aromatic acids are usually odourless, whereas most aliphatic acids are odorous.

12. Fully reduced aromatic bodies have odours similar to those of fatty substances—*e.g.*, cyclohexane, hexahydrobenzoic acid.

13. Fully reduced heterocyclic bodies also develop aliphatic odours—*e.g.*, piperidine.

14. Esters have fragrant fruity odours. This includes esters of weak inorganic acids such as boric.

15. Strong odour is often found accompanied by volatility and chemical reactivity—*e.g.*, aldehydes. Chemical reactivity and unsaturation run parallel to odour.

16. Esters of diacids have good odours, but those of dihydric alcohols have weak odours.

17. Ketones generally have pleasant odours.

18. Whereas introduction of a hydroxyl group frequently destroys odour, the etherification of this group usually restores the odour.

19. Lactones have fragrant ester-like odours.

20. The alkyl halides have sweet smells which become heavier in type as we pass from chlorine to bromine and to iodine. Two or three halogen atoms have an additive olfactory effect.

21. When a halogen is already a substituent, a hydroxyl group behaves abnormally and increases the odour.

22. The odour of amines is more ammoniacal when dilute than when concentrated, and the fishy odour is stronger in concentrated than in dilute solutions.

23. Nitrogen compounds frequently have an "animal" odour. Compounds not containing nitrogen do not ordinarily have an "animal" odour.

24. An oxygen linkage is frequently associated with a pleasant odour—*e.g.*, esters, lactones, nitrates.

25. Many nitriles have a bitter-almonds odour.

26. Compounds in which an element functions at a valency lower than its maximum usually have offensive odours—*e.g.*, hydrogen sulphide and the isonitriles.

27. Many sulphur compounds, particularly where the sulphur is divalent, have offensive odours—*e.g.*, mercaptans.

28. Sulphur and nitrogen and oxygen atoms in a ring do not play their usual olfactory role. Their influence is subordinate to that of the ring—*e.g.*, thiophen, furan.

29. If a heterocyclic body is completely reduced, the sulphur or nitrogen or oxygen atoms regain their normal olfactory effect.

30. Whereas unsaturation is often a contributory factor to odour, ring unsaturation appears to have a negative olfactory action.

31. The main factor in determining odour is the architectural type of the molecule.

32. The osmophoric groups play a part subordinate to that of the architectural style. In small molecules this part is greater than in large molecules.

33. Some substances change their odour on dilution—*e.g.*, indole, amines.

34. In ring compounds, the number of ring members often determines the odour:

5–6   members give bitter almonds and menthol odour.
6–9   members give transitional odour.
9–12   members give camphor or mint odour.
13   members give woody or cedar odour.
14–16   members give musk and peach odours.
17–18   members give civet odours.
More than 18 give faint or no odour.

The odour of compounds with rings from 9–20 members is largely independent of the substituent groups.

35. For a musk odour in macrocyclic compounds the basic ring structure must be between 14 and 19 atoms and at least one carbonyl or imine group is necessary. Musk odours are not confined to macrocyclic compounds.

36. One heterocyclic atom increases the odour of macrocyclic compounds, two reduce it.

37. In the ionones, the position of the double bond in the ring is unimportant, but unsaturation in the side chain is essential for the violet odour.

38. Arsenic compounds are usually garlicky or ill-smelling (cacodyl), but not if the arsenic is a heterocyclic member of a ring.

39. In a mixed ether-ester compound, the ester group has a dominant olfactory effect.

40. Branching of a chain usually enhances odour.

41. There is no relation between the odours of isomers with important structural differences.

42. Structurally similar isomers usually have similar odours. As the difference in molecular structure or architectural style of isomers increases, so do odour differences.

43. The position of a side-chain influences the odour. The nearer the side-chain to a polar group, the stronger the odour—*e.g.*, alpha-substituted lactones have stronger odours than gamma-substituted.

44. Position isomerism in the benzene ring has a marked influence on odour, *e.g.*, o-biphenylyl ethers are odorous, para are odourless.

45. The 1 . 3 . 4 arrangement in the benzene ring usually leads to a pleasant odour, but not if the substituent groups are heavy.

46. Para-substitution often introduces a soft anise note.

47. Meta-substitution usually enhances the power and pungency of an odour.

48. Ortho-substitution often gives a floral odour.

49. With equal substituents the para influence overwhelms the meta (or ortho)—if both are present,

50. Where methyl and chlorine occur as substituents in a benzene ring the latter has the greater influence.

51. The odour of a substituted aromatic compound depends more on the position than on the nature of the substitutent groups.

52. Stereoisomers may have different odours. The differences are not usually very great.

53. Finally, the general conclusion is that odour is determined by the architectural arrangement of the molecule. Osmophoric groups (*sic*) have a secondary influence, only in so far as they modify the general arrangement. The great difficulty is, of course, the subjective nature of odour classification. Once this difficulty is removed and it is possible to define exactly the quality of an odour, then logic and precision will reduce chaos to order, and the relation between odour and chemical constitution will be disclosed to us with mathematical exactness.

PHYSICAL PROPERTIES

Although this chapter heading indicates a close adherence to chemical constituency, it becomes necessary to introduce certain facts more closely identified with physical properties. Those substances capable of imparting odors were associated by Tyndall as early as 1871 with the capacity of high heat absorption. This rule has many exceptions. Zwaardemaker is credited with the statement that only those substances with molecular weights falling between 17 and 300 are odor stimulating. This appears to be in error, since highly numerous substances with molecular weights in excess of 300 are known to be odoriferous. Eosin, with a molecular weight near 624, and curcumin, molecular weight 368, are but examples. Of course, the odors encountered may in truth originate in impurities or in decomposition products of low molecular weight value, and this possibility is not denied.

Odor-generating substances are commonly associated with the property of surface-tension depression. Watson noted that the order of decreasing minimum odor-detectable concentrations coincided with the order of increasing depression of surface tension. The International Critical Tables state: "All odorous substances lower the surface tension of water and therefore [one may] produce static electricity by spraying an aqueous solution of the odorivector against a disc well insulated with amber and paraffin. The value is expressed as 10^{-10} coulomb per cubic centimeter of a saturated solution."

Dyson in 1938 recorded that all odoriferous substances examined exhibited one or more Raman shifts with frequencies between 1500 and 3500. He observed a close correlation between the magnitude of the shift and the type of odor emitted. The alkyl mercaptans, with characteristically similar odors, create lines in the narrow range represented by 2567 to 2580, the acetylenes at 2100, the chlorinated aromatic hydrocarbons near 2300, the ethers near 2700.

Volatility and solubility are closely linked with odor impartation. It is widely recorded that all odorous substances are soluble both in water and in lipides. While the more odorous substances conform to dual solubility, rigidity in this respect probably does not exist. Volatility is requisite to odor stimulation. All substances possess some vapor pressure, so the mere property of a vapor pressure in itself is no assurance of odor stimulation. The minimum concentration that will produce odor stimulation is approximately 10^{-11} gm. per normal inspiration under most favorable conditions for olfaction. This approximately is the equivalent of a concentration of 3×10^{10} molecules.

SUMMARY

With respect to neither inorganic nor organic chemical compounds may it be held that any single pattern of structure provides or influences odor properties. Few elements in atomic state are accessible to odor appraisal. Only seven elements give rise to odors in molecular state; these are arsenic, bromine, chlorine, fluorine, iodine, oxygen as O_3, and phosphorus. These seven elements produce only two fundamental odors, namely, alliaceous for arsenic and phosphorus, haloid for the remainder. Odors from inorganic compounds are chiefly offensive and often irritating. Pleasant odors foremostly are associated with organic compounds, although the most offensive odors are likewise a product of organic compounds. Many known chemical radicals and molecular arrangements influence odors. Their import is ably set forth in Moncrieff's principles.

usually Correspond to IR

1500 cm-1   6.66 μ
3500 cm-1   2.86 μ
2567 - 2580   3.91 to 3.88 μ
2100   4.76
2300   4.35
2700   3.7

Chapter IV

Odor Classification

Odors do not at this time lend themselves to precise classification. In the case of color, as a part of vision, or of taste there exist primary bases. There may be a hundred shades of red, but all bear some relationship to primary spectral red. Quinine and cascara may not be identified by the single fact that each is bitter, but both enter a common taste category of bitterness. For odors there are no well-established primes. Odors will attain to exact classification when the energy of odor stimulation is precisely translated into measurable physical units. Until that time reliance must be placed upon a heterogeneous lot of convenient but palpably inadequate groupings.

The very number of presently employed classifications attests the shortcomings of all. To the credit of all sponsors of particular grouping arrangements, none has claimed completeness. Foremostly odors are now designated as "like" some other odor. An analogy exists between the method of odor designation and the language origin of words on the basis of onomatopoësis. Thus, "bowwow" is a good word since it sounds like the sound it describes. So in the case of odors; confronted with an uncertain one of animalistic repulsiveness, for example, we may toss it into the "goaty" category. Goats are not liked nor is the odor liked, so "goaty" it becomes. To avoid the lack of dignity of "goaty," we appropriate the word "hircine" or possibly "caprylic." Is it not possible that, in part we register our aversion rather than describe an odor?

During the days of the potential danger from gas warfare, thousands of civilians and of military personnel earnestly seeking to grasp the lore of war-gas identification approached nervous breakdown trying to convince their noses that this or that gas's odor resembled "ensilage" or "rotting wood" or "newly cut hay." Would there have not been profit in otherwise stating "This gas has a peculiar and recognizable odor. Memorize that odor"?

Because of many opportunities for vagaries, with some justification it may be asserted that with today's knowledge of odors there is little foundation for all-embracive classification. Some odors defy all sharing of their olfactory qualities. Let him who may be able acceptably classify as an entity the odor of overripe cucumbers rotting in the field.

Many odors appearing in classifications as choice examples are, on better appraisal found to embrace six or more distinct odors. These do not blend into any odor unit. Scarcely any substance possesses a single odor.

REPRESENTATIVE ODOR CLASSIFICATION SCHEMES

These cited examples of odor groupings are not set up solely as targets for condemnation. All have value; and, if no other values were apparent, they serve to portray the difficulties in this domain.

Zwaardemaker's Classification (after Crocker)

1. Ethereal or fruity: characteristic in general of fruits and due in most cases to the presence of various esters; includes also beeswax and certain ethers, aldehydes, and ketones
2. Aromatic
   a. Camphoraceous: borneol, camphor, eucalyptole
   b. Spicy: eugenol, ginger, pepper, cinnamon, cassia, mace
   c. Anise-lavender: anethole, lavender, menthol, thymol, safrole, peppermint
   d. Lemon-rose: geraniol, citral, linalyl acetate, sandalwood
   e. Amygdalin: benzaldehyde, oil of bitter almonds, nitrobenzene, prussic acid, salicylaldehyde
3. Fragrant or balsamic
   a. Floral: jasmine, ilang-ilang, orange blossoms, lilac, terpineol, lily of the valley
   b. Lily: tuberose, narcissus, hyacinth, orris, violet, ionone, mignonette
   c. Balsamic: vanillin, piperonal, coumarin, balsams of Peru and Tolú
4. Ambrosial: musk and amber. This odor is present in the flesh, blood, and excreta (referable to the bile) of certain animals
5. Alliaceous or garlic: onion, garlic, and many compounds of sulfur, selenium, tellurium, and arsenic
   a. Alliaceous: hydrides of sulfur, selenium, and tellurium, mercaptans, organic sulfides, thioacetone, asafetida
   b. Cacodyl fish odors: hydrides of phosphorus and arsenic, cacodyl compounds, trimethylamine
   c. Bromine odors: bromine, chlorine, quinone
6. Empyreumatic or burnt: as in tar, baked bread, roasted coffee, tobacco, benzene, naphthalene, phenol, and products of the dry distillation of wood
7. Hircine or goaty: due in the case of this animal to the caproic and caprylic esters contained in the sweat and typified also by perspiration and cheese
8. Repulsive: such as are given off by many of the narcotic plants and by acanthus
9. Nauseating or fetid: such as are given off by products of putrefaction (feces, etc.) and by certain plants

Earp's Mildly Proposed Physiologic Effect Classification.—Reverting to the earlier work of Shields, Earp suggests the grouping of odors for sanitary and hygienic purposes in terms of physiologic action. Thus wintergreen, heliotrope, and violet are known to increase the flow of blood to the brain and to stimulate heart action. Carried further, there might be odors that cause nausea and vomiting, others that increase the flow of saliva, that increase or decrease the respiratory rate, etc.

However desirable, this concept possesses unsurmountable difficulties. After the breathing of the odoriferous hydrogen sulfide gas, death might occur, constituting a definite departure from the physiologic normal, yet death could not be attributed to the odor but to the gas itself. Physiologic modifications are more likely to arise from emotional reactions to odors than from any direct odor action. Palpably the majority of odors will achieve no physiologic departures either directly or indirectly through emotional responses.

Henning's Odor Classification.—This investigator conceived that all odor stimuli are embraced in six basic types, with possible combinations within the six. Henning's grouping is now presented.

1. Spicy: conspicuous in cloves, cinnamon, nutmeg, etc.
2. Flowery: conspicuous in heliotrope, jasmine, etc.
3. Fruity: conspicuous in apple, orange oil, vinegar, etc.
4. Resinous: conspicuous in coniferous oils and turpentine
5. Foul: conspicuous in hydrogen sulfide and products of decay
6. Burnt: conspicuous in tarry and scorched substances

The Crocker-Henderson Classification.—This represents a condensation of the Henning arrangement, leading to four fundamental odor sensations as follows:

1. Fragrant or sweet
2. Acid or sour
3. Burnt or empyreumatic
4. Caprylic, goaty, or oenanthic

These sponsors claim that the order is that of decreasing pleasantness; but this may be questioned, since for most persons the odor of burnt putrescing material is far more disturbing than a caprylic one.

The Numerical Rating of Odors.—Faced with some futility in attempting to appraise all odors through similarity to a single "standard" odor, at the present time it may be preferred practice to recognize several odor qualities and intensities and to express these in a four-digit number. Employing the four fundamental odor sensations in the Crocker-Henderson classification, in order from left to right, the first digit refers to the degree of "fragrance," the second to the "acid" quality, and so on. Intensity is rated on an ascending empiric scale from 0 to 8. On this basis a substance without any odor would appear as 0000. Ethanol in this form of odor standards appears as 5414. This consensus number when interpreted means that as to odor ethanol is substantially fragrant, moderately acid, scarcely burnt, and fairly caprylic. A large number of chemicals have been assigned odor numbers, but it does not follow that identification may be established through this measure. The odors of several dissimilar agents might fall into the same numerical category. This method, like all others, relies upon the human nose as the test instrument and thus is subject to human vagary.

Some values on this numerical rating basis are now introduced.

Table I.—ODOR STANDARDS* (REVISED, 1944†) CROCKER

Fragrant		Acid	
1112	n-Butyl phthalate	7122	Vanillin
2424	Toluene	7213	Cinnamic acid
3336	α-Chlornaphthalene	5335	Resorcinol dimethyl ether
4344	α-Naphthyl methyl ether	2424	Toluene
5645	Cymene	5523	Isobutyl phenylacetate
6645	Citral	5626	Methyl phenylacetate
7343	Safrole	5726	Cineole
8453	Methyl salicylate	3803	Acetic acid (20% solution)

Burnt		Caprylic	
5414	Ethyl alcohol	——	No suitable standard found
7423	Phenylethyl alcohol	7122	Vanillin
5335	Resorcinol dimethyl ether	7343	Safrole
4344	α-Naphthyl methyl ether	5624	Phenylacetic acid
4355	Veratrole	5645	Cymene
6665	Thujone	3336	α-Chlornaphthalene
4376	Paracresyl acetate	2577	Anisole
7584	Guaiacol	3518	2,7-Dimethyl octane

* A single substance may serve for several standards. The substances included in this table have been chosen because they are reasonably reproducible in odor from lot to lot, safe to breathe in quantities required for comparisons, readily available from chemical sources, and reasonably stable against changes in use or on standing.

† See also 1947 revision.

Percentage Odor Appraisal.—Since most odorous substances reveal a multiplicity of odors, it is now fairly common practice among odor analysts to associate with each component, or with a single odor if only one is detectable, a percentile figure. Thus in some instances there might be recognized the odor of apple, anise, and acetate. Marking the most intense apple odor ever experienced as 100 per cent, the apple odor now contemplated might be accepted as at the 10 per cent or 30 per cent level; so also for the anise and the acetate. This scheme shuns any attempt to thrust the actual odors faced into any near artificial category. It will be obvious that in this method there is no purpose to sum up to 100 per cent; the totality of the odor content might not exceed 8 per cent.

In much of this taxonomy may be found the failure to dissociate the functions of the olfactory and trigeminal nerves. It may be anomalous to introduce "pungency" as one of the qualities in a general odor disposal classification if, in truth, pungency is a quality prehended by the trigeminal on a common chemical sense level.

Properly interpreted, this section's intent is that at this time real odor classification cannot be accomplished. In the meanwhile, many arrangements serve highly practical purposes. The detection of the place of electrical energy of odor stimulation within the electromagnetic spectrum is awaited as the foundation of genuine odor gradation.

During the course of publication of this book it is possible that this desideratum may have been accomplished. Drs. Beck and Miles working at Yale University have developed evidences associating odor perception with infrared rays emitted by the organism's receptors. Their observations derive chiefly from work with low life forms such as bees and roaches. These investigators state:

"According to the proposed theory, olfaction results when the radiation of heat from an organism's receptors is accelerated. The source of heat is the organism itself. The organismic source defines the critical region of the infrared spectrum as that in the neighborhood of the maximum of a black body at approximately $290°\text{-}313°K$. The receptors, being of the dimensions of the wave lengths in the region of this maximum $(8\text{-}14\mu)$, can, by virtue of their size and shape, radiate selectively. Any substance having an absorption band in this region and coming within the radiation field of these receptors will cause them transiently to lose energy. This transient loss of energy is presumably the initial event in the process of stimulation of the olfactory receptors. Differential radiation losses of the receptors account for olfactory quality as spatial stimulation. . . .

"The present theory rationalizes the experimental literature on olfaction. Among other points, it distinguishes odorous from inodorous substances; explains adaptation as the return of the receptor system to a new thermal equilibrium in the presence of an odorous substance; accounts for the differences between micro- and macro-osmatic animals on the basis of the larger absorption chambers of the latter; accounts for the anomalies in the chemical theory; and provides a basis for the reinterpretation of some of the classic work in olfaction." [*Science*, **106**, 511 (1947).]

This concept of odor prehension tends to remove the odor sense from the chemical category and to locate it as anticipated in the realm of the electromagnetic spectrum. Distinctly, man is hypoosmatic, which fact handicaps tests with human beings, but man is not so hypoosmatic that it may not be anticipated that crucial tests may not be carried out with humans. The information available at the time of the preparation of this book is meager. On this account there is no warrant for the final acceptation of this revolutionary theory. Equally there is no disposition to deny the validity of this constructive work and further developments are awaited.

Chapter V

Odor Detection and Measurement

THE QUANTITATION of odors is attended by grave uncertainties. Since odors are sensations, ultimately human appraisal must rely upon the olfactory mucosa. Quantitation by some lower animal forms probably is effected continuously. When moths unerringly fly long distances to a nuptial mate, they, by all evidence, follow the gradient of increasing odor intensity until the exact location of the female is reached. While the claim has been made that this may be achieved downwind, this feat may be doubted.

Clinically no physician is confronted with difficulty in determining that an individual suffers from impaired olfactory capacity or is endowed with increased faculty for odor perception. This does not constitute odor measuration to greater degree than an individual's vision quantitates light.

Man quantitates his odors in crude fashion. His nose may be trusted to locate the dead dog under the front steps. However, the minimum difference of odor levels recognizable by the average person is near 30 per cent. If arbitrarily an odor value is fixed at 10, then only at 7 or 13 is an intensity variation appreciated. Odor responses conform to the Weber-Fechner psychophysical law, alike applicable to all sense organs, in that a change in intensity is not recognizable unless the alteration is sufficient to constitute a definite functional increment—positive or negative in varying situations—of the acting concentration or stimulus.

Efforts to produce objective methods for odor measurement have been numerous. Various appliances have been designated as scent meters, odorimeters, olfactometers, osmoscopes, etc. Some such named devices clearly are not to be associated with attempts to measure odors; rather they measure conditions favorable to odor detection. Pollard's "scent meter," highly esteemed among fox hunters, is a complex apparatus for recording temperature, humidity, air motion, wind direction, light intensity, etc. Its application, in truth, may disclose conditions favorable or unfavorable for the hounds in following the prey's path, but this does not constitute odor measurement. On a higher level at least two procedures possess practical values more closely related to odors themselves. These are (1) devices directed to the determination of the minimum identifiable odor and (2) chemical methods relating on countered odor intensities to determined quantities of the odorivector. Before these are introduced, it may be productive to refer to earlier sections in which reference is made to Raman phenomena, surface tension modification by odors, and measurements of electrical potentials in connection with odor sensation. Recent attainments in the field of microelectrical activity now warrant the belief that the molecular energy at the solution moment may be measured. Practical application to functioning olfactory mucosa may yet be distant. There is the field of promise. What is now presented represents the methods employed today.

THE DETERMINATION OF THE MINIMAL IDENTIFIABLE ODOR

The highest dilution of air containing an odorous substance that may be identified as an odor has been designated as the M.I.O. This implies the dilution of an odorivector until such a point is attained. Most of the instruments

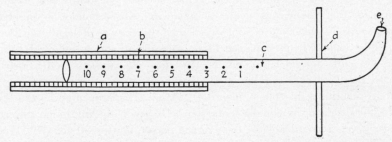

Fig. 1.—Diagram of Zwaardemaker's single olfactometer. (*Best and Taylor, "The Physiological Basis of Medical Practice," The Williams & Wilkins Company.*)

now in use, some of which will shortly be described and illustrated, are merely devices for the controlled dilution of odorous substances in gaseous or vaporous form. Extensive inquiry has been directed to the establishment of the M.I.O. for many hundreds of substances. If by consent the M.I.O. is assigned an empiric value of 1, it does not necessarily follow that 47 or 89 times as much will impart an odor recognizable as 47 or 89 times as great. The M.I.O. for any one substance is unlikely to be the same for many in a group of persons, and for one person it may vary at intervals.

However limited the worth of this procedure, its services are numerous. (1) If odors are relied upon to act as warning agents for dangerous materials, manifestly that quantity of the warning agent employed must far exceed the M.I.O. of the mixture. (2) In industrial toxicology, frequently, but not always acceptably, one may hear "any quantity of that gas sufficient to impart an odor already has reached the toxic threshold." (3) The travel limits of odors are best determined by the M.I.O. (4) Some hyperosmatic animals may be conditioned to anticipate food in connection with some specific odor (not food odor). Thus it becomes possible to introduce comparative olfactometry by determination of the respective M.I.O. for man and lower animals.

Zwaardemaker's Olfactometer.—In 1895 or slightly earlier, Zwaardemaker

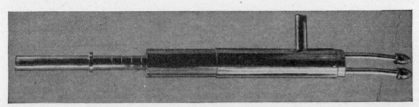

Fig. 2.—Fair and Wells Osmoscope. Odorless air enters osmoscope through side tube where it is mixed with odorous test air which enters from end tube. The degree of dilution is measured on the calibrated scale. (*Courtesy of Fair and Wells.*)

created his odor-measuring device, which consists of two telescoping tubes (Fig. 1). The odorivector is coated onto the inner surface of the outer tube. The inner tube is at its proximal end fitted with tubular devices to be inserted

Fig. 3.—Osmoscope operator testing odor intensity of test chamber by use of Fair and Wells Osmoscope. End of osmoscope protrudes through hole in wall chamber. Side tube (near left hand) draws in odorless air outside chamber. (*Florida Chemical Research, Inc.*)

into the nostrils. Obviously, as the inner tube is moved away from the outer tube, increasingly more surface is exposed to impart odor-stimulating substances to the air drawn through the inner tube in inhalation. The inner tube is graduated. If an odor is perceptible after only one unit of withdrawal, that amount is designated as one "olfactie." If it is necessary to disengage the two tubes by two units to provide an odor stimulus, two olfacties are involved, and so on (see Fig. 1). It will be apparent that unless temperature and humidity are maintained at constant levels readings are likely to be aberrant.

The Fair-Wells Osmoscope.—In 1935 Fair and Wells created the device that is now in greatest use, although complaint has been made that a "brassy" odor arises that is disturbing to appraisal of the odor under consideration. In

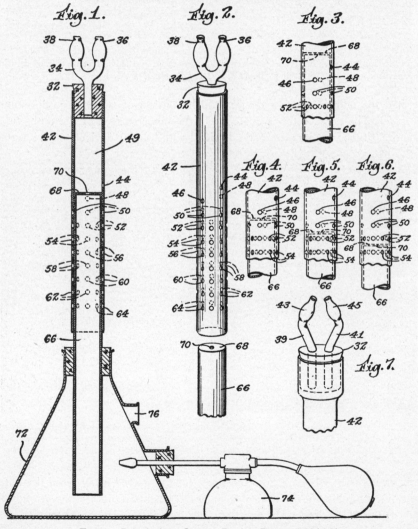

Fig. 4.—Details from Letters Patent. Patent 2,136,844.

general this device consists of two brass telescoping tubes complexly arranged for highly modified odor dilution. The odorivector is not applied within the osmoscope directly but may be contained near by in a flask or otherwise may derive from the general atmosphere under appraisal (Figs. 2 to 4). Further

Fig. 5.—Katz and Allison Odorimeter. Apparatus for measuring odor intensities. (*U.S. Bureau of Mines.*)

description of this useful instrument may be found in United States Patent 2136844. Among numerous claims made for it are the following:

1. It provides new and improved procedure for measuring or determining odors, using dilution processes and activation by the nose.

2. It provides an easily discernible scale of odor measurement.

3. It determines the dilution required to bring a given odor to an approximate threshold value.

4. It is adapted for prompt and momentary use in order to prevent errors that might otherwise arise as a result of fatigue.

5. It provides means for compounding odor intensities of substances that may be mixed to provide a desired compound odor.

6. It provides means for neutralizing odors physiologically by testing the odor intensities of substances that may be mixed to counteract each other physiologically.

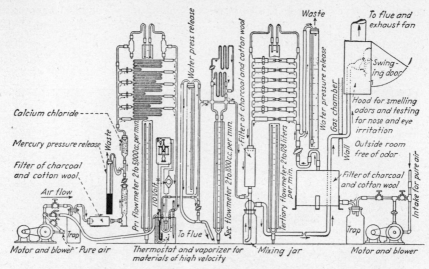

FIG. 6.—Details of Odorimeter shown in Fig. 5.

Katz and Allison Odorimeter.—This device first appeared about 1920, but it has since been modified, so that perhaps the best form is that utilized by Fieldner, Sayers, Yant, Katz, Schohen and Leitch in 1931[1] (Figs. 5 to 7). This

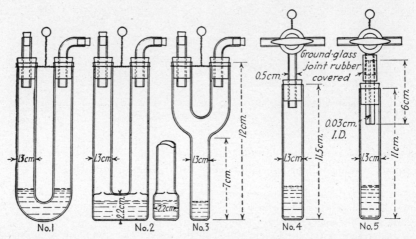

FIG. 7.—Vaporizers for adding warning-agent material of different volatilities to Katz and Allison Odorimeter. (*U.S. Bureau of Mines.*)

instrument has been described as an apparatus for determining weights of vapors volatilized at uniform rates and diluting the vapors to various concen-

[1] "Warning Agents for Fuel Gases," U. S. Department of Commerce, Bureau of Mines, Monograph 4, American Gas Association, New York, 1931.

trations by means of measured streams of air. Ultimately this device depends upon appraisal by the human olfactory mechanism.

Elsberg and Levy Blast Method.—This instrument possesses as its novel feature facilities for thrusting upon the olfactory mucosa air containing predetermined quantities of odorous substances. In this way is avoided the uncertainty that attends many other methods as to whether or not the odor stimulation actually reaches the perceptive area. In application, 30 cc. of the test liquid is placed in a large bottle. This is connected with (1) a graduated syringe for forcing measured quantities of air into the bottle and (2) a

Fig. 8.—Elsberg and Levy blast method of olfactometry. (*Redrawn from Best and Taylor, "The Physiological Basis of Medical Practice," The Williams & Wilkins Company.*)

tubular connection for introduction into the nares, thus providing for a one-blast thrust of the total odor-laden air onto the olfactory mucosa (Fig. 8). By increasing the volume of the blast a point may be reached at which the odor is first perceived.

Bach in 1937 provided a review of odor-detection methods and devices and there included some not mentioned in the present publication (Figs. 9 to 11).

Based on M.I.O. values, DallaValle, in evaluating the odor nuisance of kraft paper manufacture, provides a long list of odor thresholds, as quoted in Table I:

Table I.—Odor Thresholds

Substance	Formula	Concentrations causing faint odor (mg. per liter) (oz. per 1,000 cu. ft.)	Remarks
Acetaldehyde	CH_3CHO	0.004	Pungent odor
Acrolein	$CH_2:CH.CHO$	0.038	Acrid odor of burning fat
"Akrol"	Mixed turpenes	0.01	Acrid pine-tar odor. Irritating
Allyl alcohol	$CH_2:CH.CH_2OH$	0.017	Alcoholic odor. Not unpleasant
Allyl amine	$CH_2:CH.CH_2.NH_2$	0.067	Odor similar to ammonia. Irritating
Allyl disulfide	$(CH_2:CHCH_2)_2S_2$	0.0001	Garlic odor. Decomposes
Allyl isocyanide	$CH_2:CH.CH_2NC$	0.0043	Sweet but repulsive odor. Nauseating
Allyl isothiocyanate	$CH_2:CH.CH_2.NCS$	0.0017	Mustard-oil odor. Nose and eye irritant
Allyl mercaptan	$CH_2:CH.CH_2.SH$	*0.00005	Very disagreeable odor. Garlic
Allyl sulfide	$(CH_2:CH.CH_2)_2S$	0.00005	Garlic odor
Ammonia	NH_3	0.037	Sharp, pungent odor
Amylene	C_5H_{10}	0.0066	Nauseating in high concentrations
Amyl acetate (iso.)	$CH_3COOC_3H_5(CH_3)_2$	0.0006	Banana odor
Amyl isovalerate (iso.)	$(CH_3)_2C_3H_3COOC_3H_5(CH_3)_2$	0.0008	Pleasant. Fruity
Amyl mercaptan (iso.)	$(CH_3)_2CH.CH_2.CH_2.SH$	0.0003	Unpleasant
Amyl sulfide (iso.)	$(CH_3)_2CHCH_2(CH_2)_2S$	0.0003	Strong and unpleasant odor
Benzaldehyde	$C_6H_5.CH:O$	0.003	Odor of bitter almonds
Benzyl chloride	$C_6H_5CH_2.Cl$	0.0016	Lacrimator. Aromatic
Benzyl mercaptan	$C_6H_5CH_2.SH$	0.00019	Unpleasant odor
Benzyl sulfide	$(C_6H_5CH_2)_2S$	0.0006	Unpleasant odor
Bromacetone	$Br.CH_2.CO.CH_2$	0.0005	Pungent and stifling odor
Bromacetophenone	$C_6H_5CO.CH_2.Br$	0.00064	Lacrimator. Odor like bromine
Butylene (β)	$CH_3.CH:CH.CH_3$	0.059	Gashouse odor
Butylene (γ)	$(CH_3)_2C:CH_2$	0.05	Gashouse odor
n-Butyl mercaptan	$(CH_3)_2CH.CH_2SH$	*0.0014	Strong unpleasant odor
n-Butyl sulfide	$(C_4H_9)_2S$	0.0011	Unpleasant odor
Carbon disulfide	CS_2	0.0026	Aromatic odor, slightly pungent
Chloracetophenone	$C_6H_5.CO.CH_2Cl$	*0.0085	Apple blossom odor. Strong lacrimator
β-Chlorvinyldichlorarsine	$Cl.CH:CH.AsCl_2$	0.014	Odor of geraniums. (Lewisite)
Chlorine	Cl_2	0.010	Pungent and irritating odor
Chlorophenol	$Cl.C_6H_4.OH$	0.00018	Medicinal odor. Phenolic
Chlorpicrin	Cl_3CNO_2	0.0073	Flypaper odor
Coumarin	$C_6H_4CH:CH.CO.O$	0.00034	Vanilla odor. Pleasant
Crotonaldehyde	$CH_3.CH:CH.CH.O$	*0.021	Eye and nose irritant
Crotyl mercaptan	$CH_3.CH:CH.CH_2.SH$	0.000029	Skunk odor
Cyanogen chloride	$CNCl$	0.0025	Bitter almonds
Dichlordiethyl sulfide	$(ClC_2H_5)_2S$	0.0013	Garlic or horseradish odor (mustard gas).
Dichlorethylene (trans)	$C_2H_2Cl_2$	0.0043	Etheral odor.
Dimethyl trithiocarbonate	$CH_3S.CS.SCH_3$	0.00018	Foul and disagreeable
Diphenylamine chlorarsine	$(C_6H_4)_2NHAsCl$	0.0025	Slight odor
Diphenyl chlorarsine	$(C_6H_5)_2AsCl$	0.0003	Shoe-polish odor
Diphenyl cyanarsine	$(C_6H_5)_2AsCN$	0.003	Odor of bitter almonds and garlic
Diphenyl ether	$(C_6H_5)_2O$	0.000069	Geranium odor. Pleasant
Diphenyl sulfide	$(C_6H_5)_2S$	0.000048	Ethereal but unpleasant odor
Diphosgene	$ClCO_2-CCl_3$	0.0088	Suffocating, disagreeable odor
Dithio-ethylene glycol	$CH_2SH.CH_2SH$	0.0016	Disagreeable, garliclike odor
Ethylene dichloride	$C_2H_4Cl_2$	0.025	Aromatic. Ethereal
Ethyl dichlorarsine	$C_2H_5AsCl_2$	0.001	Irritating, biting
Ethyl isothiocyanate	$CH_3CH_2N:C:S$	0.038	Mustard oil. Irritating odor
Ethyl mercaptan	$CH_3CH_2.SH$	*0.00019	Odor of decayed cabbage
Ethyl selenide	$CH_3CH_2.Se.CH_2CH_3$	0.000062	Garlic odor. Putrid and nauseating
Ethyl seleno mercaptan	$CH_3CH_2.Se.H$	0.0000018	Very foul and disagreeable odor
Ethyl sulfide	$(C_2H_5)_2S$	0.00025	Garliclike, foul odor. Nauseating
Hydrogen cyanide	HCN	0.001	Odor of bitter almonds
Hydrogen sulfide	H_2S	0.0011	Odor of rotten eggs. Nauseating

Table I.—ODOR THRESHOLDS (Continued,

Substance	Formula	Concentrations causing faint odor (mg. per liter) (oz. per 1,000 cu. ft.)	Remarks
Methyl anthranilate	$NH_2.C_6H_4.CO.OCH_3$	0.00037	Floral essence. Fruity odor
Methyl dichlorarsine	CH_3AsCl_2	0.0008	Slight odor. Irritating
Methyl mercaptan	CH_3SH	0.0011	Odor of decayed cabbage or onions
Methyl sulfide	$(CH_3)_2S$	0.0011	Odor of decayed vegetables
Methyl thiocyanate	$CH_3S.CN$	0.0096	Odor of almonds. Unpleasant
Nitrobenzene	$C_6H_5.NO_2$	0.03	Odor of bitter almonds
Oxidized oils	....	0.0011	Unpleasant and irritating
Ozone	O_3	0.001	Slightly pungent, irritating odor
Phenyl isocyanide	$C_6H_5.N:C$	*0.000029	Repulsive, nauseating odor
Phenyl isothiocyanate	$C_6H_5.N:C:S$	0.0024	Cinnamon odor. Pleasant
Phosgene	$COCl_2$	0.0044	Odor of ensilage or fresh-cut hay
Propioaldehyde	$CH:CCHO$	0.0022	Acrid, irritating odor
Propyl mercaptan	C_3H_7SH	0.000075	Unpleasant odor
n-Propyl sulfide	$(CH_3CH_2CH_2)_2S$	0.00081	Foul odor. Nauseating
Pyridine	C_6H_5N	*0.0037	Disagreeable, irritating odor
Skatole	C_9H_9N	0.0012	Fecal odor. Nauseating
Sulfur dioxide	SO_2	0.009	Pungent, irritating odor
Thiocresol	$CH_3C_6H_4.SH$	0.0001	Rancid, skunklike odor
Thiophenol	C_6H_5SH	0.000062	Putrid, nauseating odor
Trinitro butyl xylene	$(CH_3)_2.C_6(NO_2)_3.C(CH_3)_2$	0.00001	Musk odor

*Average value of observations obtained with material of varying purity.

FIG. 9.—Modern determination of odor properties at times requires elaborate mechanical facilities. (*Florida Chemical Research, Inc.*)

Fig. 10.—Odor appraisal may necessitate modification of atmospheric pressure. View of decompression room showing entryway to odor test chamber. (*Florida Chemical Research, Inc.*)

CHEMICAL OR PHYSICAL ANALYSIS OF ODOROUS SUBSTANCES

In loose fashion the level of odor intensity may be expressed in relation to the quantity of the odorivector in the air. Thus by appropriate chemical procedure it might be established that a certain air contained 100 p.p.m. of hydrogen sulfide and that an odor accompanied this concentration. Another atmosphere similarly tested might reveal only 25 p.p.m. Any odor sensation

FIG. 11.—Much odor appraisal is based upon odor comparison. Section of one odor reference bank of more than 4,000 items. (*Florida Chemical Research, Inc.*)

FIG. 12.—The "Stinkometer," a chemical method for evaluating freshness of foods through determination of volatile odors. Two-unit portable arrangement of apparatus. *A*, aeration flask; *F*, flow meter; *T*-1, *T*-2, reaction vessels; *W*-1, concentrated H_2SO_4; *W*-2, *W*-4, re-distilled water: *W*-3, 10 per cent alkaline potassium permanganate or activated carbon. (*Lang, Farber, and Yerman, and the Hooper Foundation, University of California, Food Industries.*)

might be expected to be of lower intensity. Distinctly this is not true for all substances and all circumstances. Low concentrations of some odorivectors may induce much higher odor intensities than the same substance in higher amounts.

Typical of several analytic devices is the inelegantly named "stinkometer" (Lang, Farber, and Yerman), now described and illustrated (Fig. 12). This apparatus is a chemical one described as a reliable means for evaluating freshness in foods by measuring volatile odors. It also can be used to measure the loss of desirable flavors. In application, aeration technique is employed, which separates the odorous substances from their points of origin and then passes them into an oxidizing reagent. After quantitative analysis appraisement is made as to the state of freshness or spoilage in specified comestibles.

Exactly reckoned, no contention may be made that odors themselves may be quantitatively measured except on the basis of extensions of minimum detectable odor levels, or instead, through such crude subjective gradations as "fleeting," "strong," "overpowering," etc. However, odorous substances at times may be measured with precision and some gradation may be established between odor intensities and known chemical quantities.

Chapter VI

The Pathology and Perversions of the Olfactory System

LIKE all other organs of the body, the olfactory apparatus is subject to defects, diseases, and dysfunctions. At the minimal level is the impairment of odor perception associated with edema and congestion of coryza. This is a common occurrence. At the highest level is the complete and permanent loss of the olfactory sense (anosmia), such as occasionally arises in connection with brain tumors, injuries, and possible infection. Some of the anomalies related to odor perception are bizarre. Within recent experience a middle-aged female, probably suffering from lues, gradually lost over a period of weeks all capacity to recognize odors. After some months and in the course of antiluetic treatment, but not necessarily as the result of it, a modified ability to recognize odors returned, but only a few classes of odors were detectable. This person was unable to discriminate between boiling cabbage and frying ham but associated with each "a food odor." This is somewhat analogous to color blindness. In another instance a young female visiting a friend in a hospital was much upset by the odor emanating from osteomyelitis. Leaving the hospital and journeying homeward on the streetcar, this woman an hour later was beset by the same odor in the absence of any other person known to be suffering from osteomyelitis. This condition is akin to afterimages in the realm of vision. It is impossible to determine the extent of hysterical and emotional factors in such situations.

The scope of this publication provides no warrant for detailed presentation of anomalies related to olfactory function. It is deemed sufficient to provide a grouping of such disturbances. In doing this the classification of Kenneth[1] is closely followed. That author notes that his classification is tentative and not altogether satisfactory. This classification follows:

1. *Cryptosmia* embraces all those conditions in which obstruction of the nasal passages prevents odor stimuli from reaching the odor-perceiving tissues. In these states the peripheral and central olfactory organs are intact.

2. *Anosmia* is applied to the complete loss of smelling capacity, permanent or temporary, due to some impairment of the peripheral or central structures. If the condition is unilateral, the term *hemianosmia* is suitable. The causes of anosmia are numerous, including gross dryness of olfactory mucosa, infec-

[1] *J. Laryngol. Otol.*, **43**, 410 (1928).

tion, trauma, drug action, congenital defects, etc. The site of impairment may be found either within the nasal areas or within the cranium. In the latter area anosmia may arise from the influence of aneurisms, tumors, bony overgrowths, injury, and infection. Functional disorders may represent etiology. On occasion a reflex anosmia may arise through unknown processes such as may derive from ovariectomy.

3. *Hyposmia* is applied to the partial loss of odor sense, whether permanent or temporary, and from all manner of causes. The application of this term may involve some overlapping with cryptosmia.

4. *Hyperosmia* is a term embracing excessive responses to odor stimuli. This state may arise in hysteria, neurasthenia, hypnosis, etc. It is chiefly to be associated with emotional states but otherwise may be the result of organic excessive irritability of olfactory tissues.

5. *Merosmia* includes those states in which there is normal odor perception for some odors but the impairment or total loss of ability to recognize other odors.

6. *Heterosmia* defines the somewhat extraordinary situation in which false odors are perceived. Thus, for example, from violets might be derived the odor of liederkranz cheese. Cheese, in turn, might yield the odor of chloroform or any other substance.

7. *Autosmia* designates the fairly common occurrence of continuous or repeated appearance of odors in the absence of any actual stimuli for such odors. A fair number of persons, for long periods of time, continuously or continually are beset by odors without the presence of the material ordinarily causing such odors. Fortunate is the person who is thus saddled with a pleasant odor. At least a portion of such condition may be accepted as odor hallucinations. Autosmia may not properly be applied to continuous odors from genuine causes, such as persistent sinus disease.

In the nomenclature of odor disturbances, many other terms have been suggested, such as cacosmia, parosmia, but it is believed that the categories just mentioned probably will include the greater number of dysfunctions of the smelling sense.

Apart from the transient impairment of odor perception relating to rhinitis with some infection or chemical cause, physicians are scarcely warranted in making favorable prognosis in odor perception anomalies. The psychological elements at times may be more difficult to eradicate than organic ones. Every individual case must be appraised within the limits of its own situation. The essence of this section is that a fair number of persons go about their affairs on a temporary or permanent basis with deviation in their odor-perceiving abilities that sets them apart from the usual.

Chapter VII

The Influence of Odors on Health and Comfort

ODORS in themselves are not the cause of organic disease. To that extent odors constitute no field of activity either for clinical medicine or for public health. It is obvious to all that some highly toxic substances, such as hydrogen sulfide, are associated with offensive odors; but the dangerous properties of this gas do not derive from the odor itself. In fact, its odor is valuable in serving as a warning of the presence of an injurious gas. Other dangerous substances are entirely odorless. The treacherous carbon monoxide possesses no odor, which very fact contributes to its danger. Methane, another common gas, is both odorless and without toxic properties beyond the capacity to act as a simple asphyxiant. The pungent odor of acetone vapors in no wise reflects danger, since this substance, in other than extraordinary cencentrations, is harmless. In general, odor or its absence serves as a fragile index of toxicity.

Average man believes to the contrary. For this fallacy he has some justification. For many generations a well-meaning medical profession believed and taught that odors were the proximate causes of many diseases, particularly fevers and diseases of the respiratory tract. These earlier physicians used the terms "miasmata," "effluvia," "exuviae." These physicians had difficulty in understanding and explaining just what these mysterious agents were like. To some they were gases or vapors; to others, odors. They granted the possibility that minute solid particles entered the air from "humid rot" and that these were the agents of disease. In this grouping there appeared the vague concept that new forms of life spontaneously generated, were transported to the healthy, and there began the undermining of their well-being. There were endless types and forms of these miasmata and effluvia. Every physician had his own accepted category. Apparently without exception these dissembling medical men agreed upon one—the miasma that emanated from the humid rotting around marshes, ponds, stagnant streams, and open sewers. How close to actual facts they were! The same marshes and ponds today are recognized as the breeding ground of mosquitos, which transport disease, and the multiplying area of bacteria that bring disease to man in such ways as through the drinking of this contaminated water.

The fervor of the medical profession to trace the origin of disease to putrescence gave rise to the "pythogenic theory." Thus typhoid fever, until times within the possible memory of many still alive, was catalogued as a pythogenic fever. In order that the state of mind of physicians as to etiology may be directly associated with his miasmata, effluvia, osmia, it may be desirable to quote various brief items in their exact language.

Dr. William Cullen, Professor of the Practice of Physic in the University of Edinburgh, in his "First Lines in the Practice of Physic," written in part in 1789, but appearing thereafter in other editions (thus attesting his eminence), writes:

Miasmata are next to be considered. These may arise from various sources and be of different kinds; but we know little of their variety, or of their several effects. We know with certainty only one species of miasma, which can be considered as the cause of fever; and, from the universality of this, it may be doubted if there be any other.

This miasma, so universally the cause of fever, is that which arises from marshes or moist ground, acted upon by heat. So many observations have now been made with respect to this, in so many different regions of the earth, that there is neither any doubt of its being in general a cause of fevers, nor of its being very universally the cause of intermittent fevers, in all their different forms.

The distinguished Dr. Cullen, in commendable effort to explain the mode of action of marsh effluvia on human beings, contributes:

To render our doctrine of fever consistent and complete, it is necessary to add here, that those remote causes of fever, human and marsh effluvia, seem to be of a debilitating or sedative quality. They arise from a putrescent matter. Their production is favored, and their power increased, by circumstances which favor putrefaction; and they often prove putrifactive ferments with respect to the animal fluids. As putrid matter, therefore, is always with respect to animal bodies, a powerful sedative, so it can hardly be doubted, that human and marsh effluvia are of the same quality: and it is confirmed by this, that the debility which is always induced, seems to be in proportion to the other marks that appear of the power of those causes.

Far from limiting fevers as the sole lot of diseases caused by strange emanations, Cullen in another portion of his published learning introduces:

Besides these cases of asthma excited by heat or cold, there are others, in which the fits are especially excited by powers applied to the nervous system; as by passions of the mind, by particular odors, and by irritations of smoke and dust.

In order not to saddle Dr. Cullen with an undue share of the onus of error, Dr. James Johnson in his third edition of "A Treatise on Derangements of the Liver, Internal Organs and Nervous System," published in 1832, but bearing a preface of 1820, likewise is noted to have recorded under the causes of asthma: "Hereditary conformation, atmospherical influence, certain irritations, as from dust, smoke, offensive odours, etc."

Johnson, apparently without meteorologic gallantry, and along with the earlier Lemnious, was highly suspicious of the evil qualities of East Wind as found in the British Isles. The East Wind, he concluded, contains vegeto-animal and other terrestrial effluvia, and implies that these qualities make men "sad, lumpish, much dejected, angry, waspish, dull and melancholy." Johnson does not claim that these are diseases, nor does he mention odors; but indeed, these are the very results of attempting to live with offensive odors. They do make men, and particularly women, "lumpish" and "wasp-ish." But these are not diseases.

Lest it be claimed that insufficient share of medical ignorance is laid in the lap of physicians in America, recourse is made to "The Theory and Treatment of Fever" by Dr. John Sappington of Missouri, who, in the year 1843, copyrighted that book and thereby claimed proprietorship for much that by today's standards would have caused him pain. In discussing the senses, as "avenues of disease" and in dealing with the "Olfactories" he may be found to be the author of this statement:

Let the olfactories meet, on every hill and every plain, in street, alley and the main, nought but mephitic gases of the dead, of men, of animals and plants, of whatever kind, of whatever hue, then the perturbation comes, the fever of the brain.

Apparently the learned gentleman is portraying the cause of meningitis. Not always did Dr. Sappington fully adhere to his odor theory of fevers, for later in this same work he seems to chide Dr. Rush, whom to condemn he quotes in derision:

On the 19th of this month (meaning August) I was requested to visit the wife of Mr. Peter LaMaigre . . . in consultation with . . . . I found her in the last stage of a highly bilious fever . . . . The most powerful cordials and tonics were prescribed, but to no purpose. She died on the evening of the next day. The origin of this fever was discovered to me at the same time, from the account which Dr. Faulke gave me of a quantity of damaged coffee which had been thrown upon Ball's wharf and in the adjoining dock on the 24th of July, nearly in a line with Mr. LaMaigre's house, and which had putrified there, to the great annoyance of the whole neighbourhood. After this consultation I was soon able to trace all of the cases of fever which I have mentioned to this cause . . . . From a conviction that the disease originated in the putrid exhalations from the damaged coffee, I published . . . a short address to the citizens of Philadelphia, with a view of directing public attention to the spot where the coffee lay, and thereby checking the progress of the fever . . . .

Shades of Arbuckle Brothers!

The boundaries of this etiologic quagmire might be extended to embrace just about all the kindred writings of that hundred-year period preceding the impact of the work of Budd and Pasteur. It is much more heartening to be able to record that in the midst of so much fallacy a few publications unequivocably denounced the concept of the causation of diseases by odors. In the Edinburgh *Medical and Surgical Journal* for 1806, in Vol. II, appears an article by Messrs. Guyton-Morveau and Chaptal, constituting a report of the Physical and Mathematical "Class" of the institute upon the question "Are Those Manufacturers Which Emit a Disagreeable Smell Prejudicial to Health?" This may not be quoted precisely since it is written in the form peculiar to the day, which may not now be well duplicated except in fac-simile. These authors, at the instigation of the Minister of the Interior, undertook an investigation of the industries known to produce offensive odors or fumes. A single paragraph mirrors their attitude:

The manufacture of poudrette is now establishing itself in all the great cities of France; and the operation by which night soil is reduced to a state of powder necessarily diffuses for a long time a most disagreeable smell. Establishments of this kind ought therefore to be formed in airy situations, and far from any dwelling, not that we regard the gaseous exhalation from them as prejudicial to health, but we cannot deny that it is inconvenient, tainted, disagreeable, and difficult to breathe.

With an eye for good public relations they presented to the "Class" this highly appropriate statement:

The making of Prussian Blue, the extraction of carbonate of ammonia by the distillation of animal bodies, in the new works of sal ammoniac, produces a great quantity of foetid vapours. In truth these exhalations are not dangerous to health; but, in these times to be reckoned a good neighbour it is not enough not to be dangerous, we must also not be disagreeable.

As a generality, they note:

We cannot too seriously advise the magistrate intrusted with the care of the public health and safety to dismiss those ill-grounded complaints, which too often are directed against establishments, daily threatening the prosperity of the honest manufacturer, retarding the progress of industry, and compromising the fate of the arts themselves . . . . He should carefully distinguish between what is only inconvenient or disagreeable, and what is really noxious or dangerous.

The editors of that journal, manifestly impressed by the merits of the report, make editorial comment even more pertinent to the needs of an investigator of odors 140 years later. The editors note: "A disagreeable smell is by no means a certain criterion of an unwholesome atmosphere."

The pythogenic theory owes its downfall more than to any other single event to the blows rained upon it by Dr. William Budd, who, in 1873, published his "Typhoid Fever, Its Measure, Mode of Spreading and Prevention." This Englishman in that book contributed a forthright example of scientific writing so precise that no opportunities were left for opponents' rejoinders. Along with its scientific potency are items of human interest that would have taken away the curse of dullness had any dullness been present. At the site of one of Dr. Budd's investigations, an open sewer,

A gentleman on horseback drew up and addressed me in these words: "Ah, I see what you are upon. The only wonder is, that all these poor people have not died of fever long ago. For, any time these last six years, but in summer especially, to anyone coming down this lane, the stink has been enough to knock a man down."

But, although—so to speak—strong enough to knock a man down, it failed all these long years to cause a single case of fever.

Nature, apparently lending a hand toward the overthrowing of a death-dealing theory as to the causes of disease, furnished Dr. Budd with perfect opportunity to confound any and all adherents of the pythogenic theory. In

Fig. 1.—Cartoon *Punch*, June 18, 1859, noting the historic "stink" of the Thames. (*Reproduced by permission of Punch, and Bradbury, Agnew & Company, Ltd.*)

the hot months of 1858–1859, the Thames River stank badly (Figs. 1, 2). For the first time in the history of man the sewage of nearly three millions of people had been brought to seethe and ferment under the burning sun in one vast open cloaca lying in their midst.

The result we all know. Stench so foul, we may well believe, had never before ascended to pollute this lower air. Never before, at least, had a stink risen to the height of an historic event . . . . For many weeks, the atmosphere of Parliamentary Committee-rooms was only rendered barely tolerable by the suspension before every window, of blinds saturated with chloride of lime . . . . The river steamers lost

OUR NASAL BENEFACTORS.

Is it true, we wonder—it should be, if it isn't—that with the view of ascertaining the exact state of the Thames, the Government have sent out a Smelling Expedition, for which service none but the sharpest-nosed M.P.s were allowed to volunteer? As we are always anxious to avoid misstatement, we should be glad, if we are wrong, to be officially corrected; but we have heard that, with the knowledge of the perils of the trip, it was agreed, that only the unmarried members should be suffered to embark on it. Lest widowhood result, none but single men were accepted for the service.

We understand, moreover, that to give the sniffers ample time for making their experiments, a Government express-boat was chartered for the voyage, as being, it was thought, the slowest craft in use, and surest to break down. No member was allowed on board who had not made his will; and an experienced *corps* of surgeons were commissioned to attend, in order to prevent loss of life, if possible. All kinds of antidotes were abundantly provided, and there was a goodly store of brandy and other tried restoratives. In short, the nauseating nature of the service being known, due arrangements were made for the comfort of the sick, and every medical appliance to relieve them was in readiness. There was a most liberal supply of hand-basins, and every member was allowed a Steward to himself, to prevent the fruitless bellowing and bawling for that officer, to which sufferers from sickness are commonly reduced.

Now the question we would moot for the reflection of the public is, how are we most fittingly to honour these brave smellers, and show our gratitude for what they have had the courage to go through for us. Their nasal gallantry must clearly not be left unrecognised. Having sacrificed their noses on the altar of their country, how are we to recompense them for their patriotic act? Shall we institute forth-with an Order of Nasal Valour, and decorate the heroes who survive to wear it? Or would it be more suitable to erect them, each, a statue? or strike a medal to commemorate their distinguished nasal service? On one side might be shown the head of Father Thames, seen in his most filthy and disgusting aspect; while the other might be graven with the outline of a nose, pressed rather tightly with a thumb and forefinger. If this design won't do, let the nation find a better. Such exalted nasal heroism we have never before known, and it is not meet that it go unrewarded.

FIG. 2.—"The Order of Nasal Valor," *Punch*, July 10, 1858. (*Reproduced by permission of Punch, and Bradbury, Agnew & Company, Ltd.*)

their accustomed traffic, and travellers, pressed for time, often made a circuit of many miles rather than cross one of the city bridges. For months together, the topic almost monopolized the public prints.

Despite the worst forebodings, the hot weather passed away and the health of London had been remarkably good. There was not only a general lowered death rate but a remarkable diminution in the prevalence of fevers, diarrhea, and the other forms of disease then commonly attributed to putrid emanation.

Thus the Thames washed away all probability that at any future time intelligent laymen or physicians would ever attribute substantial diseases to odors.

In connection with odors there is scant reason beyond historic interest to disentomb the now whitened bones of the miasmata. Such reason as may be warranted derives from the desire that the interment of the miasmata and the effluvia unfailingly include the osmia as well. The embracement of odors in this neubulous lot of imagined disease causes ever was murky. It is always difficult to define a nonexistent thing. Like the dragging forth for parading of the crumbling bodies of the nobility of the Incas, so from time to time and usually for litigious parades odors still are resurrected as the stem of disease. Tribute to fallacy!

With full intent of minimizing the role of odors in relation to the causation of impaired health, it still becomes necessary to recognize those indirect ways in which odors may contribute detrimentally to well-being. The discomfiture and disagreeableness that may be brought about by foul odors are so substantially grounded that it would be somewhat remarkable if these aesthetic affronts did not serve an ill end, even though relatively unimportant and temporary. Nor is it necessary to make the claim that those persons who are upset by odors are necessarily hyperosmic. The disturbances occasioned by odors that fringe upon ill-health, include lowered appetite for food, lowered water consumption, impaired respiration, functional nausea and vomiting, insomnia, and mental perturbation.

LOWERED APPETITE FOR FOOD

In the most offensive of trades, in which putrescent flesh is partly processed by hand and in which grossly fetid and obnoxious odors may permeate the immediate premises, groups of workers at mealtimes may be seen to be consuming hearty meals with relish. This is a regular procedure—a banquet in the midst of carrion. Consulted, these workers, who in truth may be of low aesthetic level, admit no awareness of odors or of visual deterrents to eating. These inured or conditioned workers at once belie any and all claims that offensive odors regularly hamper the intake of proper amounts of foods. By way of controls, but not scientific controls, it is common experience that the casual visitor or worker cannot join in these banquets. Usually they are exercising all the discipline at their command to avoid display of their tremendous disgust. Hours after an investigating group may have left offensive work premises, and after the individual members have bathed and changed garments, some, when suddenly confronted with what ordinarily would have been savory food, such as a boiled ham hock, experience a tumultuous revulsion that cannot be hidden. In this total recital are many of the elements that enter the complex situation as to disturbing odors and impaired appetites—inurement, olfactory paralysis, sensitivity, temporariness, varying aesthetic levels, afterimages, etc.

This matter of appetite and odors has been better investigated in the laboratory. Some results are incredible, some painstaking and commendable. A few are now epitomized and subjected to comment.

About 1895 Alessi, working at the University of Rome, undertook to establish the response of small laboratory animals to odors that at least are offensive to man. The services of rabbits, guinea pigs, and rats were elicited, 494 in all, including a meager seven as controls. For the rabbits and guinea pigs the source of the feculent odors were pans of fecal material placed beneath the animal cages. Provisions for the rats were made by locating their cages over an untrapped water closet. While the study as made was a highly serious affair, perhaps it is permissible to wonder how it was determined that these odors were objectionable to the animals involved. Possibly these rats, left to their own devices, might have elected to give up their cages and make their permanent abode in near-by dunghills of their own selection. At any rate, after three to six days of this embarrassing exposure, these animals "lost their usual vivacity and pined away in spite of eating voraciously." At various times after exposure the animals were injected with harmful bacteria and in some groups 90 per cent died, while none of the controls so injected died. Later 56 rats and guinea pigs were exposed for such periods as 14 days to one or more of the gases deemed likely to have been present in the feculent atmosphere. The lot included hydrogen sulfide, ammonia, and methyl sulfide. These animals, although injected with bacteria at a later time, did not die. This seriously made investigation has not been accepted equally seriously, and the only conclusion that may not be challenged is that in spite of everything the animals "ate voraciously."

A more important inquiry was made by the New York State Commission on Ventilation, through Winslow and Palmer, in 1915.[1] For this work human subjects were exposed to the ordinary air of an unventilated room containing whatever polluting substances might be given off by bodies and garments. These persons were exposed for from four to seven hours daily, with many variations over long periods of time. The chief finding, and an unexpected one, had to do with differences in the consumption of food on test days and on control days. About 5 per cent more of the furnished food was consumed when the supply of air was fresh. These authors state, "These experiments seem to warrant the conclusion that there are substances present in the air of

[1] *Proc. Soc. Exp. Biol. Med.*, **21**, 141 (1915).

an unventilated occupied room (even when its temperature and humidity are controlled) which, in some way, without producing conscious discomfort or detectable physiological symptoms, diminish the appetite for food."

At a still later time Winslow and Greenberg[1] reverted to the Alessi sources of odors, resorting to human or dog feces for the strong feculent odors, but provided a more elaborate and better protected experimental arrangement. Guinea pigs were utilized as the test animal, and at proper times within the experimental procedure these animals were inoculated with the colon bacillus or with diphtheria toxin as a measure of any diminution of vital resistance, in keeping with the older work of Alessi.

This work failed to live up to the Alessi claims, but it was noted that early in the experiment there was a slight and transitory depression in the growth curves compared with those of the controls. These authors concluded that putrefactive odors exert a passing effect upon the appetite for food in human beings and apparently so in guinea pigs, since weight increases for a short time did not quite equal those of controls.

Shortly prior to 1935 Winslow with Herrington, working in the John B. Pierce Laboratory of Hygiene, reentered the complex field of the influence of odors upon appetite.[2] These authors readily foresaw the genuine difficulties attending the study described. Eight young males constituted the test group. On four or five mornings each week for several winter months, these individuals were under observation for a period of three hours. Well-controlled conditions of ventilation were provided, and the particular odor chosen for the odor days was that from heated house dust carefully prepared. During these weeks the subjects were not aware whether any particular day was a test day or a free day. At noon the real test was supplied in the form of lunch, which varied through three menus, with food alterations carefully introduced to meet special requirements of preference, monotony, attractiveness, etc. The odors, as introduced, while not detectable by the subjects, were such as to be obvious to anyone entering the room for the first time, and the quality of the odor was such as to be recognized as the odor of heated dust. At the end of the meal, and as the important matter, the food left over, plate by plate, was weighed day by day. The results obtained were highly useful but somewhat entangled with influences of monotony, coming of spring weather, and natural preferences for certain foods over others. A liking for potato salad led to no difference between odor and no-odor days during the early weeks of this study, but for the unwanted macaroni and cheese there was a prompt rejection by 13 per cent on odor days. But this situation was made complex by the fact that in the later weeks this reduction was only 6 per cent. From out the lot of well-considered technical features, the substantial finding was

[1] *Am. J. Pub. Health,* **8,** 759 (1918).
[2] *Am. J. Hyg.,* **23,** 143 (1936).

that in the presence of odoriferous atmosphere less food was eaten, but let the authors speak for themselves.

This study seems to justify the conclusion that the odor given off from heated house dust (even when not consciously perceived) has a clearly demonstrable effect in reducing the appetite for food and hence may be considered as definitely harmful to health.

From a general physiological standpoint, the results seem to us of some importance. They furnish, so far as we are aware, the most convincing evidence which has yet been offered (indeed, the only controlled objective evidence which has been offered except for the results of the New York State Commission on Ventilation) of the effect of mild organic odors upon human health and comfort.

Without intended detraction from this meritorious work in a difficult field, it is noted that highly different conclusions and interpretations might have been drawn from this study. Instead of the foregoing, we might conclude that odors, by diminishing the intake of an excessively high caloric diet, serve to protect against the baneful results of overeating.

It comes to be autopical that odors, should they hamper the intake of proper foods to the point that nutrition is disturbed on a pathological level, are detrimental to health.

LOWERED WATER CONSUMPTION

The nose, situated on the cliff above the mouth, long has been trusted as the "censor" or the "sentinel" for what passes through the mouth or the nares. The nose is the "outer guardian" and the tongue's taste buds are the "inner," each supplementing the other. In these capacities, these organs are great failures. Neither is capable of detecting those agents most capable of destruction. These outer and inner guardsmen let bacteria pass without challenge. Moreover, these sentinels are alarmists. They cry "danger" when there is no danger. In particular, neither is a perfect judge of drinking water.

The healthy human body's need for water is highly labile. A myriad of men may rebel over any suggestion that more than two glasses daily be consumed. Such persons appear to thrive. A lusty molten-steel worker on a summer's day may perspire a quart of sweat every hour and may consume an equal quantity of water during some hours. He thrives. The enthusiasts' daily imbibition of boastful lots of water frequently represents habit rather than the meeting of physiologic demand. It follows that the limited and temporary curtailment of water use on account of odors or other extrinsic causes need not be rated as a major calamity.

In any community accustomed to an odorless public drinking-water supply, the occurrence of an odor or taste promptly will lead to flurry and sometimes furor. At once widespread curtailment of water drinking arises, along with resort to bottled drinks including at times alcoholics, chiefly beer. Intelligent apprehension may be in order, and here is a laudable circumstance for the entry of public-health activities into the odor realm. More often than otherwise these odors reflect no condition that renders the water unpotable. A spate flooding a tarred roadway and later draining into a stream serving as a water supply may cause that stream to acquire and retain for days an odor that alarms the residents but is harmless. Such an odor may defy removal.

The odor of chlorine in treated drinking water has long, but decreasingly, hindered the universal application of this beneficent treatment. Paradoxically, the possible trace odor of chlorine in water to which objection may be raised is in itself evidence of the probable absence of the effete substances against which the nose in its proper function might warn. Chlorine gas in concentrations of relatively low magnitude is harmful, but the mere odor of chlorine may be a token of water purity.

In other communities the ground-water supplies habitually have an offensive odor or taste or both. Chiefly these are sulfur-bearing waters. The citizenries of these hundreds of localities long since have lost all awareness of objectionable qualities. There is no known proof that in these communities water consumption is at any lower level than the general average or that in any wise the community health is impaired. Only visitors to such towns and cities are outraged by the water's odor.

The spas that attract the afflicted include many sulfur springs from which the outpouring water releases a stench that trademarks the town. Joyously the hopeful go about the drinking of this odoriferous liquid, at times relying on the odors themselves to restore health.

In fine, only mild vilification of the usual odor-bearing water is in order. Disgust is impermanent; water abstinence is fleeting. At best there is but meager indication of water starvation on account of odors. Of course if there are those who deprive their bodies of the minimum requirements of water on account of osmic disaffection, the same bodily impairments may arise from thirst as from any other cause, but conceivably there might be more pathology in the head of the nonwater drinker than in prospect from the consumption of the odoriferous water.

IMPAIRED RESPIRATION

At the first impact of an unwanted odor, the tendency is to engage in two or three deep appraising sniffs. If the verdict is that something noxious is astir, the next effort is to diminish the depth of breathing in order to keep the odor stimulus low in the nasal spaces and away from the vault-placed odor-perceiving mechanism. Breathing temporarily becomes slow and shallow. Resort may be made to mouth breathing, but this is not fully protective, since the taste buds in some measure stand in aid to the nose.

Depressed voluntary breathing may not long be sustained. Respiratory demands dominate the ventilatory. Actually, because of panic or agitation, more energy may be expended and more breathing thus required. Much of this takes place without the cognizance of the one concerned.

Between the minimum breathing of a person lying calmly at rest and that of the fatigued but still hard-working individual the differential ratio may be as 1 to 30. Both are on a physiologic basis provided the mentioned fatigue is not of pathologic order. No valid assertion may therefore be made that, when the odor-offended one slumps into inaction in order to indulge in lowered breathing to lessen odor perception, the body is threatened with any decimating shortage of atmospheric gases.

Often the claim is made that in the presence of community-wide offensive odors, particularly at night, it becomes necessary to seal off all inlets of air. Then come vivid stories of suffocation. The actualities are to the contrary. In the unventilated, stuffy, foul-smelling room, the chemicals essential to breathing are little modified and are sufficient. Doctors condone their patient's throwing wide open the winter windows, but the doctors themselves are prone to keep theirs closed or cracked just enough to underslide the index finger. Foremostly, ventilation is a matter of the skin and not of the lungs, of physics and not of chemistry. The virtues of ventilation center about temperature, humidity, and air motion, not about carbon dioxide and the exuviae.

FUNCTIONAL NAUSEA AND VOMITING

The actual presence of any foul substance within the stomach may lead to vomiting. This is one of nature's therapies—she expels the harmful agent. So deeply seated within our lives is this protective measure that on many occasions, without the actual presence within the body of anything offensive, the stomach by its prodroma of nausea indicates what it would do if invaded. This reflex, which is far more complex than here implied and which includes the gradients of peristalsis, is set into operation under circumstances remote to gastric affront. Some persons sensitive to cold often vomit on passing from warm to chilling atmospheres; the tired, playing child may vomit; sexual unniceties may provoke vomiting and consternation. The reflexes may be so conditioned as to come into play under the most aesthetic circumstances. For example, a very few persons might vomit if handed a rose, all because of some well-buried disturbing associations.

Scents, tastes, and visual images are the chief stimuli to functional nausea and vomiting. Offensive odors stand near the top. While long familiarity may dispel this response to outraged nostrils, a job-hardened investigator on a new odoriferous inquiry may make himself laughable as readily as his high-school assistant on a first assignment.

The relative item is: "How significant is this to health?" The answer is fairly simple. Apart from the loss of needed food, a little vomiting is harmless. Trauma to a sensitive ego may be more important. No proud woman enjoys unexpected vomiting as her streetcar glides by the egg-powder plant. Occasionally in the presence of continued odors a few persons may suffer persistent vomiting. Then more substantial causes, such as childhood mal-events, should be sought by the physician.

INSOMNIA

For many millions of persons the acquisition of refreshing and sufficient sleep is regularly a difficulty. Any additional disturbing factor multiplies the difficulty. The causes of insomnia are protean. Offensive odors may be accorded a nonconspicuous place in this array. Some odors are quite capable of rousing from deep sleep. One of the properties of the ideal odorific warning agent is just that capacity. Unfortunately, some of the continuous odors are more intense or more noticeable at night, owing to humidity and temperature changes and to the absence of the destructive action of sunlight. Resentment over odor-broken sleep may perpetuate insomnia long after the odor wave has passed. To the extent that odors may be proved to interfere with sleep, and provided the total sleep is physiologically inadequate, these odors are related to health. All considered it is the intent to place this item in the category of the trifling.

MENTAL PERTURBATION

The concept that an angry person is a sick person, and at times a dangerous person, possibly constitutes the soundest of reasons for regarding offensive odors as contributory to ill-health. Long-continued odor exposure for some persons drives away all semblance of poise and restraint. Otherwise calm persons may become mildly maniacal, hysterical, capable of carrying out acts or making threats entirely foreign to their composed selves. In short, anger is the poison. Entire communities may be aroused to the point of near rioting by offensive odors. Such unreasonable and preposterous claims are made in connection with odor situations that these very claims through their ridiculousness are apt to defeat them. When in the presence of litigation involving odor nuisances, the defendant denies any responsibility for outbursts of anger, rage, or temper on the part of those claiming injury, he is always on such solid ground as regularly to have the better of the situation.

Odors are credited with providing the shortest route into the subconscious. Granting the assertion, it is emphasized that, on a day-by-day basis, individuals and groups of the public evince a notable vulnerability to vexations from offensive odors, be they trivial or thumping.

SUMMARY

Sanitation and medicine are still mildly handicapped by the traditional belief that odors breed disease and impair health. Generations ago, physicians themselves created this error. While physicians long since have disassociated their activities based on the concept of odors as causes of disease, it is far more difficult to remove this fallacy from the minds of a large portion of the public.

The genuine part played by odors in relation to health is minor and dips deeply into emotions and neuroses. At the extreme of likelihood, offensive odors unfavorably influence health only through the possibilities of lessening food and water intake, disturbing sleep, promoting nausea and vomiting, and provoking anger with its attending evils.

Chapter VIII

Human Body Odors in Health

INESCAPABLY, offensive odors in the form of body odors confront every person. The many persons who fortunately are little aware of the offensive trades, open sewers, stockyards, chemical works, and such, may not expect to travel far afield without disturbance from human body secretions and excretions. The foremost service rendered by air conditioning designed for human well-being is not the promotion of health but the riddance of the atmosphere of outraging smells, some of human origin. The presence of unwanted body-surface odors is a far more complex thing than the mere matter of insufficient bathing or inadequate change of garments. For this reason this chapter undertakes in epitomized form a portrayal of the anatomy and physiology of the skin's secretory organs as a preliminary to the presentation of useful methods for combating the odors involved in the process of skin functioning.

NATURAL BODY ODORS AND BODY-ODOR VAGARIES

Many races, apart from hygienic practices, exhibit odors more or less peculiar to themselves. Always these odors are more readily perceived by persons of other races. The Chinese and Japanese are relatively free from any special race odors, which partly is attributed to their low-nitrogen, cereal diet. This statement is not well attested by experience with the Japanese under conditions of warfare. Bitter condemnation has been directed to the odors of Japanese individuals, military camps, and cities. Granting such realities, these odors may not constitute particular race odors such as characterize some other races. The small number of individuals among such races who suffer from such affection as osmidrosis are accorded greater disdain than is found among some other groups. The Negro, both in Africa and elsewhere, is the best known of the racial offenders. In his case, the number of skin glands conducive to offense is probably increased. Among other groups diet rather than glandular plenitude may be the source of added offense. Orientals complain of buttery odors of Europeans, including in this instance the inhabitants of North America. Particularly, Orientals find difficulty in adjusting to the odors of European and American women. The residents of Balkan areas are set apart as having a characteristic odor, usually described as feculent. The

73

Eskimo smells like the blubber that he eats. The Mayan Indians of the Middle Americas, noted for scrupulous personal hygiene insofar as ablutions are concerned, are little blamed for body odors, but some other Middle American stocks may not be equally exculpated.

Further south the Brazilians are afflicted with body odors said to be negroid in type but much less offensive. Some of the people living along the lower Andes are credited with a high frequency of odorous bodies, but this represents no condemnation of all groups residing in high altitudes. The high consumption of animal flesh in contrast to fundamental diets of fish and vegetables is believed to be a factor in body-odor causation. Lady Dorothy Nevill, as cited by Bienfang[1] from "Table Topics," is credited with saying in noting her dietary adventures during the siege of Paris, "I tried eating donkey, too, but I had to stop that, it made me stink." Those races given to fondness for alliaceous foods prove offensive apart from the odor of such comestibles on the breath. In the widespread contempt among the races, nearly every race is prone to charge all other races as being "smelly." A much publicized and somewhat dubious aphorism is to the effect that "we are what we eat." Greater justification might attend the statement "we smell like what we eat."

As to individuals and smaller groups, it may be noted that the young and old are less odorous than the middle-aged. The very lean and the very fat may be more offensive than those blessed with normal nutrition, brunets more than blonds, women more than men. It is conceded that special acts and circumstances provoke the secretion of different odorous chemicals within the sweat. Within the jargon of those investigating odors may be heard the term "platform odor," one arising when a person is under the excitement of speechmaking or appearance in court as a witness. A somewhat different odor might appear in the same person, a "ladder odor," if perched precariously and anxiously on a ladder. However, if he were chased up this ladder or into a tree by a vicious dog or an angry bear, a third distinguishable odor might arise, a "fear odor." Admittedly, such fine gradations may represent some degree of speculation. The menstruating woman or the pregnant woman may present odors apart from those possibly to be associated with the genitalia. Prior to the beginning of a menstrual flow some women provide odors telltale of that impending state. Many drugs, later to be mentioned, eliminated by the body in part through the skin give rise to temporary periods of odor offense. Many other chemicals applied externally may be equally as disturbing as the odors that they are presumed to mask. The choice of perfumes or the quantities employed by some women make them socially undesirable, and the use of such drugs as iodoform to mask the odors of infection may merely substitute one offender for another.

[1] "The Subtle Sense," University of Oklahoma Press, Norman, 1946.

SKIN GLANDULAR SYSTEM

Some body odors associated with surface areas as to origin may derive from disintegrating tissues, such as of the feet; some may be created by skin lesions of disease states, but these are not here contemplated; some may result from application of substances to the skin by way of therapy or as cosmetics; some may represent discharges from the alvine or genitourinary tracts; some attributed to the body may in fact be limited to clothing from previous contacts with the body. Laying aside these origins, but without acquitting them as sources of odor offense, the prime cause of body-surface odors is to be found in the secretions or exuviae of the skin's glands, of which there are numerous types or at least variations in morphology or function. The outpourings of these glands may be offensive on first appearance on the skin, but, preponderantly, subsequent chemical alteration is responsible. For these reasons, description of the anatomy of the skin's glandular structure is warranted, but without any full presentation of the gross or minute anatomy of the skin as an organ entity.

The glands of the skin, without inclusion of mucosal surfaces, fall into two broad groups, the sebaceous and the sweat glands—each with its own subdivisions and special functions.

Sweat Glands.—In number these surely exceed 2,000,000 and by some are reckoned as high as 15,000,000, and their total

FIG. 1.—Coiled portion of sweat gland from axillary region of a man. (*Huber and Adamson,* "*Contributions to Medical Research*," *University of Michigan,* 1903.)

length would attain over eight miles. These sweat glands (merocrine glands, coil glands, sudoriparous glands, glandulae sudoriparae, glandulae glomiformes), are situated in the skin itself and in the subcutaneous tissues but empty upon the skin surface. Their openings are popularly termed "pores," although this name may apply to the openings of some classes of sebaceous glands. These coiled or balled glands if straightened out would be tubular with a single layer of secreting epithelial cells surrounding a lumen (Figs. 1 to 3). Toward the terminus at the skin surface the structural arrangement becomes somewhat modified, to assume a corkscrew shape. The tubular structure is associated with a few muscular fibers running as spirals about the tube. If straightened out the entire gland might attain in length several millimeters but as coiled simulates a length approximately 2 to 3 mm. These glands lie embedded in the fibrous and fatty structure of the subcutaneous areas and extend outward through the true dermal layers. Greater numbers per skin-area unit are to be found on the palms and soles than elsewhere.

Two types are recognized and by designation are the "eccrine" ("exocrine") glands, which are the smaller and secrete a simple fluid, and the "apocrine glands," which are larger in size, secrete a more complex output, including some cell protoplasm, detritus, and possibly some oil, and are somewhat more

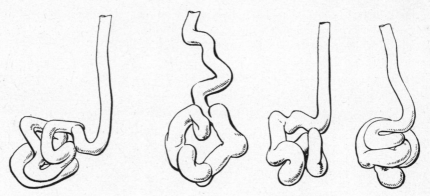

Fig. 2.—Variation in sweat-gland structure. Coiled portion and part of duct from wax model. Two at left from infant. Two at right from eight-month fetus. (*Huber and Adamson,* "Contributions to Medical Research," *University of Michigan, 1903.*)

closely identified with hairy structures. These are found chiefly in the axillae, in the pubic regions, about the nipples, the anus, etc. These glands are little active until the time of puberty. Their openings may be into the hair follicle or directly upon the skin surface. The embryologic developments of these two varieties is somewhat dissimilar.

It is probable that the apocrine glands are far from comprising a single anatomical type or a single function. Dissimilarity of odors that may arise from the same apocrine area under changing emotional stresses suggests that certain odorous secretions may be linked with special gland types, possibly equipped with different innervation or other stimulating source.

The chief function of the sweat glands is as a part of the heat-regulating mechanisms of the body. Resulting odors are only indirectly related to heat regulation. The lesser excretory sweat-gland function is to be more closely related to odors. Gland for gland, the apocrine glands are more significant to odors than the eccrine sort. The chemistry of sweat appears in a shortly following section.

The Sebaceous Glands.—These (holocrine glands, sebiparous glands, oil glands, glandulae sebaceae) are more complex in structure than sweat glands (Fig. 4). They are racemose or acinous, commonly connected with hair fol-

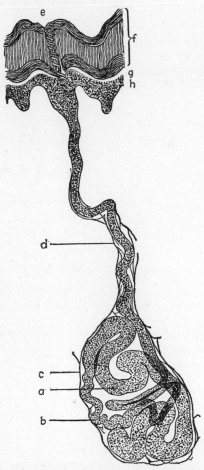

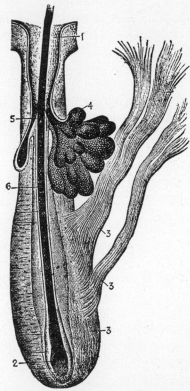

Fig. 3.—Complete sweat gland [duct and outlet (higher magnification)]. *a*, coils forming gland; *b*, beginning of excretory duct; *c*, a few muscle fibers may surround glandular structure; *d*, excretory duct; *e*, sweat pore; *f*, corneous layer; *g*, stratum lucidum; *h*, granular layer (Von Brunn). (*Stelwagon and Gaskill, "Diseases of the Skin," W. B. Saunders Company.*)

Fig. 4.—Sebaceous gland around hair follicle of scalp. 1, intrafollicular portion of hair shaft; 2, hair papilla; 3, smooth muscles attached to follicle (arrectores pilorum); 4, sebaceous gland. (*Rooker and Obermeyer, "Modern Dermatology and Syphilology," J. B. Lippincott Company, after Sappey.*)

licles but otherwise emptying directly upon the skin surfaces; some are located on nonhairy surfaces such as the lips, the glans penis, the inner surface of the prepuce, and the labia minora. The prime function of these glands is the oiling of the skin and contact surfaces. Secretion is intermittent, as needed by the skin.

Six types or modifications may be described. The commonest are the sebaceous glands linked with the hair shaft and hair follicle. From two to six glands empty into the hair follicle and contribute to the oiliness of both hair and near-by skin. The second is limited to the lanugal hair growth; but the hair and the gland duct opening, while adjacent, are separate. Histologically these glands are large and complex. A third form is found apart from hair and is distinctly limited to areas where mucosa meets skin—the lips, the nipples, the near orificial surfaces of the genitalia. These glands are stigmatized as the glandulae odoriferae of the male and female.

The three remaining differential sebaceous units are the large Meibomian glands of the eyelids, the ceruminosal glands producing ear wax (cerumen), and the glands of Tyson of the prepuce, which may not be other than the third form earlier mentioned.

Brunets and persons of dark races are equipped with more sebaceous glands than blonds and are credited with a higher frequency of odor offense. It is possible that sebaceous glands may be invaded by organisms (not the usual folliculitis causative organisms) including one animal parasite, an acarus. Their contributions may add to the odor situation attending sebaceous gland functions.

THE CHEMISTRY OF PERSPIRATION AND OF SEBACEOUS SECRETIONS

The composition of perspiration is highly variable both as to individuals and for the same individual throughout the day. The usual quantity of insensible perspiration is somewhere near 700 cc. for adults. On a hot summer day or in hot trades hard-working laborers may perspire this amount hourly. This is essentially normal and is not to be regarded as representing a pathologic hyperidrosis. Obviously the fluids excreted onto the skin surface represent a mixture of both sweat and sebaceous secretion, so that precisely it is sometimes difficult to associate with respective glands responsibility for some constituents. Sebaceous secretions probably undergo fewer variations than is true for sweat.

The usual perspiration has the following composition:

	Parts
Water	991.0
Solids	9.0
Sodium chloride	5.2
Urea	1.2

	Parts
Organic nitrogen	1.2
Calcium phosphate	0.2
Potassium carbonate	0.1
Sulfates	0.6

The specific gravity of sweat ranges from 1.002 to 1.008. Its pH ranges from 3 to 7.5, but varies greatly, the reaction being acid, alkaline, or neutral. Prolonged sweating usually eventuates in greater alkalinity. At any one time the pH may be different at divers portions of the body. With some exceptions as to constituency, sweat may be accepted as resembling a diluted urine of the same moment.

Over and above these basic elements scores of others may appear in traces. No less, these trace quantities may be the prime source of unpleasant odors. Their entry into perspiration may not indicate any abnormal state. From a knowledge of dietary habits, some odorous constituents of sweat may be anticipated; but it is scarcely possible to predict the sweat modifications that may result from anxiety, excitement, hysteria, sexual activities, fright, etc. The more important in the group of minor constituents of perspiration are acids such as formic, acetic, proprionic, butyric, valeric, capric, caproic, caprylic, palmitic, stearic. The corresponding ethers are sometimes present, such as butyric, and likewise esters. Lactic acid appears during exertion; bile derivatives may appear on occasion; pyridoxine, ascorbic acid, and other substances related to vitamins may be present if an excess exists in the body. Sterols, chiefly cholesterol, may appear. Sugar and acetone may arise in diabetes and uric acid under some circumstances. No small part of offensive odors originates from the decomposition of cells themselves, in part comprising gland-cell decomposition and in part the disintegration of desquamated skin. The interaction of sweat upon sebaceous secretion and sweat upon cellular tissues contributes to the sum total of odor possibilities.

A large number of medicaments may provide body odors through appearance in perspiration. Representative are sulfur, arsenic, iodides, bromides, phosphates, ether, tars, turpentine, asefetida, musk, copaiba.

Sebum, the secretion of the sebaceous glands as apart from sweat glands, represents as to composition a complex mixture of fatty acids, higher alcohols, esters, lipoids (chiefly cholesterol), and glycerides together with cells destroyed in the process of secretion.

CONTROL OF BODY ODORS

Laying aside as obvious the virtues of sufficient ablutions, and accepting as sometimes excusable the use of perfumes solely for the purpose of odor masking, the chief measures for the control of body surface odors are

1. Systemic treatment for the curtailment of perspiration
2. Localized X-ray therapy
3. Local application of chemical antiperspirants and deodorants

Systemic Treatment for the Curtailment of Perspiration.—Since body odors more often than not appear on a physiologic rather than a pathologic level, little warrant exists for any widespread resort to systemic treatment, and never other than under the direction of a competent physician. In pathologic states of hyperidrosis and osmidrosis, physicians may provide therapeutic measures along the following lines: The perspiration output may be diminished by such drugs as atropine, arsenic, morphine and agaricin, the last named being introduced orally in tablets or capsules in maximum doses of 0.02 gm. Various calcium components and camphor likewise have been accorded some praise. To a limited extent the salicylates have been recommended; ergot with picrotoxine has been advocated. As a substitute for atropine, its less active derivative, methyl atropine, may be introduced. Aconite, jaborandi, pilocarpine, and phenol have their advocates. This systemic approach to the control of hyperidrosis is little favored.

Localized X-ray Therapy.—Unquestionably, Roentgen therapy applied to limited areas such as the axillae will act to curtail the flow of perspiration. Recourse to such procedure should be limited to the last resort level. Sponsorship by knowing physicians is requisite. Eller[1] states:

Roentgen ray therapy has been useful in lessening or controlling excessive sweating in localized areas, such as the hands, feet and axillae. However, great caution must be exercised in the dosage and filtration in order to avoid roentgen injuries. If the irradiation has been given up to the skin tolerance, it must be discontinued even though the excessive sweating persists. For many years I have used roentgen ray therapy in the following dosage and filtration with satisfactory results: doses of 80 to 100 *r* units with a filtration of 1 mm of aluminum, using the following factors: 85 kv, ma 3, distance eight inches. This dose is administered once weekly for five treatments. After this treatment has been discontinued, it is advisable that a daily application of a ten percent solution of aluminum chloride be used.

Local Application of Chemical Antiperspirants and Deodorants.—Antiperspirants act to curtail the quantity of perspiration output. Deodorants serve through masking, neutralizing, or counteracting odor-producing substances. Since some substances may be both antiperspirants and deodorants, no effort is here made precisely to segregate these two classes of active agents.

Although some antiperspirants and deodorants may induce dermatitis and/or damage garments, these qualities do not condemn as undesirable a large number of prescription and proprietary odor-banishing substances. Prior to the introduction of a listing of various active agents and a long series of formulas, it must be recorded that the exact mechanism through which odors are banished is not precisely established. It is convenient indeed to believe that the antiperspirants foremostly destroy the secreting gland and that foremostly

[1] Body Odor, *Med. Record,* **154,** 167 (1941).

deodorants mask with their own odor the less desirable body odor. Such statements are but confessions of incomplete understanding of the nature of odor destruction. In addition to whatever may be the specific action on odorous material or the glands producing such material, it may be recognized that antiseptic action in the case of some deodorants and antiperspirants may contribute an added value.

Among other active agents in this domain are the following:

Deodorants (antiseptic in action): Sodium perborate, zinc peroxide, magnesium peroxide, oxyquinoline sulfate, salicylic acid, benzoic acid, and boric acid.
Antiperspirants (astringents): Aluminum chloride, aluminum sulfate, alum, aluminum acetate, menthol, camphor, and zinc sulfocarbolate.
Deodorant and antiperspirant: Formalin, formic acid, tannic acid, and zinc sulfocarbolate (Eller).

Harry's list* is as follows:

Those which operate by diminishing the flow of perspiration: Aluminum salts, particularly the chloride and sulfate, formaldehyde, alcohol, tannins and tannic acid, iron salts (ferric chloride, etc.).

Deodorizing agents: Zinc peroxide and oxide, hexamine, oxyquinoline sulfate, chloramine—T, chlorthymol, essential oils and perfumes, etc., sodium perborate, etc.

Deodorants and antiperspirants may be applied as liquids, creams, powders, and sticks. The long list appearing below derives chiefly from the publications of Goodman,[1] Eller,[2] and Harry.[3] It may be believed that some of the formulas utilized did not originate with any one of these investigators. No apology is made for the inclusion of a great number of formulas, since no two odor producers will with certainty respond to the same agent. Slight variations in formulation may represent the difference between success and failure. On a trial and error basis it may be necessary on occasion to try out, one after another, several of the preparations now indicated.

LIQUIDS

| Aluminum chloride | 16.–20. | drams | 4–5 |
| Distilled water, enough to make | 100. | ounces | 3 |

Dissolve and filter.

Oxyquinoline sulfate	5%
Alcohol	10%
Water	85%

*R. G. HARRY, "Modern Cosmeticology," Chemical Publishing Company, Brooklyn, N. Y., 1940.
[1] H. GOODMAN, "Cosmetic Dermatology," McGraw-Hill Book Company, Inc., New York and London, 1936.
[2] *Supra*
[3] *Supra.*

Aluminum chloride (salt)	25.0		
Borax	0.8		
Water	75.0		

Aluminum chloride	4.–16.	drams	1–4
Salicylic acid	2.	drams	½
Glycerin	10.	drams	2½
Cologne water, enough to make	100.	ounces	3
Zinc phenolsulfonate	5.–10.		
Water to	100.		

Alum	6.	drams	1–4
Aluminum chloride	10.	drams	½
Glycerin	6.	drams	1½
Water, enough to make	100.	ounces	3

Hexamine	3.		
Eau-de-Cologne spirit	50.		
Water	8.		

Alum	2.	drams	½
Aluminum chloride	10.	drams	2½
Oxyquinoline sulfate	1.	grains	15
Alcohol	6.	drams	1½
Water, enough to make	100.	ounces	3

Aluminum chloride	15%
Water	85%

Aluminum chloride	10.	drams	2½
Formaldehyde	0.6	minims	9
Boric acid	10.	drams	2½
Alcohol	6.	drams	1½
Water, enough to make	100.	ounces	3

Aluminum sulfate	25%
Water	75%

Aluminum sulfate	32.	drams	8
Potassium permanganate	6.	drams	1½
Water, enough to make	100.	ounces	3

Potassium oxyquinoline sulfate	1.
Water	99.

Aluminum acetotartrate	4.	drams	1
Water, enough to make	100.	ounces	3

Aluminum chloride	12%
Zinc sulfocarbolate	3%
Alcohol	5%
Water	80%
Perfume, q.s.	

Salicylic acid	3.	drams	¾
Benzoic acid	4.	drams	1
Glycerin	16.	drams	4
Alcohol	50.	ounces	1½
Cologne water, enough to make	100.	ounces	3

Dissolve acids in alcohol; add glycerin and Cologne water to make 100 parts.

Sodium perborate	15%
Sodium bicarbonate	5%
Glycerin	5%
Water	75%

Oxyquinoline sulfate	4.	drams	1
Formaldehyde	1.	minims	15
Alcohol	10.	drams	2½
Water, enough to make	100.	ounces	3

Arnica	12.	drams	3
Camphor water, enough to make	100.	ounces	3

Potassium oxyquinoline sulfate	1.
Aluminum sulfate	10.
Water	89.

Sodium perborate	12.	drams	3
Sodium bicarbonate	2.	drams	½
Glycerin	6.	drams	1½
Water, enough to make	100.	ounces	3

Formic acid	2.	drams	½
Chloral hydrate	2.	drams	½
Camphor	0.6	grains	9
Alcohol	80.	ounces	2½
Cologne water, enough to make	100.	ounces	3

Dissolve camphor and chloral hydrate in alcohol; add other ingredients and mix.

CREAMS

Boric acid	10.	drams	2½
Zinc sulfocarbolate	2.	drams	½
Glycerin	16.	drams	4
Water	40.	drams	10

Mix and add:

Zinc stearate	20.	drams	5
Kaolin	4.	drams	1
Talc	6.	drams	1½

Diglycol stearate	20.
Hexamine	5.
Water	75.

Dissolve the hexamine in 15 ml. of the water. Melt separately the diglycol stearate and add to the water when both are at 170° F. When the mixture is emulsified, add the warm solution of hexamine and stir until cold.

Oxyquinoline sulfate .... **2.**   drams   ½
Glycerin .... **4.**   drams   1
Water .... **64.**   ounces 2
Dissolve and add to melted:
Glyceryl monostearate .... **20.**   drams   5
Liquid petrolatum .... **8.**   drams   2
Stir to emulsify

Absorption base 20%
Mineral oil 5%
Aluminum sulfate 15%
Oxyquinoline sulfate 3%

Glycerin 5%
Water 52%
Perfume, q.s.

Benzoic acid .... **1.**   grains 15
Salicylic acid .... **2.**   drams   ½
Zinc oxide .... **6.**   drams   1½
Lanolin, anhydrous .... **10.**   drams   2½
Petrolatum, enough to make .... **100.**   ounces 3

Formalin .... **10.–20.**   drams   2½–5
Lanolin .... **20.**   drams   5
Petrolatum, enough to make .... **100.**   ounces 3

Glyceryl monostearate 22%
Mineral oil 10%
Oxyquinoline sulfate 3%
Glycerin 4%
Water 61%

Menthol .... **1.**   grains 15
Thymol iodide .... **4.**   drams   1
Magnesium carbonate .... **12.**   drams   3
Borax .... **2.**   drams   ½
Zinc stearate .... **8.**   drams   2
Lanolin emulsion, enough to make .... **100.**   ounces 3
   Incorporate powders in emulsified lanolin.

Acimul .... **26.**
Liquid paraffin .... **24.**
Melt and add to:
Water .... **30.**
Both the above being at 75°C. When cooled to about 60°C. add slowly, a little
at a time:
Potassium oxyquinoline sulfate .... **5.**
Water .... **15.**

Glyceryl monostearate 18%
Mineral oil 5%

Glycerin	4%		
Zinc sulfocarbolate	3%		
Alcohol	10%		
Water	60%		
Perfume, q.s.			

Boric acid	12.		
Zinc oxide	25.		
Petroleum jelly	66.		

Oxyquinoline sulfate	2.	drams	½
Zinc sulfocarbolate	2.	drams	½
Glycerin	20.	drams	5
Water	24.	drams	6
Dissolve and add by sifting:			
Zinc oxide	10.	drams	2½
Zinc stearate	16.	drams	4
Kaolin	4.	drams	1
Talc	20.	drams	5

POWDERS

Menthol	0.2	grains	3
Thymol iodide	4.	drams	1
Zinc stearate	12.	drams	3
Magnesium carbonate ....:.	12.	drams	3
Talc	24.	drams	6
Precipitated chalk, enough to make	100.	ounces	3

Acetanilide	40.	drams	10
Boric acid	40.	drams	10
Thymol	12.	drams	3
Menthol	1.	grains	15
Methyl salicylate	2.	grains	15
Precipitated chalk, enough to make	100.	ounces	3

Boric acid	20.–32.	drams	5–8
Zinc peroxide	32.	ounces	1
Talc, enough to make	100.	ounces	3

Talc	10.		
Magnesium stearate	5.		
Zinc phenolsulfonate	0.5–1.0		

Formalin	1.	minims	15
Thymol	1.	grains	15
Zinc oxide	32.	ounces	1
Talc, enough to make	100.	ounces	3

Magnesium carbonate	32.	ounces	1
Alum, fine powder	66.	ounces	1
Talc, enough to make	100.	ounces	3

Zinc peroxide 30%
Zinc stearate 5%
Boric acid 25%
Talc 40%
Perfume, q.s.

Zinc peroxide	1.	grains	15
Benzoic acid	1.	grains	15
Talcum, enough to make	100.	ounces	3

Chloramine-T .... 3.
Boric acid .... 30.
Talc .... 30.
Magnesium stearate .... 30.

Boric acid	32.	ounces	1
Zinc peroxide	20.	drams	5
Zinc stearate	10.	drams	2½
Talc, enough to make	100.	ounces	3

Talc .... 50.
Magnesium stearate .... 15.
Chalk, precipitated .... 30.
Zinc peroxide .... 5.

Zinc sulfocarbolate	10.	drams	2½
Sodium perborate	6.	drams	1½
Boric acid	12.	drams	3
Sodium bicarbonate	6.	drams	1½
Magnesium carbonate	10.	drams	2½
Talc, enough to make	100.	ounces	3

| Oxyquinoline sulfate | 10. | drams | 2½ |
| Talc, enough to make | 100. | ounces | 3 |

STICKS

Sodium perborate .... 9.
Hydrogenated palm kernel oil (50/52) .... 12.
Beeswax .... 20.
Paraffin wax (Ceraflux) .... 10.
Petroleum jelly .... 20.
Liquid paraffin .... 25.
Zinc oxide .... 10.
    Melt wax base and the powders mixed by trituration until the mass is sufficiently stiff for the purpose.

Oxyquinoline sulfate	2.	drams	½
Zinc sulfocarbolate	2.	drams	½
Talc	20.	drams	5

Mix into melted:

Beeswax	10.	drams	2½
Paraffin	32.	ounces	1
Petrolatum	24.	drams	6

Stir until homogeneous.

Cocoa butter, enough to make	100.	ounces	3

Beeswax	36%
Paraffin	5%
Lanolin	4%
Cocoa butter	12%
Petrolatum	16%
Oxyquinoline sulfate	3%
Aluminum sulfate	15%
Talc	9%
Perfume, q.s.	

Oxyquinoline sulfate	4.	drams	1
Zinc sulfate	2.	drams	½

Zinc sulfocarbolate	2.	drams	½
Talc	16.	drams	4
Beeswax	32.	ounces	1
Paraffin	10.	drams	2½
Lanolin	6.	drams	1½
Petrolatum, enough to make	100.	ounces	3

While a great number of these preparations are substantially harmless, there is no assurance that any one may not on occasion lead to skin irritation or to sensitivity. More than one is quite capable of damaging garments.

Commercial Antiperspirants and Deodorants.—Consumers' Research Bulletin in October, 1945,[1] published an appraisal and rating of certain antiperspirants and deodorants of that period. The following derive from that publication and are cited with the permission of its editor.

ANTI-PERSPIRANTS

B. INTERMEDIATE

POWDER

Sno-Mist (The Phillips & Benjamin Co., Waterbury, Conn.). Essential ingredients: talcum, zinc stearate, boracic acid, and an oxyquinoline derivative, with perfume.

CREAM

Arrid (Carter Products, Inc., 53 Park Pl., New York 7). Essential ingredients: water, spermaceti, aluminum sulfate, and titanium oxide; faintly perfumed.

Etiquet Deodorant Cream (distributed by Lehn & Fink Products Corp., Bloomfield, N. J.). Essential ingredients: water, titanium oxide, aluminum sulfate, in a stearate base, slightly perfumed.

[1] 16, 4, 11.

Fresh Cream Deodorant (The Pharma-Craft Corp., Inc., 405 Lexington Ave., New York 17). Essential ingredients: water, aluminum chloride, aluminum formate, in a stearate base, perfumed.

Lor-Odo, Scentized, Underarm Deodorant Compact (distributed by Parfum L'Orle, Inc., 6 E. 39 St., New York 16). Essential ingredients: white petrolatum, water, aluminum sulfate, zinc oxide, perfumed.

Lor-Odo, Men's. Essentially the same as Scentized Lor-Odo, except that aluminum sulfate content was slightly higher, water content slightly lower.

Stag Deodorant Cream for Men (Langlois, Inc., 43 Leon St., Boston 43; distributed by Rexall Drug Stores). Essential ingredients: water, aluminum sulfate, benzoic acid, in a stearate base, perfumed.

The following had certain characteristics that were considered undesirable; they were judged to merit a somewhat lower B rating.

CREAM

Ever Dry (Ever-Dry Corp., 2113 San Pedro, Los Angeles 11). Essential ingredients: aluminum chloride, aluminum phenol sulfonate, aluminum sulfate, water, in a stearate base, perfumed.

Odo-Ro-No Cream (distributed by Northam Warren Corp., 50 E. 57 St., New York 22). Essential ingredients: ammonium aluminum sulfate, zinc sulfo-carbolate, titanium oxide, glycerine, water, in a fatty base, perfumed.

LIQUID

The active ingredient of the following was aluminum chloride, present to the extent of less than 15%. They would be fairly effective as perspiration inhibitors; they were distinctly acid in reaction, and might cause discoloration of some dyed fabrics and disintegration of certain fabrics with which they came into contact.

Ever-Dry (Ever-Dry Corp.).

Odo-Ro-No Instant (distributed by Northam Warren Corp.). Also contained aluminum sulfate.

Perstop (distributed by Carter Products, Inc.).

DEODORANTS

The following preparations are effective in varying degrees in covering the offensive odor of perspiration, but do not interfere with its flow. If clothing is to be protected from perspiration stains, a product of this type will need to be used in conjunction with dress shields.

B. INTERMEDIATE

POWDER

Amolin (The Norwich Pharmacal Co., Norwich, N. Y.). Essential ingredients: boracic acid with a small amount of talc and thymol.

Quest (distributed by International Cellucotton Products Co., 919 N. Michigan Ave., Chicago 11). Essential ingredients: talcum, zinc oxide, and calcium carbonate.

CREAM

Amolin Cream Deodorant (The Norwich Pharmacal Co.). Essential ingredients: boracic acid and zinc oxide in what appears to be a petrolatum base, perfumed.

Hush Cream Deodorant (distributed by Hush Sales Co., 114 Market, Philadelphia 6). Essential ingredients: zinc oxide, white petrolatum, perfumed.

Marvelous Cream Deodorant (Richard Hudnut, 113 W. 18th St., New York 11). Essential ingredients: zinc oxide, benzoic acid, and white petrolatum, perfumed.

Mum (Bristol-Myers Co., 630 Fifth Ave., New York 20). Essential ingredients: zinc oxide, titanium oxide, and white petrolatum, perfumed. Cream considered somewhat heavy, and might be objectionable to some on that account.

Yodora (McKesson & Robbins, Inc., Bridgeport, Conn.). Essential ingredients: zinc oxide, boracic acid, sodium salicylate, and petrolatum, perfumed. Cream considered somewhat greasy and might be objectionable to some on that account.

LIQUID

Immac Lotion Deodorant (distributed by Mystic laboratories, Division of Affiliated Products, Inc., Jersey City, N. J.). Essentially an alcoholic solution of perfumes with a small amount of benzoic acid, and a very small amount of formaldehyde.

Park & Tilford Perfumed Deodorant (distributed by Park & Tilford, 485 Fifth Ave., New York 16). Essentially an alcoholic solution of perfumes with a small amount of benzoic acid and a very small amount of formaldehyde.

THE HYGIENE OF BODY-ODOR CONTROL

Along with the desire to avoid odor offense to others, every person should entertain another desire—not to subject the body to undue chemical affront. To this end a number of generalities are pertinent.

1. Do not use any antiperspirant or deodorant unnecessarily. Depend upon soap and water ablutions if these successfully may eliminate body odors. However, bathing should not be made a fetish, since water alone and many soaps are quite capable of inducing a dermatitis equal to that from chemical odor removers.

2. If necessary to use an odor chemical, apply only to those parts of the body believed to be the source of odors; commonly these are the axillae, genital region, breast region (in women), and feet.

3. Apply as little of the deodorizing substance as is necessary to combat odors.

4. Apply no odor-combating substances in the case of any present or recent skin disease.

5. Avoid the application of most odor-controlling agents, particularly aluminum-containing ones, immediately after a bath.

6. If any deodorant proves to be a skin irritant and it is still necessary to use some deodorizing agent, choice should be made of a class not containing the chief constituent in the offending type. Thus, if an aluminum type proves irritating, shift should be made, after the disappearance of inflammation of the former, to a variety not containing aluminum.

7. In case of inflammation from odor-controlling agents, patch tests carried out by a physician ordinarily may establish the precise ingredient responsible and thus may guide to a choice of substitutes.

8. After application of any odor-controlling agent, provide a few minutes for drying prior to donning of clothing for that area.

9. Lower incidence of irritation is to be expected from the use of preparations containing not more than 15 per cent of aluminum salts. This percentage is ordinarily sufficient to retard the flow of excessive perspiration.

10. Shaving of such areas as the axillae, if properly performed, is not highly detrimental. However, avoid application of antiperspirants or deodorants immediately after shaving, since microscopic nicking of the skin is inevitable.

11. If confronted with the problem of any extraordinary degree of perspiration quantity or body odor, consult and rely on a physician rather than upon any odor-dispelling medicament.

Chapter IX

Human Body Odors in Disease

THE POTENTIAL content of this section is so closely identified with that of the preceding and following chapters as to necessitate much duplication should the three be developed to minutiae. For this reason there is reserved to this chapter only the discussion of those body-surface diseases in which persistent offensive odors constitute the chief complaint of the patient or of persons in contact with the patient. Although the scope of this chapter is thus limited, the authors have no disposition to ignore the social significance of odors in many other conditions, such as pulmonary abscesses, infected tonsils, halitosis, etc.

BROMIDROSIS

This disease of the sweat system is likewise termed "osmidrosis" and "stinking sweat." It is commonly associated with excessive sweating, although this is not a constant phenomenon. Persons so afflicted secrete perspiration with much more highly offensive odor than that which marks all sweat on long standing on the body or in clothing. This disease may exist in spite of admirable efforts toward personal hygiene. Immediately after a full bath any perspiration may be offensive (usually not), but naturally less so than after a long interval following bathing. All portions of the body may be involved, but more blameworthy are the armpits, genital region, and feet. A few persons may bathe the feet and change hosiery as many as four or five times daily but still cause offense, chiefly to other persons, and an entire household, room, or office may be made unlivable by the presence of one so afflicted.

Accompanying this disease there may or may not be discernible skin lesions. The offending odor is not constant for all victims, nor does anyone invariably yield the same odorous material. On rare occasions the odor may be pleasant rather than disagreeable.

The cause of this condition is not surely known, but it is more often associated with frail, anemic, undernourished, alcoholic, or neurotic individuals. The state may be intermittent. A wide variety of drugs and a few foods may occasion this disease on a transient basis. The number of drugs embraces asafetida, sulfur, benzoic acid, copaiba, bromides, selenides, tellurides. Closely related is the obvious fact that the offensive odors may long persist in a home or office.

It is not the purpose of this book to present full treatment for this or any other disease state mentioned. Ordinarily the underlying disease should govern the treatment, and the services of a competent physician should be sought. For minor degrees of severity the following items may be of some value:

1. Frequent ablutions are in order.

2. The use of body deodorants is warranted but always at the peril of some damage.

3. Boric-acid solution and dusting powder may be serviceable.

4. For fetid feet an earlier generation resorted to bathing with chromic acid, 1 to 5 per cent. However efficacious, this dangerous chemical should be accorded respect and probably should be eschewed.

5. Potassium permanganate solution about 1 to 1,000 frequently suffices.

6. If the involvement is limited to small areas, such as the axillae, X-ray exposure at levels lower than the erythematous dose may be effective. This also may be dangerous.

7. A weak formaldehyde solution such as from 1 to 5 per cent may produce happy results.

8. The more extensive the bromidridic area the milder the local application should be. Conversely, if the condition is limited to small areas such as the toes, increased justification for more heroic measures obtains (see previous chapter).

HYPERIDROSIS

This borderline disease state, which has many names, may be reduced to the simplicity of "excessive sweating." Since all sweat is offensively odorous on standing, it follows that those persons who sweat most and into the realm of a pathologic degree are likely to become the chief offenders on a sweat odor basis.

Apart from any patent skin diseases, many persons without exertion and in the absence of high atmospheric temperatures continually are given to copious sweating, clammy hands and feet, and dripping clothing. Such persons, in addition to providing offensive odors, are a liability in the conduct of many kinds of work, since they cause the staining of metal, the smearing of artist materials, the discoloring of fabrics, the contamination of confections, etc.

Hyperidrosis may be general or local; all degrees of severity may occur; and the condition may lead to maceration of the skin with increased susceptibility to contact irritants such as would not damage a more nearly normal individual.

The persons susceptible to hyperidrosis are much the same as those who are afflicted with bromidrosis. In particular they include the obese, the tuberculous, the victims of hyperthyroidism, and hysterical individuals, along with scattered numbers suffering from severe forms of nervous disorders. Persons with flat feet are more prone to this disease than their normal-footed friends.

The treatment of this derangement of the sweat function is almost identical to that of its counterpart, bromidrosis. All the injunctions and precautions set forth for bromidrosis apply to hyperidrosis, but this condition much less frequently reaches the state of requiring the services of the medical profession in the absence of significant underlying disease. The mildest treatment relies upon the action of dusting powders, talc, boric acid, magnesia, or starch. Some will prefer the use of lotions containing formaldehyde 1 to 5 per cent, tannic acid, alum, or potassium permanganate. If treatment is designed for odors only and without regard to the quantity of sweat, some one of the deodorants previously mentioned may suffice, but always these should be used with the knowledge that some risk is involved.

Under the guidance of a physician relief may be found through the use of such medicaments as the following: 1 per cent of any water-soluble quinine salt, diachylon ointment, naphthol ointment, salicylic acid preparation, strong solutions of potassium permanganate, iron perchloride, or aluminum chloride in 25 per cent strength.

As a last resort, always under medical sponsorship, Roentgen therapy may be advocated, but only for localized involvement.

URIDROSIS

The previously discussed condition is of everyday occurrence. The pathologic condition uridrosis is comparatively rare. It represents that abnormal state in which body waste ordinarily discharged in the urine leaves the body in perspiration, so that the offensive odor is that of urine and is chiefly ammoniacal. The body odor encountered is not highly different to that from persons without full control of the urinary bladder. Any neglected infant presents the same odor, not because of uridrosis but on a wet-diaper basis. This disorder may arise in any individual with kidneys failing in their proper function. It rarely may occur in otherwise perfect health. On a palliative basis the treatment is precisely as for the disease last discussed, but always the significance of uridrosis is such that medical guidance should be secured.

BACTERIUM FOETIDUM INFECTION

Affections associated with abnormalities of sweating may be the perfect ground for action of one or more bacteria, fungi, or yeast. In any fungal infection, notably of the feet, offensive odors may be severely disturbing. It is somewhat academic to set apart the extent of odors attributable solely to decomposing flesh in contrast to the fungi themselves. It no less remains that fungal disorders may be far more odorous than other affections of equal severity in the same area. It appears probable that odorous offense from members, chiefly feet, may occur on a parasitic basis in the absence of open lesions. The growth of such organisms in the nearly normal interdigital maceration may be sufficient to produce odor offense. Individuals with such relatively innocuous infections as tinea versicolor may present disturbing odors, chiefly associated with clothing and recently occupied beds.

The treatment of these parasitic odor offenders in the absence of substantial skin lesions lies largely in the domain of proper personal hygiene, with recourse to such medicaments as formaldehyde, potassium permanganate, etc. Severer conditions require medical supervision.

The authors are aware that this chapter fails to mention all skin diseases in which disagreeable odors may exist and nonskin diseases with odorous features. Instead, through design, comment has been limited to surface conditions in which malodors are likely to be the foremost manifestation. Related comment appears in chapters devoted to odors in the diagnosis of disease, odors of food, and body odors in health.

Chapter X

Odors in the Diagnosis of Disease

BENJAMIN FRANKLIN is credited with the observation that an odor of violets characterized the urine of persons who had been poisoned by turpentine or who merely ingested that substance as a medicament. Such olfactory diagnostic criteria continually were sought out by physicians of that general period. These physicians prided themselves that through odor alone they were able to recognize such diseases as diphtheria, measles, lung abscesses, and some forms of insanity and that by odors they could differentiate between the many forms of "fevers." In some measure that physician blessed with the greatest nasal acuity was to be accepted as the best physician in the community—winning by a nose.

It may not be inferred that the present-day diagnostician scorns odors in the achievement of his diagnosis, but the difference is that odors are now less important in diagnosis than formerly. Nowadays almost without exception there are earlier and better methods leading to the disclosure of a disease's nature. A hundred years ago, and somewhat before and after, a disease odor may have been the major and final discipline in diagnosis. Today that same odor is still added into the general appraisal but frequently only as contributory evidence.

Odors as encountered in the work of the physician may reveal other things than a disease itself. Almost unconsciously the physician, through odors alone, may record the impression that a patient is a tobacco user, an alcoholic, or given to low personal hygiene, that he works in a certain trade or with certain chemicals, that he hails from an institution, that she is menstruating, that certain drugs are being used in medication, or that certain foods have been ingested.

The import of odors in diagnosis fans out into several categories, but at times with overlapping. The material here presented is not to be regarded as all-embracive, but chiefly as illustrative.

ODORS AS DISCLOSERS OF ETIOLOGIES

Under many circumstances, but chiefly in the realm of general and industrial toxicology, the probable cause of an affection may be disclosed by odors of the breath or the clothing or by odors emitted at autopsy. The worker in selenium may so identify himself, sick or well, through a garliclike odor of his breath. Tellurium and arsenic provide similar odors, and without further information differentiation may not be made. Unfortunately, garlic itself, used as food and widely so, may upset any odor hint toward diagnosis. The odor of ethyl alcohol is so readily detected that suspicion of drunkenness at once becomes warranted. Many diagnostic errors arise, since the drinker, without being profoundly drunk, may be the victim of any of a long list of severe conditions leading to unconsciousness and thus to involuntary noncooperation. Many other alcohols, with less familiar odors, known to industry but not to bars, may through fortuitous circumstances be the source of intoxication. Allyl alcohol, with its characteristic odor, exemplifies these less familiar alcohols. Phenol and kindred chemicals, such as cresol, and various trade preparations, such as Lysol, sometimes used for purposes of suicide, possess revealing odors and thus facilitate diagnosis. The well-known almond odor associated with the presence of various substances deriving from or related to hydrocyanic acid is so precise as to justify a working diagnosis of poisoning by some one of that group. At autopsy this odor may pervade all tissues; but, if the autopsy be long deferred, it is possible that this odor may originate as one product of decomposition. In the case of mercury poisoning, the pronounced odor about the mouth sometimes encountered is prone to result from stomatitis; but on rare occasions a metallic odor may appear. Less frequently, the same metallic odor may appear in lead poisoning. In like manner, telltale odors may be associated with exposure to such other substances as carbon tetrachloride, trichlorethylene, gasoline, benzol, etc. Only slightly dissimilar are those other or possibly the same odors originating from harmful substances unwittingly applied to the exterior body. A few permanent-wave solutions disintegrate with the formation of hydrogen sulfide. Absorption through the skin provokes prompt injury, but the odor alone may facilitate the diagnosis. Rarely and carelessly carbon tetrachloride or some similar chlorinated agent may be used as a shampoo with evil results. Encountered early, odor may direct the trend of diagnostic inquiry. Medicaments applied in the form of ointments, with ensuing skin sorption, may prove to be quickly injurious, and a diagnostic lead may be found in the ointment odor still present.

ODORS DERIVED FROM INGESTED DRUGS AND FOODS

In the relationship between physician and patient, patients may hold back from the examiner frankness as to recent antecedent intake of drugs or foods. The patient on a rigid diet piously may claim rigid compliance with regimes only to have deception brought out, for example, by the odor in the urine so characteristic of asparagus. Only a few foods and drugs possess this property. The recent imbibition of beer, considered as a food, shouts that fact through its odor; likewise more potent alcoholics. Local applications, such as mouth washes, are often unmistakable. A patient may have a desire to conceal the use of bromides but be betrayed by a bromidic odor in sweat. Sulfur compounds taken by ingestion may impart sulfur odors to perspiration. The few alliaceous drugs utilized in medicine regularly emit their garlic odors. It is probable that adrenalin contributes a body-surface odor, imperceptible to man, but highly noticeable for dogs. It is conceded that the number of drugs that readily identify themselves after intake is so low as not to constitute a major diagnostic aid.

ODORS CONCOMITANT TO INFECTIONS

Odors resulting from some infections are nondescript but from others highly specific. The pronounced offensive odor from an open pulmonary empyema may warrant a diagnosis (which ordinarily already has been made) from an observer who merely stands at the doorway of a room sheltering an empyemic patient. This odor, although involving the same system—that is, the pulmonary system—is wholly unlike the equally disturbing odor of bronchiectasis. Of all body odors, that from lung abscesses or lung gangrene is perhaps the most disturbing. On a crowded streetcar anyone who has encountered the odor of a pulmonary abscess is in position make an exact diagnosis of such condition even though the exact victim is not recognized. Open osteomyelitis imparts to the air its own characteristic odor. Apart from the odors attributed to tuberculosis originating along the pulmonary tract, such patients, particularly when the disease is well advanced, present a general body odor at least somewhat limited to this infection. For rheumatic fever there has been described a highly differentiated skin odor set apart as sour or acid and said to be encountered in no other disease. In the case of putrid odors from the mouth, difficulty may arise in determining the exact cause. Gingivitis, stomatitis, purulent tonsillitis, Vincent's angina, bridgework, carious teeth, some pulmonary and gastric involvements—all may contribute a somewhat similar odor. Only the thoroughly skilled may differentiate with accuracy. Yet day by day diagnoses are made through the aid of oral odors. The dentist after drilling into an offending tooth may be observed to sniff his drill after the dental canals have been reached. What he does after that may largely depend upon the odor that he perceives. The odor of ozena, a nasal affection, is dreadful and characteristic. Laryngeal diphtheria in the necrotic stage emits a well-defined odor, but long before this period the diagnosis should have been made through superior procedures. Such infections as typhoid fever, measles, scarlet fever, and smallpox possess their own peculiar odors, none of which may be described as one apart from the others.

Great effort has been made to define such odors in terms of distinctive properties; thus, the smallpox odor is said to resemble that of sweet potatoes. It is here desired to avoid these farfetched, dubious descriptions.

ODORS IN THE DIAGNOSIS OF OTHER DISEASES

Figuratively speaking, the shortest path into the subconscious is along the olfactory nerve. The psychiatrist and the psychoanalyst continually are confronted with the neuroses, inhibitions, and incompatibilities of domestic life. In this realm, disturbing odors may play a tremendous and often unrecognized role in the etiology of disaffection. While these odors may not be accessible to the investigating psychiatrist, still his inquiry may lead to odors as the provocation of marital maladjustment.

The acetone breath odor (apart from a worker employing acetone) immediately suggests the possibility of diabetes and calls for more precise examination. Gout is sometimes accompanied by an odor from the skin, pathognomonic of that disease. Disintegrating surface cancer reveals itself by characteristic odor; however, long before this state is reached, a diagnosis will have been made. The epileptic, before, during, and after convulsions, may disclose the presence of the disease by odor; on occasion, odor may serve as a foreboding of imminent seizure and may permit of helpful preparation. Apart from the common odor of aural suppuration, another, questionably resembling that of Camembert cheese, appears in the presence of choleastomatous impactions. Strangely enough, in some corneal ulcers of the eye, the breath assumes a malodor. Likewise, a breath odor may follow some ovarian operations although not laparotomies in general. Pregnancy, quite apart from any odor from the genitalia, may disclose itself by odor. Endocrine disease and notably Froelich's syndrome may be accompanied by characteristic odors. In some instances atrophic rhinitis (ozena) in women, in which there is no constant odor, may come to present a disturbing odor at the time of menstruation. Over and over the odor of a urine specimen may indicate the nature of the patient's pathology.

It may be observed that odors may also be evoked in forensic medicine. A single example will indicate the opportunity. In the possibility of previous rape or attempted rape of a recently murdered female, the peculiar odor of semen competently observed is fairly conclusive. The skeptic at once will (rightly) contend that microscopic examination for spermatozoa or other laboratory procedure is vastly superior. This is obviously true, but there remain numerous communities without any facilities for such, and in some instances through neglect of opportunity no samples of suspected material are collected. Thus the sole competent evidence may come to reside in odor.

To a minor extent the absence of odor may attain medical import. When fresh feces, usually highly odorous, possess little or no odor, attention should be directed to the possibility of hepatic disease. It is a medical dictum that in the presence of well-established jaundice the feces may be odorless.

Far from relegating odors to an outmoded past and rating them as unworthy of a place in modern diagnostic methods, time and again every good diagnostician confronted with odors or their absence introduces this evidence into his comprehensive appraisal. For him, unlike his remote predecessor, odor acuity is seldom a boasted prime implement.

Chapter XI

Household Odors

THE HOUSEHOLD is the reservoir of nearly every conceivable odor associated with human activity. It duplicates in miniature the places occupied by human beings during each hour of the day, notably offices, stores, restaurants, hotels, and night clubs. It takes on an aromatic personality of its own that records and retells the habits, desires, and difficulties of the family members and their friends.

As we approach the mid-point of the present century we are informed by press and radio that the domestic atmosphere is no longer a private matter, but that to the contrary we should conduct our household affairs in a way that will deserve the approval of an American public having a universal preference for country-fresh air. The concern for our osmic pleasure has brought forth a rash of new preparations that surprisingly enough employ many of the deodorizing procedures of earlier centuries. Some of these new products have enjoyed phenomenal acceptance by householders, who tacitly admit thereby that all is not well with their olfactory environment.

The homemaker is admonished in the fertile language of advertising that present standards of domestic cleanliness demand the control of odors generated by cooking, smoking, bathing, nursing, and refuse disposal. To get along socially the house must be free of offensive odors, otherwise known as "stinch" in the copy of an enterprising advertiser. In short, we learn that fresh odor-free air in the home is a twentieth-century necessity.

Household odors arise from the occupants—including body odors, cosmetics, tobacco, and apparel—from the preparation and service of foods and beverages, from the activities of painting, varnishing, papering, laundering, and housecleaning, and from household commodities such as textile, leather, and rubber products, glues or adhesives, pharmaceuticals, and cleaning compounds. Manufacturers of the many articles for domestic consumption are learning the value of deodorizing and reodorizing their products, with the result that unpleasant foreign odors in the household have gradually depreciated in intensity. Methods of controlling the odors of manufactured goods have improved in recent years to the point of utilizing the skills of professional blenders from the essential oils and synthetic aromatic chemicals industry. Further discussion of this will be found in Chaps. XVII and XVIII.

AROMATIC PERSONALITY OF THE FAMILY HOME

The receptacles for fragrant perfumes in ancient Egyptian tombs contained materials that presumably would evaporate through the ages despite their confinement; when archaeologists opened these tombs and their contents many centuries later, the aromatic vapors were still present, though doubtless in modified form.

The family home accumulates thousands of odorous vapors, including many having an almost ageless stability. There is little occasion for wonder at the infinitely complex variations in household atmospheres as we visit one home after another. The processes of condensation, adsorption, and chemical change are continuously recording the events that lead to aerial dispersions, and the entire body of furnishings and interior decorations becomes impregnated and saturated with substances arriving by way of the air. The less volatile substances may remain trapped for years, while giving off infinitesimal contributions to the indoor air. Ventilation temporarily reduces the concentration of these odorous substances to an imperceptible level, but their presence in the room is quickly made known when the house has been closed over a weekend.

It is furthermore well known that those who live continuously in a given space become inattentive to its characteristic odors. Only the guest has an opportunity for significant appraisal. And it must be realized that the inherent aromas of occupied spaces may be either pleasant or unpleasant to the casual visitor. Strong or overpowering odors of almost any type are liable to offend, while faint odor impressions have the best opportunity of pleasing.

Closed rooms acquire an atmosphere that is eminently difficult to describe. Our collection of adjectives includes: stuffy, close, heavy, dead, flat, lifeless, and oppressive. Such air is not without odor, but is simply lacking in the odors freely circulated from the activities of occupants or the events conducted outdoors in the vicinity. We appreciate the "dynamic" odors of daily activity according to our occupations or avocations, and it is natural to miss these odors when they have been excluded from a room or building.

Closed rooms also acquire odors that represent decay or deterioration arising from the presence of microorganisms, insects, or animals that find their way into the space unmolested by human sanitary procedures. Musty or putrefying odors may replace the usual odors of human living and may superimpose themselves upon the initially stale or flat effect caused by temporary disuse of the space.

Odors of all types have become more apparent in modern buildings with sealed windows and recirculating air-conditioning systems. The desire to reduce the load on heating, cooling, and air-cleaning apparatus has accented the demand for internal air recirculation accompanied by the restriction of outdoor air quantities to as little as 10 per cent of the total air movement. The modern well-insulated home with storm windows and weather stripping has a very low rate of air replacement by normal infiltration of outdoor air, and care must be taken to provide modern methods of ventilation compatible with high-quality insulated construction.

Fortunately our improved standards of household and personal cleanliness offset to some extent the tendency to build tighter homes in the colder climates. We have come a very long way from the domestic conditions related by Green in 1897.

Sweet odors are thus the natural disguisers of evil smells. They are the only resource of rude and dirty times against offensive emanations from decaying animal and vegetable substances, from undrained and untidy dwellings, from unclean clothes, from ill washed skins and from ill washed stomachs. The scented handkerchief in these circumstances takes the place of the sponge and the shower bath; the pastille hides the want of ventilation; the attar of roses seems to render the scavenger unnecessary; and a sprinkling of musk sets all other stinks and smells at defiance. The "sixty stinks of Cologne" may thus be at once the parent and grand consumer of its artificial rivers of scented water. The fiercest demand for the luxury of civilized perfumes may exist where the disregard for healthy cleanliness is the greatest. Even the burning of incense at the altar may find a merely rational use in disguising the dank and unwholesome smells which damp walls and floors engender, and in hiding from the senses of the worshiper the noxious effluvia which slowly decaying bodies in hidden vaults are continually giving off.[1]

Two hundred years ago, Benjamin Franklin gave his readers a critical lesson on domestic odor control. In his "Pennsylvanian Fire-Places," first printed at Philadelphia in 1745, he observes the unwise habits of those who appeared to resist the use of the "Franklin stove," as it was later called.

There are some objections commonly made by people that are unacquainted with these fire-places, which it may not be amiss to endeavour to remove, as they arise from prejudices which might otherwise obstruct, in some degree, the general use of this beneficial machine. We frequently hear it said, "They are of the nature of Dutch stoves; stoves have an unpleasant smell; stoves are unwholesome;" . . . it must be allowed there may have been some cause to complain of the offensive smell of iron stoves. This smell, however, never proceeded from the iron itself, which in its nature, whether hot or cold, is one of the sweetest of metals, but from the general uncleanly manner of using those stoves. If they are kept clean, they are as sweet as an ironing-box, which though ever so hot, never offends the smell of the nicest lady; but it is common to let them be greased, by setting candlesticks on them, or otherwise; to rub greasy hands on them; and, above all, to spit upon them, to try how hot they are, which is an inconsiderate filthy unmannerly custom; for the slimy matter of spittle drying on, burns and fumes when the stove is hot, as well as the grease, and smells most nauseously, which makes such close stove-rooms, where there is no draught to carry off those filthy vapours, almost

[1] *Sci. American Supp.*, **44**, 17936 (July 3, 1897).

intolerable to those that are not from their infancy accustomed to them. At the same time nothing is more easy than to keep them clean; for when by accident they happen to be fouled, a lee made of ashes and water, with a brush, will scour them perfectly; as will also a little strong soap and water.

Franklin's warning about cleanliness on stoves still applies in this century. The most modern electric range can become very offensive if care is not taken to keep the hot surfaces of the burners and the oven scrupulously clean and free of food accumulations. The acrid and scorched odors generated by the combustion of food particles or fluids, especially in the oven, where removal may be difficult, are extremely irritating or annoying to some persons.

ODORS FROM THE KITCHEN

Nelson and Wright[1] express a contemporary architectural dismay at the most prolific source of odors in the average home—the kitchen.

The average kitchen is a Pittsburgh in miniature, where particles of soot, burned food and grease fly off into the atmosphere and eventually settle on walls, windows and furniture. Laboratory tests show that some of the fish mother fries on the stove is likely to condense on an upstairs windowpane in a matter of seconds.

Unfortunately, the streamlined kitchen of this era generally does not incorporate the best systems of ventilation that engineers have learned to apply to industrial and commercial installations. The desire for smooth, unbroken contours had years ago made obsolete the canopy hood connected to a generous flue pipe; from the standpoint of fire safety, this was an improvement. The development of gas and electric ranges reduced the air contamination from burning coal or wood and to some extent permitted the discard of the overhead hood. Concurrently, the appearance of inexpensive wall fans seemed at that time to be the answer to a desire for streamlined kitchen ventilation. In certain cases the results were satisfactory, but all too often the home owner has finally discovered that general ventilation by means of a fan located several feet from the range, even though directly overhead, does not whisk away the gaseous and odorous products of food preparation.

Likewise, the ventilating engineer has decided that simple propeller-fan ventilation in the wall or ceiling does not represent the most effective control of cooking odors. A recent study by the American Gas Association[2] indicated that the humble canopy hood with adequate rates of airflow did the best job of confining cooking odors to the kitchen (Table 1). Better methods of grease removal from the exhausted air have lessened the fire hazard of grease-filled ducts and flues, and return of the canopy hood to modern kitchens would not restore the former dangers of fire. However, smaller hoods placed at the rear

[1] "Tomorrow's House," Simon and Schuster, Inc., New York, 1945.
[2] A Study of Various Methods of Kitchen Ventilation, *Research Bull*. 40, Cleveland, 1946.

Table I.—RESULTS OF TESTS ON THE REMOVAL OF COOKING ODORS BY VENTILATION*

Ventilating hood	Burners employed	Food cooked	Air removal rate, c.f.m.	Cooking odors remaining
Wall-type hood (slot exhaust at rear of range; two 4-in. by 9½-in. openings)	Oven	3.87-lb. rolled rib roast	171	Very slight odor
	2 rear top burners	Cauliflower and cabbage	283	Strong odor in kitchen
	2 rear top burners	Cauliflower and cabbage	528	Slight odor in kitchen
	All top burners	Potatoes, meat, onions and cabbage	528	Strong odor
	All top burners	Potatoes, meat, onions and cabbage	900	Odor slightly reduced
Canopy hood (12 in. above range)	All top burners	Potatoes, meat, onions and cabbage	830	Odors confined to small area around range
	All top burners	Potatoes, meat, onions and cabbage	570	Slight odor in doorway to kitchen
	All top burners	Potatoes, meat, onions and cabbage	290	Perceptible odors in hallway leading to kitchen

* From AGA *Research Bull.* 40, p. 21 (1946).

of the stove or range using sufficient ventilating rates may appeal to architects and home owners as more harmonious with the remaining equipment in the food center (Figs. 1 to 4). Also, to many persons, the conventional canopy hood as used in commercial kitchens would seem to be a return to nineteenth-century design, with all its cumbersome disregard of compact electrical air movers.

Home builders of the future who have been disappointed with the performance of kitchen ventilating fans can expect better control of cooking odors, as well as of heat and humidity, by means of equipment that does not disturb the eye or upset the budget. The preparation of cabbage, cauliflower, onions, or fish need no longer be an occasion for family debate.

Many cooking odors are highly desirable and will be welcomed with enthusiasm throughout the household. The housewife certainly would not deny to her family the aromas of roasts and steaks, breads and pastries. When the program in the kitchen anticipates an enticing aromatic creation, there is no easier way to disseminate the inviting vapors than restricting or interrupting the mechanical ventilation. Engineering design is not obliged to offer a system of ventilation that fails to control unwanted odors to a degree that will permit other desirable odors to emerge from the kitchen. The maximum

Fig. 1.—Cabinet duct ventilation for kitchen range. (*Rochester Gas & Electric Corporation.*)

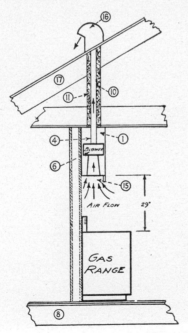

1 Cupboard.

4. Oval Transite duct or equivalent.

6. Blower.

8. Floor joists.

10. Discharge duct of Transite pipe or equivalent, carried through weather head in roof.

11. Insulation around discharge pipe in attic.

15. Blower inlet with Control Damper in.

16. Weatherhead for Roof discharge.

17 Rafters.

Fig. 2. Installation diagram for cabinet duct system. (*Rochester Gas & Electric Corporation.*)

Fig. 3.—Ventilated kitchen range with direct oven flue connection. (*Rochester Gas &
Electric Corporation.*)

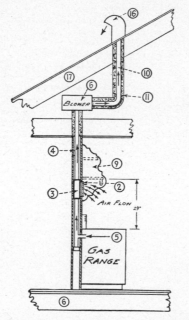

2. Wall Register.
3. Damper Box.
4. Oval Transite duct or equivalent.
5. Oven connection.
6. Blower.
8. Floor joists.
9 "What Not Shelf."
10. Discharge duct of Transite pipe or equivalent, carried through weather head in roof.
11. Insulation around discharge pipe in attic.
16. Weatherhead for roof discharge.
17 Rafters.

Fig. 4.—Installation diagram for range ventilation with direct oven flue connection.
(*Rochester Gas & Electric Corporation.*)

capacity of air-exhausting equipment should be based instead on the characteristics of highly odorous foods that the housewife generally desires to confine to the kitchen, and even, if possible, to the range itself.

ODORS FROM THE BATHROOM AND NURSERY

The domestic bathroom is years behind its commercial counterpart. Frank Lloyd Wright reminded us decades ago that bathrooms and kitchens should be so ventilated that air would move through the house toward and not from these prime odor offenders. Industrial ventilating engineers have long employed the method of local and booth ventilating to keep irritating, dangerous, or offensive gases and vapors confined to a restricted area. Many of the better homes today are designed to take advantage of this principle of controlled air movement.

Natural ventilation for bathrooms is notably unreliable. In the summer, the movement of air through open windows is subject to the direction of outdoor air travel, and it is not uncommon for air from the bathroom to be forced into other parts of the house by natural movement through windows. In the winter, bathroom windows are generally closed to prevent chilling by the cold outdoor air. Window ventilation, required by the building codes of most cities, is then a theoretical rather than actual provision.

The "inside" bathroom, so named because it has no outer wall exposure, generally offers better odor confinement because of the mechanical exhaust ventilation required by modern building codes. Ventilation is a year-round accomplishment. Air exhausted from the bathroom is replaced by air from other areas of the house, which, in turn, usually receive sufficient air by the infiltration of outdoor air, even during the wintertime. The inside bathroom with mechanical ventilation has been an economic necessity for large hotels and apartments for many years, but very few patrons appreciate the odor-control significance of this arrangement.

Architects of modern homes who desire to give their clients natural window lighting and positive ventilation in the outside bathroom have persuaded the owners to install efficient, quiet exhaust fans discharging the air directly outdoors. In this case windows may be either movable or fixed, as building codes generally permit the substitution of mechanical ventilation for the conventional movable window of specified size.

The odors in bathrooms, nurseries, and sick rooms fluctuate with the fortunes of the family with respect to communicable disease and vary according to the age distribution of the family members. The very young and very old need the kind of care that often presents deodorizing problems. Antiseptics and germicides, together with generous use of cleansing materials, have acquired the additional designation of deodorizers by reason of the control they exercise over decomposition or putrefaction of organic matter. In fact, sanitarians have pointed out for generations that one of the most effective means of odor control is simple cleanliness, never permitting putrescible material to proceed to a state of gas-forming decomposition. We have learned to tolerate the odors of phenol, cresol, or formaldehyde in moderate concentrations when their use arrests the more offensive odors of animal wastes in decay. Association of these "medicinal" odors with indirect deodorization even created a demand for their presence in modern preparations as an evidence of genuine germicidal and deodorizing value. The appearance of relatively odorless disinfectants is a fairly recent demonstration of the fact that an antiseptic-deodorant does not have to "smell like an antiseptic" to be powerfully effective.

Robert Spurr Weston is the source of the following item, which should serve to remind us that our contemporary domestic sanitary problems are relatively trivial and that our desire for further control over the sources of odors is perfectly reasonable when compared with the remarkable advances of the past 75 years.

Many of the so-called sewers of the seventies excluded fecal matter, and earth closets and open privies were common even in large cities. Bath tubs and sanitary plumbing were rare objects. The writer remembers the slow-filling, slow-emptying copper tub and the complicated hopper water closet of his boyhood home, also the "odorless" excavator which made the rounds of the cesspools and pumped their contents into a tank wagon for conveyance to a suitable disposal area. It is hard to believe the authentic story that when President-emeritus Eliot, now ninety-two years of age, was a teacher at Harvard there was but one bath tub in the whole college. This was the property of a wealthy student from New York, and even this was diverted from its intended purpose and used as a store for wines.[1]

TOBACCO-SMOKE ODORS

Most of us have observed that the odor of stale tobacco smoke is quite objectionable, while that of the freshly formed smoke may be fairly agreeable to many persons. Yaglou and Witheridge were able to confirm this impression experimentally, as shown in Fig. 5. Tobacco smoke for these experiments was created both by normal smoking and by a suction-fan device, and in all instances the odor intensity rose for a few hours before it finally underwent a gradual disappearance.

Crocker suggests that the volatile odorants used in pipe mixtures and cigarettes, such as ionone, coumarin, and hydroxycitronellol, tend to alleviate or neutralize the unpleasant stale tobacco-smoke odors by reason of their concurrent absorption by hangings and furnishings.[2] The smoke from cigars and certain English brands of cigarettes is considered to be more objectionable because of the absence of flavoring or odorizing ingredients.

[1] *Ind. Eng. Chem.*, **18,** 899 (1926).
[2] *Chem. Inds.*, **56,** 777 (1945).

Tobacco smoke has been the occasion of much domestic dissent. In some homes it contributes an unmistakable component to the total aromatic personality of the dwelling. In others it drives the several members to isolated quarters and leads to architectural demands that are difficult to provide on a modest building appropriation. Forced-air heating systems effectively distribute tobacco odors throughout the entire house, along with all other odors,

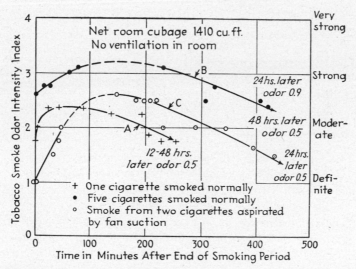

Fig. 5.—Disappearance of tobacco smoke in a closed room. (*Yaglou, C. P., and W. N. Witheridge, Ventilation Requirements, Part 2, Trans. Amer. Soc. Heating Ventilating Engrs.*, **43,** 423, 1937).

no matter where they originate. The housewife may find the merchandising arguments for a new household deodorant or aromatic vapor dispenser especially attractive and even apply the new materials with such diligence that the final combination is more offensive than the original.

INSECTICIDE AND AROMATIC SPRAYS

Designers of aromatic gadgets for household use realize that odorous medicated inhalants for respiratory diseases have a forceful appeal, that fly and moth sprays should smell efficient, and that atmospheric "fresheners" are more readily marketed if they simultaneously "humidify" the room air. Consequently there is an endless array of combinations of the functions of humidifying, odorizing, deodorizing, medicating, freshening, oxidizing, fumigating, repelling, and insect killing.

Liquids are atomized or vaporized by assorted ingenious devices, ranging widely in cost and convenience. They may be motor-driven or hand-operated atomizers, or unattended evaporators with automatic dripping arrangements mounted on walls, or simple exposed wicks disposed throughout the house as desired. Practically all the proposed methods can disperse the required amounts of material into the air according to the tolerance of the occupants, and their success is largely dependent upon the character of the aromatic ingredients. Their ability to perform all the sanitary, germicidal, insecticidal, or therapeutic functions included in the claims is usually somewhat less than their ability to provide the desired fragrance, such as pine, cedar, rose, lemon, or geranium.

Insect sprays are more acceptable for interior use than they were years ago. The inevitable odorous kerosene base has generally given way to more completely refined petroleum fractions having less residual odor and thereby lending themselves to more successful odorizing with pleasantly faint perfumes.

THE STORAGE OF CLOTHING

The preservation of textile and leather goods is traditionally associated with pleasant as well as troublesome odors. The paradichlorobenzene or naphthalene moth balls and crystals have found their way into nearly every home in the country. They have also yielded their intense odors to the effective blending of synthetic aromatics, with the result that many persons do not realize that they are still using these conventional repellents.

Cedar-lined closets, chests, and bureau drawers have long competed with the flat or lifeless atmospheres of less aromatic woods and have in turn given way to fragrant sprays, sachets, and volatile oils. The cedar odor however is still a favorite and has even been incorporated in a special plaster lining for clothes closets. A trace of cedar oil is even added to garments in the course of laundering or dry cleaning to please the customer or to suggest the effectiveness of mothproofing treatments.

The dry-cleaning industry is acutely aware of the troublesome odors that tenaciously remain in some types of fabrics. "Odorless" dry-cleaning fluids do not remain that way without constant vigilance on the part of plant personnel. Garments may be received and placed in storage by the customer only to give forth a surprising aroma of dry-cleaning origin when later removed from the clothes closet for use. Some of the new synthetic fabrics have peculiar odors of their own that are accentuated or revealed by the dry-cleaning process. Chests and closets themselves may acquire an unpleasant musty atmosphere that seems to transfer itself to the contents. It is not, therefore, unreasonable for the householder to seek refuge or relief in the aromatic sprays or evaporators offered for use in storage compartments and on garments to freshen or deodorize.

BASEMENT AND CELLAR ODORS

The traditional odor from basements and cellars is the indefinable "sewer gas," judging from the hundreds of complaints made yearly by householders to municipal authorities. Occasionally a dry trap may permit the escape of gases into a basement, or odorous water may back into the basement during exceptionally wet weather; but often the odors are of quite different origin. Fuel-burning appliances may be inadequately vented, so that combustion products can enter the basement air. Oil or gas leaks may develop in heating appliances. Garbage or refuse incinerators may be overloaded or improperly operated, with odorous results. Rats or mice may die in inaccessible spaces after fumigation and give forth an exciting odor. Dampness may encourage the formation of mildew or accentuate the odors of discarded furniture stored in the basement. Even the water-suspended, casein-base paints may generate unwholesome odors in the presence of moisture on basement walls.

Basement dampness is aggravated by laundering and clothes drying. However, sufficient heat will keep any basement dry, and convected and radiated heat from the furnace in the wintertime usually suffices to maintain a dry con-

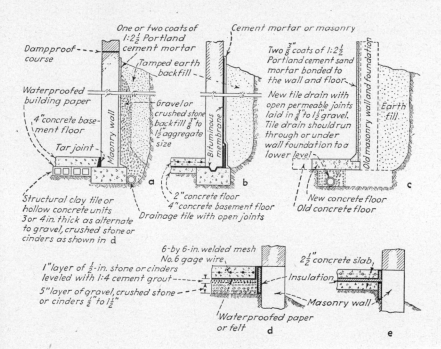

Fig. 6.—Methods of waterproofing basement walls and floors. (*From the National Bureau of Standards, Letter Circular 813, by Dill and Persons,* Jan. 25, 1946.)

dition. In the summer, heat from a water heater may be sufficient to prevent moisture condensation from the basement air onto walls and floor. It has even been suggested that such heaters might better be left uninsulated during the summer, if possible, wherever there is a need for some means of drying the basement.

Hygroscopic materials are on the market for extracting the moisture from basement areas; they succeed more or less according to the amount of absorbent surface provided and the humidity of the air. The usual material supplied for this purpose is calcium chloride. As it absorbs the moisture from the air, it goes into solution. This solution is quite corrosive, and care should be taken to dispose of it by generous flushing into the sewer.

Ventilation or airing of the basement is generally effective in removing excess moisture due to condensation or capillary transmission from the ground. When this fails consistently even in fairly dry weather, the only successful remedy may be extensive draining, waterproofing, or repairing procedures as illustrated in Fig. 6.

A dry basement with reasonable care will be a clean-smelling basement. A damp basement despite almost endless attention will sharpen the odors of all its contents and even, at times, make an otherwise delightful recreation room completely uninhabitable.

Chapter XII

Odors of Waters and Foods

FLAVOR is the professional word for the combination of taste, feel, and odor in foods. While its use as a verb in the subjective sense is a grammatical possibility, it has not been so honored by contemporary philology. Thus, when we flavor our food, we are *modifying* rather than *perceiving* its quality. By colloquial default, *taste* has acquired the broad connotation of odor *with* taste; and, moreover, for some foods and waters it may even be technically synonymous with *odor* and *smell* without taste. To the scientist taste means chiefly the perception of salt, sour, sweet, and bitter. To the layman, taste is everything his chemical senses register whenever he eats or drinks.

Aroma or odor is unquestionably the most versatile element in our enjoyment or dislike of foods. Whether we realize it or not, the "off flavors" or "off tastes" that are damaging both to manufacturer and to consumer are nearly always "off odors" in the preferred language of sensory perception. The possibilities in variation of aromatic constitutents in foods are literally tremendous in comparison with the opportunity for aberrations in the taste factor of flavor. A misplaced aroma is anathema, and the lack of aroma is intolerable.

The aromatic part of flavor is present in exceedingly small concentrations— so small, in fact, that a major problem in food processing is the preservation or retention of the elusive aromatics. This applies alike to the commercial packer and canner, the restaurateur, the caterer, and the cook at home. With justified fervor, Crocker has described the dilemma as follows:

The gourmet knows that order-cooking is best, with the minimum time spent between the oven or saucepan and the table. He knows that needless evaporation of even a little water from the hot food will carry off with it much of the precious aroma that has persisted through the various stages of preserving, storage, and preparation. He sighs when he must eat at large banquets, when foods are likely to be dearomatized. However, he puts on some butter and other seasonings and hopes to build up a palatable flavor. How must he feel at a cafeteria with steam heat under the uncovered serving dishes assuring that evaporation will proceed until the volatile flavors are gone? . .

[1] *Food Inds.,* **17,** 247 (March, 1945).

The importance we unconsciously attach to aroma is no better illustrated than by the manufacture of concentrated apple juice. The volatile aroma from the boiling fruit juice is condensed and set aside while the residue is concentrated to a thick sirup. By returning the aromatic distillate to the parent sirup after concentration has been completed, the apple juice later prepared from this sirup is made pleasantly similar to the fresh product.

The natural odors of foods are so low in concentration in most cases that foreign or unpleasant taints may easily overtake them and produce inedible substances. At least, that is the present-day consequence, for consumers have been gradually trained to demand high quality in their foods. Centuries ago it was not quite so easy to discard unfresh foodstuffs. As with practically all other odor-control necessities, the suppression of unsavory food odors began as a problem in masking; and seasonings and spices helped to salvage the foods that were highly susceptible to decomposition. To this day we value the complex array of natural and artificial seasonings not only for the interest they add to our diets but even to mask off flavors in food that are believed to be still safe for human consumption.

ODORS ACQUIRED BY FOODS DURING STORAGE AND PROCESSING

If the time between harvesting or slaughtering and consumption were always a matter of hours or days at the most, the flavor of foods would be easy to control. They might even in fact be monotonous to the epicure, for meats in particular are improved with moderate aging. There is ample evidence that our preference in flavors is materially influenced by the command of necessity. In Moncrieff's words: "Cheese is ripened, and a bird is hung, but no unnecessary delay is countenanced in the case of an egg." The situation furthermore is cause for international debate, for, as illustrated by classical anecdote, an American ridiculed a Chinese for eating "rotten eggs," whereupon the Chinese replied that the "rotten milk" eaten by Americans was much worse—he referred of course to cheese.

With regard to the evolution of our attitude on flavors we again refer to Crocker, the eminent flavorist of the present generation.

Poultry suffers greatly in flavor when an appreciable time interval elapses between killing and evisceration, particularly when there is not immediate chilling. Sulphury-smelling ingredients from the intestines diffuse into the tissues of the bird in appreciable amount in a matter of hours when the poultry is not refrigerated, or in a few days at just above freezing. Transfer of this unpleasant flavor is much retarded by a solidly frozen condition. While this type of "gutty" or "gamey" flavor is relished by some sportsmen in pheasants, it is highly objectionable in chickens, turkeys and other domestic fowl. The evisceration of poultry before freezing eliminates intestinal-flavor transfer. It is safe to predict a steady increase in this practice, which is still a far from general detail of preparation.[1]

[1] *Food Inds.*, **17**, 247 (March, 1945).

Processing advancements will continue to alter the American taste in food products. Deep freezing brings the possibility of return to the natural flavors of many familiar foods, but at the same time it creates new flavors never before encountered that are directly related to the frigid environment. During and throughout this dynamic progression of the flavors of modern foods, the processor will constantly be reminded of the inertia of public desires and will learn by necessity how to maintain his products in the most popular condition during their storage and distribution period. If he does not bow to the authority of the consumer, his foodstuffs will be discounted in price for their failure to comply.

The development of undesirable aromas or flavors is a complex process for most foods. It comprises one or more of the following transitions, in some cases despite all that is known in the field of food technology: (1) transfer of odors from one food to another; (2) absorption of odors from the package or environment; (3) changes produced by processing into currently marketable items; (4) alterations caused by the treatments used to prevent microbial decomposition; (5) changes resulting from the inherent life processes of respiring fruits and vegetables; (6) modifications caused by high and low temperature and high and low humidity; (7) changes produced by the impact of visible and invisible radiant energy; (8) changes produced by vibrations, whether or not perceptible to the human being; (9) alterations resulting from chemical or enzymatic reactions within the food tissues; (10) atmospheric oxidation; and (11) the paramount mechanism of microbial decomposition, including bacteria, yeasts, and molds, whereby the elements and molecules of life are constantly rearranged.

One of the best demonstrations of the complexity of off-odor sources that we have encountered is the tabulation by Crocker of the reasons for flavor defects in milk, butter, and cheddar cheese (Table I). Dairy products of

Table I.—Flavor Defects and Their Causes for Three Important Dairy Products*

MILK

Barny, cowy ....Absorbed from the surroundings in the process of production.
Feed, ensilage ......Feeding immediately prior to milking; also certain weeds and feeds that the cows may eat in pasturage (garlic, onions, turnips, etc.)

Metallic, card-   Four Principal Causes:
board, oxidized,   1. Natural conditions affecting the cows (often whole herds)
tallowy, oily,   2. Copper and iron catalysts, dissolved from pasteurization equipment
burnt feathers   ment
     3. Action of sunlight (important principally for homogenized milk)
     4. Irradiation by ultraviolet light (often cause of burnt-feather defect)

High acidity, sour ..Improper handling—inadequate refrigeration and age
Salty ....Diseased udder (mastitis, etc.)

*Compiled by E. C. Crocker in "Flavor," McGraw-Hill Book Company, Inc., New York, 1945.

Bitter ....Bitter-flavored weeds in feed; lipase
Disinfectant ....Sometimes the early stages of oxidized flavor
Neutralizer ....Excessive addition of neutralizer
Rancid ....Enzyme action and bacterial toxins

BUTTER

Salty ....Excessive salt used
Rancid ....Old, oxidized products used in the butter or improper storage temperatures; also bacterial action
Metallic ....Frequently is incipient rancidity; occasionally due to dissolved metals
Fishy ....Enzymatic action setting free amines
Feed ....This can be caused by garlic, onion, and other objectionable feed flavors
Unclean or musty ..Many possible causes; sometimes due to yeasts and molds
High acid ....Excessive acidity due to high-acid cream used improperly in its manufacture
Neutralizer ....Excessive neutralizer in cutting the acidity of the cream
Putrefaction and
cheesy ....Protein decomposition

CHEESE (*Cheddar Type*)

Musty ....Old culture, or contamination by wild yeasts and molds
Old ....Indication of runaway or other faulty curing
Metallic ....Metals dissolving from equipment used in manufacturing
Salty ....Too much salt; or abnormal milk
Flat ....Not enough acidity or salt; improper manufacture or curing; or defective culture
Bitter ....Uncontrolled enzymatic action, due to improper processing or curing

course are especially susceptible to foreign odors because of the absorbability of their fat content; but nearly all foods have oleaginous components, and those that do not may have large quantities of water, also a good solvent for natural food aromatics.

ABSORPTION OF ODORS BY FOODS

We have all had experience in the transfer of flavors within the household refrigerator. Aromatic substances are sufficiently soluble in both water and fats so that practically all foods are subject to this process. Some foods offend because they are unusually volatile, such as melons, citrus fruits, onions, cheese, and fish; others are troublesome because they avidly absorb any odor within reach, such as cream cheese, cottage cheese, butter, margarine, whole milk, and apples. The obvious remedy is airtight segregation, not always possible in a limited space. Even water and ice cubes will absorb strange odors wandering inside the refrigerator, and ice-cube compartments are seldom airtight. It is not surprising therefore that many investigations have been carried on to determine the best means of deodorizing the atmosphere inside refrigerators and cold-storage rooms. The most promising material is activated carbon, further discussed in the chapter on Sorption. Ozone is important in many cold-storage applications, principally for the inhibition of molds, and its use is considered in the chapter on Chemical and Physical Destruction of Odors.

Foods are by no means the only source of misplaced aromas or flavors. The processing environment may contribute such unfortunate vapors as gasoline, paint and lacquer solvents, disinfectants and fly sprays, chemicals from a neighboring industry, and the musty odors from poorly ventilated, hot, and humid food-handling rooms. The materials of storage-room construction likewise may be at fault, namely, volatile woods, cork insulation, caulking or sealing compounds, and various surface treatments in the interest of good sanitation. Package or container materials may give off strange odors, and in this category may be mentioned pine woods, cardboard or strawboard, bottle- or jar-top gaskets, waxed paper, and the recently synthesized plastic containers and films.

MICROBIAL DECOMPOSITION OF FOODSTUFFS

The years of study that have been devoted to the organic reactions associated with life processes have uncovered some of these complicated mechanisms, but principally they have reminded us that the chemical processes of life are intricate and incessant. In support of this dynamic state of living tissue, the destruction of one form of life is the basis for construction of another. The microscopic forms that keep this mechanism running are aided by the presence of powerful catalytic agents known as "enzymes"; of these we are here specially concerned with the lipolytic and proteolytic enzymes, capable of splitting fats and proteins respectively. The result we call "biological decomposition."

Microbial activity has by evolutionary methods adapted itself to a wide range of environmental conditions. Although heat in sufficient degree is universally destructive, evidence in the form of prehistoric cold-preserved tissues suggests that some organisms are highly resistant to low temperatures for long periods of time. Bacterial activity may be either anaerobic or aerobic, according to the absence or presence of elemental oxygen. If gaseous oxygen is not available, the end products of decomposition are generally odorous and offensive, represented by such compounds as sulfides, amines, volatile fatty acids, aldehydes, ketones, and thiocyanates. If further oxidation is possible, the products are generally inodorous, represented by carbon dioxide, water, nitrates, and sulfates.

The preferred methods of controlling odors caused by microorganisms are preventive—the use of agents or the creation of environmental conditions that are bactericidal, fungicidal, bacteriostatic, or fungistatic. They include the following: (1) heat-treatment or pasteurization, with care to avoid the creation of caloric odors; (2) chemical agents or preservatives, both in foods and environment; (3) dehydration of foods or dehumidification of environment; (4) refrigeration; (5) storage in inert gases, such as carbon dioxide; (6) storage in high, inhibitory concentrations of oxygen; (7) ozonation of the environment, at concentrations below those producing "oxidized" flavors; (8) storage in vacuum; (9) storage in solutions of controlled acidity; and (10) irradiation of foods and environment with ultraviolet light.

The use of chemical preservatives in foodstuffs is somewhat in disfavor for two reasons. One is the fact that some of the compounds are harmful to humans when consumed in regular though very small amounts. The other is the fact that the use of such chemicals may give the food processor an unwarranted feeling of security from rather unsanitary techniques in the course of food handling.

The use of chemical agents in the environment to destroy or inhibit bacteria, yeasts, and molds is good sanitary procedure; but, as mentioned before, it must be done in a manner that will not contaminate or odorize the foods stored or processed therein. The use of disinfectants to prevent biological decomposition is in large measure responsible for the frequent cataloguing of these agents as chemical deodorizers.

RANCIDITY IN EDIBLE FATS AND OILS

All forms of plant and animal life contain some measure of concentrated energy in the form of fats or oils. Fatty substances are present in the tissues of animals—between and within the muscles; in and around various organs as the liver, kidney, stomach, and intestine; in bone marrow; immediately beneath the skin; and in specialized locations, such as in cavities of the head and jaw in the porpoise and sperm whale. They are present in eggs and in the seeds and nuts of the vegetable kingdom. We recognize the animal oils and fats as butter, lard, tallow, fish oils, and blubber; and the vegetable oils as cottonseed, olive, palm, coconut, linseed, sesame, peanut, rapeseed, cashew nut, soy bean, tung, castor, and almond.

The terms "fats" and "oils" are often used interchangeably, but the preferable distinction is their physical state—the oils being liquid and the fats solid. One cause of confusion is the fact that temperature differences around the world are enough to make a liquid oil in a warm country appear as a solid fat in another of colder climate.

We are concerned with the fats and oils because they are found in nearly everything we eat. It is true that in some cases the quantities may be minimum, but the odorous products of chemical change can create rancidity or tallowiness in extremely low concentrations. The natural fatty materials are composed of complex mixtures of glycerides, phosphatides, cerebrocides, sterols, waxes, pigments such as chlorophyll, carotene and xanthophyll, vitamins, resins, and essential oils. From the standpoint of odors we are chiefly concerned with the glycerides, which are esters of glycerol and the saturated and unsaturated fatty acids.

Rancidity in fats and oils is variously known as "oxidative" or "aldehydic," "hydrolytic," and "ketone" rancidity. Oxidative or aldehydic rancidity is generally considered to be more offensive, possibly because the majority of edible fats and oils do not contain substantial amounts of the "volatile fatty acids," such as butyric, caproic, caprylic, and capric. In fact the principle component fatty acids, either free or in combination with glycerol, are oleic, palmitic, linoleic, stearic, and myristic. Myristic, palmitic, and stearic acids are saturated low-volatile compounds, which are practically odorless, as indi-

Table II.—COMMON SATURATED FATTY ACIDS*
General formula $C_nH_{2n}O_2$

Name	n	Melting point, °C.	Volatile in steam	Odor
Butyric	4	−8	Yes	"Rancid"
Caproic	6	−1.5	Yes	"Rancid"
Caprylic	8	16	Yes	"Rancid"
Capric	10	31	Yes	"Weak"
Lauric	12	44	Slightly	Odorless
Myristic	14	54	Very slightly	Odorless
Palmitic	16	63	No	Odorless
Stearic	18	70	No	Odorless
Arachidic	20	77	No	Odorless
Behenic	22	82	No	Odorless
Lignoceric	24	86	No	Odorless

* Adapted from tabulation by C. H. Lea, "Rancidity in Edible Fats"; *Special Report* No. 46, Department of Scientific and Industrial Research, H. M. Stationery Office, London, 1938; reprinted by Chemical Publishing Company, New York, 1939.

cated in Table II. Oleic and linoleic acids are unsaturated and are present in neutral fats as the unsaturated glycerides. According to Lea, oleic acid is by far the most abundant constituent of natural fats.

Oxidative rancidity is said to be aldehydic because the oxidation of an unsaturated glyceride is accompanied by the formation of aldehydes, some of which have the typical sharp, unpleasant odors of rancidity. Bailey gives the following equation for this reaction[1]

[1] "Industrial Oil and Fat Products," Interscience Publishers, Inc., New York, 1945.

$$CH_3(CH_2)_x \overset{\overset{\displaystyle H}{|}}{C} = \overset{\overset{\displaystyle H}{|}}{C} - R + O_2 \rightarrow CH_3(CH_2)_x \overset{\overset{\displaystyle H}{|}}{\underset{\underset{\displaystyle O-O}{|}}{C}} - \overset{\overset{\displaystyle H}{|}}{\underset{\underset{\displaystyle |}{|}}{C}} - R \rightarrow CH_3(CH_2)_x \overset{\overset{\displaystyle H}{|}}{\underset{\underset{\displaystyle O}{\|}}{C}} + \overset{\overset{\displaystyle H}{|}}{\underset{\underset{\displaystyle O}{\|}}{C}} - R$$

Unsaturated Glyceride   Peroxide   Aldehydes

Hydrolytic rancidity is the deteriorative change brought about by the hydrolysis of glycerides in the fats or oils, liberating the fatty acids of low or medium molecular weight. Although hydrolysis may occur with the esters of any of the fatty acids, rancidity in this case is the consequence of releasing the volatile acids from butyric to capric. Dairy products offer the best opportunity for this type of rancidity.

Animal and vegetable fats, as they occur in the tissues, are invariably accompanied by enzymes capable of hydrolysing them. These lipases vary somewhat in properties with the source from which they are derived, but all are capable of decomposing neutral fats into free fatty acids and glycerol, and all are inactivated by heat. In the living organism the enzyme is held in check, probably in the form of an inactive zymogen. . . .[1]

In addition to these lipolytic enzymes capable of producing hydrolytic rancidity if certain volatile fatty acids are present, there are oxidizing enzymes that evidently accelerate the development of oxidative rancidity with production of damaging aldehydes.

Ketone rancidity, sometimes called "perfume" rancidity, appears to be due to the formation of odorous methyl ketones—propyl, butyl, amyl, hexyl, heptyl, and nonyl—from the C_6 to C_{12} fatty acids. This means that fats or oils that do not contain appreciable quantities of acids lower than myristic are not likely to develop ketone rancidity. This type of rancidity is reported to be due to the action of molds, principally penicillium and aspergillus, and occurs most readily in dairy products and in coconut and palm-kernel oils.

The saturated fatty acids are usually quite stable in air. Banks and Hilditch reported that palmitic and stearic acids have been recovered from Egyptian tombs 3,000 to 5,000 years old, probably buried as the beef-tallow constituents of cosmetics.[2] However, these acids will oxidize in air in the presence of ultraviolet light or in the presence of metallic catalysts at high temperatures.

Oxidative rancidity is accelerated by heat, ultraviolet and visible light extending from about 3,000 to 5,000 angstroms, and the presence in fats of catalytic quantities of cobalt, copper, or vanadium. Metals such as iron, manganese, nickel, and chromium are less active in this respect, while the least effective are tin and aluminum. In view of the catalytic or accelerating activity of copper, the stainless steels appear to have an important advantage over

---

[1] Lea in "Rancidity in Edible Fats."

[2] *Analyst*, **58**, 265 (May, 1933).

tin-coated copper for processing equipment, since the coating of tin is naturally subject to wear or abrasion. With respect to the accelerating activity of radiant energy, there is good reason to use protective wrappers for oleaginous foods that will exclude as much light as possible below 5,000 angstroms, which means that yellow, brown, or red materials would be suitable.

Both animal and vegetable oils contain remarkable substances called "antioxidants," which protect the oil against deterioration during its natural life. Animal fats, however, are not so well protected as are the vegetable oils, and consequently they may be fortified with additions of minute quantities of vegetable or plant antioxidants or synthetic chemicals. The concentrations of antioxidants naturally present in the fats or oils may be not more than a few hundredths or even thousandths of 1 per cent. Among the materials suggested and used for antioxidants are guaiac resin, cereal flours, glucamine derivatives, maleic acid, lecithin, esters of gallic acid, ascorbic acid (vitamin C), and nordihydroguaiaretic acid (NDGA). Most of the useful antioxidants are covered by patents.

DEODORIZATION OF FATS AND OILS

The deodorizing of oils for edible purposes was an unknown, even unnecessary art, until comparatively recent years. The ancients were acquainted with olive oil and undoubtedly with coconut oil, but in early practice both of these oils were expressed by means of cold-pressing processes, from fresh raw materials and both therefore were entirely suitable for edible uses without further processing of any sort.[1]

The forces of agricultural economics caused the storage and shipping of oil-containing seeds and fruits in greater and greater quantities and over increasing distances, with the result that the natural changes outlined above brought on gradual deterioration of the valuable oils. Processing methods were improved to permit higher yields from the oil-bearing raw materials, also resulting in some impairment of quality.

Early methods of controlling the odors and flavors of edible oils included (1) their masking with agents like coumarin, saccharin, vanillin, menthol, thymol, oil of mirbane, oil of lemon, oil of peppermint, ethyl nitrate, oil of celery, oil of sage; (2) washing out of the odoriferous components with various solvents; (3) chemical destruction or neutralization of the odorous compounds; (4) sorption by materials such as fuller's earth or charcoal; (5) sweeping out the odorous vapors with inert gases at high temperature; and finally (6) the development of steam deodorizing procedures of many varieties.

Steam distillation for deodorization is now carried out with high vacuum

[1] A. P. Lee and W. G. King, Edible Oil Deodorizing Equipment and Methods, *Oil & Soap*, **14**, 263 (October, 1937).

and high temperature to facilitate the removal of volatile odorous compounds. The desirable fatty components of the oils are relatively nonvolatile, and this makes the steam treatment feasible. An important advantage of the steam atmosphere is its ability to prevent oxidative decomposition of the oil by the exclusion of air.

Lee and King found the inventive trends in the development of steam deodorization to be somewhat as follows:

. . . superheating of the steam; addition of vacuum apparatus; the use of higher and still higher temperatures, of lower and still lower absolute pressures; intro-. duction of baffles of various designs to secure intimate contact between steam and oil; variation in design of heating apparatus, of entrainment breakers, or catchalls, of steam distributors, and of vacuum apparatus; construction of the equipment from various inert or noncorrosive metals; and the development of continuous apparatus . . . .

Jamieson describes a contemporary continuous deodorizer as follows:

. . . the alkali-refined bleached oil is first heated by pumping it through a heat exchanger into the evacuated top section of the deodorization tower, where it is rapidly deaerated. From there the oil is passed through an external heater, into the top of the deodorizer column; it then flows downward in very thin streams through the bubble trays at the same time that low-pressure superheated steam rises counter-current to the oil, carrying off its odoriferous volatile constituents. The deodorized oil which collects at the bottom of the deodorizer is pumped into a heat exchanger through which the oil to be deodorized is also flowing, and after passage through another cooler, it goes into the storage tank. The deodorization of the oil by this method is completed within a few minutes.[1]

The Foster Wheeler Corporation's continuous deodorizing system using Dowtherm is shown in Fig. 1.

ODORS OF BEVERAGES

Good organoleptic technique is the classical attribute of professional tea-tasters, coffee-cuppers, wine samplers, brandy tasters, and, recently, water samplers for taste and odor control. The distillates, fermentates, decoctions, infusions, and simple solutions that are sold to the public have all been subjected at one place or another to the quality control of human appraisal. Manufacturers of beverages, both alcoholic and otherwise, are quite sensitive to the impact of off-flavors in their products. No test is quite equal to the discriminating response of the professional taster.

As everyone knows, the control of aromatic composition is the actual function of the aging of liquors. Raw spirits contain a number of alcohols that have disagreeable odors, and long periods of storage give them time to

---

[1] "Vegetable Fats and Oils," American Chemical Society Monograph, No. **58**, 2d ed., Reinhold Publishing Corporation, New York, 1943.

convert into pleasantly odorous esters. Moreover, by storage in wooden containers, the flavors and colors are strengthened by absorption and extraction of woody constituents. While activated carbon may be used to remove strange flavor components, it may also take away some of the esters and aldehydes; and the presence of tannin and furfural in brandies is desired by some for

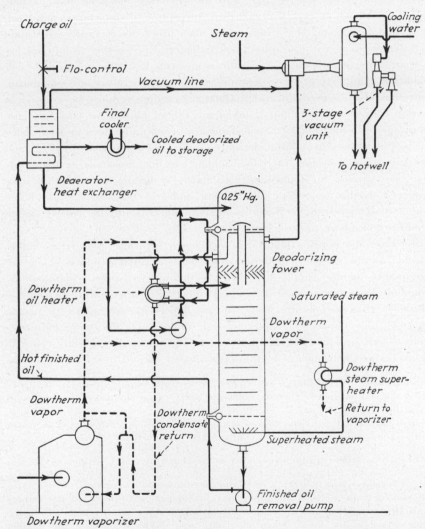

Fig. 1.—Continuous steam deodorizing system for oils. Flow diagram showing the path of oil through the deodorization system. Stripping steam carries off the undesirable constituents and is exhausted through the booster ejector and barometric condenser system. Dowtherm for heating is circulated from the vaporizer to the oil heater and steam superheater, returning by gravity to the vaporizer. (*Foster Wheeler Corp.*)

their effect on character and body. Tolbert and Amerine note that "treatment of a spirit (by carbon) for fusel oil removal alone is likely to be impractical, as better results can be obtained more economically by careful separation of the tails during distillation."[1]

Wines and beers are susceptible to absorption of environmental odors during fermentation and storage, and the offending materials may include such divers items as molds, cork, rosin, turpentine, disinfectants, paint solvents, and fumigants. The solutions for such problems generally are found in better maintenance, sanitation, ventilation, and processing techniques.

Apart from the abominable variations in methods of brewing coffee, over which the manufacturer has essentially no control, there are several precautions that are observed during production. The beans must be roasted to develop fully the flavor, "but if taken too far an unpleasant empyreumatic odour appears which makes the subsequent infusion nauseous," in Moncrieff's words. Coffee loses its volatile elements rapidly when exposed to the air and consequently is best preserved by vacuum packing, especially if the beans have been ground for immediate use. Many of the dry extracts that were developed during the Second World War and are now available for home use clearly demonstrate the difficulty of retaining faithfully the elusive aroma of coffee throughout the concentrating processes.

Breweries and bottling plants for carbonated beverages require a "highly polished" water supply to avoid unusual odors in their products. Even the high-quality potable supply delivered by the water-treatment plant to the community may have sufficient residual chlorine or other barely perceptible substances that do not mix well with the flavors of beverages. Ice plants, bakeries, confectioneries, creameries, and similar food-processing industries likewise need an odor- and taste-free supply of water and frequently resort to the use of privately operated granular-activated carbon filters or adsorbers.

In December, 1927, Chicago experienced in its water supply probably the greatest contamination due to phenols (carbolic acid) ever experienced by any large city in the country. Damages, largely to food products, were estimated to be fully one half million dollars. Food cooked in the water in perhaps 200,000 homes tasted so strongly of chlorophenol that it could not be consumed.[2]

Offutt reported a similar experience some years later at Williamson, W. Va.

A local bakery had to scrap a thousand pies during the week because the water had tainted them so badly that they were unsalable. This siege led the owners to install a granular carbon filter to prevent any further taste troubles. Even the coffee served at the local restaurants was unpalatable because of the distinct chlorophenolic taste.[3]

[1] *Ind. Eng. Chem.*, **35,** 1078 (October, 1943).
[2] MANTELL, C. L., "Activated Carbon," Industrial Chemical Sales, New York, 1930.
[3] *Taste Odor Control J.*, **7,** 3 (July, 1941).

ODORS IN POTABLE WATER SUPPLIES

The control of odors in foods and in water differs in one significant respect. In water there must be *no* odors, according to present public de-

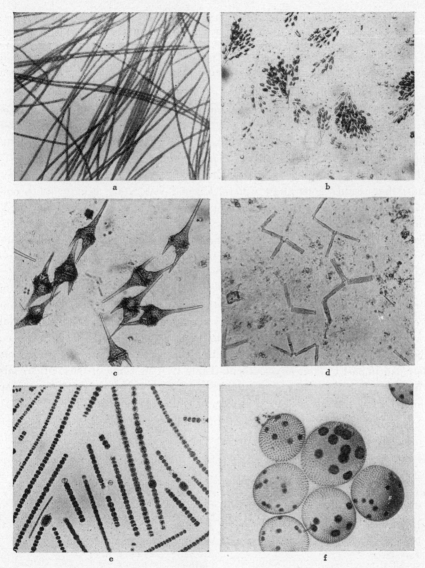

FIG. 2.—A few microorganisms responsible for odors in water. (*a*), Aphanizomenon (*Chlorophyceae*), 150×; (*b*), Dinobryon (*Protozoa*), 200×; (*c*), Ceratium (*Protozoa*), 150×; (*d*), Tabellaria (*Diatomaceae*), 200×; (*e*), Anabaena (*Chlorophyceae*), 200×; (*f*), Volvox (*Chlorophyceae*), 55×. (*Phelps Dodge Refining Corp.*)

mand, while in foods and beverages there must be the *correct* odors. The difficulties of the food industry in this goal are immeasurably relieved by the availability of the odorless water that many of us now take for granted.

People have learned to accept characteristic tastes and odors in characteristic places. Thus they will relish fresh cucumber in a salad, but they cannot be depended upon to enjoy the cucumber taste of synura in a water supply. Nothing tastes more like green algae than watermelon. The flavor is delicious when found in watermelon, but please be cautious about permitting it to get into your distribution system.[1]

The raw water supplies of a community are generally classified as surface, shallow-well, deep-well, rain, and spring water. They are *surface* supplies when taken from streams, rivers, lakes, ponds, or reservoirs, and *ground* supplies when taken from wells or springs. Odor-control problems are generally offered by surface supplies because of the many and complex contaminants that readily enter these waters. Ground waters are usually quite palatable, as a consequence of their long contact with particles of soil and sand, which act as absorbers or adsorbers; but occasionally they may be contaminated with hydrogen sulfide, methane, or industrial wastes passing into the ground. Hirsch estimated that ground waters are the source of approximately two-thirds of the public water supplies in the United States.

Surface supplies are subject to practically every type of contamination conceivable. It is often contended that the free-floating organisms or plankton are the chief source of trouble, even when the highly offensive industrial wastes are considered. There is no doubt that the myriads of microscopic plant and animal organisms are exceedingly versatile in the kinds of aromas they can impart to their environment. Table III lists some of these organisms with the odors they have generated. Figure 2 shows a few as they appear under the microscope. Figure 3 is offered without comment.

Table III.—Microorganisms Responsible for Odors in Water Supplies

Organisms	Odor
Diatomaceae, Bacillarieae:	
Asterionella	Aromatic, geranium, fishy
Cyclotella	Faintly aromatic
Diatoma	Faintly aromatic
Meridon	Aromatic, spicy
Pleurosigma	Fishy
Tabellaria	Aromatic, geranium, fishy
Synedra	Earthy

[1] Welch, W. A., Milestones in Taste and Odor Control, *J. Am. Water Works Assoc.*, **38**, 57 (January, 1946).

Chlorophyceae:

Actinastrum ....Slightly grassy or earthy
Dictyosphaerium ....Grassy, nasturtium, fishy
Eudorina ....Faintly fishy
Pandorina ....Faintly fishy
Staurastrum ....Grassy
Volvox ....Fishy
Gonium ....Slightly fishy

Cyanophyceae, Myxophyceae, Schizophyceae:

Anabaena ....Moldy, grassy, nasturtium, pigpen
Aphanizomenon ....Grassy, nasturtium, pigpen
Coelosphaerium ....Sweet grassy
Clathrocystis ....Grassy, nasturtium, pigpen
Cylindrospermum ....Grassy
Microcystis ....Grassy
Oscillatoria ....Spicy, moldy
Rivularia ....Moldy, grassy

Protozoa:

Bursaria ....Irish moss, salt marsh, fishy
Ceratium ....Vile stench
Cryptomonas ....Violets
Dinobryon ....Fishy, like rockweed
Glendoinium ....Fishy
Mallomonas ....Aromatic, violets, fishy
Peridinium ....Fishy, like clam shells
Synura ....Cucumber, muskmelon, fishy
Uroglena ....Fishy, oily

Lake Winnebago in Wisconsin is renowned for its prolific and lush growths during favorable weather. The Indians made certain that its fame would be preserved by giving it a name that meant "stinking water" in their language.

Added to the odors introduced by the organic inhabitants of water are decayed vegetation, community sewage, contamination by animal life, and trade-waste pollution. Public officials learn to accept each new problem with reserve. In one of these incidents, "complaints came in from the general public so rapidly during the spring and fall periods that all of the telephones in the City Hall were constantly ringing, and accusations were being made that horses and possibly cows had fallen into and been drowned in the lake."

Perhaps not the most voluminous but nevertheless the most intense types of water contamination are those which the industries discharge with their liquid wastes. Water-treatment plants in highly industrialized areas, as well as many miles downstream, are constantly seeking better odor-control methods to keep pace with the rising standards of organoleptic quality and the increasing number of offensive wastes. The kinds of industry that may offend are so varied that they may be found in practically every community in the country. A list would include chemical plants, oil refineries, coke ovens, gas plants, synthetic-rubber plants, paper mills, steel mills, creameries, tanneries, canneries, sugar refineries, breweries, distilleries, textile mills, dye works, and meat-packing plants.

THE WATER THAT JOHN DRINKS.

THIS is the water that JOHN drinks.

This is the Thames with its cento of stink, That supplies the water that JOHN drinks.

These are the fish that float in the ink- -y stream of the Thames with its cento of stink, That supplies the water that JOHN drinks

This is the sewer, from cesspool and sink, That feeds the fish that float in the ink- -y stream of the Thames with its cento of stink, That supplies the water that JOHN drinks.

FIG. 3.—Cartoonist's appraisal of water odors. (*Reproduced by permission of Punch, and Bradbury, Agnew & Company, Ltd.*)

Methods of water treatment for odor control have progressed through many stages during recent decades, beginning with aeration and including chemical oxidation, filtration, removal with coagulants, chlorination, and treatment with chlorine-ammonia, activated carbon, and most recently chlorine dioxide. Ozonation has been used for some years in European countries and in small industrial supplies, but evidence now appears that it may be extended in this country to the water supplies of moderately large communities. Further consideration of some of these processes may be found in Chaps. XVI and XIX.

Aeration was the only treatment used for odor removal for many years. Its use was based on the premises (1) that odorous materials are sufficiently volatile to escape from the water; (2) that some of these substances are readily oxidized if given good opportunity; (3) that replenishing the oxygen content of the water would prevent odorous anaerobic decomposition; or (4) that removal of iron and manganese would deprive some microorganisms of their food supply. Many waters have been substantially improved by aeration, but unfortunately the standards of water quality have outrun the capability of this method in competition with more recent systems of control.

The designs of aerators have been endless, interesting, and in some cases spectacular (Fig. 4). Their parklike decorative possibilities have undoubtedly endeared them to many communities. Aerating devices have included spray nozzles, spray towers, cascades, splash trays, coke-tray percolators, carborundum or alundum bubblers, perforated submerged pipes or plates, and riffle or stair-type gravity-flow aerators. Haynes and Grant have described a moderately successful use of high-pressure aerators in a recent chemical odor control problem in West Virginia.[1]

In addition to chemical treatments discussed elsewhere, the control of odors due to microorganisms has comprised two effective techniques. One is the "carbon blackout" procedure apparently innovated by Bailey at Council Bluffs, Iowa, and also known as the Bailey Blackout. It depends on the facts that odor-producing organisms require light for their growth and that by applying finely divided carbon in a liquid suspension over the surface of a reservoir or small lake it is possible to reduce the light intensity enough to inhibit such growth. Quantities of carbon required vary from about 1/4 to 1 lb. per 1,000 sq. ft. of water surface on a sunny day.

The other method of controlling the growth of microorganisms is a carefully calculated application of copper sulfate over the surface of the reservoir. The method was introduced in 1904 by Moore and Kellerman of the U. S. Department of Agriculture. The quantities of copper sulfate required to destroy each type of organism and the limiting concentrations to avoid poisoning of fish life have been compiled by Hale and are too comprehensive for

---

[1] *J. Am. Water Works Assoc.*, **37,** 1013 (October, 1945).

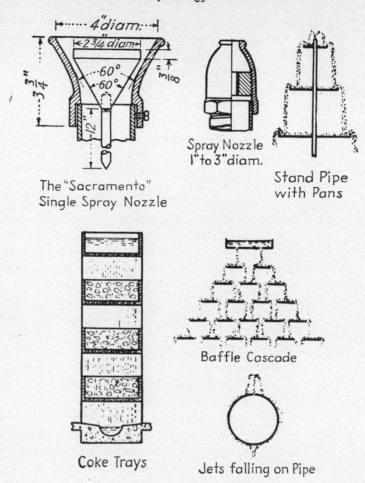

The "Sacramento" Single Spray Nozzle

Spray Nozzle 1" to 3" diam.

Stand Pipe with Pans

Coke Trays

Baffle Cascade

Jets falling on Pipe

FIG. 4.—Several types of aerators. (*Baylis, "Elimination of Taste and Odor in Water."*)

inclusion here. It may be stated in summary that required copper sulfate concentrations range from 0.1 to 10 parts per million, while the limiting safe dosages for protection of fish range from 0.14 part per million for trout to 2 parts per million for black bass.[1]

Hirsch indicates that copper sulfate may be applied to a reservoir from a skiff or motorboat by the following methods:

1. Sacks or perforated cans, one hung on each side of the boat are dragged through the reservoir while traveling in lanes about 25 feet wide, criss-crossing the area . . . .

[1] HALE, FRANK E., "The Use of Copper Sulfate in Control of Microscopic Organisms," Phelps Dodge Refining Corporation, New York, 1942.

2. A barrel or tank containing copper sulfate solution discharges overboard at the stern so that the propellor causes mixing . . . .

3. A powder is blown from a feed table by a fan. The dust settles on the surface and dissolves in the upper layers where algae are most numerous . . . .

4. A solution is sprayed over the surface of the reservoir.

To treat a small reservoir conveniently, a sack of crystals may be submerged at the inlet.[1]

[1] HIRSCH, A. A., "Manual for Water Plant Operators," Chemical Publishing Company, New York, 1945.

Chapter XIII

Industrial Odors

A MAN living all his life in the open is said to be able to smell the bad air of a city the moment he steps inside its gates. We who live and smother in our own and our neighbors' exhalations grow accustomed to the stench.

Ellen Richards, the internationally honored sanitarian at the turn of the century, by her careful indictment of city air was eminently more gracious than Shakespeare's Gloucester: "Let him smell his way to Dover." But she could not resist an observation that left no doubt about responsibility for community disgrace:

"Air is abundant and is kept in constant motion by forces of nature beyond human control, so that, save in the neighborhood of an exceptionally offensive factory, man does not foul the free air of heaven."

Industry has not always been so vulnerable. The housekeeping habits of the early cities of the world were indeed never calculated to inspire cleanliness on the part of industrial or commercial enterprise. Rivers and streams were generously polluted with all forms of filth, and each citizen on the waterway contributed his share. The scavenging of assorted refuse on land was left to the community hog, dog, and vulture population, although in some United States towns the preference was for geese—and they accordingly roamed the streets to keep the place tidy. In 1926 Tribus congratulated the American city for its sanitary reformations by painting a picture of contemporary old-world indifference:

The Oriental and near-Oriental sensibility to smell and sight does not seem as keen as that of the conglomerate and amalgamated American with its Anglo-Saxon predominance; so the dog and vulture scavengers that comprise the street-cleaning personnel of many populous cities are even yet tolerated. The speaker is glad that he visited Constantinople before the thousands of street dogs were destroyed, and saw the groups of mangy curs, large and small, appropriating the sidewalks, while pedestrians walked in the streets. These groups knew their own districts, perhaps by virtue of dog vote and determination, for it was immediate destruction for any dog to step outside his own territory. Not a scrap of any edible refuse could long be found in the streets of that wonderful cosmopolitan city. The unpaid, non-uniformed, four-footed corps did the trick, until finally banished to a neighboring island.[1]

[1] *Trans. Am. Soc. Civil Eng.*, **92**, 1297 (1928).

That we have progressed a long way in our standards of both liquid and aerial sanitation is no better revealed than by the incredible conditions still tolerated in other parts of the world. The "water system in Teheran is a series of open ditches running through the streets. Iranians use it for drinking, bathing and washing clothes, gradually turning the water dirty brown as it flows through the city. Social life centers on these ditches."[1]

This is precisely the situation we struggle to avoid on the streams in this country, sometimes at great expense. Industries have accepted the dictum that they do not have an unlimited right to turn the water "dirty brown as it flows through the city." With progressive management, they have also arrived at the conviction that community patience is wearing thin on the subject of aerial sewage.

THE METEOROLOGY OF ODOR NUISANCE

It is not required that one travel into the city through its gates to encounter the gases and vapors of the essential industries. As any careful observer can attest, the odors of industry will not only travel over the gates and tall buildings and trees and hills to become intercity odors; with favorable geography and meteorology they will also arrive at the state boundary and immediately become interstate odors. Well over a decade ago the residents of many western Kansas and Oklahoma communities were thoroughly convinced that "sour gas" discharges from the oil fields in the Texas Panhandle had traveled from 100 to 150 miles in their direction before sufficient dissipation and dilution terminated the nuisance.

It may be fair and justifiable to consider any widespread odor attack extending even as far as 50 miles as more of a phenomenon than a nuisance. Gage[2] was commissioned in 1920 to investigate the odor nuisance from oil refineries in the Metropolitan District of Providence, R. I., and from this study he concluded that a nuisance is most likely to occur in "light airs" or when the wind velocity is between 5 and 15 miles per hour. Odors might conceivably travel several hours at this velocity in one direction before complete dissipation, but the evidence from most investigations seems to indicate that the range of an odor nuisance is seldom greater than 5 to 15 miles and is usually within a radius of 1/2 to 2 miles.

In the Providence survey, an odor was observed on only one instance when the recorded wind velocity was greater than 25 miles per hour, and in only nine instances when the wind velocity was greater than 20 miles per hour. In some instances odors travel high and at other times with apparently similar conditions they may travel low. In one instance an odor was traced from hilltop to hilltop for some distance, but could not be detected in the intervening valleys. In certain instances

[1] *Life*, Apr. 8, 1946, p. 35.
[2] *Trans. Am. Soc. Civil Eng.*, **89**, 349-360 (1926).

an odor settled in what was probably an air pocket and remained a source of offense for some time after it had ceased to be produced at its source, this condition generally occurring when there was some fog and little wind. Strong odors were also observed on the wind blowing up certain streets while parallel streets only a block distant were practically free from odor.[1]

There is general belief that odors will remain with the prevailing wind direction and that accordingly a plant may be located downwind from a residential district with reasonable security from odor complaints. Actually the concept of "prevailing wind" is a statistical device that can be misleading. Examination of Weather Bureau records will disclose that, for nearly every station where measurements have been made over many decades, the wind blows in every direction around the compass at some time or another and that it is not unusual for the weather vane to point for many minutes in every direction during a single day. It is true that the pattern of a nuisance zone around a plant will be displaced in a general direction parallel with the axis of prevailing wind and that winds may be strong enough in some communities to afford good protection. In most places this will not be the case, and there will be enough air movement in all quarters so that location of a plant in an urban district with dependence upon the prevailing wind does not appear to be a reliable method of odor control.

Pearson claimed that while living in Jersey City a few decades ago he was able to predict the weather by the impressions on his nose and ears—without getting out of bed!

Northeast winds brought tobacco fumes from a tobacco factory and rain or snow. Steamboat whistles from the Hudson denoted east winds and bad weather. Odors from a soap and perfume factory were wafted by a southeast wind, when fog would often follow. Whistles from a railroad were plainly heard when it was balmy south. Smells of low tide denoted southwest winds and mild weather. Smoke odors with westerly winds from the Jersey Meadows brought good weather. Pronounced whistles from the two other railroads were indicative of a cold northerly wind.

The case of topography is different. If the plant is located in a valley or at the base of high hills, the effect on direction of air currents moving away from the plant will be substantial. If a residential section should be located at the top of the hill, air currents moving up the hill will carry a good sample of the industry's activities. Residents who may be located at the base of the hill on the other side will be better protected from odor offense. An extensive forest or wooded area seems to be a good barrier in some cases, but quite often the real factor is the distance and not the presence of trees. Skinner had a different view of the utility of a generous vegetation.

If trees and shrubs which give off pleasant odors are planted about the premises in masses sufficient to affect the atmosphere, they will be noticed at times for their

[1] *Ibid.*, 352.

beauty and for their pleasant odors and at other times will serve to disguise unpleasant odors by their presence.[1]

The classic incident of teamwork between topography and air pollution occurred in the Meuse Valley in Belgium. In the winter of 1930 the residents of the valley suffered a "fog disaster," in which a calm atmosphere and dense fog joined forces with toxic industrial gases and a low-lying terrain. The results were the loss of many human and domestic animal lives and the death of countless small wild animals and birds. The circumstantial evidence against the industries in the valley was overwhelming, although the toxicology of the incident is still debated.

Temperature and humidity deserve all the attention the investigator can give them. The arrival of hot summer weather in the vicinity of an uncontrolled source of odor is accompanied by a rising tempo of neighborhood excitement. But curiously the worst time of day is generally evening and not midday or midafternoon, when the heat may be greatest. Furthermore, the warm, muggy, humid summer night becomes even worse if the temperature drops low enough to bring fog. Temperature "inversions" may blanket the lower atmosphere, particularly on a still clear night. The implications are at once complex and disturbing. A knowledge of meteorology is decidedly helpful.

The glider pilot knows the power of thermal updrafts in the atmosphere near cities; the commercial transport pilot knows the settling or stabilizing effect of sundown, usually appreciated in terms of a smoother ride. The meteorologist identifies the "thermals" by their white-tipped clouds, and the Pacific Islanders can locate their tiny pieces of land by these telltale temperature signals. In short, the forces of odor dissipation in a vertical direction are substantially greater during the daytime in summer, and the observations of hundreds of investigators confirm this fact.

The approach of evening may produce at least two effects of importance in odor nuisance. The dropping air temperature takes the power from the vertical convection currents over the city and permits any gases or vapors to remain at a low level above the city, even though they may be initially discharged at fairly high temperatures. The air movement or wind velocity may be low enough to avoid the churning of these odorous gases into the city atmosphere, with the result that on some days the stratum of odorized air over the city will be high enough to avoid nuisance at ground level. However, on many days, air movement will be substantial, and failure of the industrial gases to escape high into the atmosphere, as they may have done during the day, leaves them low enough to contaminate the air near the ground. This applies naturally to the effluent from any establishment operating late in the day or all night long.

[1] *Trans. Am. Soc. Civil Engrs.*, **89**, 381 (1926).

Another effect of dropping temperature as night approaches is the condensation of moisture to produce a fog. Observers for many years have been careful to report that many odors are aggravated during periods of dense fog in the evening or early morning. It is well known that many of the malodorous organic vapors are water soluble or can be condensed. It is quite within reason for such materials to contaminate and remain with fog or mist particles in the nuisance zone with gradual accumulation to a relatively high concentration. The passage of such air into the nasal cavity, whether or not the fog is revaporized upon entering a dwelling, should result in a high order of olfactory stimulation.

An additional factor that is worthy of consideration is the reduction of air density with increasing humidity. This is contradictory to the conventional belief that humid air is heavy air, but the fact remains that large amounts of water vapor in the atmosphere reduce the density of the air-vapor mixture and likewise, therefore, its barometric pressure. Humphreys, the great meteorological physicist, has recorded his convictions on the fundamentally sound relationship between outdoor odors and the state of the weather.

On cloudy, muggy days the aromas of the abattoir, of the glue factory, and many other such smellful places, remain concentrated near the surface instead of being carried up and diluted beyond perception by the convection of sunshiny weather; and therefore, on such occasions, the leeward town often wonders whether the source of its wealth may not be a trifle tainted! In a sense the townsmen smell the direction of the wind and state of the sky. Through their noses they perceive the weather. Similarly, on the edges of stagnant ponds, by the sides of fetid swamps, and wherever else the earth is full of decaying matter, we often can "smell" the fall of the barometer and the near approach of a general rain. We then smell the breath of the earth, for the earth does breathe, inhales when high pressure forces air into every crevice, and exhales when low pressure lets it out again. This outgoing air, this breath of the earth, carries with it some of the foul gases of decaying matter. It is this that offends the nose, an offense that is a clear perception of an effect of low atmospheric pressure, the common prelude to bad weather.[1]

Finally, an effect of the weather that will receive more attention in the years to come is the irradiation of odorous gases with sunlight. Although the fact is obscured by the contemporaneous action of other phenomena in the outdoor air, there is some evidence now available that odor intensities on a sunny day may be somewhat reduced by the combined forces of ultraviolet activation of gaseous molecules and the instant availability of oxygen for destroying some compounds by photochemical reactions.

SOLID, LIQUID, AND GASEOUS WASTES

The continuous appearance of new industrial activities and products, especially from organic synthesis, makes any attempt to itemize the sources

[1] "Ways of the Weather," The Jaques Cattell Press, Lancaster, Pa., 1942.

of industrial odors misleading, presumptuous, and unwarranted. It is our intent here to generalize in a way that will demonstrate to any industry the kinds of activities and problems that are related to odor offense to the community as well as to the worker. We recognize the scarcity of reliable information in this field in spite of the hundreds or thousands of independent investigations, reports, and publications, for much of the material now in print is repetitive or contradictory. Our hope is that the appearance of this discussion will stimulate more intensive study and more frequent reporting of odor-control experiences in industry as a basis for a growing body of analytical and remedial information for the specialist in this field.

The final state of an odor nuisance is a gas or vapor reaching the person by aerial transport. The initial state may be solid, liquid, or gaseous, and the odor-control methods correspondingly variable. In all cases there is an economical conflict between the cost of disposing of an odorous waste and the saving or profit by recovery of valuable materials therein. The recovery process itself may create a new odor problem. The costs of recovery may consume all the by-product value but still may be profitable if the cost of disposing of the unsalvaged waste is substantially high. Furthermore, the expense attending the control of offensive odors is not always certain to the designers of new processes, for this element in planning has been too long neglected. Even the movement of an industry into a community may be economically ill-advised from an odor viewpoint, although promoted with vigor by the chamber of commerce. And zoning commissions still lack the comprehensive information they need to pass judgment on the potentialities of a new industry nuisance. Many officials have discovered that an odor will not "stay zoned."

The untreated waste may be in the form of gases discharged into the atmosphere through stacks, liquids discharged into a lagoon or over a sewage farm, or solids deposited on an open dump. Treatment for the gaseous waste may be combustion, chlorination, ozonation, scrubbing, adsorption, or any other operation to alter its character or reduce its quantity. Treatment for the liquid waste may be dilution in an available stream or lake, nitration, chlorination, sedimentation, neutralization, or pumping into the ground. Treatment for the solid refuse may include burial, dumping at sea, incineration, or maceration with introduction to the sewerage system. In every case, the possibility of gaseous escape at the end of the treatment process or at the destination of the waste must still be anticipated and avoided, inasmuch as the abatement of odor nuisance may be the paramount reason for treating these wastes in the first place. In many cases the elimination of odors is the *only* reason for treatment.

Thus, it does no good to scrub the odor from a gaseous waste and then discharge the wash water into a stream that cannot dilute it below an acceptable level. It is no solution to reduce solid wastes to a form that will enter a sewer when the consequence is a terrific stench at the sewerage outlet. There is no advantage in burning a gaseous waste when the products of combustion are as bad as, or even worse than, the primary substance.

Some of these methods of odor control are analyzed further in Chaps. XVI and XIX. They include the destruction of odors by chemical or physical means and their collection by absorption or adsorption. Additional methods of odor prevention or odorless waste disposal are suggested in the remaining sections of this chapter.

ODORLESS DISPOSAL OF SOLID WASTES

Slag piles, sludge beds, and dumps are no asset to the community appearance; but when they burn, putrefy, or vaporize foul gases, tolerance comes to an end. Man, of course, is not among the most orderly creatures in the animal world, for he has strewn his wastes over the earth for milleniums. Once in a while he buries his refuse, as do some of the well-bred animal relatives, but the work and expense seem so often unnecessary that eventually the cycle returns to the open-face dumping ground.

In this country and in England we have arrived at a new stage in outdoor housekeeping. The City of New York through its Department of Sanitation has carried the disposal of solid wastes to the notable point of municipal reclamation. In defiance of the public antipathy toward anything that simulates a "dump," highly trained technicians, engineers, and public health personnel have refined and studied the methods of *sanitary land fill,* whereby all garbage and refuse in practically any proportion is quickly buried and covered with enough earth, and the area is converted into limited-use land. The method deserves the study of any community or industry that finds itself in the position of owning or creating any solid odorous wastes that are difficult or costly to destroy. In England the method is comparable to the one developed here but is known to the British as "controlled tipping."

The land-fill procedure is not an impractical dream that ignores all advances in the technology of garbage disposal by incineration or reduction or by the salvage of refuse, but it is an accomplished scientific procedure in the hands of competent workers. The perennial problem of waste disposal in New York City, which inspired the search for better procedures, has been effectively summarized by Rice and Pincus.

Some of you may be familiar with the endlessly smoking Rikers Island dump, the smouldering Corona dump, the Barren Island reduction plant—spreading odors for miles in the neighborhood, the ill-fated Staten Island reduction plant—closed after a year's operation, and, finally, the disposal of waste by dumping at sea, which was discontinued 6 years ago by order of the United States Supreme Court.

For the past 3½ years, mainly two methods have been used by the city for the disposal of its refuse and garbage: (1) destruction by incineration, and (2) the sanitary land-fills. . . .

In New York City, the Sanitation Department is disposing of 9,000,000 cubic yards of refuse and garbage per year through the use of land-fill. That department has completed 5 land-fills and retrieved for useful purposes a total area of 325 acres. . . . The complete cost of disposal of waste by land-fills has been 7½ cents per cubic yard as against 30½ cents per cubic yard when incineration is used. . . .

By disposing of 4,000 truckloads of waste material daily through land-fills, the Department of Sanitation has been able to close up 11 of the smaller and less efficient incinerators out of the total of 22 incinerators formerly in operation.[1]

A schematic description of the technique in this operation is given in Figs. 1 and 2. Almost any earth-moving equipment may be used, but the most convenient device for the moderate-size land fill is currently known as the *bull-clam* tractor. Large-scale fills are conducted with the drag-line crane, bulldozer, and other accessory machinery. Discussion of this process is available in detail in the *Engineering News-Record*.[2]

While the sanitary land fill has been used in modified form in a few cities for some years, such as San Francisco and Fresno, Calif., Portland, Ore., and Tacoma, Wash., there are many communities where other methods will continue in preference.

Garbage may mean any mixture from the limited content of animal and vegetable waste from homes, restaurants, or hotels to a heterogeneous combination of food waste, tin cans, glass, paper, cardboard, rags, leather, leaves, grass, wood, metal, rubber, and ashes. Most cities, however, now require some segregation of wastes, chiefly between the combustible and noncombustible components, also distinguished as organic and inorganic, putrescible and nonputrescible, garbage and rubbish.

Current methods of disposal in addition to dumping and land filling are usually incineration or thermal reduction for organic material, and mechanical salvage for inorganic-organic mixtures containing paper, cardboard, wood, metal, glass, and rags. Outdoor odor problems are characteristic of the garbage-disposal processes but are seldom encountered in the vicinity of salvageable refuse plants. In the latter case, the conditions within the plant may become annoying, but even so the odors are apt to be less troublesome than the dust and the noise.

A summary of the causes or sources of odors associated with the handling of putrescible solid wastes as prepared by Greeley some years ago is still appropriate and should be carefully weighed by any investigator of a complex odor complaint in an urban community.

1. The House Treatment—Odors may come from accumulations of garbage in the can or house receptacle and from accumulated piles of garbage spilled from the

[1] *Am. J. Pub. Health*, **30**, 1091 (1940).
[2] **129**, 851 (1942).

can. In some apartment houses, the garbage is spouted to the ground and these spouts may become foul.

2. The Collection—If the collection wagons are not cleaned, or are difficult to clean, they may become quite odorous. Leaky and overloaded wagons may spread odor-producing material along the route. A proper covering of collection units is desirable and may be important.

3. The Transportation—In cases of long haul, the garbage may be transported from a transfer station to the disposal works in scows, freight cars, or large trucks. Poorly designed and maintained transfer stations with inadequate facilities for

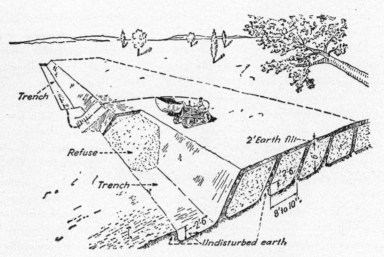

Fig. 1.—Disposing of solid waste by land-fill using a bull-clam tractor. (*War Dept., Tech. Bul. Eng. 1, December, 1943.*)

washing are likely to produce odors. Such conditions may be aggravated if the garbage is not removed from the transfer station frequently . . . .

4. The Final Disposal

    a. If the plant capacities are such that garbage must be stored at the plant for several days during peak seasons, odors will result. The age of the garbage as delivered to the plant also affects the odor situation . . . .

    b. At incinerating plants, incomplete combustion may permit odorous gases to escape from the chimney top. In the reduction process odors may come from the vapors escaping from open grease-skimming tanks, from hot materials when exposed, and from leaks about piping and tanks. Odors may also come from the digester vent gases and from the drier gases.

    c. Some odors may come from the products of disposal, as for instance, half-burned garbage from incinerators delivered to ash dumps; or the accumulation of tankage, tailings, and sewage at a reduction plant.[1]

The solids in sewage that may be collected as a filter cake on drum or rotary filters become an asset in the form of fertilizer. The "milorganite"

[1] *Trans. Am. Soc. Civil Engrs.,* **89,** 364-366 (1926).

marketed by the Milwaukee Sewage Disposal Plant is a notable example of profitable disposal of waste solids.

TRADE WASTE WATERS AND SEWAGE

Although sewage is a combination of liquids, suspended solids, and dissolved gases, it is conveniently designated as "liquid waste." Apart from the obvious and in many places successful method of diluting the sewage or trade

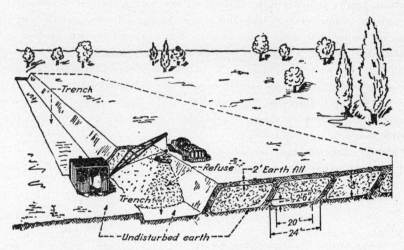

FIG. 2.—Disposing of solid waste by land-fill using a drag-line crane and truck. (*War Dept., Tech. Bul. Eng. 1, December, 1943.*)

waste with enough water where available, the selection of a good treatment for such matter has been troublesome for centuries. In a history of sewerage and drainage of towns in this country, Eddy stated that it was not until about 1850 that the water-carriage system for liquid wastes, including excretal matter, began to come into wide use. Before then it was common among the communities to prohibit the discharge of fecal matter into their drainage systems, because of the intolerable odors usually created. Early drains were not properly designed to handle solid materials, which might settle or collect where odorous decomposition could proceed undisturbed. Baltimore carried its legal opposition to the introduction of offensive or dangerous solids into the drains until the year 1911, when a new comprehensive system of sewerage and sewage treatment was ready for use, independent of the storm-water drainage system.

The liquid wastes from industrial activity are seemingly endless in variety. In addition to the sources shown in Table I, there are dye works, chemical plants, synthetic-rubber plants, oil wells, refineries, gas plants, coke ovens, wood distillation plants, slaughterhouses, glue factories, woolen mills, breweries, distilleries, laundries, corn-products plants, and gasoline filling stations. In wastes from most of these sources there is adequate organic matter of nitrogenous or sulfurous nature to give rise to the noxious products of biological decomposition. From the standpoint of odor the worst of these gases are sulfides, mercaptans, indoles, and amines. In addition to organic products, the waste waters from many establishments contain dissolved gases of malodorous quality that are little affected by the natural forces of self-purification in the watercourse or lake and carry for miles to degrade the environment of commercial shore lines, bathing beaches, and resorts, as well as to odorize the potable water supply and the waters inhabited by oysters or small fish. Pleasure boating may be impossible on some waters because of the odors of dissolved gases carried in with the industrial wastes. It is alleged that the fishing industry in Saginaw Bay, for a time suffered serious losses through the decrease in value of fish that acquired the taste of their liquid environment.

Eldridge indicates that the phenol content of the ammonia liquor and still wastes from gas-coke manufacturing plants is of the order of 2,000 p.p.m.;

Table I.—Population Equivalents of Typical Industrial Wastes*

Industry	Population Equivalent
Milk condensery	1,500– 2,000
Cheese factory	2,000– 3,000
Dairy and creamery	800– 1,000
Pea cannery	6,000– 8,000
Corn cannery	2,500– 4,000
Tomato cannery	3,000– 4,000
Squash cannery	6,000– 8,000
Red-beet cannery	2,000– 3,000
Paper mill	4,000– 5,000
Pulp mill, sulfite	250,000–400,000
Tannery, vegetable	18,000– 20,000
Beet-sugar factory, straight house	65,000– 75,000
Beet-sugar factory, Steffens	115,000–125,000
Cotton-textile mill	2,500– 6,000
Silk-textile mill	15,000– 22,000

*From Eldridge, E. F., "Industrial Waste Treatment Practice," McGraw-Hill Book Company, Inc., New York, 1942.

from a pentane-extraction plant about 4,000 p.p.m.; and from wood distillation plants about 100 p.p.m. A phenol concentration of 0.1 p.p.m. in potable water can be detected by some persons. If the phenol should become chlorinated either in the course of water treatment or as a result of admixture of phenolic and chlorinous liquid wastes before the water appears at the treatment plant, the chlorinated phenol that results is detectable in a concentration as low as 0.02 p.p.m.

One of the methods of disposing of gaseous wastes is their extraction from air by washers or scrubbers. In many instances the results are commendable, for dilution in waterways that are capable of biologic purification effectively disintegrates the organic matter. Unfortunately, however, a good many wastes are not readily oxidized or consumed as organic food, and the absorption of odors by industrial waters may then be not odor control but simply odor transfer from one point to another.

It is generally known that a stream has ability to rejuvenate itself by the metabolic activities of its microscopic inhabitants. An old Arab proverb says that "when water turns over seven times it is purified." Many are familiar with the ancient adage, "Running water purifies itself." This fortunate circumstance is outlined by Eldridge in the following manner:[1]

> The purification process in a stream takes place in a series of overlapping steps. These steps, more or less in the order of their happening, are as follows:
> a. Wastes discharged into a stream may have an immediate oxygen demand because of the presence of compounds, such as hydrogen sulphide, calcium sulphite, etc., which unite chemically with oxygen. This reaction takes place within a short distance below the point of discharge.
> b. Suspended material is deposited on the bed of the stream, causing the formation of sludge beds.
> c. Colloidal and soluble material is precipitated biologically by the action of the stream organisms. Much of this material also settles on the stream bed and adds to the sludge deposits.
> d. Anaerobic and aerobic decomposition of both precipitated and soluble material takes place with the depletion of oxygen. The organic matter is liquefied or gasified by the reducing and oxidizing action of the organisms.

In this process the dissolved oxygen content is the vital component. In sewage nomenclature also, oxygen is decisive: if the sewage is "fresh" it contains dissolved oxygen; if "stale," the oxygen has been exhausted; and if "septic," the organisms have begun to deoxygenate the most susceptible compounds, with highly odorous results. According to Eldridge, the amount of oxygen required to avoid odor nuisance is about 2 p.p.m. For the support of slow-moving bottom-feeding fish it is 4 p.p.m., and for game fish the requirement is from 6 to 10 p.p.m., which is possible only in cold-water streams.

The quality of sewage or industrial wastes is currently judged by its "biochemical oxygen demand," or B.O.D. This index is the amount of oxygen that the sewage would consume at 20° Centigrade during a period of five days. The test has been standardized in sewage technology and research activities to the point that a value of 0.167 lb. has been established as the B.O.D. of domestic sewage per capita of population per day. With this convenient device the oxygen demand of organic industrial wastes can be com-

[1] ELDRIDGE, E. F., "Industrial Waste Treatment Practice," McGraw-Hill Book Company, Inc., New York, 1942.

pared to that of domestic wastes and accordingly expressed as the "population equivalent," as in Table I here included.

One of the earliest methods of sewage treatment was "broad irrigation" or "sewage farming," which in fact is still practiced in many parts of the world. Because of the large amounts of land required, and for aesthetic reasons, the method has never been widely practiced in this country as a primary process. Irrigation makes use of the natural purifying forces of the land micro-organisms, in a manner similar to stream purification. As will be readily appreciated, the odor potentiality is serious and, unless it is tolerated by the neighbors because of the fertilizing effect, the "farm" or "lagoon" must be carefully isolated. Cannery wastes and sewage-plant effluents are still extensively lagooned in certain communities; but preliminary treatment, including chlorination and nitration, has effectively suppressed the greater portion of the nuisance.

The odors of sewage treatment are practically legendary. So little is known by the public concerning the high stage of sewage-treatment development that invariable surprise is expressed when a citizen visits his community's modern establishment. The handling of sewage is now scientifically conducted under careful bacteriological control and advanced engineering design. Not all the problems have been solved, to be sure, for some plants are subjected to the most complex and obnoxious mixtures conceivable. In other cases, the municipal authorities may not fully appreciate the technical responsibility that accompanies sewage-plant operation, with the result that qualified and competent personnel are difficult to attract on a limited budget.

The surprising freedom from offense achieved by scores of such treatment plants in this country is an object lesson in intensive research combined with scrupulously careful management of the works. Many of the offensive industries would do well to observe not only the excellence of design and construction of recent plants but also the attitude and caliber of the operating personnel. In support of this appraisal of the current status of sewage-plant management, we reproduce here in full the meritorious advice given by Cohn on the method of obtaining nuisance-free operation:

About a decade ago I coined the expression "The Three C's of Odor Control." The C's are: Care, cleanliness and chlorination. In this succinct phrase, I believe, is summed up the secret of nuisance-free plant operation. Each plant can supply its own interpretation of these three factors, yet they remain basically the same for every problem, regardless of the nature of the sewage treated, the type of plant, the location of the plant and the personnel of operation.

Care in operation will prevent many odors which might take a pound of cure to correct. Interwoven with this fundamental of odor control is efficient operation of treatment units. Proper sewer servicing, intelligent care of grit chambers, screens, tanks, digesters, and like facilities will prevent the production of odors. Septicity can be prevented in many cases and the reward of care is carefree service.

Cleanliness in operation is an inviolable rule. The clean plant is normally clean smelling. The presence of debris around the plant units is offensive to the eye—and what offends the eye offends the nose. There is little excuse for improper disposal of screenings, skimmings, sludge and other odor-producing materials which arrive at the plant in unending stream. Cleanliness means plant upkeep. The plants with nice lawns, trim roadways, intelligently laid-out flower beds and clean buildings are builders of favorable public opinion. They seldom are the whipping boys of neighborhood complaints. Cleanliness extends to the plant personnel. Unkempt workmen mean unkempt workmanship. Dress up the men and you achieve safety and a pride in the job, both of which result in a cleaner plant and a fresher plant. The fellow who spits in the corner of the power house or pump room may cuss about "sissy stuff" when he is told that such slovenly methods do not go, but he will soon perk up and see filth and odor-producing materials which he never saw before.

Chlorination is the outstanding odor destroyer in the sewage treatment field. The intelligent use of chlorine will prevent the septicity of sewage, or correct such conditions when they exist. Prechlorination of sewage will result in improved conditions around screen and grit chambers, settling tanks, etc. The agitation of sewage in treatment devices, flowing over weirs, passing into dosing tanks, being distributed over trickling filters and even flowing in channels is a definite source of odor dissemination. The use of chlorine will prevent these points from becoming foci of objectionable conditions.

The best advice I can give the operator is—"Practice the Three C's of Odor Control." Your plant will benefit, and the neighbors will bless you.[1]

MALODOROUS GASES AND VAPORS

The emergence of odors from smokestacks and vents is traditional, almost to the point of hallucination in some cases. In one famous incident the citizens had been anticipating trouble from a new garbage incinerator for so long a period during its construction that, when the first smoke began to rise from the visible stacks, complaints immediately poured in that the burned garbage stench was intolerable. The plant had not even been put into operation but was simply undergoing preliminary boiler tests with only coal as the fuel.

Although industrial odors are conceived as disseminated gases and vapors, this does not preclude the good possibility that finely divided solid or liquid particles of colloidal magnitude may also carry offensive odors over widespread areas. The solids may either be composed of substances with sufficient vapor pressure to yield an odor or have odorous gases adsorbed on their surfaces. The malodorous mists may comprise foul liquids prior to complete vaporization or may likewise carry impurities of offensive materials, in this case in solution.

DallaValle and Dudley concluded in their study of odor nuisance originating in kraft-paper mills that the most seriously offending air contaminant was the large quantity of chemical smoke containing sodium sulfate particles with adsorbed organic sulfur compounds. In this case electric precipitation was an

[1] *Sewage Works J.*, **13**, 1237 (November, 1941).

indicated control method, notwithstanding the well-known fact that gases and vapors themselves cannot be removed from the air by electrostatic precipitators.[1]

Many disappointments have followed the construction of enormously high stacks. The vagaries of air currents in the outdoor atmosphere are entirely capable of returning the stack gases to the earth no matter how high they may be discharged. The high stacks built for smelters, reaching 500 or 600 ft. into the air, have generally succeeded in reducing the concentration of sulfur dioxide to a permissible point from the standpoint of vegetation, but such structures are prohibitive for the majority of industries. Even in the kraft-paper-mill nuisance cited above, the erection of a superstack did not completely eliminate the odor problem, although it did succeed in spreading the offense over a much wider area at substantially reduced intensity.

The conclusion reached on many occasions has been the inevitable necessity of treating the stack gases before they are discharged. The choice of deodorizing procedures is extensive and at the same time uncertain, and large-scale installations are best selected as a result of preliminary experiments with small models or in the laboratory. The methods of scrubbing, combustion, chlorinating, ozonating, and adsorption are treated in detail elsewhere in this book.

Development of the techniques of industrial-process ventilation has greatly reduced the merit of any excuse for offensive odors inside industrial plants. It has likewise made the escape of odorous gases through windows, doorways, and leaky roofs quite untenable when the plant is not isolated. In fact, the rising standard of air purity inside factories has increased the amount of odorous air contaminants collected by exhaust systems and conducted to ventilating stacks on the roof, with the natural result that neighborhood complaints in an urban community have increased in volume and intensity.

In consequence of this tendency, not only must deodorizing procedures now be applied to the tall stacks of conventionally offensive industries; they must also be considered for incorporation into the general or local exhaust systems going into manufacturing plants in increasing number. Whereas a toxic air contaminant near an industrial process may be adequately diluted by the simple expedient of discharging it outdoors, if the substance is simultaneously a potently foul odor, such as hydrogen sulfide, the atmospheric dilution achieved by mechanical exhaust may be notably inadequate.

The specialized ventilating equipment for indoor atmosphere control around industrial processes is beyond the scope of this book. Furthermore, although a good many installations of industrial exhaust systems are frankly for the olfactory comfort of plant personnel, the primary function of the largest number is the prevention of occupational disease, dust explosion, flammable vapor

[1] *Public Health Rept.,* **54,** 35 (Jan. 13, 1939).

escape, or property damage due to corrosive air contaminants. Methods of ventilating industrial processes may therefore be found in the rapidly growing literature of air conditioning, industrial hygiene, fire prevention, and safety engineering.

For the investigator of odor nuisances, the peculiarities of outdoor air movement are highly significant and require much study to master. For the designer of control procedures, odor travel habits may influence the point of discharge into the atmosphere and the degree of odor reduction before discharge is permitted. For the owner or manager of a potentially offensive industry, the eccentricities of odor nuisances should clearly lead to the conclusion that little dependence can be had on the deodorizing activities of natural atmospheric forces and that, instead, the plant and its equipment should be conceived and operated to minimize the escape of offensive air contaminants.

Especially to be commended is the development of a consciousness of potential odor nuisance at all levels of industrial and community enterprise, so that in advance of plant operation, serious consideration may be given to the possibility that a new product or process will bring offense along with economic advantage. The benefit, we are sure, will accrue not only to the public; much costly redesigning, rebuilding, and relocating will be avoided, to the montetary advantage of owners and operators.

Chapter XIV

The Offensive Trades

B EGINNING AT a time long past, all forms of production of wares were so divided that one special category was designated as the "offensive trades." The common denominator of these trades was offensive odor. These low trades commonly centered about dead animals, the slaughtering of animals, secondary products from animals, such as glue or fertilizer, and the disposal of human wastes and human dead. The nature of such operations is reflected in such trade terms as fellmongering, blood boiling, gut cleaning, tripe boiling, knacking, hide tanning, glue manufacturing, fat rendering, tankage reduction, garbage dehydration, poudrette manufacturing, stockyards, shambles, suture processing, privy cleaning, corpse bearing. Offensive trades as determined by the Massachusetts Supreme Court are the keeping of swine, rendering, soap works, slaughterhouses, oil refineries, fish-handling plants, glue works, gasworks, liquor distilleries, breweries, abattoirs, tanneries, varnish works, rubber works, smelters. These do not preempt the possibility of other inclusions.

The early forms of these occupations were attended by two varieties of social opprobrium. The workmen engaged commonly represented the lees of humanity, near to social outcasts. For some centuries slaughterers were not permitted to serve on juries in trials involving death penalties—this on the theory that the sensibilities of slaughterers would have been so hardened by continuous proximity to blood that human life would be held in low esteem. During the same period these workmen were not permitted to serve as witnesses in important issues on the same ground—that hardened sensibilities would lead to their becoming incorrigible liars. Secondly, the community demand was for the segregation of these lowly rated operations. The worst of the offensive trades were banished beyond the city walls, and the workmen were not permitted to live within the walled cities. Some less offensive trades were tolerated in the city itself, but only in specifically designated areas. What with no steam cooking, no condensers, no water carriage of wastes, no chemical treatment of odorous gases, it may be conceded that much of the disaffection, if not apprehension, over the spread of diseases by odors may have been justified.

Ramazzini, in his "De Morbis Artificum," published in the year 1700, strangely omits reference to the greater number of the offensive trades as he may have observed them in Italy. The two that he describes, "Privy Cleaning" and "Corpse Bearing" earn the right to extensive quotation here as a record of the fearsome attitude of the ancients toward odors attending these humble means of livelihood.[1]

Privy Cleaning

I will relate the incident that first gave me the idea of writing this treatise on the diseases of workers. In this city, which for its size is thickly populated, the houses are naturally close together and of great height, and it is the custom to take the houses one by one every three years and clean out the sewers that run in every direction through the streets. While this work was going on at my house I watched one of these workmen carrying on his task in that cave of Charon and saw that he looked very apprehensive and was straining every nerve. I pitied him at that filthy work and asked him why he was working so strenuously and why he did not take it more quietly so as to avoid the fatigue that follows overexertion. The poor wretch lifted his eyes from the cavern, gazed at me, and said, "No one who has not tried it can imagine what it costs to stay more than four hours in this place; it is the same thing as being struck blind." Later, when he had come up from the cesspit, I examined his eyes carefully and observed that they were extremely bloodshot and dim. I asked whether cleaners of privies regularly used any particular remedy for this trouble. "Only this," he replied, "they go back at once to their homes as I shall do presently, shut themselves in a dark room, stay there for a day and bathe their eyes now and then with lukewarm water; by this means they are able to relieve the pain somewhat." Then I asked him: Had they a burning sensation in the throat or any respiratory troubles or attacks of headache? Did that stench hurt their nostrils or cause nausea? "Nothing of that sort," he replied, "in this work our eyes only are injured and no other part. If I consented to go on with it any longer I should very soon become blind, as has happened to others." Thereupon he wished me good-day and went home, keeping his hands over his eyes. After that I saw several workers of this class with eyes half-blinded or stone-blind begging alms in the town. I am not at all surprised that so foul a reek injures the rather delicate texture of the eyes. In Baillou there is a case of a poor workman in Paris who contracted Ophthalmia, and Baillou ascribes the malady to the man's occupation; he was a street-cleaner. But as for the reason why the eyes only are attacked by this cruel affliction while the other organs escape injury, the lungs for instance which are also made of very soft tissue, or the brain by way of the nostrils—why, I say, these are not at all affected by that foul stench is what astonished me from the first and still does; I am at a loss to account for this fact.

It seems likely that Ramazzini has furnished an excellent description of the toxic action of hydrogen sulfide gas on the eyes. The toxic action of this gas is a thing apart from its offensive odor.

Corpse Bearing

In cities and towns, at least in Italy, every family of rank has its family tomb in the principal churches, but the common people are buried in their own parish churches, promiscuously in great burial vaults, and the corpse-bearers have to go

[1] Latin ed., 1713, trans. by Wright, pp. 95 and 151.

down into those terribly fetid caverns full of decomposing corpses and lay in them the bodies that have been brought there; hence they are exposed to very dangerous diseases, especially to malignant fevers and to sudden death, cachexy, dropsy, suffocative catarrh, and other serious diseases; their faces are always corpse-like and they look ghastly, as men well may who themselves have an appointment with death before long. Could one imagine any surer or more certain way of inviting pestilential diseases than to go down into the vaults where they must for some time breathe that foul air? To inhale it is to contaminate the animal spirits, whose ethereal nature must be preserved or they become too feeble for their proper function, which is to sustain the whole vital machine. Hippocrates says with justice: "Air is the father of human life and of human diseases." Now the air in such a vault cannot fail to be highly pernicious for the corpse-bearers and to corrupt the blood mass. In antiquity the public slaves were doomed to this vile task as they were to the mines and sewers; their heads were half-shaved, and they were called "the branded." Martial says: "Four branded slaves were carrying a pauper's corpse; a miserable pyre receives a thousand such."

Nowadays, filthy lucre or sheer need and poverty compels free men to do this sort of work, but fortune frowns on them; so far I have never seen an old corpse-bearer. We all know how terribly the decomposing bodies of any kind of animal can taint the air; for it has often been observed that unburied corpses after great battles or ancient tombs carelessly opened have given birth to frightful plagues that decimated whole populations; no wonder then that corpse-bearers and those who conduct funerals invite pestiferous diseases by handling corpses, unlocking the doors of vaults, or going down into them. A certain well-known corpse-bearer called Pisto, after laying in the vault a young man who was well dressed and wore new shoes, noticed a few days later, about midday, that the doors of the church were open, so he went to the vault, removed the stone, and went down, but he had no sooner taken off the shoes than he collapsed on top of the corpse and there breathed his last; he paid the penalty he deserved for violating the tomb.

There are so many tombs in the churches, and they are so often opened that this abominable smell is too often unmistakable, however much they fumigate the sacred edifices with incense, myrrh, and other aromatic odors, and it is obviously very injurious to those present. In his learned treatise on various burial customs, Lilio Giraldi very properly censures our modern custom of interring the dead in churches; for in remote times and in the earliest days of the Christian faith only the bodies of martyrs were deposited in churches; the rest of the faithful were buried near a sacred edifice or in cemeteries. Our country-people bury the dead more decently than is done in towns; when one of the family dies, they place the body in a narrow wooden box, dig a deep pit in a meadow near their parish church, and commit him to the earth; these last rites are discharged by the friends and relatives. Admirable indeed, by Hercules! was that practice of the Romans of carrying their dead outside the city, like the Athenians who deposited theirs in the Ceramicus; they placed them on a pyre and stored the ashes in urns of stone or brass in the Via Latina and the Flaminia, and the military roads especially were in high repute among the Romans because they had so many monuments to the dead. So Juvenal says: "I will try what is safe to say of those whose ashes lie under the Latin and Flaminian roads." According to the worthy Giraldi, this was done for three reasons; first, that those monuments might encourage travellers to pursue virtue, which is why ancient epitaphs are nearly always addressed to the wayfarer; secondly, that whenever the city was in danger from a siege the citizens might fight the enemy more fiercely in defence of the ashes of their kin; but the third and most powerful motive was to preserve the city from the fetid exhalations that come from decomposing corpses. It was the unique privilege of the Vestal Virgins and the Emperors that they could be buried within the city; furthermore, as we read in Cicero, a law of the Twelve Tables provided that no funeral pyre, even outside the city, might be placed near another man's house: "Let no pyre, or new funeral mound be placed within sixty feet of another man's house against his will." So Cicero says, and this was not from fear of fire, as he says, but because of the horrible smell of burning corpses. So careful were the ancients, so heedful of the purity of the air for the sake of the public health, that they banished beyond the city walls not only all unclean things but even the ashes of their kindred.

Beyond the historic there is scant reason for the perpetuation into the present of any concept of "untouchables" among man's industries. Perhaps without exception all these stigmatized trades which are still carried out may be operated as to provide no offense. Actually, not all are.

THE ODOROUS GASES OF THE OFFENSIVE TRADES

Insofar as the offensive trades are associated only with operations connected with animal bodies, excreta, etc., in distinction to petroleum refining and rubber manufacture, sometimes accepted as offensive trades,. it may be pointed out that the gases or vapors concerned are similar, but of course not constant. On this account there are now introduced some data related to such gases and vapors, chiefly derived from the work of Ronald,[1] since his estimable publication is not widely available in the United States.

From the totality of the Ronald experiments the following conclusions were reached as a result of chemical inquiry:

1. That the gases driven off during concentration are almost entirely soluble.
2. That the insoluble gases are so minute in quantity as to be incapable of determination.
3. In an airtight plant the volume of noxious vapours or gases to be deodorized consists of the air which overlies the charge and is displaced by heating, together with the small quantity of air from the condenser water, and the insoluble gases.
4. That most of the gases given off during concentration belong to the amine group. Ammonia and monoethylamine from flesh, and ammonia and monomethylamine from fish, form the largest proportion of these gases, followed by trimethylamine, sulfuretted hydrogen and dimethylamine from fish, and diethylamine and sulfuretted hydrogen from flesh. Trimethylamine is the most offensive, apart from a substance which remains undetermined.
5. That this undetermined gas, though exceedingly small in quantity, taken together with small quantities of the soluble gases which pass the condenser, is capable of fouling a large volume of air.
6. That, in consequence, all air leaving the plant which has been in contact with the interior of the plant must be deodorized.
7. That notwithstanding the noxious nature of these gases, they and any air which has been in contact with them can be completely deodorized by chlorination.

[1] "Handbook on Offensive Trades," William Hodge & Company, Ltd., London, 1935.

Table I.—FISH

Analyses of the condensate from surface condenser and condenser effluent from spray condenser derived from the concentration of *fish* in a fresh and stale condition expressed as parts per 100,000, percentages, and pounds of substances per ton.

Constituents	Parts per 100,000				Expressed as percentages				Pounds of substances distilled from 1 ton of fish			
	Surface condenser		Spray condenser		Surface condenser		Spray condenser		Surface condenser		Spray condenser	
	Fresh fish	Stale fish	Fresh fish	Stale fish	Fresh fish	Stale fish	Fresh fish	Stale fish	Fresh fish	Stale fish	Fresh fish	Stale fish
Water	.....	.....	.....	.....	63.9374	78.6617	.....	.....	1432.199	1762.022	.....	.....
Ammonia and mono-methylamine	39.10	123.38	0.450	4.521	0.0250	0.0975	0.0234	0.6312	0.560	2.184	0.637	14.129
Dimethylamine	2.40	5.77	0.019	0.029	0.0015	0.0046	0.0012	0.0040	0.034	0.103	0.027	0.090
Trimethylamine	31.00	128.65	0.228	1.124	0.0198	0.1016	0.0144	0.1568	0.444	2.276	0.323	3.512
Sulfuretted hydrogen	0.90	0.85	0.007	0.067	0.0006	0.0007	0.0005	0.0093	0.013	0.016	0.010	0.208
Carbonic acid	19.80	117.20	.....	.....	0.0127	0.0926	.....	.....	0.283	2.074	.....	.....
Oil (nonvolatile at 100° C.)	.....	6.64	.....	.....	.....	0.0052	.....	.....	.....	0.116	.....	.....
Other nonvolatile organic matters (at 100° C.)	4.70	45.72	.....	.....	0.0030	0.0361	.....	.....	0.067	0.808	.....	.....
Dissolved oxygen taken up in 5 days	2.44	3.92	0.58	0.50								
Oxygen absorbed from permanganate N/80 in 3 min.	0.92	3.51	0.02	0.18								
in 4 hr.	4.01	10.34	0.21	0.46								

Table II.—FLESH

Analyses of the condensate from surface condenser and condenser effluent from spray condenser derived from the concentration of *flesh* in a fresh and stale condition expressed as parts per 100,000, percentages, and pounds of substances per ton.

Constituents	Parts per 100,000				Expressed as percentages				Pounds of substances distilled from 1 ton of flesh			
	Surface condenser		Spray condenser		Surface condenser		Spray condenser		Surface condenser		Spray condenser	
	Fresh flesh	Stale flesh	Fresh flesh	Stale flesh	Fresh flesh	Stale flesh	Fresh flesh	Stale flesh	Fresh flesh	Stale flesh	Fresh flesh	Stale flesh
Water	.....	.....	.....	.....	62.7466	67.0368	.....	.....	1405.524	1501.386	.....	.....
Ammonia and mono-ethylamine	52.30	578.80	0.416	3.901	0.0329	0.3913	0.0314	0.2500	0.736	8.765	0.704	5.600
Diethylamine	Traces	19.67	Traces	0.288	Traces	0.0133	Traces	0.0185	Traces	0.298	Traces	0.414
Triethylamine		34.83				0.0236				0.528		
Sulfuretted hydrogen	4.30	3.52	0.040	0.116	0.0027	0.0024	0.0030	0.0069	0.061	0.054	0.068	0.155
Carbonic acid	21.20	98.27	.....	.....	0.0133	0.0664	.....	.....	0.298	1.487	.....	.....
Oil (nonvolatile at 100° C.)	.....	64.50	.....	.....	.....	0.0436	.....	.....	.....	0.976	.....	.....
Other organic non-volatile matters (at 100° C.)	7.20	26.00	.....	.....	0.0045	0.0226	.....	.....	0.101	0.506	.....	.....
Dissolved oxygen taken up in 5 days	15.76	13.40	0.88	0.81								
Oxygen absorbed from permanganate N/80 in 3 min.	6.15	24.41	0.07	0.18								
in 4 hr.	14.80	37.33	0.30	0.46								

8. That if the chlorine is derived from a solution of calcium or sodium hypochlorite, the amount of available chlorine in the liquor should never fall below 0.35 per cent, and the period of contact should not be less than half a minute.

9. That the maximum rate at which moisture is driven off during concentration is about four times the average rate when the internal temperature of the vessel is 148°C. (298°F.), equivalent to steam at a pressure of 50 lb. per sq. in.

10. That the volume of gases given off during concentration as well as their noxiousness is greatly increased when the raw material is in a stale condition.

11. That if the quantity of water used in the condenser is sufficient to reduce the temperature of the effluent to between 33 and 49°C. (90 to 120°F.) the effluent containing the dissolved foul gases is much below the standard suggested by the Royal Commission on Sewage Disposal for a purified sewage effluent.

12. That if the gases are cooled in a condenser to a temperature not exceeding 49°C. (120°F.) no nuisance will be caused by the effluent.

With the prospect of increasing population density for the United States for a few oncoming generations, and with the prospect, however undesirable, that large cities will grow still larger, only waning hope may be entertained that the traditionally odor-disturbing industries may be so located that through location alone all basis for complaint will disappear. These industries serve the communities within which they exist, and their banishment might lead to grosser olfactory offense. A fat-rendering plant dedicated to the utilization and disposal of meat-market waste in Detroit could not practically and economically exercise that function if relegated to some island in Lake Erie.

It is widely believed by the public that most of the meat supply of all large cities represents shipments from the packing-house areas of the Midwest. To the contrary, as much as 80 per cent of the fresh meat supply for many a city far from the packing cities is furnished through local animal slaughter. Always there will arise products apart from edible flesh. No sane person will want to demand that all cattle hides be destroyed on the premises rather than shipped to some tannery. Leather from hides is almost as essential to life as the comestible flesh. The nonedible products of slaughtering are as characteristic of these trades as their more highly favored ones.

Already means are at hand whereby garbage may be fully minced and harmlessly dumped into water-carried sewage; or instead garbage may be incinerated on the householders' premises without offense to any. Still it will be a long time before the smelly, fly-ridden garbage truck becomes a relic.

He who elects urban residence must accept as inescapable some degree of prospective annoyance from a multitude of disturbing odors. This small peril as a disadvantage offsets some other advantage that characterizes city life. The contention is not that nothing ever may be done in the control of odors; rather that, after all possible has been done, cities regularly or irregularly will harbor some unwanted odors. That is a feature of city life (Fig. 1).

Laying aside as impossible the exiling of the gory trades to points beyond the "walls" of the city and the denying of the plyers of such trades admission into the city, what are proper approaches to the regulation of the odorous trades? The following responses are by intent only general:

1. Through due city planning and zoning, all industries including the more offensive ones should be located in districts best suited to the total interests of the community. Unfortunately in most cities zoning if accomplished at all was so belated that industries, particularly the ancient ugly ones, beat the city to the locality and may not with propriety be dislodged. The industry leads to the city rather than otherwise.

NEW USE FOR GUTTA PERCHA.

In addition to drinking-cups, driving-bands, whips, hats, splints, portable soup, shoes, elastic heads, coats, candles, tubing, tenpenny nails, theatrical banquets, picture-frames, saveloys, buttons, baskets, biscuits, and other various forms into which that universal material Gutta Percha has been converted, we beg to suggest a new and sanitary employment from this multiform substance, to which its connexion with the gutter would seem naturally to adapt it.

We would suggest that masks with pipes of Gutta Percha might be employed in London and other large towns, for enabling the wearer to breathe the upper and purer currents of air, in the neighbourhood of our slaughter-houses, cattle markets, graveyards, bone-boilers', soap-makers', and cat-gut manufacturers'. Without some such arrangement we do not see how the Londoner is to enjoy the "sweet airs that give -delight and hurt not" which we are assured by philosophers *do* exist somewhere above our heads, and of which we may be allowed to breathe the name, if we cannot breathe any more substantial part of them.

Fig. 1. *Punch's* 1049 satire on the offensive trades. (*Reprinted by permission of Punch, and Bradbury, Agnew & Company, Ltd.*)

2. In any event, a citizenry is entitled to the virtues of the best developments within the trade in the way of protective mechanisms against odors. For all, or nearly all, offensive trades odor-controlling machines or practices exist. A citizenry has warrant to demand of that other citizen, the offensive industry, the introduction and proper operation of these odor-controlling measures. The convincing example of good odor control may be found in the crematoria for human bodies. After years of early revolting apprehensions, actual conduct of this business has led to no known offense. Similar or at least other suitable measures may be made equally successful in many industries. There may be some exceptions; the very nature of stockyard operations makes them well-nigh unsusceptible of control at this time.

3. It is not sufficient merely that suitable appliances be installed. Proper operation and maintenance is an essence. Apart from inevitable mechanical breakdown, the crucial test of suitable appliances and practices is the substantial absence of odors. Legal regulations to this end are in order as part of the totality of legal control.

4. The transportation of effete odorous materials, whether by truck, scow, or train, falls within the category of offensive trades, not exempting the city's own garbage trucks. Clearly, such haulage may be accomplished without defiling a street block by block. Equipment is obtainable; but odors from garbage collection, filling house after house, may not always be escaped.

5. Timing is to be accepted as a right for a citizenry in the avoidance of noisome odors. There may be reasons aplenty why a dead horse shall be disposed of by proper rendering, but to allow this swelling and festering beast to lie two days before collection from an inhabited area and another two days before it reaches the rendering pots is a nasal affront against which prompt complaint from those affronted may not be denied.

Little sponsorship may be promised that future urban life will be wholly spared the very presence of offensive trades as neighbors. But without equivocation it may be held that these neighbors may become substantially odorless and thus lose the opprobrious designation, "offensive trade." That term now should be reserved for those plants which fail to keep pace with modern odor-control measures and thus still are to be labelled "offensive trades."

CONTROL OF ODORS FROM THE OFFENSIVE TRADES

There is no warrant for the setting apart of the offensive trades as requiring peculiar methods for odor prevention and elemination. Indeed, the need for such practices may be greater in these industries, but basically the requirements and the methods are not other than those specified for odor prevention and control in general. For this reason, reference is made to those other chapters devoted to the divers methods of odor suppression.

Chapter XV

Air Conditioning and Odors

MOST of us believe that outdoor air has some one or more properties, still undefined, which account for its "freshness." The exhilaration experienced in the "wide-open spaces" is actually the product of many kinds of stimuli, including sounds, odors, colors, horizons, and complex variations in temperature, radiation, humidity, and air movement. It is reasonable to suppose that olfactory impressions play a dominant role in this harmony of sensation.

Man has tried in a good many ways to duplicate indoors the invigorating attributes of outdoor air. His attempts range in diversity through ozonation, ionization, ultraviolet radiation, perfuming, deodorizing, washing, and thermal adjustment. None of these experiments has been a solution, but all have helped to carry us by stages toward the anticipated goal of fresh indoor air.

AIR COMPOSITION AND STANDARDS OF VENTILATION

In view of the long and fascinating history of alchemy, it is rather amazing that man did not know that air contained *oxygen* gas as the respirable constituent and *carbon dioxide* gas as the respiration product until nearly 1800; and not until 1900 did he learn that artificial ventilation of occupied buildings was not required to prevent oxygen suffocation or carbon dioxide poisoning. And today, in 1947, we still have not analyzed all the components of *fresh air*.

Measurement of carbon dioxide concentrations in spaces occupied by human beings had been standard practice among ventilating engineers for many years, until Yaglou, Riley, and Coggins reported in 1936 the results of their experiments on ventilation requirements. They concluded that carbon dioxide concentrations "in the air of occupied rooms proved to be an unreliable index of ventilation, from the standpoint of both outdoor air supply and odor intensity," and suggested that "a great deal of unjustified effort would be saved by discontinuing the usual measurements of CO_2 in ordinary ventilation work, except perhaps in instances in which the air flow is well under 10 cfm per person."

Many research workers and writers during the present century have recognized that the existence of 0.1 to 0.5 per cent of carbon dioxide in spaces occupied by human beings is not of itself dangerous. Some still express the belief, however, that such an increase in carbon dioxide from a normal outdoor level of 0.03 to 0.04 per cent indicates the presence of unhealthful constituents as a result of the *vitiation of air* by human respiration. This question is by no means settled to the satisfaction of the layman, who still demands in many cases that determinations be made of both oxygen and carbon dioxide concentrations in his atmospheric environment.

Evidently Carl Wilhelm Scheele (1742–1786) introduced the expression "vitiated air" to denote the air or gas remaining after burning substances in ordinary air. He gave this name to the residual air because it would not support further combustion. He also concluded from his experiments that living animals change "fire-air" (oxygen) into "aerial acid" (carbon dioxide) and perhaps was one of the earliest alchemists to recognize the similarity between respiration and combustion.

The term "vitiated air" is still a respectable item in the lexicology of writers on ventilation. However, its current implications are far less spectacular than those of the early nineteenth century, as for example: vitiated air "produces deformity, imbecility and idiocy"; "encourages pusillanimity and cowardice"; "encourages vice"; "encourages intemperance in the use of intoxicating drinks"; "produces inaptitude for study and, therefore, ignorance."

The current use of odors as indexes of ventilation requirements is viewed by certain wary individuals as an unwarranted scientific neglect of some fundamental hazard to life and health. Nevertheless, public health workers and sanitary-ventilation engineers are generally convinced at present that oxygen and carbon dioxide concentrations in the air of buildings at normal barometric pressures are not of concern to health in the absence of substantial nonhuman disturbances of air composition, such as the operation of industrial processes or the storage of foods that may consume oxygen or generate carbon dioxide.

The 1923 Report of the New York State Commission on Ventilation[1] contained the following statement:

Human occupancy produces five different alterations in the air of a confined space. The oxygen is decreased; the carbon dioxide is increased; products of organic decomposition are given off from mouth, skin and clothing (as evidenced by the "body odor") ; the temperature is raised; and the humidity is increased. The first three of these changes having been shown by careful physiological examination to be relatively unimportant, it would seem natural to turn to the last two.

But nearly thirty years earlier, Billings, Mitchell, and Bergey did not consider the odorous emanation of human bodies "to be relatively unimportant." Instead they observed that: "The discomfort produced by crowded, ill-ven-

[1] E. P. Dutton & Company, Inc., New York.

tilated rooms in persons not accustomed to them is not due to the excess of carbonic acid, nor to bacteria, nor, in most cases to dusts of any kind. The two great causes of such discomfort, though not the only ones, are excessive temperature and unpleasant odors."[1]

Several decades prior to Billings and his coworkers, DeChaumont proposed that the air of a room should be maintained at such a state of purity that a person coming directly from the outside should perceive no difference between the odor quality of the room and that of the outer air.

During the early part of the present century, when many engineers turned their attention to the thermal aspects of ventilation requirements, Soper conducted a careful and thorough survey of the atmosphere in subways both in New York City and in European cities. He was sensitive to the odor quality of the air and made keen observations on their characteristics and sources. With respect to human odors, he reported the following:

Odors of human origin were sometimes present, but almost always close to people. They were most common during warm, damp weather and where there was much crowding. These odors often came from the clothing of the passengers. It was sometimes possible to learn the occupation of a workman by the odor of his clothes. Odors of coffee, garlic, bad teeth, liquor, cheese, and perfumery were some of the personal odors noticed.

The peculiar odor given off by clothing which had been hung in a kitchen was frequently noticed.

In fact, under the conditions of crowding, amounting frequently to close personal contact, it seemed that odors of practically every character connected with human existence were noticeable.[2]

VENTILATION REQUIREMENTS FOR HUMAN OCCUPANCY

Ventilation is now understood to be necessary for the control of body odors, tobacco smoke, cooking odors, and other odorous impurities for which the human occupants of residential and commercial spaces are responsible, and not to preserve the oxygen-carbon dioxide balance of the indoor atmosphere. The intense interest in ozone, following the First World War, as a possible purifier of vitiated indoor air helped to refocus attention on the use of odor as an index of air requirement, this time without the implication of organic poisoning, but with direct admission that indoor air should be clean-smelling air (see Chap. XVII, on Odor Masking).

Yaglou, Riley, and Coggins conducted a series of experiments on ventilation requirements for human occupancy at Harvard University and found that the intensity of body odor perceived upon entering an occupied room from relatively clean air varied inversely with the logarithm of the quantity

[1] The Composition of Expired Air and Its Effects upon Animal Life, *Smithsonian Contributions to Knowledge, Publication* 989, Washington, D. C., 1893.
[2] "The Air and Ventilation of Subways," John Wiley & Sons, Inc., New York, 1908.

of outdoor air supplied and the logarithm of the air space allowed per person. Table I summarizes the results of their experiments.

Table I.—Outdoor or Odor-free air Requirements for Dilution of Body Odors[*]

	Air space per person, cu.ft.	Clean air supply per person, c.f.m.. [†]	Type of occupants and kind of ventilating equipment[‡]
A	100	29	School children; average personal hygiene
	100	25	Sedentary adults
	100	22	School children; best personal hygiene
B	200	38	School children; poor personal hygiene
	200	23	Laborers
	200	21	School children; average personal hygiene
	200	18	School children; above average personal hygiene
	200	16	Sedentary adults
C	200	12	Sedentary adults; air washed by centrifugal atomizing humidifier
	200	<4	Sedentary adults; summer season; air cooled and dehumidified by spray washer; water changed daily
D	300	17	School children
	300	12	Sedentary adults
E	500	11	School children
	500	7	Sedentary adults

[*] Yaglou, C. P., E. C. Riley, and D. I. Coggins, *Trans. Am. Soc. Heating Ventilating Engrs.*, **42**, 133 (1936).

[†] Based on impressions of persons entering experimental room from relatively clean air at "threshold" odor intensity. Allowable odor intensity of 2 on a scale ranging from 0 for no perceptible odor to 5 for nauseating or overpowering odor.

[‡] Heating season, air not washed or conditioned, except as noted in group C tests at 200 c.f.m. per person.

Later experiments on ventilation requirements by Yaglou and Witheridge[1] demonstrated that

. . . air space per occupant in a room not only affects the disappearance rate of body odors and hence ventilation requirements, but also the efficiency of ventilation systems. Large rooms have an advantage over small ones, as they act like reservoirs, allowing body odors to disappear with a minimum outdoor air supply and maximum ventilation efficiency. A small room would require a greater air supply per occupant for the control of body odor. An increased air supply entails a loss of ventilation efficiency, as the air passes quickly to the exhaust without removing a full share of odors, heat, and moisture.

With respect to tobacco odors, however, their tendency to become more offensive during the first few hours after smoking indicated that retaining them longer in the occupied space by increasing the volume of the space

[1] *Trans. Am. Soc. Heating Ventilating Engrs.*, **43**, 423 (1937).

actually was a handicap. The conclusion was that, for tobacco-smoke control by dilution ventilation, small volumes of air space with high ventilation rates per capita would be a preferable combination, in spite of the probable decreased efficiency in utilizing the air supply.

Table II suggests ventilation rates for the dilution of tobacco smoke and body odors in various types of occupancy.

Table II.—RECOMMENDED OUTDOOR AIR QUANTITIES PER PERSON

(Air cleaning or odor adsorbing devices not in use. Space not less than 150 cu. ft. per person, or floor area not less than 15 sq. ft. per person.)

Outdoor Air, c.f.m. per Person	Type of Space or Occupancy
5–10	High ceiling space such as a bank, auditorium, church, department store, theater; room with no smoking
10–15	Apartment, barbershop, beauty parlor, hotel room; room with light smoking
15–20	Cafeteria, drugstore with lunch counter; general office, hospital room; public dining room, restaurant; room with moderate smoking
20–30	Broker's board room, private office, tavern; room with heavy smoking
30–40	Cocktail bar, directors' conference room, night club; room with heavy smoking

State and city codes should be consulted to make certain that minimum outdoor air requirements are provided.

EFFECT OF TEMPERATURE AND HUMIDITY ON ODORS

It is generally believed that high temperatures and humidities accentuate odors in air. The reason for this widespread observation may lie in the concurrent effect on the odor source, rather than the effect of heat and water vapor on the olfactory process. Lemberg, Brandt, and Morse[1] were unable to confirm the belief that high humidities intensify the odor of occupied rooms. A very slight increase in odor intensity was recorded at the higher temperatures and humidities used in their experiments, but the difference did not appear to be significant or important.

ODORS RETAINED BY AIR-CONDITIONING EQUIPMENT

Accumulations of dust, moisture, and organic matter inside the ducts and mechanical equipment of air-conditioning systems may become a troublesome source of odors, popularly known as the "air-conditioning smell." The common practice of recirculating up to 90 per cent of the indoor air to conserve the energy of heating or cooling favors the accumulation of air contaminants in the absence of effective air-cleaning appliances.

The experiments of Yaglou, Riley, and Coggins (1936) indicated that "the usual processes of washing, humidifying, cooling and dehumidifying recircu-

[1] *Trans. Am. Soc. Heating Ventilating Engrs.,* **41,** 157 (1935).

lated air apparently removed a considerable amount of body odor, and under certain conditions practically the maximum amount possible by the use of known processes." It is clear, therefore, that spray water used in air-conditioning systems must be constantly renewed to avoid the return of odorous materials to the airstream by the mechanism of aeration of the wash water as it approaches saturation with the body-odor constituents.

Hassler reports the use of activated carbon in the spray water of an experimental air-conditioning system subjected to odors of fish, onion, boiled cabbage, cantaloupe, pyridine, and butyric acid. The carbon was powdered and applied in the form of a slurry, which undoubtedly would introduce operating difficulties in conventional equipment. A granular carbon bed filter probably would be equally effective, and less troublesome, if the desire for water conservation could justify the expense of odor removal. In the experimental unit it was possible to recirculate the spray water from 10 to 50 times longer than without carbon treatment.[1]

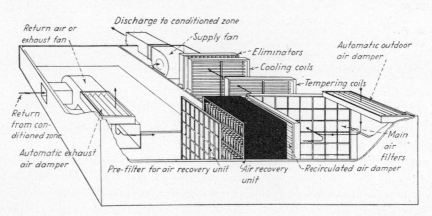

FIG. 1.—Diagram of a central air-conditioning system showing the location of an air-recovery unit for odor control. Note that recovery is in the return air circuit. (*W. B. Connor Engineering Corp.*)

Disinfectants and deodorants have been added to the recirculating spray water of air-conditioning systems to reduce the consumption of water as well as to introduce low concentrations of aromatic or germicidal vapors into the air stream. The practice is limited, however, by the difficulties of maintaining a constant air quality in the face of many seasonal variables, and it appears to be more satisfactory to add volatile materials directly to the air as it passes through the ducts or plenum chambers (Fig. 2).

Particulate matter such as dust and smoke likewise may aggravate the odor retention of air-conditioning equipment because of the ability of such par-

[1] *Taste Odor Control J.*, **4** (No. 4), 2 (December, 1937).

ticles to absorb or adsorb gaseous materials from the air in addition to the odors that may be inherent in their composition. Consequently there are some cases where effective dust and smoke removal must be provided together with adsorption of gaseous contaminants for completely satisfactory odor control. A combination of electrostatic precipitation and activated carbon adsorption is highly effective in controlling all forms of impurities that may accumulate in the recirculating system (see Chap. XIX, on The Sorption of Odors).

OUTDOOR ODORS ENTERING THE AIR SUPPLY

As an outcome of urban living habits and the advancement of air-conditioning demands, the engineer now finds at times that odors originating outside buildings in industrial or business districts have a decisive effect on the kind and capacity of equipment he must provide for a high-quality air-supply installation. They may determine, for example, whether odor-removal equipment can be limited to the recirculated air duct as shown in Fig. 1 or must be applied to the outdoor air supply. Outdoor odors may persuade the owner

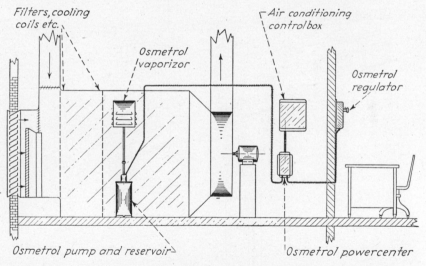

Fig. 2.—Vaporizer system applied to central air-conditioning equipment.
(*W. H. Wheeler, Inc.*)

to provide extensive year-round air conditioning, so that windows and doors can be closed against offensive odors during the summertime as well as in the wintertime.

Congested business and manufacturing districts in poorly zoned cities are especially vulnerable to atmospheric "cross connections." Kitchen odors from near-by restaurants, gasoline fumes from service stations, paint-spray fumes, internal-combustion-engine exhaust gases, and a multitude of others can be discharged from neighboring buildings and then be recaptured by their respective air supply systems. Office buildings may receive contaminated air in exchange for relatively clean air, while a restaurant may discharge cooking

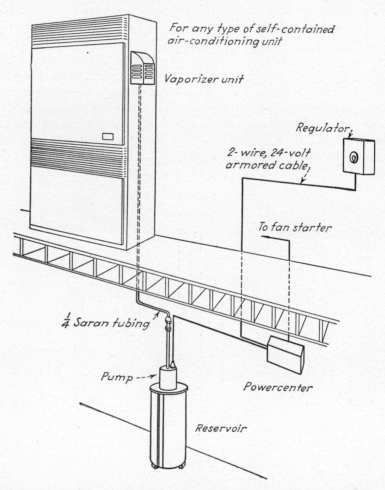

Fig. 3.—Vaporizer system applied to a "packaged" unit air conditioner. Liquid reservoir may be located out of sight and regulator placed at a remote point. (*W. H. Wheeler, Inc.*)

odors and receive in return the pentrating odors of a dry-cleaning establishment.

Community planning and zoning should avoid these atmospheric incompatabilities in the cities of the future, but the air-conditioning engineer must provide some relief during the interim by cleaning both the air supplies and the air exhausts of ventilated buildings in heterogeneous districts.

Two principles of odor control in air conditioning are in use. One is the introduction of a gas or vapor at each occupied space or at some central point, with the object of masking, canceling, or destroying objectionable odors. Illustrations of this method are given by Figs. 2 and 3. The other principle is the removal of odorous bodies from the air by absorption in washers, scrubbers or condensers or by adsorption in activated carbon (Fig. 1).

The extended indoor use of odor-control procedures described in subsequent chapters will bring about further revisions in outdoor air requirements. Eventually it may be possible to approach 100 per cent recirculation of indoor air even in the presence of highly odorous contaminants. Certainly the possibility of operating an air-conditioning system without the use of outdoor air will depend upon future discoveries in the realm of air "freshness" and whether these developments may convince the occupants that a synthetic atmosphere is fresh, healthful, and desirable.

Chapter XVI

Chemical and Physical Destruction of Odors

THE FIRST method of odor destruction by man was combustion. Then came the tossing on fire of aromatic combustibles, as the spices and resins, to overpower an incompletely oxidized stench; thereafter, the alkalization and sorption of odors by covering with wood ashes, followed by the suppression of smells with calcined earths, disintegration by inorganic reagents, deodorization with synthetic organic chemicals, and now the photo-activated decomposition of odorous molecules. The last method is not man's innovation, but rather a landmark in his knowledge of solar radiation.

The destruction of odors often has the aspect of a hopeless task. Knowledge of the chemical constitution of a complex odor is invariably meager, while almost as troublesome as composition is the possibility of multiple odor sources. Furthermore, the application of chemical agents to an indoor odor is not satisfactory unless good exhaust ventilation methods are used to carry the contaminated air to a point of treatment remote from the occupied environment. Most chemicals that are known to be active or powerful deodorants against airborne substances are too toxic to human beings in the concentrations required for odor destruction in the respired atmosphere. The classical experiments of Lister with carbolic acid are exemplary; even his reason for conducting these experiments is significant here, for his attention was drawn to carbolic acid by discovery of its use to deodorize sewage in the English village of Carlisle about 1866.

Lister thought that infection was carried into wounds by the air. . . . This assumption was natural both from the ideas prevailing in regard to "miasmas" and the harmful effects of night air and also from Pasteur's work. Lister did not recognize at first that the real source of infection was on the surgeon's hands and instruments. He went to great lengths in his attempts to abolish the germs in the air, and for this purpose he injected a spray of carbolic acid into the air of the entire operating-room. The carbolic acid was unpleasant and often dangerous to inhale. It was the basis of the objections made by many surgeons to the adoption of Lister's work; they mistakenly thought that he had introduced a medicine, carbolic acid, and failed to grasp the fundamental principle of his work. Lister continued to develop the antiseptic method, and finally gave up the carbolic spray and the elaborate dressings used to exclude air from the wound. The antiseptic method gradually merged into the aseptic.[1]

[1]HAGGARD, H. W., "Devils, Drugs, and Doctors," Harper & Brothers, New York, 1929.

Chemical destruction of odorous organic matter grows more complex day by day. The patent literature receives almost weekly a new chemical deodorizing agent or process, and many of these are limited to highly specialized reactions that are effective only under the carefully controlled conditions well appreciated by the organic chemist. There are literally endless possibilities for the discovery of new methods of disintegrating the foul substances we recognize as stenches, and any concentrated exploration in a research laboratory is certain to uncover some of them. Each industry must first discover the chemical identity of the extremely small quantities of material that are causing odor nuisance and then submit this information to qualified study. In some cases the solution will be evident. It may suffice to use one or more of the specific deodorizing techniques outlined in this chapter. On the other hand, the cause of odor may turn out to be too involved for selective chemical treatment, and it may then be necessary to resort to a relatively nonspecific procedure such as combustion, ozonation, or adsorption.

The specific treatments that depend on a thorough knowledge of the chemistry of the odor source can be named in the terminology of chemical reactions: neutralization, acidification, alkalization, oxidation, reduction, hydrolysis, polymerization, stabilization, precipitation, sedimentation, and perhaps others. No attempt is made here to review the organic and inorganic chemistry of odor destruction. It may be said at least that the problem is one of rearranging or subdividing the molecules of mercaptans, mercaptides, aldehydes, ketones, thiocyanates, isocyanides or carbylamines, methylamines, ethylamines, diamines such as putrescine and cadaverine, pyridines, pyrroles, indoles including skatole, thiomides, hydrogen sulfide, ammonium sulfide, organic acids, phenols, cresols, and many other compounds discharged by chemical process industries. Thus it is seen that the chemistry of offensive odors, while not exclusively, is certainly for the most part the chemistry of organic sulfur and nitrogen compounds. If the gaseous wastes of an industrial process are known or can be predicted with some assurance, their possible destruction may be ascertained by a study of the literature or treatises on these compounds. For this purpose are recommended the first volume of a compendium by Suter, "The Organic Chemistry of Sulfur,"[1] possibly to be followed soon by a companion volume by the same author. Also Sidgwick's "Organic Chemistry of Nitrogen," revised by Taylor and Baker[2] will be of great interest.

The control of odors by alteration of the chemistry of an industrial process must not be overlooked in the search for methods of chemical destruction. Although prevention at the source may not be called true odor destruction by chemical agents, study of the constitution of offensive vapors or gases is

[1] John Wiley & Sons, Inc., New York, 1944.
[2] Oxford University Press, London, 1942.

closely allied to the study of chemical means for their prevention as well as their disintegration. The chemistry of modern industrial processes is sufficiently involved to require the advice of a chemist who is familiar with the processes and product, because the selection of a deodorant or of a deodorizing change in the process must be done in consideration of the effect on the product and on the environment of the workers from the standpoint of occupational poisoning. In a good many cases it will be necessary to compromise deodorizing proficiency with product quality. In many others the results will be surprisingly beneficial in more ways than odor control. The tanning industry provides an example.

Perhaps the most wholesome advance made by science in tanning was the substitution of purified trypsin for the obnoxious dungs used in the operation called bating. In 1876, after the skins and hides had been limed, unhaired, and washed, it was practically a universal rule to soak them in vats containing warm infusions of the dung of dogs or fowls. This treatment prior to tanning gave a finished product with a much smoother and finer grain surface than could be obtained by any other treatment then known. The tanner had no idea as to what constituent of the dung was responsible for the observed effects nor as to the mechanism of the reaction taking place in the skin. This made it difficult to control the operation of bating and consequently much leather was spoiled in the process.[1]

The same may be said of atmospheric deodorization by chemical reaction. The probability of a reaction going sufficiently to completion in low air dilution to effect substantial relief requires careful study of the operating conditions, including temperature, radiant energy, permissible concentrations of the opposing chemicals, effects on mechanical equipment, relative costs of several possible agents, and degree of attention required by the one selected.

COMBUSTION OF ODORS AND THE SOURCES OF ODOR

The oldest method of odor destruction is still one of the best. It has been said that nothing but cremation will accomplish so rapidly that which the putrefactive process does so slowly and so disastrously.

Doctor Kilvington, president of the Board of Health of Minneapolis in 1888, addressed the sixteenth annual meeting of the American Public Health Association in that year as follows:

After all has been said and done in favor of all other means of ridding ourselves of the waste products of city life, history repeats itself in the suggestion of fire as the only competent agency at our command. I say history repeats itself—for ancient civilizations and yet older pagan peoples long since, and again and yet again, arrived at the same sanitary conclusion to which we have come. Cremation of the human body, to say nothing of human waste, was in vogue among all early nations excepting those of Egypt, Judea, and China. It was from the effete civilization of the latter country that Christian peoples derived the insanitary and inhuman

[1] WILSON, J. A., *Ind. Eng. Chem.*, **18**, 934 (September, 1926).

practice of earth burial. In a great part of Asia and South America the fire is still employed to destroy the remains of the dead and the refuse of the living. The method was followed by several North American tribes. Even the Israelites burned the bodies of Saul and his sons at Jabesh; the Jews cremated the victims of the plague in the vale of Tophet; and, outside the walls of Jerusalem, they cast their offal, garbage, and dead animals into the unquenchable fire which burned perpetually in the pit of Gehenna, three thousand years ago. Cremation was practiced, undoubtedly, among the early Christians, while it was still resorted to by the Swiss in the eighth century.

The sharp, pungent odors in the fumid products of combustion, accompanied by the dynamic movements of the flame, gave the ancient Greek philosophers all the evidence they needed to elevate fire to the status of the "princely element." The devastating tetrahedral shape of its hypothetical particles gave it the divine power to disintegrate any material thing into the basic elements, earth, water, air, and fire—for fire itself was held in reserve in all substance. Fire was the most versatile of the elements; for a time it dominated all scientific thought as well as all daily life. It could release the soul of man and did so on many funeral pyres. The fire in men literally enlivened them to action. Fire was a sharp, biting devil, with a sulfurous stench, who lived on dry wood. Its sting was due to the sharp cutting edges of the tetrahedral particles of which it was thought to be composed. As did all living things, fire consumed its combustible food, or "pabulum," and discharged the various residues into its own environment, sometimes generating so much of the fuliginous vapor that it stifled itself.

The "sulfureous principle" was so long associated with fire that it actually served as one of the elements of the seventeenth-century "Spagyrists," whom Robert Boyle so despised and ridiculed. To the Greek philosophers, lightning was a form of fire and had the smell of sulfur. Pliny said that sulfur was an agent of great power over substance, and such power of course was derived by its close association with fire. The fire and brimstone of the nether regions, which occasionally came forth from the volcano, had the legendary odor of the Evil One.

So the early civilizations had among them careful and accurate observers, even if not the most foresighted scientists. They knew that the burning of all sorts of earthly substances was invariably accompanied by the release of some overpowering and irritating vapors, and they naturally arrived at the conviction that a mysterious evil spirit was responsible. Our theories of the constitution of matter are now vastly different, but we still are unable to prevent the formation of nitrogen and sulfur oxides along with carbon dioxide and water as the products of complete combustion. We know now, of course, that the odor of lightning is not an oxide of sulfur, but an oxide of oxygen—ozone. And we are not surprised that the odors of nitrogen oxides should be blamed on sulfur.

Combustion is not a method of odor control unless it is *complete* combustion. Even then, the burning of nitrogenous and sulfurous organic matter with the evolution of pungent oxides of nitrogen and sulfur is not the ideal conclusion to an odor-destruction process, but slight nuisance is often preferred to the sickening offense of the unburned vapors. Partial combustion may be even worse than no combustion, as the neighbors of incinerators and rendering plants will testify. Incomplete combustion in Diesel and internal-combustion engines yields the irritating and sickening aldehydes, with formaldehyde as the principal ingredient in the malodorous group.

While the creation of irritant gases may not be considered a real solution, in the great majority of such cases the gases are effectively discharged through high stacks at a rate that will not overtax the capacity of the atmosphere to dilute or dissipate them on the wind. Admittedly there are some cases, notably ore smelting, where it is necessary to remove the destructive and irritating gases and mists before discharging the gaseous wastes outdoors. In modern plants this is frequently done at a profit rather than a loss, for the recovered acid gas is a valuable raw material.

The minimum combustion temperature for the complete destruction of garbage, meat refuse, corn-products waste, and the like, may range from 1400 to 2000° F., according to the type of waste so treated and the construction of the incinerator, cremator, or furnace. Even higher temperatures may be necessary in some industries.

The following suggestions for the combustion of refinery wastes have been extracted from the American Petroleum Institute's bulletin, Disposal of Refinery Wastes: II. Waste Gases, Vapors, Sludges, and Dusts.[1]

The best method for the ultimate disposal of all combustible odorous compounds occurring in the refinery is high-temperature oxidation. The principal products of combustion are carbon dioxide, water, and sulfur dioxide; these are discharged from the top of high stacks. Sulfur dioxide is much less objectionable than the original sulfur compounds . . . .

It is recommended that at no time should the sulfur-dioxide content of the air beyond the refinery boundary, and solely attributable to the refinery as its source, be greater than three parts per million . . . .

The amount of excess air required for complete oxidation (in waste-gas furnaces) is approximately 50 per cent, and the temperature carried in the combustion chamber should range from 1600 to 2000 deg. F. The temperature of flue gas leaving the stack should be above its dew point . . . .

For liquid sludge-disposal furnaces:

A uniform temperature within the range 1800 to 2400°F. should be established throughout the combustion area in order to prevent the formation of coked sludge at the cold spots. These would later be dislodged and travel through the stack as incandescent spongy lumps of coke—constituting a serious hazard in the vicinity of flammable material . . . .

[1] 2d ed., 1938.

Regardless of the type of furnace used for disposal, efficiency must be secondary to proper temperatures and sufficient excess air in order to insure complete destruction of the malodorous compounds.

Complete details for the design and operation of these waste-disposal systems are given in the bulletin above cited.

Combustion may be the only treatment or it may be the final step in a multistage air-cleaning installation. For example, the airborne waste products of an industrial process may contain dust, fume, condensable vapors, and uncondensable gases. They may first be *scrubbed* to remove the dust and soluble or condensable vapors, then passed through an *electrostatic precipitator* to capture fume and mist particles too small to be retained in the condenser or scrubber, and finally filtered through an *activated carbon bed* because of the highly offensive character of the insoluble, noncondensable gaseous wastes. The process is not complete, however, because some disposal must eventually be made of the accumulation on the carbon; it seldom is wise to discard the carbon after one use. The final step, then, is release of the offensive gases by high temperature regeneration, leading the concentrated gases to a combustion chamber at a rate that will not interfere with the economical operation of the furnace or boiler. The objection to the method of passing all the contaminated air initially through the firebox and out the stack with the gases of combustion may be the high cost of heating large volumes of ventilation air to a temperature that will destroy its malodorous components.

ANTISEPTIC AND DISINFECTANT DEODORIZERS

These words have been synonymous to the layman for decades and to medical science for many years before. Lister demonstrated that he believed in the antiseptic-deodorizing power of carbolic acid by saying that "wounds and abscesses no longer poison the atmosphere with putrid exhalations . . . since the antiseptic treatment has been brought into full operation."

Although a disinfectant might be a deodorizer only when the cause of odor is microbial decomposition, this is not inevitably so. Many of the organic and inorganic chemicals that qualify as disinfectants also have good power to decompose malodorous substances that are not the immediate result of microscopic metabolism. Formaldehyde is the outstanding example, for it is a highly important link in many organic reactions.

With the *antiseptic* interpretation of a deodorizer, it would be possible to include all the processes of combustion, oxidation, pasteurization, refrigeration, ultraviolet radiation, ultrasonic vibration, ozonation, chlorination, and fumigation, in a complete listing of deodorizing agents. Clearly we might be in danger of assigning to an antiseptic many deodorizing attributes it does not possess.

The list of chemical agents that are known to have some antiseptic-deodorizing property is large and still growing. The discovery of some organic chemicals that can be called "odorless" deodorants, to the surprise of many who believe that a disinfectant must have the smell of its strength, is an example of the continuous activity in this field of research. Hundreds and perhaps thousands of the agents that are toxic to microscopic life have no value whatever in those problems of odor control not related to bacterial decomposition.

Lister might have ignored a disinfectant that did not have an efficient smell. On the other hand if he *had* found and tried a nontoxic antiseptic with no odor, the practice of air sterilization with liquid sprays might have continued through the last decades of the nineteenth and first decades of the twentieth centuries concurrently with water-borne and food-borne bacteria control. (Consider, for example, the present use of odorless amounts of glycol vapors to destroy airborne bacteria.)

Fifty years ago Green wrote the following: "All disinfectants act chemically. They either decompose or they combine with the noxious substances and produce new compounds which, if not always void of smell, are comparatively harmless in their action upon the human body."[1] His statement reflected the belief of that century that the substance of offensive odor was also the substance of contagious disease.

The 1939 edition of the Encyclopaedia Britannica has the following definition: "Deodorizer: a disinfectant which acts by oxidizing or otherwise changing the chemical constitution of volatile substances disseminated in the air. It also prevents noxious exhalations from organic substances, and in virtue of its properties is an effective disinfectant in certain diseases." This is not very much different from Green's definition and may appear to future generations as evidence that we did not know the difference between a disinfectant and a deodorizer.

Bryan and Bryan have grouped the principal disinfectants somewhat as follows:

1. Coal tar derivatives—cresols, cresote, carbolic acid, or phenol.
2. Oxidizing agents—hydrogen peroxide, sodium peroxide, potassium permanganate, calcium hypochlorite, sodium hypochlorite.
3. Acids—nitric acid, sulfuric acid, boric acid, salicylic acid.
4. Halogens and their salts—chlorine, bromine, iodine.
5. Gaseous agents—formaldehyde, sulfur dioxide, hydrogen cyanide, chlorine.
6. Salts of metals—silver nitrate, mercuric chloride, potassium mercuric iodide.
7. Certain non-toxic dye products, as gentian violet, neutral acriflavine.[2]

[1] *Sci. American Supp.*, **44**, 17936 (July 3, 1897).
[2] "Principles and Practice of Bacteriology," 3d ed., Barnes & Noble, Inc., New York, 1942. See also McCulloch, "Disinfection and Sterilization," Lea & Febiger, Philadelphia, 1945.

ALKALIS AND ACIDS FOR THE CONTROL OF ODORS

Long before men knew the true nature of combustion, the Greeks used the word "kaio," meaning *burn,* from which they derived "kausticos," which we still use as "caustic." In the ancient philosophy of the four Aristotelian elements, fire, air, earth, and water, combined with the four qualities, hot, dry, cold, and moist, there was every reason to believe that the corrosive action of the ashy residue of burned wood was a manifestation of the fiery element still lingering after its destructive deed. The power of fire was also in some degree the power of the caustic ash.

The application to an odor source of lime, quicklime, caustic lime, or milk-of-lime, otherwise known as "calcium oxide" or "calcium hydroxide," is a time-worn expedient that still has its advocates. Lye, comprising either or both caustic soda and caustic potash, also known as "sodium hydroxide" and "potassium hydroxide," is highly respected for its ability to disintegrate organic tissues and wastes. Soda ash, the commercial sodium carbonate, is an industrial alkali of great versatility.

The *liming* of stench pots had a genuinely sound basis. Hydrogen sulfide does not form in strongly alkaline solutions, and even solid materials that are potentially putrefactive can be kept in an alkaline state on the surface by a covering of caustic having high affinity for water. This method, however, ignores the possibility of existence of organic products of decomposition that are unaffected by an alkaline environment and that may even find such an environment favorable.

Acidification of waste liquids and solids with such agents as sulfuric acid, nitric acid, or hydrochloric acid is generally a dangerous procedure from the viewpoint of odor control. The refining industry in particular has experienced the unhappy consequences of accidental or uninformed acidification of caustic liquors used to remove sulfides from petroleum products. Since hydrogen sulfide is rapidly formed from the sulfides that may be present in acid solution it is best not to attempt this method of treatment; in fact, it is wise to avoid all possibility of a liquid waste becoming acid during its course through the plant or sewerage system. Likewise it is not desirable to permit a liquid waste to become too strongly alkaline, because of the detrimental effect it may have on the treatment processes at the sewage plant. If the dilution of waste in a near-by stream is permissible without leading the liquid to the disposal plant for treatment, care must be taken to avoid the introduction of concentrated materials that will destroy or inhibit the natural purifying organisms of the stream. This applies not only to acid and alkali wastes but to any chemical waste discharged into a body of water serving as the disposal system.

HYPOCHLORITES FOR ODOR CONTROL

The superiority of chlorinated lime over the caustic earths for suppression of odors has been known for many decades. In the last decade of the nineteenth century, Green told his readers:

Chlorid of lime . . . possesses a remarkable power of oxidation; it burns up many of the offensive neutral bodies evoked during decay. It exerts this influence even upon sulphuretted hydrogen. Spread in the solid form upon any fermenting mass, it destroys the noxious bodies as they are formed. Dissolved in water and sprinkled over bad smelling chambers, or mixed with more or less fluid collections of putrid matter, it bring sweetness everywhere.[1]

The familiar "bleaching powder" served the needs of odor destruction by chlorination or oxidation long before liquid chlorine was available for the treatment of water, sewage, and stack gases. Ronald successfully applied a solution of calcium hypochlorite to the uncondensed vapors from meat- and fish-rendering processes by introducing the chemical into the spray water for air from the condensers, as shown in Fig. 1. The mixing tank, stock tanks, and clear liquor runoff indicated in this diagram refer to the equipment for preparing and delivering the hypochlorite solution to the spray-nozzle piping. Ronald stated that "if the chlorine is derived from a solution of calcium or sodium hypochlorite, the amount of available chlorine in the liquor should never fall below 0.35 per cent, and the period of contact should not be less than half a minute."

Specially prepared hypochlorites are widely used in the water-treatment field as reserve or stand-by sources of available chlorine as a supplement to the conventional liquid chlorinating systems. It is likewise used in sewage-treatment practice at occasional odor sources where application of a solid material is more convenient than use of liquid chlorine.

HTH is a true calcium hypochlorite with a composition in which the active element exists as $Ca(OCl)_2$. It has a concentration of available chlorine not less than 70%, and an inherent stability that maintains its concentration at summer temperatures. A low calcium chloride content has eliminated hygroscopic tendencies, so that the powder remains dry and free-flowing even when exposed for some time to natural atmospheric conditions.[2]

ODOR DESTRUCTION BY CHLORINATION

The use of chlorine as a disinfecting agent for public water supplies was begun in this country about 40 years ago. The equipment for applying chlorine has now reached a high degree of perfection, and its use has made it pos-

[1] *Sci. American Supp.*, **44**, 17936 (July 3, 1897).
[2] Mathieson Alkali Works, Inc., New York.

sible to deliver a bacteriologically safe water in nearly every major community in the country. Although chlorine will destroy some odors, notably hydrogen sulfide by precipitating free sulfur, it has introduced others nearly as troublesome. Perhaps the worst offenders have been the chlorophenols that are formed when chlorination is applied to phenolic waters. In an attempt to solve this problem, water-treatment practice moved through several stages, including superchlorination with subsequent dechlorination by the use

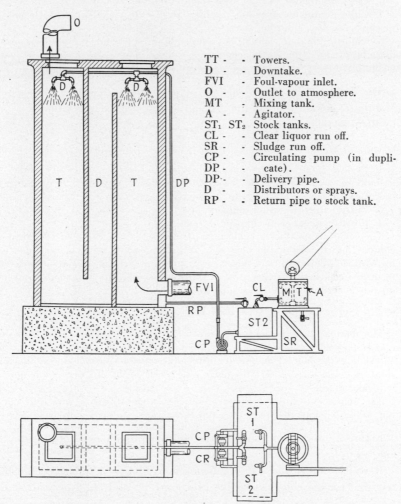

TT -	-	Towers.
D -	-	Downtake.
FVI	-	Foul-vapour inlet.
O -	-	Outlet to atmosphere.
MT	-	Mixing tank.
A -	-	Agitator.
ST_1 ST_2	-	Stock tanks.
CL -	-	Clear liquor run off.
SR -	-	Sludge run off.
CP -	-	Circulating pump (in dupli-
DP -	-	cate).
DP -	-	Delivery pipe.
D -	-	Distributors or sprays.
RP -	-	Return pipe to stock tank.

FIG. 1.—Two-stage deodorizing system for the uncondensed gases from a meat-rendering process. (*Ronald, "Handbook on Offensive Trades," Wm. Hodge & Company, Limited, 1935.*)

of such agents as sodium thiosulfate, sodium bisulfite, or activated carbon, chlorine-ammonia treatment to circumvent formation of chlorophenols, "breakpoint" chlorination, a technique that has been vigorously contested and in some places has yielded no relief from phenolic tastes, and most recently a technique for applying chlorine dioxide.

Two advantages and one disadvantage are cited for chlorine dioxide.

1. Chlorine dioxide has 2½ times the oxidation capacity of chlorine.
2. Chlorine dioxide does not combine with other chemicals to form chlorinated products, as does chlorine.
3. Chlorine dioxide cannot be produced in bulk and stored until wanted. It must be produced in low concentrations at the point of application and used immediately.[1]

The development of this method of chlorination has been directed by the Mathieson Alkali Works, and its application to water treatment is outlined by them as follows:

Outline of Method for Taste and Odor Control with Chlorine Dioxide

1. Pre-chlorination with enough chlorine to sterilize the water and to insure a small residual through the filter.
2. Coagulation in the usual manner.
3. Filtration in the usual manner.
4. Post treatment with chlorine dioxide.
The chlorine dioxide is generated by metering a solution of technical sodium chlorite into the discharge hose of a standard vacuum chlorinator, such as made by Wallace & Tiernan, and passing this mixture through a small mixing chamber to insure complete reaction to the chlorine and chlorite to generate the chlorine dioxide according to the following reaction:

$$Cl_2 + 2NaClO_2 \rightarrow 2NaCl + 2ClO_2$$

The mixing chamber consists of a 12" length of 4" Pyrex pipe filled with unglazed porcelain Rachig Rings installed in a vertical position with the mixture entering at the bottom and the chlorine dioxide solution leaving at the top. This solution is run directly into the clear water well at a point where complete mixing will take place.

The amount of chlorine dioxide required naturally varies with different waters but we have found that 0.5 to 1.5 p.p.m. has been sufficient.

Figure 2 shows the location of the chlorine-dioxide generating equipment in one type of water-treatment plant.

It will be noted that liquid chlorine delivered by a standard chlorinator is required for the chlorine-dioxide procedure. Liquid chlorine will continue to be applied in many ways for water treatment and sewage treatment and for destroying the odors in stack gases. The chlorinating mechanism is essentially an automatic flow-regulating device for delivering the gas from standard

[1] SYNAN, J. F., *J. Penn. Water Works Operators' Assoc.*, **17**, 55 (1945).

pressure cylinders. Figures 3 and 4 illustrate this equipment as applied to water chlorination and Figs. 5 and 6 as applied to sewage treatment.

In 1922 Henderson and Haggard received a patent for their process of "deodorizing offensive gaseous emanations from organic matter," as illustrated in Fig. 7. In their patent application they stated:

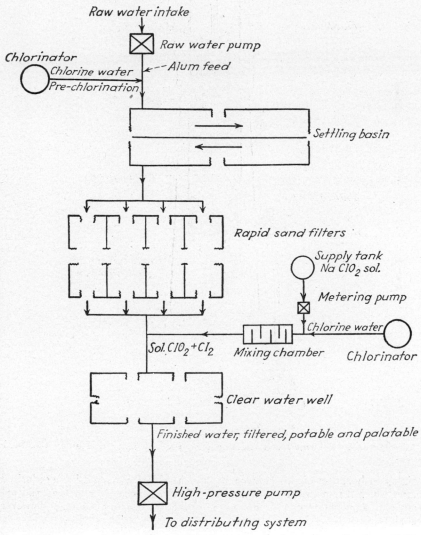

Fig. 2.—Flow sheet showing chlorine dioxide treatment of water supplies for removal of tastes and odors. (*Mathieson Alkali Works.*)

We are aware that liquid chlorine has been used in the field of sanitation to sterilize water and sewage, liquid industrial wastes and tannery effluents. We also are aware of the use of chlorine gas in the disinfection of buildings and factories in place of fumigants, but we believe that we are the first to deodorize the effluent air of ventilating systems by injecting chlorine gas into confined effluent air and

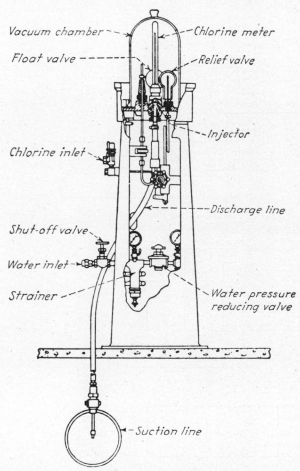

Fig. 3.—Manual-control chlorinator, solution feed type. (*Wallace & Tiernan Co., Inc.*)

retaining such effluent air in confinement until its chlorine content has deodorized it, after which it is permitted to escape into the atmosphere. Our method and apparatus are applicable to the deodorization of the effluent air of garbage, however treated.

Also in their application they listed as the odoriferous compounds that are nullified by the use of their chlorination process:

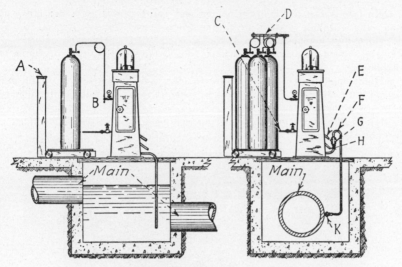

Fig. 4.—Vacuum chlorinator, solution feed type, large capacity.
(*Wallace & Tiernan Co., Inc.*)

Fig. 5.—Master chlorinators supplied by central distribution system. Municipal sewage
treatment at Cleveland, Ohio. (*Wallace & Tiernan Co., Inc.*)

I. Odoriferous organic hydrosulphides and sulphydrates such as: ethyl mercaptan, ethyl sulphide, methyl mercaptan, etc.

II. Aldehydes, ketones, and aromatic alcohols with disagreeable odors.

III. The secondary amines which have unpleasant odors, as, for example: trimethylamine.

IV. Higher members of the olifine series, the carboxy derivatives of the paraffines, and fatty acids and their derivatives, such as: butyrate, valerianate, heptylate, laurate, myristicate.

V. Besides the above many odoriferous compounds of extremely complex and little known structure.

Fig. 6.—Battery of chlorinators fed by high-pressure gas-distribution system. Municipal sewage treatment at Detroit, Michigan. (*Wallace & Tiernan Co., Inc.*)

In describing their experiments with the use of chlorine, Henderson and Haggard indicated that the presence of moisture appeared to be an essential condition for success. They reasoned that the chlorine formed hypochlorite with the water, which then oxidized the organic gases. In the case of the unsaturated fatty acids a direct addition reaction with chlorine was suggested. In the case of vapors from manure, their laboratory work indicated that most of the chlorine finally reached the form of ammonium chloride.

Chlorine cannot be applied to stack gases indiscriminately. As stated earlier, reasonably complete knowledge of the types of compounds discharged is a prerequisite to chemical destruction of odors. This certainly applies to chlorine, even though it has high reactive ability, inasmuch as there is ample evidence in the literature on organic nitrogen and sulfur compounds to indicate that occasionally the chlorinated compounds are equally as offensive as the unchlorinated variety.

OZONATION FOR ODOR DESTRUCTION

When ozone is introduced into water, its action on many forms of organic matter is highly destructive. It will decolorize, deodorize, and sterilize in the

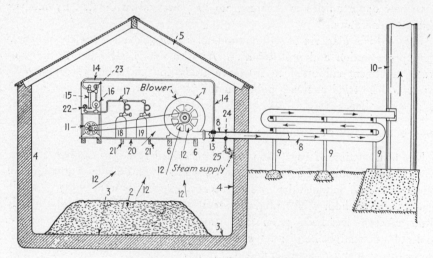

FIG. 7.—Henderson and Haggard system of chlorinating offensive organic gases. From Patent 1,410,249.

same operation. It is claimed that it does not form new odorous compounds (not confirmed by all observers), and its presence in small quantity in water is not objectionable. In fact, ozone cannot remain long in water without returning to the oxygen state.

Ozone has been used in Europe for municipal water purification for many years. In this country the development of activated carbon was sufficiently rapid and inexpensive that ozone did not become a conventional method of treatment. Evidence is beginning to arrive that better equipment and higher yields of ozone per unit of electrical energy may give ozone a more equitable showing in the field of odor control, both in water treatment and in the destruction of offensive gases and vapors inside chimneys or discharge stacks from industrial processes. In the latter case ozone concentrations can be raised to the necessary concentration without concern for the physiological effects on human beings. Used inside ventilating systems to prevent an outdoor nuisance by malodorous vapor discharges, it is in no way similar to the masking action it promotes when applied to the indoor environment of human beings.

So far the only important development has occurred in the water-treatment field. Recent installations in cities of moderate size have been made to overcome the troublesome phenolic odors that are anchored in the water by chlorination. It is not possible yet to decide what success ozone may have in competition with powdered activated carbon, but unquestionably there will be many cities favorably located for electric power and unfavorably impressed by treatments so far applied to their potable water supply where ozone will have new opportunities to demonstrate its power when created by modern efficient generators.

Figure 8 is a diagram of two methods of applying ozone to water purification, preozonation and postozonation. As with nearly all other methods of water treatment subjected to intensive study in this country, ozone most likely will be tried at many points in the plant before its optimum location has been settled.

PHOTOCHEMISTRY OF ODOROUS COMPOUNDS

The construction of vegetation by the combined forces of sunlight, water, carbon dioxide, mineral salts, and chlorophyll has been the classical enigma of photochemistry. So much time in fact has been expended on the study of photosynthesis in the hope of learning the secret of chlorophyll that comparatively little attention has been given to the systematic disintegration of organic molecules that might be of interest to odor specialists. Perhaps it is only fair to state that many difficulties and delays have been encountered with inadequate electrical equipment and that some of the latest devices for creating narrow bands of the visible and invisible radiations, believed to be most importantly photochemically, have already released the investigator from a certain measure of frustration.

Photolysis, or photodecomposition, is the opposite of photosynthesis, the latter usually reserved for the construction of vegetable compounds in nature. Photolysis is the process of most interest to the student of odor-control methods, for it appears that photosynthesis rarely occurs in the atmosphere to create larger molecules; evidently the life of the activated state of the molecule is so short that its opportunity for suitable contact with a reacting molecule in the gaseous phase is slight. Investigations with organic compounds indicate that they are variously dissociated into such fragments or new molecules as hydrogen, carbon monoxide, carbon dioxide, methane, ethane, and similar small groups of atoms. The photochemical decomposition of hydrogen sulfide into hydrogen gas and free sulfur has been studied by Stein[1] and by Forbes, Cline, and Bradshaw.[2]

Table I indicates the near-ultraviolet absorption spectra of the vapors of aldehydes. These compounds are known to separate into smaller fragments

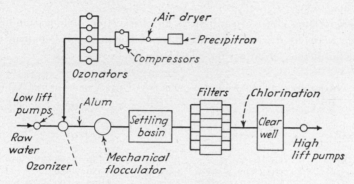

Pre-ozonation

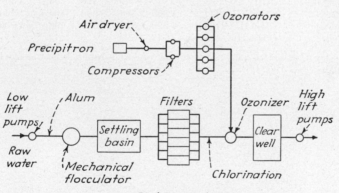

Post-ozonation

Fig. 8.—Location of ozonators in water treatment for either preozonation or postozonation. (*Ozone Processes, Inc.*)

under the influence of the appropriate wave lengths of light, and the table is inserted here as a demonstration of the kind of information that will be needed for a great many odorous molecules before the tool of photolysis can become practicable.

[1] *Trans. Faraday Soc.*, **29**, 583 (1933).
[2] *J. Am. Chem. Soc.*, **60**, 1431 (1938).

There seems to be a reasonable future chance that knowledge of the photo-lytic wave lengths for a given offensive odor molecule will make it possible to irradiate the gas with a frequency giving the highest "quantum yield" in the confines of a discharge stack or ventilating system as a means of effecting its destruction. If the analysis of stack gas shows a number of offensive con-stituents, then activation or dissociation wave lengths could be studied to determine where on the spectrum it would be most efficacious to expend energy of decomposition.

The deodorizing effect of sunlight is an observation of long standing. We may once again by discovery of new facts of science finally confirm the un-scientific suspicions of an earlier generation.

Table I.—Near-ultraviolet Absorption Spectra of the Vapors of the Aldehydes*

Substance		Spectrum range, angstroms		
Name	*Formula*	*Discrete*	*Diffuse*	*Continuous*
Formaldehyde......	$HCHO$	3,570–2,750	2,750–2,500	<2,670
Acetaldehyde.......	CH_3CHO	3,484–3,050	3,050–2,660	3,484–~2,400
Proprionaldehyde...	C_2H_5CHO	....	3,400–2,700	3,400–~2,400
n-Butyraldehyde....	nC_3H_7CHO	....	3,400–2,700	3,400–2,350
i-Butyraldehyde....	iC_3H_7CHO	....	3,400–2,700	3,400–2,350
Acrolein..........	$CH_2{:}CHCHO$	4,000–3,300	3,300–2,800	4,000–2,400
Crotonaldehyde.....	$CH_2CH_2{:}CHCHO$	3,850–3,350	3,350–2,900	4,000–2,600
Benzaldehyde.......	C_6H_5CHO	3,747–2,599	2,428–2,349	

* Data compiled by Rollefson and Burton, "Photochemistry and the Mechanism of Chemical Reactions," Prentice-Hall, Inc., New York, 1939.

Chapter XVII

Odor Masking

ASKING, blanketing, disguising, and overpowering of unpleasant odors, all were the duty of the ancient perfumer. Centuries ago godliness and cleanliness were joined with personal fragrance for those who could purchase the Arabian oils. For the less privileged multitudes, godliness demanded aromatic sacrifices to the special deities. Burnt offerings would offend the gods unless augmented by the magical aromas of properly compounded incense.

The presence of strong perfume in the air has so long been associated with the disguising of smells that we now automatically suspect all sorts of disreputable violations of the laws of cleanliness. This coupled with the fact that potentially pleasant aromas become offensive in high concentrations has created the current demand for faint, elusive, and almost imperceptible fragrance. The consequence has been the development of the art of odor "cancellation" as a branch of industrial perfumery, whereby the aromatic chemist attempts to counteract an offensive odor by blending it with a number of other volatile substances on the basis of his long experience in the creation of perfumes from both fragrant and foul odoriferous ingredients. Not so with the early apothecary-perfumer. The obliteration of bad odors with strong aromatics was the conventional treatment. Furthermore, the pagan gods desired powerful olfactory stimulation in the belief of their worshipers, and many a religious procession was sanctified by the intense aromas of concentrated oils. Delicate perfumery would not do, because the competing odors had great strength in themselves.

The need for vigorous overpowering of bad odors remained with our ancestors until modern conveniences reduced the high cost of cleanliness. At the close of the nineteenth century Green recorded his philosophy of odor sanitation in terms that are substantially appropriate in the present generation:

Where evil smelling decay of any kind commences, or where volatile substances which disagreeably affect the organ of smell escape into the air from any source, we naturally desire to rid ourselves of the unpleasant sensation. This we generally wish, and always ought, if possible, to do by removing the substance to which the noisome smell is owing, In the great majority of cases, however, we merely overpower or disguise it. We are content to mingle with the smell we dislike some odor

185

we can enjoy, and to leave floating in the air around us the evil and the good together, to produce unheeded their natural effects upon the system.[1]

In obedience to the common belief that the easiest way to eliminate an objectionable odor is to cover it with something agreeable, the New York subway began its operation in the first decade of this century with a sanitation policy that included the use of pungent proprietary deodorants and disinfectants in the underground station toilet rooms. Soper discovered in his survey of subway ventilation that these disinfectant odors were so powerful that they were occasionally evident on the streets outside the subway stations. He also observed that in the course of decorating some of the newly built stations with ceramic tile, a cheap and highly odorous grade of fish oil was used in the tile cement. "In order to disguise the fishy odor, creosote was freely mixed with the oil before mixing it with the cement. The result of these intermingled odors was peculiarly unpleasant."[2]

PRINCIPLES OF ODOR MASKING

It is not the purpose here to summarize the many ways in which man has employed the process of odor masking. Instead we aim to establish as best we can the general principles of this method of odor control to the end that those who study the problems of masking, counteracting, neutralizing, absorbing, or destroying odors will desire in the future to record their findings in terminology more specific and directive than the perennial and contemporary "deodorizing."

Throughout this chapter the important principles or characteristics of the masking process are illustrated or implied. We summarize these principles now as a point of reference for the discussion that follows:

1. Odor masking is the process of obliterating one odor by superimposing another to create a more compelling sensation, preferably pleasant.

2. The masking agent does not alter the composition of preexisting odors, but simply covers such odors during the period of its addition to and presence in the air.

3. Masking is an effect produced at the point of sense perception in the respiratory passages together with the final interpretation in the brain and does not constitute an aromatic correction of the aerial components.

4. The application of an inherently pleasant masking agent to an offensive atmosphere may result in a final combination that is still objectionable as a consequence of odor incompatibilities.

5. The objectionable odor concentration must not be so intense that the masking agent is itself required in objectionable concentrations. In such cases, other odor control methods are indicated.

[1] *Sci. Am. Supp.*, **44**, 17936 (July 3, 1897).
[2] "The Air and Ventilation of Subways," John Wiley & Sons, Inc., New York, 1908.

COMBUSTIBLE AROMATICS AND INCENSE

Although the more formal religious denominations still practice incense burning on important occasions, the concept that inhalation of the products of burning incense is an inherently religious experience will not be unanimously subscribed to by the many contemporary beliefs. That continued and repeated use of incense at special services or offices can evoke a powerful religious association is not denied. Many have acquired this association, while it is equally true that many others respond negatively, even to the point of despising the burning aroma.

Even in the early struggle between the Christian and heathen worshipers the status of incense was controversial. "Thus Tertullian, while ready to acknowledge its utility in counteracting unpleasant smells ("si me odor alicujus loci offenderit, Arabiae aliquid incendo"), is careful to say that he scorns to offer it as an accompaniment to his heartfelt prayers."[1]

In the literal sense, the words "incense" and "perfume" have practically the same origin. Perfume was the aroma given off with the smoke of any odoriferous material as it was burned:

perfumare—fumigate—perfume
incendere—incendiate—incense

Perfume has since acquired so many additional connotations in the course of time that its original meaning is now quite out of order in our language.

The function of incense was probably threefold in early times—symbolic, hypnotic, and hygienic. Even in the case of hygiene, the effect of the heavy oriental fragrance was no doubt more psychologic than physiologic or antiseptic. Combustion has long been associated with purification, both in a religious and in a medical sense; and it is not unusual that sacrificial and fumigating fires should be treated with aromatic substances in an attempt to offset the acrid, pungent, sickening odors of burning organic matter. Cremation of the dead has been practiced throughout man's history; but even when present methods of interment were used, the ancients burned incense at their funerals and burial processions, a practice still followed in some parts of the world. The development of sanitary techniques for the handling of departed relatives did not and would not result in a prompt discard of rituals having as strong an olfactory appeal as the burning of aromatic woods, gums, spices, flowers, and seeds.

Modern formulas for incense may include almost any of the ingredients available to the aromatic chemists: sandalwood, rosewood, cedarwood, bayberry, balsam, pine, spruce, dried flowers, fruits and seeds, spices, essential oils, isolates, synthetic chemicals, and the traditional galbanum, onycha,

[1] *Encyclopaedia Britannica.*

stacte, olibanum or frankincense, benzoin, storax, and cascarilla bark. With so many possible variations it is certainly important that the formula be carefully designed to avoid the production of objectionable by-products of combustion.

The flame-coloring materials lately devised for use in fireplaces are sometimes odorized to add olfactory interest to a pyrotechnic display.

Fumigating pastilles, with sulfur as a common ingredient, have been subjected to a masking treatment on occasion. The pungent, noxious odor of burning sulfur is mingled with the products of some of the conventional incense ingredients to modify the resulting atmosphere—not always with success to be sure, for sulfur dioxide is an excellent masking agent in itself. Ordinary sulfur matches have been used on occasion for temporary odor masking in confined spaces.

Bienfang paints an interesting picture of the early practice of kindling huge fires in the vicinity of a communicable disease epidemic as a desperate attempt to halt its progress.

More dramatic was the burning of cedar and pine boughs in the narrow cobbled streets in the hope of quelling the disease. One can almost see the darkened and saddened houses, full of sick and dying attended by those still on thir feet, while outside the cries of men in the street accompanied the crackling of the flames, which cast first light then dark on the time-stained stones of the buildings, and over all was a pall of acrid, aromatic smoke, coursing its way into windows and up to the starlit sky.[1]

Incense burning has been tried in retail merchandising establishments with indifferent success; the stale or musty odors of a poorly air-conditioned space can easily be overtaken by the aromatic smoke, but the customer reaction is dangerously mixed. This atmospheric treatment is preferably restricted to halls of worship and the mysterious apartments of the occult sciences.

In the same division of odor masking by combustion is the homely practice of kindling various items in the domestic kitchen to overcome the less desirable cooking odors. The pungent odor of a smoldering strand of grocery twine was the solution of some ingenious housewives to the problem of combating the odors of onions or cabbage. Even incense has been used for this purpose, but the combination is apt to be unkind to the appetite. Again, the best solution to unwanted kitchen odors is not their mixture with other odors but instead their mechanical removal by well-directed air currents—in other words, good exhaust ventilation.

THE MASKING OF TEXTILE ODORS

Perhaps some of the earliest attempts to overcome strange odors by masking were related to the wearing apparel of our indoor ancestors. This does not

[1] "The Subtle Sense," University of Oklahoma Press, Norman, 1946.

imply that body odors were the only offenders, for it is certain that some of the materials of fabrication themselves gave forth unpleasant vapors. Natural coloring matters have long been associated with characteristic odors, but fortune did not provide the appropriate aromas for every occasion. In Hibbert's excellent discussion of dyeing scents is a reminder that modern colorists have inherited a problem that has undoubtedly existed as long as textiles have been decorated: "Considering the remarks of Bancroft, one is inclined to wonder how the kings who were clothed in purple managed to endure the scent of their royal robes, and what powerful and beautiful scent was used to disguise the disagreeable odour of the buccinium."[1]

The literature of perfumery contains frequent allusions to the profuse application of aromatic oils in early days to an extent that would evidently now be considered disgusting. Certainly one of the reasons for such generosity on the part of those who could afford the precious oils was a desire to move any and all distracting odors into the background, in addition to whatever ethereal glamour or aphrodisiac allure might have been contemplated. No doubt the garment fabrics received their share of such treatment, both to disguise inherent odor defects in the materials and to serve as the vehicle for an aromatic environment. In modern society these refinements are applied indirectly to avoid the deterioration of delicate fabrics.

The colorful and odoriferous occupations of our forefathers also contributed their odors to the wearing apparel. We have the proof still with us in the form of clothing worn by workers in the contemporary offensive and odorous trades, such as rendering, slaughtering, chemical manufacture, rubber processing, and sewage disposal. Today it is comparatively easy to remove these odors by efficient cleaning methods, but our ancestors were not so fortunate. Whether they actually resorted to the masking of objectionable odors acquired by clothing is perhaps speculative at this period of time, but the possibility was certainly not overlooked by those who had the price of the precious aromatic oils.

The ability of textile materials to acquire the odors of their environment has even been recorded in the Bible. In the twenty-seventh chapter of Genesis, it is related how Isaac was deceived in his attempt to identify his son Esau by the simple device of exchanging garments; ". . . and he smelled the smell of his raiment . . . and said, See, the smell of my son is as the smell of a field which the Lord hath blessed."

In recent times the odors of dyed fabrics occasionally have been accepted as inevitable. They have even served to identify the dye as a genuine treatment, and with characteristic eccentricity customers have sometimes insisted on the genuine dye odor in spite of a disagreeable quality. Dyers were so impressed by the demand for an indigo-dyed fabric that smelled as well as

[1] *J. Soc. Dyers Colourists*, **42**, 254 (August, 1926).

looked genuine that a preparation known as "vat odor" was developed to simulate the odor of real indigo.

Laird reports that he has observed people, blindfolded, distinguish dyed goods from white goods solely by their odor.

In his reminiscences of the dyeing trade in Great Britain, Pennington stated that one of the most extraordinary incidents he recalled was the receipt of a sample of fabric in a small tin box together with an order for yarn dyed to the "enclosed shade and smell."[1] Although he presented it as a curiosity, the time may come again when the customer devotes a portion of his attention to the odor as well as the color of textile materials, especially if the innovations in synthetic fibers continue to confront the market with fabrics carrying inherent odors never before encountered on the drygoods table.

Textile odors are by no means limited to coloring materials. They include the odors of the animal or vegetable fibers, the oils used for lubricating the fibers during weaving, the substances applied to impart weight or body to the finished goods, and materials deposited on the goods by cleaning processes. Even bacterial or fungus decay may odorize as well as deteriorate the individual fibers. Since the modern demand seems to be for fabrics that have virtually no odor, or at most a "neutral" odor weak enough to be readily overlooked, the opportunity for masking objectionable textile odors by the simple expedient of impregnating the goods with a definitely noticeable perfume seems to be negligible. Instead the industry is seeking aid from the aromatic-chemicals industry and the skilled perfumers to blend carefully selected ingredients for each type of fabric that will result in a practically imperceptible combination so far as most customers are concerned. This procedure we prefer to designate as odor "cancellation," and it is the subject of another chapter.

SOAP ODORS AND MASKING

Perhaps the most versatile method of odor control is the use of soap and similar detergents. It removes the organic wastes and debris that generate so many offensive odors. It serves as the vehicle for carefully selected aromatics that blend with unpleasant odors almost to the point of complete cancellation; or it carries relatively strong odorous components that will frankly mask the odors of the body or occupied space. Germicidal components may fortify its ability to destroy microorganisms and thereby prevent the odors of decomposition. And even the soap itself is subject to the process of odor masking, for its ingredients may include odors that are undesired both during and following its use.

The soap industry has been a principal consumer of aromatic materials, both

[1] *J. Soc. Dyers Colourists,* **42,** 182 (June, 1926).

natural and synthetic, for many years. Although generally we are not aware of the fact, practically every type of soap on the market includes some aromatic ingredient. Advancements in the purification and refinement of soap constituents have made it possible to cover toilet-soap odors with relatively light perfumes, with the result that the residue on the skin is only faintly odorous and does not include harsh or rancid odors of basic ingredients. The odorizing of soap has progressed well beyond the need for masking its own basic scents to the present point of its function as an odorizer of animate and inanimate surfaces. Cleansing compounds and janitor supplies frequently combine the functions of dirt removal, perfume deposition, and bacterial destruction. The overpowering residues of highly "medicated" soaps are still encountered on occasion and remind us that odor masking has not been overlooked by the manufacturers and users of soap products.

MASKING OF PAINT, VARNISH, AND LACQUER ODORS

The public demand for more comfortable aromatic stimulants in the indoor atmosphere has now invaded the paint industry. Interior finishes have been a source of irritation and annoyance for years, with the painters themselves being the most consistent victims. The earliest remedies were of course applied to the vehicles and drying oils, but today these constituents are greatly improved. Fish oils and castor oils are specially processed to remove most of the offensive components, and the vehicles or solvents are more highly refined and more carefully selected to reduce the odor intensity of interior paints, varnishes, and lacquers.

The problem of masking the odors of drying paint is an instructive lesson in the masking process. The volatile thinners are not the sole offenders, as is often implied. Although the solvent odors may be highly nauseating to some persons, some of the most irritating and objectionable scents are developed during the oxidation of the drying oils. Successful masking of paint odors therefore requires skillful blending of aromatic substances of graduated volatility to follow as closely as possible the gradual release of odors from the paint film as drying progresses. The U. S. Patent Office granted a patent to Shuger on the strength of his development of the principle of progressive volatility in the masking formulation (Patent No. 2,103,830; 1938). An important advantage of this system is the possibility of extending the masking period throughout the evaporating and drying period of the paint without an excessively high concentration of masking agent when the paint is first applied.

The types of odors used for masking are limited primarily by the majority opinion of the persons exposed. The favorite odors of pine, rose, lemon, vanilla, cedar, eucalyptus, and peppermint, as well as others, have all been tried. The following excerpt from a report by the National Paint, Varnish, and Lacquer Association shows that the vanillin odor is especially well received:

In tests made at this laboratory there was also included ordinary vanillin in the same concentration as the other materials, namely, one part to 2000 parts of paint. The vanillin was rated very highly by most observers, but it is slightly more expensive than certain other types of industrial perfumes. Vanillin may be dissolved in turpentine or linseed oil to make a concentrated base which can be added in the proportion referred to above when treating interior paints.[1]

Most persons do not object to the odors of interior paint after the initially high concentrations have worn off. In fact, the clean, sanitary effect of a freshly painted house is highly attractive to a great many tenants and owners. It is one of the odorous components of a newly built house that contributes to the anticipated or realized pride of ownership. Although the masking of initially applied paint may develop to a highly effective stage, even to the point of true cancellation, it is not likely that home owners will be deprived completely of the olfactory pleasure of an attractively painted interior.

AROMATIC SPRAYS AND VAPORS

Reference was made in Chap. XI, on Household Odors, to the use of various combinations of fly sprays, perfume atomizers, and aerial disinfectants in the home. Long before the modern gadget age, housewives used effective and interesting devices to modify the unpleasant atmospheres of poorly ventilated dwellings. In addition to the simple devotion to aromatic flowers and plants in proper season, there were rose jars for alcoholic extracts of rose petals, powdered cloves sprinkled in important locations, apples and oranges generously punctured with horny cloves, and small cloth evaporators impregnated with lavender water or other perfumed solution. These are but a few examples, for the odor problems of householders were bound to stimulate many ingenious counteractions.

When the circus attendant sprays the elephant with an aromatic fluid, he is masking the animal emanations as well as repelling insects. When the odorous fly spray in a research animal laboratory is imperceptible to the human nose, the masking effect of animal odors is responsible.

The best example of odor masking with aromatic sprays is the time-honored application of fragrant mists and vapors in theaters and motion-picture houses. Many of us still remember the raw perfumes atomized up and down the aisles to combine with the musty and stuffy air of a poorly ventilated hall. They are still used in some places as a substitute for good air conditioning and even to correct some of the characteristic odors of unsanitary air-conditioning equipment. The ingredients may include almost any

[1] GARDNER, HENRY A., *Circ.* 496 (November, 1935).

scent that the manager believes will please or deceive his patrons, such as pine, eucalyptus, sassafras, lemon, lavender, rosemary, cinnamon, thymol, or violet. The risk of annoying a large portion of the audience would appear to be real, inasmuch as most of us have definite likes and aversions in the realm of aromatics. The latest concession to the dictates of American audiences is the type of aroma best described as a "country-fresh outdoor scent," which everyone is presumed to enjoy.

The day seems to be near when motion pictures will appeal to the eyes, ears, and noses of the assembled observers with the odor-effects man in immediate command. Giles reports what may have been the first attempt to project an aromatic motion picture.

Last year in Berne, Switzerland, two chemists invited newspaper men to attend the first motion picture enhanced with scent. While the lover guided his lass through hayfields the scent of new-mown hay filled the auditorium, and when he handed her a bunch of violets you could smell them. These inventors claim that it takes no magic to introduce—and eliminate—a thousand odors through modern air conditioning systems.[1]

Perhaps these experimenters are rashly optimistic, for the problems of instantaneous odor transition would seem to be potentially difficult. Thus, as Kalischer reminds us, it would never do to permit the clear smell of a pine forest to carry over into a stockyard scene, if the scenario writers compelled this sequence. However, with carefully planned script for consideration of the odor-effects man and his air-conditioning collaborator, an occasional aromatic scene does not seem to be an impractical speculation.

Aromatic vapors are consumed in large quantity in the washrooms, toilet rooms, and locker rooms of practically every type of building for human occupancy. Everyone has encountered at one time or another the sanitary use of paradichlorobenzene and naphthalene blocks or crystals. Their odors have become so monotonous and even obnoxious that the latest versions of these volatile chemicals are simultaneously colored and perfumed to provide a masked masking agent with antiseptic or insecticidal powers.

Volatile oils with any desired fragrance are also marketed for sanitary use with the frank purpose of deodorizing by masking. They may be applied to an aerated wick to facilitate evaporation or constantly dripped into toilet bowls or urinals (Figs. 1 and 2). The ingredients may well combine several functions, such as odor masking, chemical destruction of organic matter, and retardation of vaporization at the surface of odorous liquids. In some respects their use is similar to the application of ozonized water for odor control by means of compact ozonators installed above urinals and water closets.

[1] *Advertising and Selling*, 31 (June, 1940).

OZONE AS A MASKING AGENT

The remarkable oxidizing power of ozone has been utilized in so many ways that it was inevitable that an attempt should be made to purify or deodorize the indoor atmosphere by the introduction of ozone. Its inhibitory effect on fungus growths in cold-storage rooms was known for some time, and it seemed quite logical to extend its "freshening" effect to air conditioning for human occupancy.

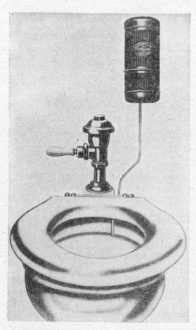

FIG. 1.—Automatic drip machine for aromatic liquids applied to a toilet bowl. (*West Disinfecting Co.*)

The ability of ozone to destroy odorous materials in the gaseous phase depends on its own concentration and on the amount and kind of objectionable odors. It is quite reasonable to expect that ozone in high concentrations will do a commendable job of destroying odorous gases that are susceptible to oxidation. This, in fact, is the case when ozone can be injected into a confined air stream before its discharge from a building as a means of abating an industrial nuisance. However, permissible quantities of ozone in living quarters are extremely low, much lower in fact than amounts used in cold-storage rooms, which generally range from 0.5 to 2 parts of ozone per million parts of air. These low concentrations in cold-storage rooms are still impossibly high for comfort air conditioning, for which the allowable concentrations are from 0.01 to 0.05 part per million. The Council on Physical Medicine of the American Medical Association has specified that the concentration of ozone produced by ultraviolet lamps shall not exceed 0.1 part per million.[1]

In view of the controversy that developed over the question of odor masking vs. odor destruction by ozone in air conditioning, Witheridge and Yaglou conducted a series of experiments in an attempt to discover the answer. A number of investigators had previously ascribed the deodorizing effect of ozone to its masking of other odors, but this conclusion encountered severe criticism from those who had committed themselves to the theory of outright destruction. There is good reason to suppose that some highly unstable odors can be readily destroyed by low concentrations of ozone, for they are also

[1] *J. Am. Med. Assoc.*, **122**, 503 (June, 1943).

evidently easily oxidized in ordinary air. However, in the experiments here mentioned, a consistent observation was that the pungent odor of ozone had to be distinctly evident in order to effect a significant reduction in body odors in the experimental room. Even at near threshold concentrations, trained observers could identify both the ozone and the contaminating odors.[1]

The summarized conclusion from these experiments is now quoted in full.

Ozone in concentrations of 0.015 ppm, that barely can be smelled by the occupants of a room, reduced the smell of body odor sufficiently to permit a reduction

Fig. 2.—Battery of automatic drip machines for aromatic liquids applied to urinals. (*West Disinfecting Co.*)

of at least 50 percent in the fresh-air requirement for odor control. Higher concentrations were irritating to the mucous membranes of the upper respiratory tract, while lower concentrations had no effect on body odors. The action of ozone on body odors appears to take place not in the air of the room by oxidation, as is sometimes assumed, but on the mucous membranes of the nasal passages by *masking*. Although ozone in sufficient strength completely obliterated the smell of body odors, it proved difficult to counteract the two so that neither could be smelled by persons entering the room from fresh air. Ozone had to be present in perceptible concentrations to do any good.

[1] Ozone in Ventilation Its Possibilities and Limitations, *Trans. Am. Soc. Heating Ventilating Engrs.*, **45,** 509 (1939).

The main objection to the application of ozone to ventilation is shown to be lack of control. Until adequate means are devised for controlling the output of ozonators from the actual concentration in occupied spaces, the use of ozone should be discouraged because of its great toxicity.

It may be possible to classify ozone as either a masking or a neutralizing agent for some odor conditions. When both the ozone and the undesired odor are near threshold concentrations, some persons cannot detect either substance, and the apparent result is neutralization for these persons. However, there is practically no need for the use of ozone under such conditions, and the operators of ozonizing equipment have generally turned off the current if other odors in the air are no longer objectionable. Ozone itself is annoying to many persons.

We have here classified ozone as a masking agent on the basis of its conventional action in air conditioning. The possibility that some oxidation of odorous materials may take place in the presence of moist tissues in the respiratory tract is not excluded. Likewise, it is expectable that some oxidation of organic matter will occur on moist surfaces within rooms and in air-conditioning equipment exposed to ozone. This effect, nevertheless, is not rapid or strong enough to eliminate the need for perceptible concentrations of ozone in the air itself, and consequently the masking effect seems to be more significant.

Further evidence in support of the masking effect of ozone is the reappearance of body odors concurrent with the disappearance of ozone odor when the generator is turned off and the room vacated. As shown in Fig. 3, from the experiments cited above,

The ozone intensity just before the subjects left was high enough to obliterate completely the body odor, but when the ozone intensity fell to the threshold, the body odor reappeared and continued to increase, gradually approaching the normal body-odor disappearance curve (dotted line) without ozone. The implication here is that ozone was incapable of destroying body odors in the air while the subjects were in the room, despite its high concentration. Odoriferous material was adsorbed on wall surfaces and when the subjects left, desorption began and continued at its usual normal rate, as if no ozone had been added.

One of the major difficulties in the operation of ozonizing equipment for room air conditioning is the variability of humidity from day to day. The ozone generators can be constructed and operated to produce fixed and known amounts of ozone at the equipment, but at present there is no room "ozostat" or "ozometer" that can regulate the output of ozone generators according to the actual concentration of ozone in the room atmosphere. Therefore, as many operators of ozone equipment have observed, the output of the ozone generator must be varied manually from day to day or hour to hour to offset changes in humidity. In other words, high humidity is just as destructive to ozone after it reaches the room air as it is in the ozone generator it-self. More ozone must be produced on humid days than on dry days if the ozone odor is to be kept at a comfortable though perceptible intensity in the occupied areas. On a very dry day the amount of ozone delivered to rooms must be held at a minimum to prevent the accumulation of high ozone in-tensities. Systems of ozonation have been removed from air-conditioning equipment because of their condemnation resulting from failure to keep

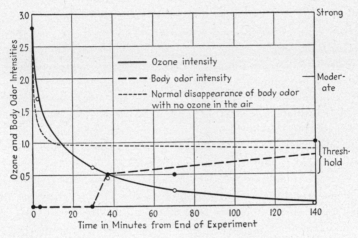

FIG. 3.—Reappearance of body odor with the disappearance of ozone.

the ozone intensity within acceptable limits by constant adjustment at the generator.

Inasmuch as room-air humidity is known to affect the decomposition rate of ozone, it is possible to use a specially calibrated humidistat to give some degree of indirect control over the quantity of ozone introduced to the room. Such a device would not register changes in ozone concentration caused by a variable rate of natural ventilation produced by changes in the setting of windows or doors. It would succeed best in connection with fixed rates of mechanical ventilation and with the occupants' consent to keep windows closed.

Chapter XVIII

Odor Cancellation and Counteraction

THERE is an apparent conception in both the technical and the popular press that odor masking, counteracting, canceling, compensating, and neutralizing are practically synonymous and interchangeable terms. We differ from this opinion and have decided to offer here in a separate chapter our reasons for believing that the effect of one odor upon another should not be described invariably as a "masking" process, any more than it can truthfully be called "neutralization" in all cases. In so doing we are not presenting an innovation, for the evidence in favor of actual cancellation or interference of unlike odors is a matter of record by many observers. The significance of these findings, however, is not often emphasized in its relation to a better understanding of the olfactory process, and we therefore desire to underline these observations for special attention at this point.

A recent example of an isolated incident in support of the prospect of true cancellation of two dissimilar odors is the following report of an experience in water treatment, in which the intimate relation between taste and odor perception is acknowledged.

Vanillin tablets have been used by the Army in large quantities for flavoring purposes. One day a GI, disliking the chlorine taste of water purified on the spot with a chlorine chemical tablet, dropped a vanillin tablet in the water to improve its taste. Imagine his surprise when he found that the vanillin tablet not only neutralized the chlorine taste, but that the chlorine taste likewise neutralized the vanillin taste leaving the water tasteless as it should be . . . .[1]

To the perfumer, this observation, even though it may have been inexact, is not an impossibility. Piesse, the English aromatic chemist, observed over fifty years ago that when it is impossible to get rid of disagreeable odors by air currents or ventilation, the best neutralizer is another volatile odor. Although he may have referred to the masking phenomenon, it is equally possible that his experiences in the blending of volatile materials gave occasional evidence of the "antagonism" of odors, in the language of modern physiology.

Sagarin offers an up-to-date definition of perfumery that is quite specific in its recognition of the opposition of odors.

[1] *Drug & Cosmetic Ind.*, **57**, 173 (August, 1945).

Perfumery is the science and art of odor. It is concerned with the creation of new odors, the duplication of others, whether they be from nature or from the laboratory. It changes the odors of materials, usually to make them smell more pleasing, *sometimes to abolish the smell entirely*, and sometimes to make it quite obnoxious.[1]

Most of us are aware of the fact that the perfumer blends odors of widely different character, not always pleasant, to obtain the enjoyable fragrance of his products. Through years of constant trial and endless experiment he has learned about antagonistic or incompatible odors, the combinations of which at times create highly obnoxious aromas and at others remove practically all trace of one another. We say "practically" because the skilled perfumer can detect odors on objects and in spaces that are virtually non-existent to the untrained nose of the average observer.

When two or more substances are present in the atmosphere at concentrations that would be definitely perceptible if experienced alone but that counteract one another when together to an extent that neither is perceptible to the majority of observers, the olfactory effects of these substances are said to be "antagonistic." Obviously, the balance between precise cancellation and outright masking may be rather precarious for some combinations. Likewise, the potentially compensating aromas may be present in the atmosphere in any proportion from the masking of *A* with *B,* through cancellation, to the point of masking of *B* with *A*. However, this does not imply that any process of masking can be adjusted to a point of true cancellation, for the primary requisite of cancellation is the selection of materials that are inherently antagonistic, and the number of these combinations is by no means unlimited. Nevertheless, it is quite likely that many of the masking processes we have experienced in our atmospheric environment might be potentially capable of true cancellation by the careful adjustment and control of the aromatic components of the air. This, in fact, is a field that we believe deserves, and will receive, a more lively interest in the research laboratories of the future.

Best and Taylor say the following about the effect of one odor upon the perception of another:

Strong odors tend to mask weaker ones. If two scents are of about equal strength a blend of the two is smelt or both are identified; but if one is considerably stronger than the other it alone, as a rule, is smelt. On the other hand, certain pairs of odors in appropriate relative concentrations are antagonistic and when the two are sniffed together both are diminished. Iodoform, for example, is antagonized by balsam of Peru, musk by bitter almonds and ammonia by acetic acid. Other pairs of neutralizing odors are cedarwood and rubber, beeswax and balsam of Tolu, benzoin and rubber, and camphor and eau de Cologne. Though the neutralizing effect may in some cases be simply chemical or physical in nature, in others

---

[1] "The Science and Art of Perfumery," McGraw-Hill Book Company, Inc., New York, 1945. Italics ours.

there seems to be a true physiological antagonism, for the phenomenon is observed when mixing is avoided by leading the two odors directly one to each nostril.[1]

The interaction between ammonia and acetic acid noted above is not a true case of odor cancellation in the sense in which we apply the term but is the kind of process for which the term "neutralization" seems more appropriate. In this connection, we agree with Parker, who called attention to the "spurious" nature of this combination.

Spurious mixed odors are those in which the gases or vapors act chemically on each other and thus produce a third substance which may or may not have an odor of its own. Thus ammonia and acetic acid both stimulate the nose, but when mixed they possess no odor for they combine to form odorless ammonium acetate. Obviously such instances are not, accurately speaking, instances of mixed odors.[2]

Zwaardemaker may have been the first to study the canceling effect of two dissimilar odors. His double olfactometer, permitting the restriction of each substance to a single nasal cavity, was used to measure the proportions of two substances required for cancellation. In Moncrieff's words, "By this method all possibility of chemical reaction between the two substances was removed, and also it shows that since different receptors are involved, the neutralization must have a central origin." Table I lists some of the antagonistic combinations reported by Zwaardemaker.

Table I.—Pairs of Counteracting Odors Observed by Zwaardemaker

Odorous Substances	Canceling Proportions in Olfacties
Cedarwood v. rubber	2.75–14
Benzoin v. rubber	3.5 –10
Paraffin v. rubber	8.5 –14
Rubber v. wax	14 –28
Rubber v. balsam of Tolu	14 –70
Wax v. balsam of Tolu	40 –90
Paraffin v. wax	10 –20

Aronsohn reported in 1886 that the odor of camphor was canceled by cologne water, by oil of juniper, or by petroleum.

Backman investigated the odors of benzene, toluene, xylene, pseudocumene, and durene and found that with definite proportions of certain combinations in this group it was possible to compensate their olfactory effects almost to the point of odor disappearance.[3]

We respect the theory, first stated by Dyson, that when two odorous substances compensate one another to the point of cancellation, they do so by

[1] "Physiological Basis of Medical Practice," The Williams & Wilkins Company, Baltimore, 1943.
[2] "Smell, Taste and Allied Senses in the Vertebrates," J. B. Lippincott Company, Philadelphia, 1922.
[3] *Verslag. Akad. Wetenschappen Amst.*, **25**, 971 (1917).

the counterbalancing or interference of their respective molecular vibrational energies. Conversely, if the vibration frequencies are so tuned as to create a resonance effect, the olfactory result may be a mutual fortification of the odor stimuli with the result of an exaggerated sensation instead of odor cancellation. With this in mind there can be no universal counteracting agent, because the effect is highly specific between two or more odorous materials, both qualitatively and quantitatively.

Ockrent, in discussing Dyson's theory on the significance of the Raman effect in odor perception, produced a highly interesting analysis of the processes of odor fatigue, masking, neutralizing, and cancellation.

. . . Fatigue due to long exposure in a concentrated atmosphere may be due to condensation into a bulk phase on the sensory surface, and since a two-dimensional phase has characteristics different from those of the bulk phase, lack of smell may result until the bulk phase is dissipated.

"Masking" may also be due to preferential adsorption. Consider two species A and B; if A, the odorous species, is preferentially adsorbed on the sensory surface, then B will not mask A; if, however, B is preferentially adsorbed then no odour will result, *i.e.*, we have catalyst poisoning.

Again if two species, A and B, both odorous, mask each other, this may be due to the Gibbs-Thomson minimum free energy effect. If the reaction A+B→AB is possible and AB lowers the interfacial free energy to a greater extent than either A or B or mixtures of the same, then the production of AB will be favoured at the interface, where it will concentrate, and if AB is nonodorous, then a "masking" effect will be apparent.[1]

In this case, as in the writings of other English students of olfaction, the term "masking" includes the process of overpowering one odor with another, the process of odor cancellation (which we elect to set apart in this discussion), and the process of chemical neutralization.

Odor cancellation is conceived here as a process that permits the odorous molecules to retain their individual identity, at least until they are removed from the area of olfactory reception. There is no chemical interaction to rearrange the elements and radicals into inodorous or less odorous substances, but rather a registration of molecular or interatomic energies that are precisely counteractive so that any residual forces still available are inadequate to evoke an odor sensation. If the deodorizing effect of a mixture of odors is a chemical reaction that creates new odorless compounds, we prefer to designate the process as "odor destruction." If neither the canceling nor decomposing processes are sufficiently complete to eliminate both of the odorous components, we prefer to classify the deodorizing effect as "odor masking." Clearly, the boundaries between the several methods of odor control may not be distinct, but a careful description of a deodorizing process

[1] *Chemistry & Industry*, **57**, 647 (July 9, 1938).

may quite properly include more than one method when the action is compound or complex.

CANCELLATION OF COMMODITY ODORS

Perhaps the most useful application of odor cancellation has developed in the manufacture of essentially odorless commodities from potentially offensive raw materials. In parallel with the history of aerial deodorization, early attempts in the dispelling of obnoxious odors in the things we wear and use were based on the principle of masking.

The interest in this field gained substantial momentum in the decade immediately following the First World War. The reaction to low-grade materials that could readily be sold in a shortage economy was building up to a point at which the quality of some articles could no longer be tolerated. The opportunities for improvement in commodity odors were almost without limit. Glues smelled like fish; oilcloth and rubber were offensively volatile. Polishes, waxes, paints, inks, and insecticides were all antisocial in a country where millions of dollars were flowing into the comparatively new air-conditioning industry in response to the rising standards of atmospheric control.

The obvious procedure for removing the unfriendly aromas was their complete domination by generous proportions of sassafras, wintergreen, citronella, pine, lavender, and anything similar. Textiles were imported from France with "indelible" perfumes to match exclusive designs. Fly and moth sprays were combined with potent synthetics or essential oils to hide the lingering odor of the kerosene vehicle. And the odorizing of rubber was carefully calculated to give a new character to hot-water bottles, girdles, footwear, adhesives, toys, baby pants, and garden hose. In fact, the "reodorizing" of rubber had progressed to such a point before the Second World War that the aromatic and rubber chemists were well prepared to demonstrate their skill in controlling the powerful odors of the new synthetics. Although synthetic products are still far from deodorized, the public in general has no conception of the nauseating potentialities of uncontrolled compounding. The rubber technicians have become so confident of their ability to deodorize their synthetics that they have announced recently that they could make synthetic powder puffs that would in no way conflict with the delicate aromas of the costliest cosmetics. And in lighter moments they have even suggested that synthetic sponge rubber can be made to smell exactly like American cheese to produce a more durable rat bait.

The idea of a universal deodorant which would, by physical or chemical action upon any odorous substance, completely destroy it and thus do away with its odor, without introducing any odor of its own, has been proposed from time to time by ambitious inventors, but so far it is still just an idea.

When all of the usual approaches to a deodorizing problem fail—and they do frequently—the art of "odor neutralization" may help. While by no means universally applicable, this method utilizes the offending odor as a constituent of a "bouquet"—as it were—of various aromatic substances, so that the offending odor is transformed to a pleasant or even a neutral one without any need of "covering it up" by sheer brute force of an overwhelming stronger odor.

The "odor neutralization" method has been successfully applied in a large number of industrial instances, such as the rubber, textile, glue, and paint industries, to mention a few. The selection of the correct deodorizer or "reodorizer" is a highly specialized job—there is no such thing as a universal deodorant in this line, either.[1]

We find in the above commentary, therefore, a recognition of the present desire for "neutral" odors in the things we buy. Although this is by no means identical with "odorless" commodities in the literal sense, it is evidence of a reaction to the highly perfumed products of an earlier decade.

Years ago Laird sensed the reaction that would develop against noticeably odorized commodities. "Actually, perfumed fabrics carrying a flowery or fruity scent are a psychological abortion and should not be taken seriously except to show what can now be done by the creative chemist to solve the perennial problem of merchandising smelly products."[2] He was equally aware of the work being done with the process of odor cancellation, notably by Kunz, and mentioned its application to the manufacture of coated paper: "The characteristic unpleasant smell of the casein is actually put to work as an element in the final olfactory blend. The result is scarcely a smell or scent in the sense in which these are usually conceived. It is more the absence of odor."[3]

Endless quotations from contemporary periodicals could be given to illustrate the forcible urge for less odorous or inodorous products. Although most of us unconsciously purchase some articles under the influence of their barely perceptible aromas, we are gradually discovering the freedom of aromatic choice that is possible when we do not surround ourselves with strange and conflicting odors contributed to our environment by hundreds of substances. Accordingly, we find these assertions in print: "Soaps for laundry and textile purposes should be as nearly as possible inodorous." "No perfume was wanted as the product was for business use and had to fit into every office." "A reodorant was used, and the raincoat had no smell of any kind, no matter what the weather." "A colorful liquid, nearly odorless, and harmless to humans but repellant to insects has been developed after a three-year study."

An important prerequisite to the possibility of canceling the odors of finished goods is the rigid control of the quality of raw materials. Whereas a faint odor may be subject to counteraction to the point of subthreshold in-

---

[1] *Sci. American,* **169,** 11 (July, 1943).
[2] *Textile World,* **76,** 1837 (Sept. 28, 1929).
[3] *The Inland Printer,* as quoted in *Literary Digest,* **109,** 24 (Apr. 11, 1931.)

tensity, a strong odor may defy the best efforts of precision compounding. There is no doubt that successful cancellation so far as the human nose is concerned is nevertheless grossly inaccurate in terms of intermolecular forces. The reduction of an odor to a level below the threshold of perception is an operation in the realm of astronomical mathematics, for the sub-threshold quantities of odorous molecules are still in the millions and billions. If the initial order of magnitude of the unwanted aroma is excessively high, the probable error in balancing electromagnetic forces will undoubtedly leave residuals of billions of molecules that can still be perceived.

The blending skill of the chemist-perfumer is improving continuously in the treatment of industrial products. The prospect of completely eliminating the faint odors of certain materials without recourse to physical or chemical destruction is fundamentally sound in the light of an electromagnetic hypothesis of odor perception.

Chapter XIX

The Sorption of Odors

W<small>E DEFINE</small> "sorption" in general as the attraction and retention of gaseous material by a liquid or solid medium. To avoid misunderstanding, this interpretation will be explained.

Two clearly separate processes of sorption are recognized in chemical engineering practice. The one, commonly termed "absorption," applies to the collection of a gas or vapor by solution in a liquid absorbent. The other, known as "adsorption," is the capture of a gas or vapor by a sorbent that is solid, rather than liquid. This distinction would be sufficient were it not for the fact that theoretical considerations have given the term "sorption" a specialized connotation that certain writers have carefully guarded. Neither absorption nor adsorption may be fully defined in the simple manner attempted above.

"Adsorption" is the phenomenon of surface attraction that is universal with all substances. It is agreed in theory that the adsorbed molecules do not penetrate the atomic or molecular structure of the adsorbent. However, at least two principal forms of this phenomenon are now recognized for solids: (1) physical adsorption, and (2) chemical adsorption, sometimes called "chemisorption." In the former there is a weak interaction between the solid and gas, similar to condensation, and this bond may be broken by a moderate elevation of temperature to drive off the adsorbate chemically unaltered. In chemisorption the interaction is much stronger, similar to chemical reaction, and any attempt to recover the gas from the solid by heating may yield instead a new chemical compound. As a third item, capillary attraction may also be important, especially where the air contaminant is a true gas or has a high vapor pressure. "Sorption" is therefore the noncommittal term technically applied to all mechanisms of surface attraction.

"Absorption" likewise is a word not without its confusing implications. It applies to a more or less uniform penetration of the absorbent by gaseous molecules and is not a concept restricted to the liquids. It is quite proper to speak of solid absorption; for a gas may enter the solid to form a true "solid solution," or it may thereupon form a new chemical compound. However in this chapter, we have limited our discussion of absorption to the conventional processes using liquid sorbents.

It is evident that distinctions of this kind are comparatively unimportant to the user of sorbents for odor control. In solvent recovery a knowledge of these mechanisms is helpful, for it is usually desired to reclaim an adsorbed solvent with its initial chemical identity. In odor-control problems the possibility of chemical change in the adsorbed gases or vapors has so far been of little consequence, because in nearly every case when the adsorbent is regenerated by steam the condensate is sent to the sewer. Only to the specialist are the various sorption processes significant—for example, the observation that chemisorption increases the holding capacity of activated carbon.

Accordingly, we have divided the material on sorption into two parts: (1) absorption or solution of odorous gases and vapors in liquids or solvents by the use of washers, condensers, or scrubbers; and (2) adsorption of odorous matter by activated carbon supported in equipment variously known as "filters," "beds," or "canisters."

ABSORPTION IN WASHERS, CONDENSERS, OR SCRUBBERS

Absorption towers are chemical process units with a history that essentially parallels the manufacture of chemicals. It is almost a certainty that no method of intimately mixing gases with liquids can now be devised that at some time or another has not already been tried. The fundamental forces of interphase diffusion that govern the process of absorption were for many years a mystery, and even now it cannot be said that our knowledge in this field is comprehensive. Chemical engineers at the present time have a great deal of empirical data with which to assemble their equipment, but much is still lacking, as the industries well know.

One of the most troublesome applications is the removal of extremely small quantities of air contaminants that create odor nuisance. The following item is now several decades old, but still pertinent.

. . . An incident occurred which indicated very clearly that scrubbing the vapors by water alone would not eliminate the nuisance. One day while observations were being made at a point about a mile from the starch works, a very severe rain storm occurred. In order to determine the effect of the rain on the odors, the observer continued his observations in the rain for about 30 minutes, and it was found that, although the odors passed through a natural mammoth scrubber about a mile in length, they were not appreciably diminished in intensity.[1]

According to Whitman's double-film concept of resistance to absorption,[2] if a gas is highly soluble in a liquid, then its diffusion into the liquid from the surface is relatively easy. In such a case it is said that the resistance of the *gas film* in this two-phase system controls the rate of gas absorption. To a chemical engineer this means that resistance to absorption may be

[1] Holmquist, C. A., *Trans. Am. Soc. Civil Engrs.*, **89**, 420 (1926).
[2] *Chem. & Met. Eng.*, **29** (July 23, 1923).

minimized by spraying the liquid through the gas, causing good turbulence on the gaseous side of the interface—that is, around the outside of the droplets. As an example, ammonia, highly soluble in water, is readily absorped by spraying water through a chamber containing ammonia gas.

On the other hand, for a poorly soluble gas, such as are many of the odorous organic compounds, if water is the solvent, the reverse would be true; it would then be said that resistance of the *liquid film* at the interface between liquid and gas would control the rate of absorption. To minimize this resistance it would be very much preferable to bubble the gas through the liquid to obtain good turbulence in the liquid phase and thereby facilitate the absorption of gas. The plate-and-bubble-cap column for gas absorption meets this requirement to a certain degree.

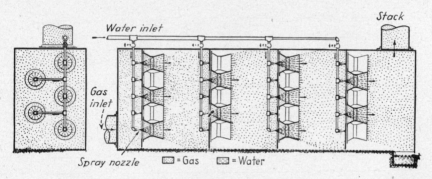

Fig. 1.—Gas-absorption system with four banks of spray nozzles. (*Schutte & Koerting Co.*)

The above explanation simply confirms in technical language the well-known fact that spray washers or scrubbers have considerable difficulty in absorbing low concentrations of some gases. Many air washers have evolved somewhat instinctively along lines of violent agitation of liquid and gas, and the results have been satisfactory in a large number of cases. An important observation is the fact that an increase in contact time or in the number of separate times the air encounters a spray zone will greatly assist the absorption of vapor. Figure 1 illustrates a four-bank spray system with carefully staggered nozzles. The vertical spray towers in Fig. 2 achieve prolonged contact between the liquid and gas phase by their three-stage arrangement. Figure 3 is an air washer of the type suitable either for dust collection or for odor condensing and incorporates the elements of water cascade, air rotation, and increased internal absorbing surface.

Air-scrubbing equipment that depends on liquid sprays or cascades is characterized by empty or nearly empty enclosures through which air or gas is passed against fairly low resistance. In Figs. 1 and 2 the contact surface is that of the liquid droplets as they fall through the air, while in Fig. 3 the contact surface is a combination of droplet areas and the sheet-metal surfaces guiding the airstream. In Figs. 2 and 3 the flow of air is vertical, upward, and countercurrent to that of the water, while in Fig. 1 it is horizontal and concurrent with the water flow. There is no standardized design for this type of equipment, and examination of the patent literature will disclose the ingenious variety that has accumulated.

While the high-pressure fog-nozzle-type washer is capable of a great air-liquid contact surface a critical point in air capacity is reached where the airstream begins to entrain or carry over the liquid. Selection of fog-nozzle size and type and liquid pressure are therefore intimately related to the velocity of air movement, and the operating specifications are necessarily a

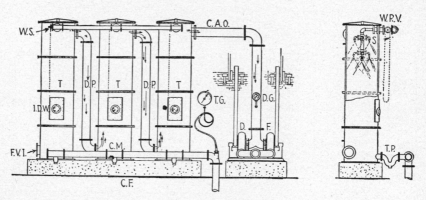

Fig. 2.—Three-stage condenser for a rendering plant. (*Ronald, Handbook on Offensive Trades," Wm. Hodge & Company, Limited, 1935.*)

compromise between high absorption efficiency and high air-treating capacity.

The most extensively used absorbers in the chemical industries are towers or vertical cylinders packed with materials like broken stone, hard coke, clay spheres, Berl "saddles," or hollow cylinders or rings made of ceramic, metal, carbon, or glass according to the chemical and structural properties needed. Figure 4 shows such a tower with spiral ring packing, similar to that illustrated by *C* in Fig. 5. Table I gives the properties of some specially designed packings. Packed towers are remarkably efficient when correctly designed, and for this purpose the treatise by Sherwood[1] is commended.

The height of an absorption tower influences its efficiency, while the cross-section area determines the air-handling capacity. For convenience in estimating capacity, the air movement through the tower is expressed in terms of "superficial gas velocity," which is defined as the velocity that would occur

[1] "Absorption and Extraction," McGraw-Hill Book Company, Inc., New York, 1937.

Table I.—PHYSICAL CHARACTERISTICS OF VARIOUS PACKING MATERIALS*

Material	Dimensions, in.	Bulk density, lb./cu. ft.	Dry surface, sq. ft./cu. ft.	Per cent free volume	Number of pieces per cu. ft.
Coke, dumped	6	10	5.5	57	
	3	24	12	50	
Quartz, dumped	6	87	6.3	48	
	4	90	9.7	46	
	3	92	13.7	43	
	2	100	22.7	37	
Raschig rings, dumped	1 × 1	58	58	73	1,350
	½ × ½	49	132	68	11,000
	2 × 2	35	14.4	73	170
Raschig rings, packed	4 × 3	52	20	64	38
Partition rings (double-crossed partition), packed	6 × 6	64	18	54	8
same	3 × 3	80	37	42	70
Single spiral rings, packed	6 × 6	53	15	58	8
same	3 × 3	53	29	64	64
Triple spiral rings	3¼ × 3¼	55	37	60	55
"Propeller" twisted prisms	6 × 6	40	16	78	13
Hollow balls	2½	52	19	33	140
"Hechenbleikner" blocks, packed	6 × 6 × 6	52	14	62	8
"Hexahelix" units, packed	4 × 4	60	20	60	28
"Prym" triangles, packed	3¼ × 3¼	60	40	72	55
Stoneware single-partition rings, packed	1 × 1	35	66	92	1,145
Metal Lessing rings, dumped	2 × 2	...	37	95	160
	1 × 1	...	74	93	1,300
	½ × ½	...	130	91	9,000
"Bregeat" wire spirals	½ × ⅞	57	144	83	9,350
	1¼ × 1¼	45	81	91	620
Vertical tubes	1 in. diam. on 1⅜ in. centers.	...	40		
	½ in. diam. on 11/16 in. centers	...	160		
Berl saddles	1.0	...	79	75	2,260

*Copyright by C. H. Butcher, London, reproduced from *The Industrial Chemist* by permission.

if no packing were present; it is thus based on the gross cross-section area of the tower. Superficial gas velocities generally range from 1 to 10 feet per second. Water or scrubbing-liquid flow rates are from 100 to 10,000 pounds per hour for each square foot of tower area.

Some designers prefer the Mach equation for estimating the pressure drop in packed towers, and those who are interested will find it on page 379 in "Elements of Chemical Engineering," by Badger and McCabe.[1]

[1] McGraw-Hill Book Company, Inc., New York, 1936.

Sherwood compares the advantages and features of packed towers and plate-and-bubble-cap towers as follows:

1. For acids and other highly corrosive solutions the packed tower is simpler and cheaper to construct than the plate tower built of glass, acid-resisting alloy steel, or other material.

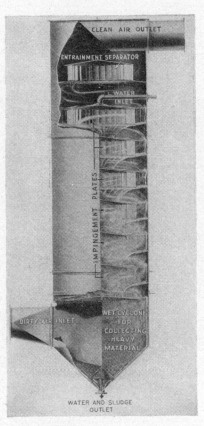

Fig. 3.—Vertical air washer suitable for either vapors or dusts. (*Claude B. Schneible Co.*)

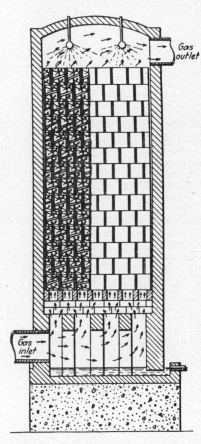

Fig. 4.—Absorption tower with manufactured spiral-ring packing. (*Sherwood, "Absorption and Extraction."*)

2. The pressure drop of the gas in passing through the packed tower can be considerably less than for a plate tower designed for the same duty.

3. The plate column avoids serious channeling difficulties of gas and liquor streams.

4. The plate column can be designed to handle liquor rates which would flood the ordinary packing.

5. A plate tower fitted with manholes can be cleaned of accumulated sediment

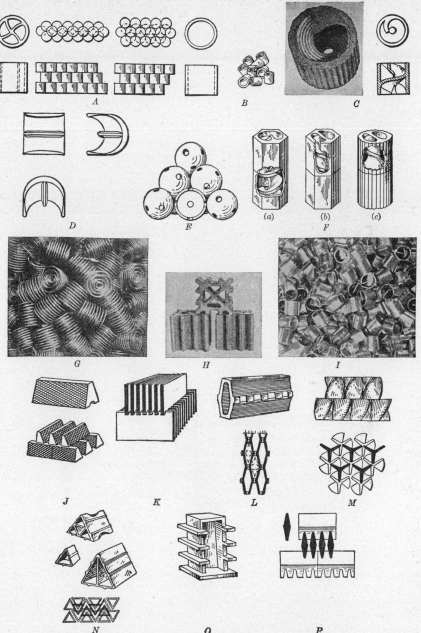

Fig. 5.—Typical manufactured packings for absorption towers. (*Courtesy of T. K. Sherwood and C. H. Butcher.*)

(*Most of the individual illustrations are the copyright of Charles H. Butcher, London, reproduced by permission.*) *A.* Partition rings. *B.* Plain Raschig rings. *C.* (Photo and diagram) Spiral rings. *D.* Doil saddles. *E.* Hollow balls. *F.* Helical packers: (*a*) single-spiral hexahelix blocks, (*b*) double-spiral hexahelix blocks, (*c*) double-spiral cyclohelix blocks. *G.* Bregeat multiple spirals. *H.* Hechenbleikner blocks. *I.* Metal Lessing rings. *J.* Prismic packing. *K.* Grids. *L.* Guttmann cells. *M.* Nielson "propeller" packing. *N.* Prym triangular packing. *O.* "Obsidianite" packers. *P.* Scherfenberg bricks. See Table I.

211

which would clog many packing materials and make necessary costly removal and refilling of the tower.

6. The plate tower lends itself readily to cooling of the liquor to remove a large heat of dilution, either by cooling coils on the plates or by external coolers through which the liquor is passed in flowing from one plate to the next.

7. The liquor holdup in the packed tower is considerably less than in the plate tower.

A water jet is utilized in the SK Obnoxious Vapor Condenser to remove the vapors from a rendering kettle or meat-scrap cooker, condense the steam and absorb odors arising from rendering meat scraps, dead animals, and similar substances.

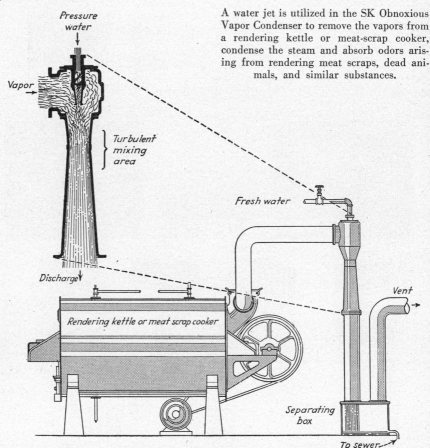

Fig. 6.—Water-jet-vapor condenser for rendering kettle or meat-scrap cooker. (*Schutte & Koerting Co.*)

8. The total weight of the plate tower is usually less than for the packed tower designed for the same duty.

9. Temperature changes are apt to do more damage to the packed tower than to the plate tower.

In all cases in which malodorous air is treated in absorbers, some form of motive power is required to confine the air in exhaust hoods and conduct it to the scrubber or condenser. Centrifugal or axial-flow exhausters are generally installed, but occasionally a type of equipment is desired that is less vulnerable to corrosion. Venturi ejectors or syphon jets may then be used, deriving their energy from high-pressure blowers located safely outside the air stream. A more satisfactory device, particularly for soluble or condensable air contaminants, is the water or steam jet exhauster shown in Figs. 6 and 7. Some types are capable of a high vacuum development, but for odor-control installations the jet is designed to operate within 0.5 to 3 in. water-gauge pressure drop.

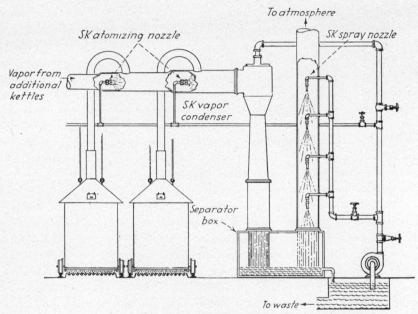

FIG. 7.—Water-jet-vapor condenser for varnish or oil-boiling kettles. (*Schutte & Koerting Co.*)

In all types of air washers it is possible to modify the solvent in accordance with knowledge of the solute. Thus a hypochlorite solution may be indicated for meat-rendering odors, milk-of-lime for a sulfur dioxide scrubber, or sodium hydroxide for a nitrogen dioxide absorption system. Special solvents such as alcohols or petroleum fractions may be used, but their use requires careful attention to the factors of flammability, volatility, solvent odor, and recovery economics. Liquids other than water may necessitate scrubber construction with expensive corrosion-resistant materials and possibly neutralization or stabilization of the waste water before discharge to the sewer.

One advantage of absorbing odorous gases in a liquid as an intermediate step toward final disposal is the possibility of more convenient or successful application of destructive treatments on the odorous substances while in solution. It is true that the availability of a sewerage system might obviate the need for further treatment once the offensive vapor has been collected or condensed in the wash water. But if the water is to be discharged into a stream, the possibility that dissolved gases may later escape into the air and create an odor nuisance at a point downstream cannot be overlooked.

ODOR ADSORPTION BY ACTIVATED CARBON

Without question the most versatile agent for odor control yet produced is *activated* carbon. Although it cannot be said to control all types of odors under any conditions, it approaches this goal more completely than any other agent to our knowledge.

A serious obstacle to the existence of a "universal deodorant" is the failure to develop chemical or physical methods to analyze the remarkably small quantities of airborne substances responsible for disagreeable odors. Since the process of adsorption is a universal phenomenon, a method of odor control making use of this property would release the designer from the necessity for air analysis. This state of affairs provides the opportunity for carbon, and in fact long before there was any theory of adsorption men were aware of the purifying or deodorizing power of charcoal.

Prehistoric man certainly discovered that if he threw wood ashes over a decaying carcass, the smell would disappear. This operation has survived many thousands of years of competition with all other experiments, and even today is well known. The presence of alkali in the ashes is of course some assistance, but even in this case the deodorizing action is selective.

Marco Polo, in his thirteenth-century travels to the Orient, found that wood ashes were used to refine sugar. In 1773 Scheele reported that wood charcoal would absorb gases. Sinclair of Edinburgh wrote in 1807 that the use of charcoal as a purifying agent was most recently discovered. In 1854 Stenhouse described a respirator filled with powdered wood charcoal for use in hospitals or sick rooms. Its purpose was protection against the foul emanations, which at that time were believed to be the cause of the dreaded disease epidemics. Constantly man has rediscovered charcoal and its odor-suppression ability, and there are many persons today who are surprised when they learn of its properties.

In 1897, Green reviewed many methods of eliminating odors and arrived at the following conclusion:

Of these deodorizers, or smell removers, charcoal in its various forms is one of the cheapest, most abundant and most efficacious. Mixed with fermenting night soil or with the contents of our common sewers, it sweetens them almost immediately, and it produces a like effect upon almost every variety of decaying animal and vegetable matter. Spread to the depth of two or three inches over a festering graveyard, or even over a decaying dead body, it is said to prevent any evil odors from rising into the air or becoming sensible to the smell . . . .

So powerful is this affinity that if a tablespoonful of finely powdered animal charcoal, or twice as much newly burned wood charcoal, be shaken up with a pint of stinking ditch water and the mixture filtered, the water will pass through bright, clear and with little of either taste or smell.[1]

"Activated" carbon, or, as some prefer, "active" carbon, has from 50 to 100 times the adsorptive power of untreated charcoal. In the process of charring, the carbon acquires, or refuses to release, some low volatile impurities, and the high-temperature activation that is the modern contribution to adsorption by carbon removes much of this foreign matter that would impair its performance. Within the carbon particles or granules there is an incredible number of tiny cavities or capillaries whose aggregate surface area in a cubic inch of high-grade coconut-shell carbon is estimated to be approximately five acres.

According to Ledoux,

The adsorption characteristics of the manufactured carbon depend considerably upon the mode and degree of activation, but also on the raw material used (coconut shell, peat, anthracite, etc.). For instance, soft woods will produce light and friable carbon which must be used in powder or agglomerated form, while hard woods will produce carbon in granular form which will have entirely different characteristics.[2]

Some of the results of Hunter's investigations from 1863 to 1872 on the adsorption of gases by charcoal made from different woods are given in Table II. It is interesting to note that he found coconut-shell carbon to be the most adsorptive substance he tested.

At the present time two principle types of active carbon are produced: (1) a dense material for gas adsorption, and (2) a more porous material for the decolorizing, purifying, or deodorizing of liquids. The properties of activated carbons vary widely, and all of them are selective to a certain degree. Many of the failures that have been attributed to carbon in deodorizing attempts have been due rather to unwise application.

The First World War provided a great stimulus to the use of carbon. As "gas-mask carbon" it represented the outcome of intensive research, as well as study of the uncoordinated findings of earlier generations. Again in the Second World War it remained as the only reliable physical adsorbing agent for protection against the anticipated poison-gas attacks. For this purpose it was one of the ingredients of civilian or military gas masks and was installed in the air-conditioning equipment of underground shelters. Figure 8

[1] *Sci. American Supp.*, 44, 17936 (July 3, 1897)
[2] "Vapor Adsorption," Chemical Publishing Company, New York, 1945.

shows its use for odor control in hospital planes; in this application a carbon bed of about 3/4 in. thickness handling 10 cu. ft. of air per minute had an odor-adsorbing life of approximately seven days.

Carbon is not the only solid adsorbent that will deodorize air. Silica gel, activated alumina, kieselguhr, and fuller's earth, all have been used. The superiority of carbon as an odor-control agent is principally due to the strong affinity of silica gel and alumina for water. Carbon, instead, will release water vapor in preference to the odorous gases or vapors. It is this property in fact that accounts for its ability to deodorize or decolorize water

Table II.—Adsorption of Gases by Charcoal from Different Woods*

(Volume of gas adsorbed per volume of charcoal at 0°C. and 760 mm. Hg)

Wood	Ammonia	Carbon dioxide
Coconut shell	176	71
Logwood	111	55
Ebony	107	47
Camwood	91	45
Fustic (Cuba)	90	58
Green ebony	90	41
Lignum vitae	89	47
Boxwood	86	31
Sapanwood	70	32
Jamaica logwood	69	33
Beech	58	
Rosewood	51	
Wistaria sinensis	44	
Vegetable ivory		50

* Hunter's results compiled by Mantell, in "Adsorption," McGraw-Hill Book Company, Inc., New York, 1945.

or liquids containing large percentages of water. Silica gel and alumina, with their special preference for water, are accordingly best employed in the fields of dehydration and dehumidification. Its strong attraction for water even makes silica gel an excellent dehydrator for liquid refrigerants, in which the presence of water, freezing at 32° F., would be intolerable.

Furthermore, carbon is used almost exclusively for solvent recovery by physical adsorption, in which high efficiency at low concentration is often imperative to justify the recovery installation.

A recent product known as "magnesol"[1] is a synthetic hydrous magnesium silicate possessing decolorizing and deodorizing properties. In consideration of its ability to adsorb colors and odors without the danger of a black residue, it has been designated by some as a "white activated carbon," particularly in its cosmetic applications.

[1] Westvaco Chlorine Products Corp., New York.

Activated Carbon in Air Conditioning.—Activated carbon for atmospheric odor control can be used successfully only with systems of mechanical ventilation, whether they are motivated by a tiny fan, as shown in Fig. 8, or provided with a huge centrifugal blower, as installed in office buildings and hotels. Carbon specifications for this use have been carefully developed, and designers of new equipment should bear this in mind. The carbon must be hard, durable, dust-free, capable of repeated regeneration, and highly absorptive for the contaminants usually found in the indoor atmosphere. The standard grades of carbon produced for this use are only fairly adsorptive

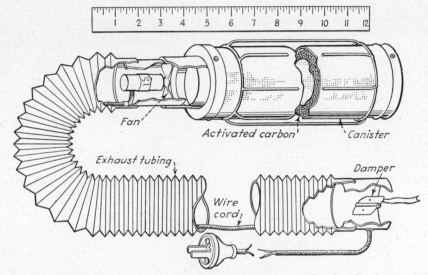

Fig. 8.—Hospital-plane litter odor adsorber. The canister is placed under the patient's blanket and the tiny fan draws the air through the carbon, preventing escape of odors into cabin. (*W. B. Connor Engineering Corp.*)

for such materials as formaldehyde, cyanogen, hydrogen cyanide, phosphine, and arsine and therefore are not recommended for use in gas masks or respirators. Munkelt offers in Table III a recently revised summary of the retentivity for gases and vapors of standard air-conditioning carbon based on experience of many years.

As a general rule, the more condensable or liquefiable a vapor is at the conditions imposed, the higher will be the adsorbability or retentivity for a given solid. However, no quantitative relation has been established between adsorbability and either the critical temperature or boiling point, and the equilibrium state of sorption for a given solid-vapor combination must be determined experimentally. Furthermore, there are cases in which the retentivity violates the condensability comparison here stated.

Table III.—Properties of Gases and Vapors* and Their Retentivity by Activated Carbon†

Substance	Formula	Molecular weight	Boiling point, 760 mm., °C.	C critical temperature, °C.	Approximate retentivity at 20°C., 760 mm., %	Remarks
Propane.	C_3H_8	44.09	-42	95.6	5	Heating gas
Butane.	C_4H_{10}	58.12	1	153.0	8	Heating gas
Pentane.	C_5H_{12}	72.15	37	197.2	12	Light naphtha
Hexane.	C_6H_{14}	86.17	69	234.8	16	Gasoline
Heptane.	C_7H_{16}	100.20	98.4	266.8	23	Gasoline
Octane.	C_8H_{18}	114.23	125.5	296.0	25	Gasoline
Nonane.	C_9H_{20}	128.25	150.0	......	25	Kerosene
Decane.	$C_{10}H_{22}$	142.28	231.0	......	25	Kerosene
Acetylene.	C_2H_2	26.04	-88.5	36.0	2	Welding and cutting
Propyne.	C_3H_4	40.06	-23.0	......	5	
Butyne.	C_4H_6	54.09	27.0	......	8	
Ethylene.	C_2H_4	28.05	-103.9	9.7	3	Illuminating gas; fruit ripener; anesthetic
Propylene.	C_3H_6	42.08	-47.0	92.3	5	Coal gas
Butylene.	C_4H_8	56.10	-5.0	......	8	
Pentylene.	C_5H_{10}	70.13	40.0	......	12	
Benzene.	C_6H_6	78.11	80.1	288.5	24	Benzol; paint solvent and re-mover
Toluene.	C_7H_8	92.13	110.8	320.6	29	Manufacture of TNT
Xylene.	C_8H_{10}	106.16	144.0	......	34	Solvent
Turpentine.	$C_{10}H_{16}$	136.23	180.0	......	32	
Naphthalene.	$C_{10}H_8$	128.16	217.9	......	30	Mothballs; reagent
Phenol.	C_6H_5OH	94.11	182.0	419.0	30	Carbolic acid; plastic ingredient
Methyl alcohol.	CH_3OH	32.04	64.7	240.0	10	Wood alcohol
Ethyl alcohol.	C_2H_5OH	46.07	78.5	243.1	21	Grain alcohol
Isopropyl alcohol.	C_3H_7OH	60.09	83.02	235.0	26	Solvent
Butyl alcohol.	C_4H_9OH	74.12	117.71	287.0	30	Solvent

Name	Formula					Uses
Amyl alcohol	$C_5H_{11}OH$	88.15	138.0	307.0	35	Fusel oil
Cresol	C_7H_7OH	108.13	202.5	422.0	30	Ingredient of creosote; wood preservative
Menthol	$C_{10}H_{19}OH$	156.26	215.0	.....	20	
Formaldehyde	$H.CHO$	30.03	−21.0	.....	3	Disinfectant; plastic ingredient
Acetaldehyde	CH_3CHO	44.05	21.0	188.0	7	Reagent
Butyraldehyde	C_3H_7CHO	72.10	75.7	.....	21	
Acrylaldehyde	C_2H_3CHO	56.06	52.5	.....	15	Acrolein; burning fats
Crotonaldehyde	C_3H_5CHO	70.09	104.0	.....	30	Solvent; tear gas
Formic acid	$H.COOH$	46.03	100.7	.....	7	Reagent
Acetic acid	CH_3COOH	60.05	118.1	321.6	40	Reagent; sour vinegar
Propionic acid	C_2H_5COOH	74.08	141.1	339.5	40	
Butyric acid	C_3H_7COOH	88.10	163.5	355.0	40	Sweat; body odors
Valeric acid	C_4H_9COOH	102.13	187.0	379.0	40	Sweat; body odors
Caprylic acid	$C_7H_{15}COOH$	144.21	237.5	.....	35	Animal odor
Palmitic acid	$C_{15}H_{31}COOH$	256.42	339.0	.....	35	Palm oil
Acrylic acid	C_2H_3COOH	76.06	141.9	.....	20	
Lactic acid	$CH_3CHOH.COOH$	90.08	122.0	.....	30	Sour milk
Methyl acetate	$CH_3COO.CH_3$	74.08	57.1	233.7	16	Solvent
Ethyl acetate	$CH_3COO.C_2H_5$	88.10	77.15	250.1	19	Lacquer solvent
Isopropyl acetate	$CH_3COO.C_3H_7$	102.13	88.9	.....	23	Lacquer solvent
Butyl acetate	$CH_3COO.C_4H_9$	116.16	126.5	288.0	28	Lacquer solvent
Amyl acetate	$CH_3COO.C_5H_{11}$	130.18	148.0	326.0	34	Lacquer solvent
Acetone	$CH_3CO.CH_3$	58.08	56.5	235.0	15	Solvent
Methyl ethyl ketone	$CH_3CO.C_2H_5$	72.10	79.6	.....	25	Solvent
Diethyl ketone	$C_2H_5CO.C_2H_5$	86.13	102.7	.....	30	Solvent
Methyl isobutyl ketone	$C_4H_9COCH_3$	100.16	115.8	.....	30	Solvent
Methyl ether	$(CH_3)_2O$	46.07	−23.6	.....	10	Ether—medical
Ethyl ether	$(C_2H_5)_2O$	74.12	34.6	193.8	15	Solvent
Isopropyl ether	$(C_3H_7)_2O$	102.17	67.5	.....	18	Solvent
Butyl ether	$(C_4H_9)_2O$	130.23	142.0	.....	20	Solvent

Table III.—Properties of Gases and Vapors* and Their Retentivity by Activated Carbon† (Continued)

Substance	Formula	Molecular weight	Boiling point, 760 mm., °C.	C critical temperature, °C.	Approximate retentivity at 20°C., 760 mm., %	Remarks
Methyl mercaptan......	CH_3SH	48.10	7.6	196.8	20	Garlic; onion; sewer
Ethyl mercaptan......	C_2H_5SH	63.13	34.7	225.5	23	Garlic; onion; sewer
Propyl mercaptan......	C_3H_7SH	76.15	68.0	....	25	Garlic; onion; sewer
Carbon bisulfide......	CS_2	76.13	46.3	273.0	15	
Eucalyptole........	$C_{10}H_{18}O$	154.25	176.0	....	20	
Camphor........	$C_{10}H_{16}O$	152.23	204.0	....	20	
All essential oils......	....	....	....	....	High	
Methyl chloride........	CH_3Cl	50.49	−24.22	143.1	5	Refrigerant
Ethyl chloride........	C_2H_5Cl	64.52	12.2	187.2	12	Local anesthetic; refrigerant
Isopropyl chloride......	C_3H_7Cl	78.54	35.4	....	20	Solvent
Butyl chloride........	C_4H_9Cl	92.57	78.0	....	25	All organic chlorides are highly sorbable
Methylene chloride......	CH_2Cl_2	84.94	40.1	....	25	Anesthetic; solvent
Chloroform	$CHCl_3$	119.39	61.26	263.0	40	Cleaning fluid; solvent; fire extinguisher
Carbon tetrachloride......	CCl_4	153.84	76.0	283.1	45	
Iodoform........	CHI_3	393.78	....	....	30	Antiseptic
Pyridine........	C_5H_5N	79.10	115.3	344.0	25	Burning tobacco
Indole........	C_8H_7N	117.14	254.0	....	25	Excreta
Skatole........	C_9H_9N	131.17	266.2	....	25	Excreta

Nicotine	$C_{10}H_{14}N$	162.23	247.3	....	25	Tobacco
Nitrobenzene	$C_6H_5NO_2$	123.11	210.9	....	20	Oil of bitter almonds; oil of mirbane
Putrescine	$(CH_2)_4(NH_2)_2$	88.15	158.0	....	25	Decaying flesh
Body odors	....	....	....	....	High	
Packing-house odors	....	....	....	....	High	
Cooling odors	....	....	....	....	High	
Food (raw) odors	....	....	....	....	High	
Sewer odors	....	....	....	....	High	
Toilet odors	....	....	....	....	High	
Chlorine	Cl_2	70.91	−33.7	144.0	15	
Bromine	Br_2	159.83	58.78	302.0	40	
Iodine	I_2	253.84	183.0	553.0	40	
Hydrogen fluoride	$HF+H_2O$	....	120.0	....	10	
Hydrogen chloride	$HCl+H_2O$	....	110.0	....	12	
Hydrogen bromide	$HBr+H_2O$	....	126.0	....	12	
Nitrogen dioxide	NO_2	46.01	21.3	158.0	10	Hydrolyzes to HNO_3
Nitric acid	HNO_3	63.02	86.0	....	20	
Sulfur dioxide	SO_2	64.06	−10.0	157.2	10 dry	Oxidizes to SO_3
Sulfur trioxide	SO_3	80.06	44.8	218.3	15 dry	Hydrolyzes to H_2SO_4
Sulfuric acid	H_2SO_4	98.08	330.0	....	30	
Hydrogen sulfide	H_2S	34.08	−61.8	100.4	3 dry	50 when oxidized to H_2O and S
Water	H_2O	18.02	100.0	374.0	None	

* Compiled as of 1946 by F. H. Munkelt, W. B. Connor Engineering Corporation, New York.

† Retentivity is the ratio of the weight of the retained substance to the weight of the carbon. It is determined by passing clean dry air at constant pressure and temperature through a bed of granular carbon previously saturated with the vapor in question until the carbon ceases to decrease in weight.

A low retentivity appearing in Table III usually indicates a proportionately low efficiency of removal by the carbon bed. In some cases, however, retention of the gas or vapor is aided by chemical reaction that proceeds after adsorption. Thus, ethylene, hydrogen sulfide, and sulfur dioxide enter into such reactions and the carbon apparently takes up much more than indicated in the table. It is considered good practice when dealing with low-retentivity gases to provide for frequent recirculation through the carbon beds.

Dauphinee, Munkelt, and Sleik estimate the carbon requirements for decontaminating air approximately as stated in Table IV.

Table IV.—AVERAGE CARBON REQUIREMENTS AND SERVICE LIFE IN AIR CONDITIONING*

Type of ventilation	Pounds of carbon per 1,000 c.f.m.	Average life between reactivations
Domestic.....................................	25	2 years or more
Commercial..................................	35–40	1–1½ years
Industrial.....................................	60 or more	½–1 year

* Air Conservation Engineering, W. B. Connor Engineering Corporation, New York, 1944.

Since the resistance to airflow through a granular carbon bed depends on the bed thickness as well as the air velocity, it is general practice to install the carbon in thin layers combined with large surface area. The most convenient system so far developed is that shown in Fig. 9, constructed under the patent issued to Dauphinee in 1941 (U.S. Patent No. 2,214,737). Figures 10 to 12 indicate the method of assembling the canister in banks and locating these banks or groups of canisters in air conditioning ducts. Figure 13 illustrates a perforated tubular arrangement for limited space, and the same type of tubular element may be arranged for deodorizing recirculated room air, as in Fig. 14.

The over-all adsorption efficiency of air-conditioning carbon is practically 100 per cent for vapors having a high retentivity value in Table III and remains so until the amount of material adsorbed is about ⅔ of the retentivity figure, independent of moisture. For substances having retentivities in the middle range, the initial adsorption efficiency would be 90 to 95 per cent, while 85 per cent might be the initial efficiency with a vapor of low retentivity. Substances with low retentivities usually give the best adsorption efficiencies when their concentrations in the untreated air are low. In any case, continued adsorption is possible beyond the period of maximum efficiency.

Activated Carbon in Water Treatment.—"In an old Sanskrit manuscript, containing a collection of medical lore, appears this advice: 'It is good to keep water in copper vessels, to expose it to sunlight, and filter it through charcoal.' The document was written about 2000 B.C."[1]

Sir John Sinclair wrote in 1807 the earliest known reference in our language to the use of charcoal for water treatment.

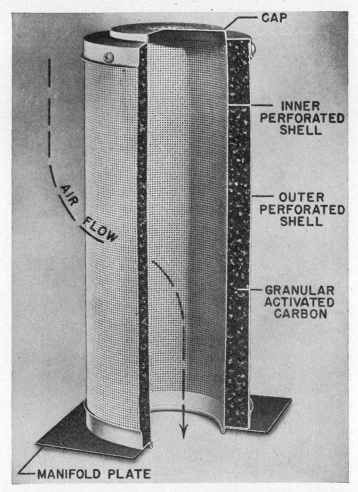

Fig. 9.—Perforated canister for granular activated carbon. Air capacities range from 20 to 40 cu. ft. per minute per canister. (*W. B. Connor Engineering Corp.*)

Another mode of improving water, and one that has been most recently discovered, is by means of charcoal, a substance which enjoys the property of preserving water from corruption and of purifying it after it has been corrupted. It has been found that one ounce and a half of powdered charcoal and 24 drops of oil

[1] *Taste Odor Control J.*, **6**, 4 (September, 1939).

of vitriol are sufficient to purify three English pints and a half of corrupted water, without communicating to it any sensible acidity. If no acid be used, two-thirds more of charcoal powder will be necessary . . . . It is said, also, that filtering the water through charcoal has been found an excellent mode of purifying it.[1]

FIG. 10.—Common method of assembling activated-carbon canisters for use in air-conditioning systems. (*W. B. Connor Engineering Corp.*)

In 1861, Dahlke read a paper before the London Society of Arts in which he stated that water filters containing sand, gravel, and charcoal had been introduced in England about seventy years previous to that date.[2]

[1] "Code of Health and Longevity," **1**, 262, 1807, Edinburgh.
[2] On Filtration—A New Medium, *Sci. American*, **4**, 353 (June 8, 1861).

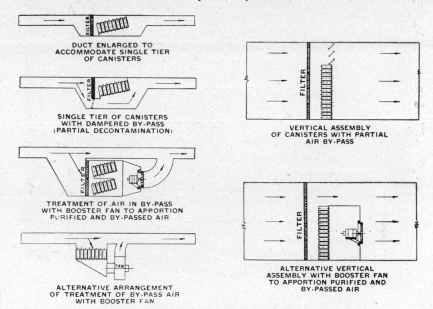

FIG. 11.—Several methods of installing carbon-canister banks in air-conditioning ducts. (*W. B. Connor Engineering Corp.*)

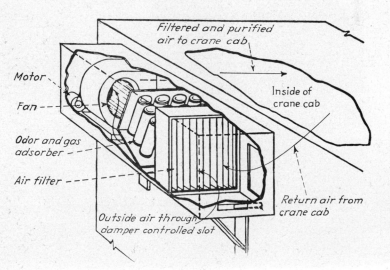

FIG. 12.—Carbon canisters used for purifying the air of crane cabs. (*W. B. Connor Engineering Corp.*)

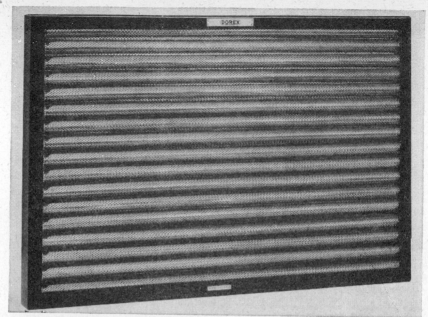

FIG. 13.—Panel unit with perforated tubes containing activated carbon. Developed especially for limited space, as in unit air conditioners or public conveyances. (*W. B. Connor Engineering Corp.*)

FIG. 14.—Air circulator with perforated tubes filled with activated carbon. Used in small areas where odor generation is moderate. (*W. B. Connor Engineering Corp.*)

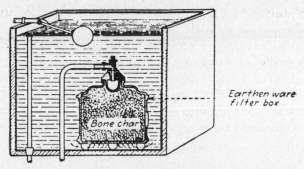

Fig. 15.—An early type of carbon filter. (*Baylis, "Elimination of Taste and Odor in Water."*)

One of the earliest forms of bone-char filters is illustrated in Fig. 15. It was used in England to a limited extent during the middle of the nineteenth century. Purification of potable water was originally limited to domestic use, and the patent literature contains many examples. Figures 16 and 17

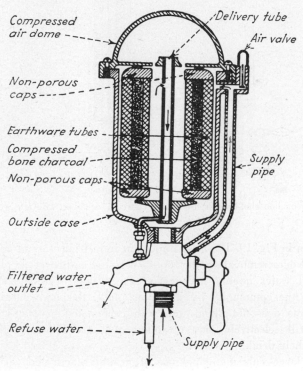

Fig. 16.—Domestic water filter manufactured about 1900. (*Baylis, "Elimination of Taste and Odor in Water."*)

indicate two methods of filtering tap water that incorporate compressed or granular charcoal. Even cisterns were specially constructed to permit the addition of granular carbon, as is illustrated in Fig. 18.

While the quality of water now delivered by municipal treatment plants is high, much of it being deodorized with powdered activated carbon, a large number of industrial plants and isolated commercial and residential establishments are currently filtering water through beds of granular active carbon. An arrangement for coagulation, sand filtration, and carbon purifica-

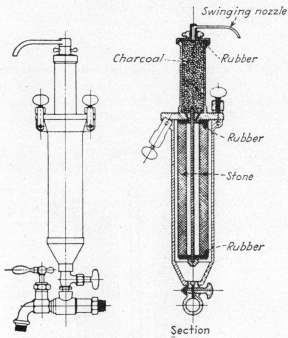

Fig. 17.—Everson household water filter with charcoal chamber. (*Baylis, "Elimination of Taste and Odor in Water."*)

tion is shown in Fig. 19. The most important industrial users of active carbon for taste and odor removal are the food-processing and beverage plants, where the required water quality may even exceed that of the general supply delivered to the community by its water plant. Residual chlorine in very small amounts does not blend well with carbonated beverages, and some foodstuffs will selectively pick up odors that are imperceptible to most persons in their drinking water.

The first large-scale municipal use of granular activated carbon in this country was the method devised by Harrison at Bay City, Mich., in 1930. His equipment is illustrated in Fig. 20; the capacity of the filter bed has been recently increased to 8,000,000 gal. per day by increasing the depth of the carbon layer to 36 in. Harrison states that 1 ft. of granular carbon is sufficient for a filtering rate of 1 gal. per sq. ft. per min., so 3 ft. of carbon will be able to purify at the rate of 3 gal. per min. per sq. ft. There are a number of such units now in use for municipal water treatment and their rates of filtration vary from 2 to 6 gal. per sq. ft. per min., with suitable depth of carbon bed.[1]

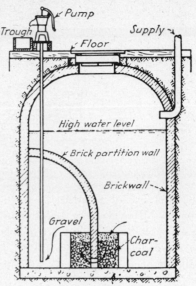

FIG. 18.—Charcoal filtering cistern in use about 1880. (*Baylis*, "*Elimination of Taste and Odor in Water.*")

In 1866, the East London Water Company began filtering through animal charcoal the water supplied to 700 occupants of lodging houses in Columbia Square.[2] The results were so successful that some persons advocated the filtering of London's entire water supply through beds of animal charcoal. Unquestionably the improvement would have been substantial, even though charcoal at that time was relatively inactive compared with the present materials.

Croes wrote that the first attempt to filter a municipal supply through layers of sand and charcoal in this country occurred at Elizabeth, N. J., in 1852.[3]

Oscar and Rudolph Adler of Karlsbad, Czechoslovakia, received a patent on the use of *activated* carbon for dechlorinating water in 1927 in their country. Patents were then granted by Great Britain in 1928 and the United States in 1930 (No. 1,771,518, July 29, 1930). Rudolph Adler came to this country in 1927 and induced the Cleveland Water Purification Plant to experiment with activated carbon for chlorine and phenol removal. The most important early work in this country, however, was begun by Baylis in 1928 at the Chicago Experimental Filtration Plant. He made his first report on this work in the following year.[4]

Baylis credits the Chicago meatpacking plant of Swift and Company with

[1] "Taste and Odor Control in Water Purification," Industrial Chemical Sales Division, West Virginia Pulp and Paper Company, New York, 1942.

[2] *Engineering*, **2**, 365 (Nov. 16, 1866).

[3] *Eng. News & Am. Contracting J.*, **10**, 277 (June 16, 1883).

[4] The Activated Carbons and Their Use in Removing Objectionable Tastes and Odors from Water, *J. Am. Water Works Assoc.*, **21**, 787 (June, 1929).

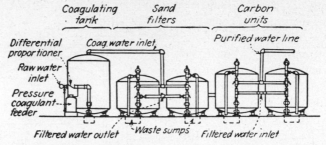

Fig. 19.—An activated-carbon installation for filtration of water, consisting of pressure coagulating tank, pressure filters, and carbon purifiers. (*Mantell, "Adsorption."*)

the first use of powdered activated carbon for water purification in this country.[1] However, he states that Spaulding of New Jersey probably was responsible for the rapid development of interest among water-plant operators in powdered carbon, as a result of his report of successful use at the New Milford plant of the Hackensack Water Company in 1930.[2]

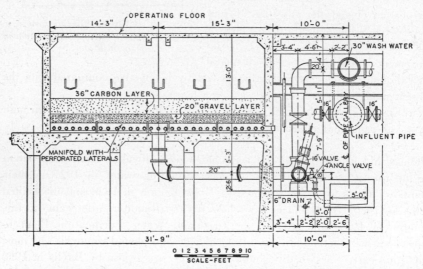

Fig. 20.—Granular activated-carbon bed for municipal-water treatment at Bay City, Michigan. (*Industrial Chemical Sales Div., West Virginia Pulp & Paper Co.*)

In 1941 it was estimated that over 1,200 municipal water plants in the United States were using powdered activated carbon for taste and odor control. It has been applied at nearly every point in the treatment process at one place or another. The quantity required is highly variable owing to the

[1] "Elimination of Taste and Odor in Water," McGraw-Hill Book Company, Inc., New York, 1935.

[2] *J. Am. Water Works Assoc.*, **22**, 646 (May, 1930).

wide differences in the quality of the raw water supplies around the continent. Sigworth writes as follows on carbon dosages:

In general, it may be stated that under average conditions 20 to 40 lbs. of activated carbon per million gallons of water will be sufficient to secure a palatable water. Where odors are quite intense or of a type difficult to remove, considerably higher proportions are necessary, ranging perhaps from 100 to 500 lbs. per million gallons. In some rare cases it has been necessary to employ as high as 1500 lbs. per million gallons for short periods of time.[1]

The dry powder is usually fed into some form of dry feed machine, of which there are many designs. One type is shown in Fig. 21. From the feeder the material is passed into water to create a slurry, and in this form the carbon may be piped to any of several points throughout the plant. Figure 22 illustrates a batch method of preparing a water suspension of powdered carbon.

Activated carbon is also applied to reservoirs in dosages ranging from 5 to 50 parts per million by weight, especially after copper sulfate treatment for destruction of algae. Death of the microorganisms is followed by severe short-term odors and tastes, and carbon effectively eliminates or at least modifies these odors before the water enters the treatment plant. The method of carbon application to a reservoir from a motorboat is shown diagrammatically in Fig. 23.

The threshold odor test now in use for water-treatment control has been standardized.[2]

MISCELLANEOUS USES OF ACTIVE CARBON

A great many miscellaneous uses of activated carbon have appeared in recent years, too numerous to review here. A few may be mentioned, such as the application to Imhoff tank gas vents, open digestion tanks, trickling filter sprays, and open-bed sludge drying in sewage-treatment practice; introduction to the liquid wastes from canneries or creameries where the broad irrigation method of disposal is used; and dusting on piles of cannery waste or other organic matter undergoing decomposition.

Carbon also has been used to a limited extent for the control of industrial-odor nuisance. An installation of this type is shown in Fig. 24. One advantage of this system is that large volumes of air may be deodorized by temporarily storing the malodors on carbon, and upon regenerating the carbon at a later time, the concentrated vapors desorbed from the carbon can be led to a furnace for destruction without seriously interfering with combustion efficiency.

[1] *Taste Odor Control J.,* **7,** 2 (October, 1940).
[2] "Standard Methods of Water and Sewage Analysis," 9th ed., American Public Health Association, New York, 1946.

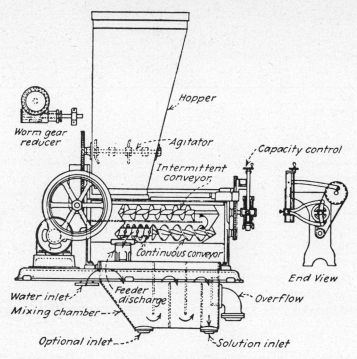

Fig. 21.—Savage-Gauntt dry-chemical feeder. (*Baylis, "Elimination of Taste and Odor in Water."*)

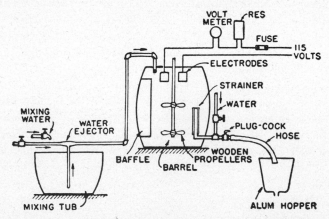

Fig. 22.—"Solution" method for feeding activated carbon. (*Industrial Chemical Sales.*)

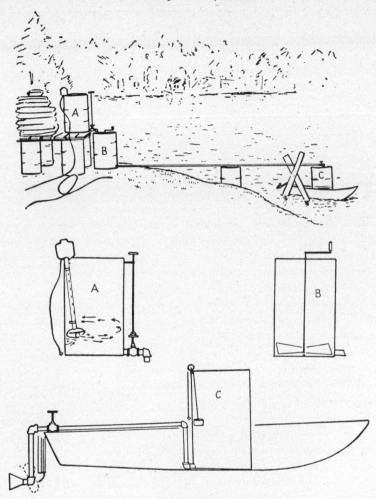

FIG. 23.—Type and arrangement of equipment suitable for the application of powdered activated carbon to reservoirs. (*Taste Odor Control J.*, May, 1946.)

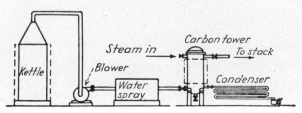

FIG. 24.—Diagram of stench-abatement installation using activated carbon. (*Mantell, "Adsorption," after Ray and Chaney, Chem. & Met. Eng.*, **28**, 1114, 1923.)

Chapter XX

Odors as Warning Agents

OUR MEMBERSHIP in the animal kingdom has favored us with a long heritage in the highly effective mechanism of olfactory warning. The ability of certain species to surround themselves with emanations most likely to disgust and repel their enemies was doubtless a formidable asset in the rugged competition of animal evolution. The ability of others to detect extremely minute concentrations of odorous molecules originating from their enemies likewise gave them providential advantage over their less acutely endowed relatives.

The instinctive association of imminent danger with foul or strange odors is now so well ingrained in the human experience that we find almost universal acceptance of the value of unusual odors as signals of possible disaster. In fact, urban dwellers have become so irritable in the presence of olfactory surprise or offense that designers of warning procedures must be careful not to create inferior mechanisms that may lead to periodic or chronic complaint or unnecessary community alarm.

Warning agents protect against fire, explosion, or gaseous poisoning that might be the accidental circumstance of leaks in utility gas lines, refrigeration systems, and storage tanks or the result of unfortunate events in the course of mining operations widely scattered deep in the earth. They depend on the fact that most of us take little heed of our atmospheric environment unless we encounter a discomforting odor, and then the degree of our reaction is directly related to the nature of the respiratory insult.

It is repeatedly argued that warning agents should simulate the odor of the hazard as commonly associated in the public mind; thus, a leak of fuel gas in the home should be revealed by an unmistakable "gassy" or "gas-house" odor. Opponents of this view suggest that the public can learn to associate a new odor with a given hazard and that other factors might be more significant in the selection of a suitable warning agent. Surveys of odor complaints have in fact revealed that a householder may in time connect strange odors with familiar hazards; thus he may complain that "cooking gas" odors are permeating the premises when the real source is an organic decay that is generating an odor similar to a sulfurous warning agent in the fuel-gas supply.

234

It is interesting to observe that some of the most effective materials for the warning process are organic sulfur compounds known as "mercaptans," widely found in nature as the products of animal and vegetable decay and in the excretions of animal life initiated by fear or anger. The unpleasant associations of such odors have been so numerous in our daily events that specific advance instructions may be necessary to ensure the correct response in the case of accidental or planned release of the warning agent. During one of the utility-gas-leakage surveys conducted by the Bureau of Mines, ethyl mercaptan was injected into the gas supply without the public knowledge, with the following curious results:

One man blamed a butcher for having sent spoiled meat. A woman threw all her husband's shoes out of a closet. Another insisted that her husband take a bath. One woman burned disinfecting candles for two or three days in different parts of the house to overcome the odor. Many people passing over a river bridge . . . where a leaking expansion joint was found, severely criticized up-river residents for dumping sewage into the river.

These instances, however, served to demonstrate not only the inability of many persons to associate strange odors with their true sources but also the comparative ease of forestalling confusion by intelligent advance instruction. In the first case, in which the gas customers were not notified of the leakage tests until they had been in progress for 10 days, many persons associated the new odor with something dead, and considerable expense and trouble was caused by tearing up floors and exploring areas under houses. In a second case, in a different community, notices of the proposed leakage tests were sent out to the customers three days in advance, and the new odor of leaking gas was in nearly all instances correctly identified and promptly reported.

The applications of warning agents, also known as "tracer gases," have steadily increased since the publication of numerous tests and reports on their properties and methods of use. They are now added to compressed or "bottled" gases such as oxygen, hydrogen, and mixed hydrocarbons; injected into fuel gases that are relatively weak in odor; mixed with explosive or poisonous refrigerants to warn of leakage; injected into ventilation and compressed air lines of mines to warn the miners of actual or potential danger; and introduced into boilers and pipe lines to reveal leaks with either air or water under pressure. In the case of temporary, carefully supervised tests, the preference is for mild or pleasant odors, such as oil of peppermint, oil of wintergreen, or amyl acetate. When the purpose is to provide in advance some means of giving automatic warning of dangerous accidental gas escape, the preference is for warning agents of the type that will arouse or excite the observers to immediate action, such as the foul mercaptans or the irritant acrolein.

Warning agents are generally grouped into two principal categories: (1) substances whose dominant warning property is an odor, without irritating properties except at impracticably high concentrations; and (2) substances whose dominant warning property is irritation, often accompanied by a mild degree of odor in concentrations required to give warning. Although we are here concerned chiefly with the odorous agents, some mention will be made occasionally of the irritant types in justice to the general subject of warning agents.

WARNING AGENTS FOR FUEL GASES

The most extensive survey of warning agents for fuel gases in recent decades was conducted by the U. S. Bureau of Mines and the American Gas Association during the period from 1926 to 1930. Some of the conclusions from this study are recorded here for their fundamental value to the knowledge of olfactory warning techniques.

The intensity of the odor or irritating properties was measured for 57 substances which were thought to include the most promising agents. These represent hydrocarbons, alcohols, esters, aldehydes, amines, iso-cyanides, nitro compounds, cyclic compounds of C, H, and N, miscellaneous compounds of C, H, and N, mercaptans, polysulphides, thio-ethers, thiocyanates, isothiocyanates, halogenated hydrocarbons, halogenated ketones, halogenated phenols, halogenated thio-ethers. seleno-mercaptans and seleno-ethers . . . .

The efficiency of various types of warning agents for waking and warning sleeping persons was studied for representative compounds of each type. The types and compounds used, and the minimum waking concentrations in pounds of agent per million cubic feet of air are as follows: nose and throat irritant—crotonaldehyde, 0.7 to 1.2; allyl alcohol, 0.75 to 1.2; allyl isothiocyanate, 1.5 to 2.1; lacrimator—chloracetophenone, 0.12; sternutator—capsaicin substitute, 0.0036 (no minimum determined); unpleasant odor—ethyl mercaptan, 11; pleasant odor—isoamyl acetate (banana odor), 32. Neither pleasant nor unpleasant odors were effective in waking persons unless present in very high and impractical concentrations. Eye, nose and throat irritants were effective in practical concentrations . . . .

Ethyl mercaptan was found to be the most promising warning agent of the unpleasant odor type. The field tests indicated that it would be transmitted through the lines satisfactorily after they had become saturated. It has a very distinctive odor and is noticeable in very high dilution with air. It was very effective in attracting attention and was the cause of more complaints of leaks than any other material used in field tests. It does not waken sleeping persons unless present in high and impractical concentrations . . . .

Butylene, amylene and Pintsch-gas condensate were transmitted through the distribution system very much more rapidly than the other substances tested. In general, highly odorous hydrocarbon products as those obtained from cracking petroleum or forerunnings from light oil offer possibilities for obtaining commercially practical agents for imparting a gassy type of odor . . . .

The odorizing of natural gas with ethyl mercaptan was found to be a practical means for detecting certain types of leaks and a much cheaper means than usual inspection methods. Concentrations of 7.7 to 9.3 pounds of ethyl mercaptan per million cubic feet of gas were found effective in indicating house leaks. It is thought that half that amount or even less would be ample to indicate leaks of significant magnitude. Concentrations of 31.0 to 46.5 pounds (possibly less than this amount) of ethyl mercaptan per million cubic feet of gas were found effective in indicating underground leaks in the mains and service lines under certain conditions. The use of ethyl mercaptan caused no inconvenience to customers unless leaks were present.

Odors are immediately perceptible on entering a contaminated atmosphere, but nasal fatigue and temporary impairment or loss of sense perception occurs rapidly with increase in period of exposure. In the case of practical concentrations of irritants there is a lag in the sense perception which increases with the period of exposure, possibly to an intolerable degree. Odors give immediate warning to persons entering highly poisonous or explosive atmospheres, but irritants are more satisfactory for warning persons exposed to such gases which are gradually increasing from low concentrations.[1]

Von Quaglio of Germany is credited with the first use of a warning agent in water gas sometime around 1880. He vaporized or atomized ethyl mercaptan inside the utility gas lines, but evidently his procedure did not meet with prompt success. Reitmayer suggested that the difficulty was due to the fact that the odor was confused with that of onions or garlic and therefore did not give an unmistakable warning of escaping gas.[2] European investigators have frequently stated that ethyl mercaptan is unsuitable for odorizing gas because of an odor allegedly similar to that of cooking cauliflower, cabbage, onions, or garlic. The surveys of the Bureau of Mines in this country did not confirm this belief, and the reasons for the difference might include such variables as kitchen ventilation standards, dietary habits, and olfactory attitudes.

In 1905, Strache and Reitmayer patented a process for introducing an oil-gas condensate into water gas to give it a characteristic coal-gas odor (German Patent No. 172,342). Also in Germany, acetylene has been added to blast-furance gas in order to make it safe for domestic use. In this country, Katz and Allison suggested amyl thioether, ethyl mercaptan, phenyl isocyanide, and pyridine as the most promising agents for use in fuel gases.[3]

Manufactured gases generally do not require warning agents. Blends of natural and manufactured gas sometimes have a low odor intensity and require odor fortification, as do straight natural gas, blue water gas (chiefly carbon monoxide and hydrogen), air carbureted with propane or butane, and liquid propane and butane. One method of adding an odorant to the gas line is illustrated in Fig. 1.[4]

[1] FIELDNER, SAYERS, YANT, KATZ, SHOHAN, and LEITCH, "Warning Agents for Fuel Gases," Bureau of Mines Monograph 4, 1931.
[2] *Jahrb. f. Gasbeleuchtung Wasserversorgung*, **50**, 318 (1907).
[3] *Bur. Mines Tech. Paper* 267, 1920.
[4] Cox, R. O., Developments in Natural Gas Odorization, *Gas Age*, p. 69, Oct. 5, 1944.

Holtz suggested in 1930 that a warning agent for fuel gases should have the following properties:

1. Harmless or nontoxic and non-nauseating
2. A penetrating odor similar to artificial gas
3. Noncorrosive or sufficiently inactive
4. Insoluble in water
5. Not absorbed by mains or meters
6. Burn completely without harmful or odorous products
7. Cheap and readily available

Opinions still differ concerning the type of odor most effective or desirable in fuel-gas supplies. The mercaptans and light-oil petroleum fractions are

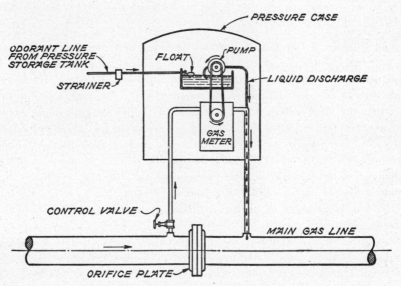

FIG. 1.—Meter-type odorizer for natural-gas line. (*Courtesy of Gas Age and Lone Star Gas Company.*)

both used for gas odorizing at the present time. Pleasant or floral odors, advocated by early investigators, have not been accepted as satisfactory odorants for fuel gases.

The prime requisite of a warning agent, and the one given major consideration by the Bureau of Mines and the American Gas Association in selecting the list of substances for study,

is ability to impart an adequate intensity of sense-affecting properties. Whether or not a substance will fulfill this requirement involves: (1) the quantity required to produce sense affection; (2) the vapor pressure of the substance, which limits the amount that can be added to the parent gas; and (3) the warning standard, or the dilution of the parent gas with air at which warning is desired.

With regard to item 3, the "warning standard," Patty and Yant reasoned as follows:

The warning properties of an explosive gas or vapor are considered adequate from a practical standpoint if the gas possesses odor intensity degree 2 (faint but readily perceptible) when present in a concentration equal to one-fifth its lower inflammable limit. A safety factor of five used in conjunction with degree 2 permits detection well in advance of a dangerous situation, and at the same time insures a much higher degree of intensity for the immediately dangerous situation. The safety factor is also designed to take care of warning persons less sensitive than the average and to help compensate for fatigue or impairment of the sense of smell.[1]

Surveys of gas leakage from underground pipe lines have disclosed that the concentration of warning agent required is generally greater than for warning of leaks into the atmospheres of rooms or buildings. It has been observed that warm weather and dry ground favor the immediate detection of underground leaks so long as sufficient warning agent has been added to overcome ground absorption. Warm weather is also more suitable for extensive surveys of leakage within buildings, as the occupants can readily move outside if dangerous or offensive gas concentrations develop within.

The Bureau of Mines found that ethyl mercaptan was highly satisfactory for leakage surveys because its odor intensity changed slowly with dilution in air. This property tends to give a fairly uniform degree of warning over a wide range of escaping gas quantities.

Table I sumarizes some of the results of warning agent studies in the field with butane-carbureted air.

WARNING AGENTS FOR LIQUEFIED GASES

Liquefied gases are marketed for many uses, including domestic and industrial fuel, where gas utilities are not available, for enriching or carbureting other gases, and for commercial and residential refrigeration. The odor intensity of butane and propane is not sufficient to warn of dangerous air concentrations from the standpoint of fire or explosion.

Odorants for liquefied or "bottled" hydrocarbon gases are similar to the petroleum fractions used for utility gas supplies. The Standard Oil Company of California markets such materials under the general trade name of "Calodorant."

It is clearly apparent that an odorant should not be more volatile than the liquefied gas, as this would result in the premature disappearance of the odorant or reduction of its odor intensity to an ineffectual level before the fuel gas is completely consumed. The odorant materials in common use are in fact less volatile than the fuel gases so charged. The process of "differential vaporization" permits the lighter fuel gases to evaporate from the

[1] *Bur. Mines Rept. Investigation* 2979, 1929.

Table I.—Field Tests on Warning Agents in Butane Carbureted Air Conducted by the Bureau of Mines*

Warning agent	Period of test in days—concentration of warning agent variable	Physiological effects of air containing warning-agent-impregnated gas
Amyl acetate (mild, pleasant odor)	7	Concentration 67 lb. per million cu. ft. gas. Diluted 1 in 1,000 or 0.067 lb. per million cu. ft. air—perceptible; diluted 1 in 500, or 0.134 lb. per million cu. ft. air—easily noticeable. Odor not striking in character.
Crotonaldehyde (nose and throat irritant)	14	Concentration 262 lb. per million cu. ft. gas. Dilution 1 in 281, or 0.93 lb. per million cu. ft. air—nasal irritation in a few seconds; 1 in 187 or 1.39 lb. per million cu. ft.—uncomfortable in one minute; 1 in 113 or 2.32 lb. per million cu. ft.—painful; intolerable in 2 to 3 min.
Ethyl mercaptan (disagreeable, repulsive odor)	26	Concentration 20.5 lb. per million cu. ft. gas. Dilution 1 in 562, or 0.036 lb. per million cu. ft. air—distinct odor; 1 in 281, or 0.072 lb. per million cu. ft.—strong and repulsive odor
Pyridine ("gassy" odor)	38	Concentration 50 lb. per million cu. ft. gas. Dilution 1 in 750, or 0.067 lb. per million cu. ft. air—definite odor; 1 in 500, or 0.10 lb. per million cu. ft.—quite distinct, though of moderate character
Butylene ("gassy" odor)	4	Concentration 818 lb. per million cu. ft. gas. Dilution 1 in 1,124, or 0.73 lb. per million cu. ft. air—detectable; 1 in 562 or 1.46 lb. per million cu. ft.—faint; 1 in 281, or 2.92 lb. per million cu. ft.—readily perceptible; and 1 in 187, or 4.38 lb. per million cu. ft.—moderate to strong
Butylene ("gassy" odor)	10	Concentration 1,072 lb. per million cu. ft. gas. Dilution 1 in 1,124 or 0.96 lb. per million cu. ft. air—detectable; 1 in 562 or 1.92 lb. per million cu. ft.—faint but distinct, minimum for warning; 1 in 300 or 3.57 lb. per million cu. ft.—faint to moderate
Pintsch-gas condensate ("gassy" odor)	6	Concentration 280 lb. per million cu. ft. gas. Dilution 1 in 750, or 0.37 lb. per million cu. ft. air—detectable, but very faint; 1 in 562, or 0.50 lb. per million cu. ft.—definite but weak; 1 in 373, or 0.75 lb. per million cu. ft.—minimum for warning

*From "Warning Agents for Fuel Gases," Fieldner, Sayers, Yant, Katz, Shohan, and Leitch, U.S. Bureau of Mines Monograph 4, 1931.

Table I —Field Tests on Warning Agents in Butane Carbureted Air Conducted by the Bureau of Mines*—*Continued*

Warning agent	Period of test in days—concentration of warning agent variable	Physiological effects of air containing warning-agent-impregnated gas
Amylene ("gassy" odor)	8	Concentration 43 lb. per million cu. ft. gas. Dilution 1 in 1,124, or 0.038 lb. per million cu. ft. air—detectable; 1 in 562, or 0.076 lb. per million cu. ft.—faint, minimum for warning; 1 in 295, or 0.146 lb. per million cu. ft. —faint to moderate
Mixed Hydrocarbons ("gassy" odor)	12	Concentration 1,350 lb. per million cu. ft. gas. Dilution 1 in 1,124, or 1.2 lb. per million cu. ft. air—a positive but very faint odor; 1 in 562, or 2.4 lb. per million cu. ft.—distinct and sufficient for warning

* From "Warning Agents for Fuel Gases," Fieldner, Sayers, Yant, Katz, Shohan, and Leitch, U.S. Bureau of Mines Monograph 4, 1931.

pressure vessel at a greater rate than the less volatile odorant, resulting in considerable variation in the odor intensity as fuel consumption progresses. To ensure satisfactory warning properties in the first units of fuel withdrawn from the cylinders, the necessary amounts of odorant of relatively low volatility are high enough to constitute wastage and nuisance in the final units of released gas, due to superfluous odorization.

Dayhuff has devised an ingenious method of regulating the rate of gas odorizing (U.S. Patent No. 2,332,617, 1943), which utilizes a solid adsorbent such as activated carbon to release the odorant into the passing gas stream within a relatively narrow range of odor concentration. Figure 2 illustrates his patented arrangement and presents data showing its superiority over the procedure of releasing the gas and odorant mixture directly into the fuel supply line. Dayhuff's curves are effectual testimony to the care required in designing warning mechanisms with full consideration of the respective properties of a warning agent and its parent gaseous or liquid hazard to health or safety.

WARNING AGENTS FOR REFRIGERANTS

Of the refrigerants now in common use, only ammonia and sulfur dioxide provide a strong warning odor or nasal irritation. Others such as the hydrocarbons of the methane series, chlorinated hydrocarbons, and chloro-fluorohydrocarbons require odorous or irritant additives to give them positive warning properties.

When refrigerants have a low order of toxicity, as the chloro-fluorohydrocarbons, the use of warning agents is usually a matter of preventing unnecessary loss of large quantities of expensive refrigerants from multiple or extensive installations.

"Where toxic gases are employed in multiple refrigeration installations, special attention should be paid to tight and durable jointing, and a warning

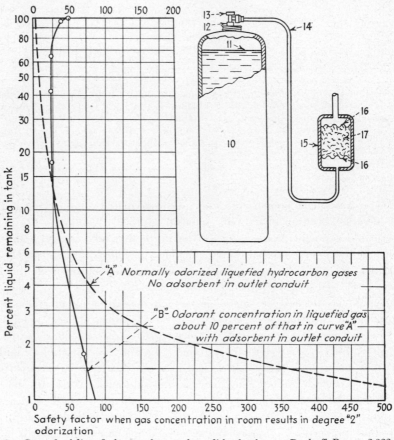

FIG. 2.—Control of liquefied gas odorants by solid adsorbents. Dayhuff Patent 2,322,617.

gas should be added to odorless toxic refrigerants (in replacing routine leakage as well as in the original installation)."[1]

Sayers, Yant, Thomas, and Berger recommended that the toxic halogen compound, methyl chloride, should contain a suitable warning agent when used as a refrigerant.[2] Investigations were promptly made, leading to the conclusion that the most suitable substance was acrolein, a warning agent of

[1] "Basic Principles of Healthful Housing," American Public Health Association, 1939.
[2] *Public Health Bull.* 185, 1929.

the irritant type. Although it polymerizes rapidly in concentrated form, it is more stable when dissolved in methyl chloride in concentrations of 1 to 4 per cent by weight. The stability of acrolein under the conditions of the refrigeration cycle is not well established, but there is some evidence that it may be necessary to replenish the acrolein in methyl chloride systems after one or more years of operation.

Schrenk, Patty, and Yant reported:

Exposure to one part of acrolein vapor in a million parts of air produces marked irritation of the eyes and nose in five minutes or less. By using this as a criterion of the amount necessary to give warning, leakage from the units would be readily detectable when the methyl chloride concentration in air was 0.04 to 0.08 percent by volume. Animal experiments have indicated that 0.05 to 0.10 percent methyl chloride in air by volume does not cause apparent harm after exposure of several hours.[1]

Such concentrations of methyl chloride are now known to be excessive for prolonged exposure.

Calcott has found that oenanthal or oenanthic aldehyde is a suitable warning agent for addition to the chloro-fluoro-hydrocarbons (U. S. Patent No. 2,283,666, 1942). It is an odorous rather than irritant agent and as such is a logical choice when the loss of refrigerant is of economic instead of toxicologic significance. In other words, the human response need not be one of immediate removal from the leakage area when the preferred objective is to reveal the location of a leak that can be repaired quickly without serious danger to the lives or health of operating and maintenance personnel. Oenanthal is recommended in concentrations ranging from 0.01 to 0.5 per cent by weight, depending on the refrigerant in which it is used and the warning effect desired.

WARNING AGENTS IN COMMERCIAL AND DOMESTIC FUMIGATION

Frequent efforts have been made in some communities to have the regulating authorities require the addition of irritant warning agents to hydrogen cyanide, which is not readily detected by some persons. Chloropicrin is the agent most commonly advocated, inasmuch as it has proved to be an effective fumigant in its own right as well as a practical warning agent used by many fumigators. However, the problems of differential vaporization, unequal rates of diffusion, and uncertain surface adsorption factors when chloropicrin is compared with hydrogen cyanide have given the opponents of the warning agent procedure several effective arguments against the legal requirement of such a practice.

It is contended, with some merit, that the cyanide would probably be gone from the fumigated space long before the chloropicrin, with the result that

[1] *Bur. Mines Rept. Investigation* 3031, 1930.

vacation of the premises would be unduly prolonged. Furthermore it is stated that adjustment of chloropicrin and hydrogen cyanide ratios to accomplish simultaneous disappearance at the earliest time of safe reoccupancy would result in inadequate warning at the beginning of the fumigation period. In view of the facts that chloropicrin is widely used in the pest-control industry and has demonstrated its usefulness as an *added* safeguard, arguments to the contrary in any community should be carefully examined for their economic as well as public-safety implications.

Cox has suggested the addition of a pungent, repulsive odor to poisonous insecticides that are available to the general public.[1] This would not necessarily remove the need for distinctive coloring agents but would instead provide an additional protection to those persons whose color perception is faulty or who may not fully realize the significance of the special coloring treatment. Notwithstanding their greater safety from the possibility of misuse, powdered insecticides with offensive odors not only would repel the careless cook, but also might drive away the prospective customer. The tendency at the present time is to odorize fly sprays and similar fluid insecticides with pleasant aromas to the end that householders will not refrain from their use. In the same spirit perhaps the powdered insecticides could be treated with warning agents of the pleasant type, relying not upon a foul odor but rather upon an unusual odor to keep the substances from becoming the ingredients of pancakes, pastries, or breads in domestic and commercial kitchens.

STENCH WARNINGS FOR MINING EMERGENCIES

The Butte and Superior Mining Company has been credited with the first experimental application of an offensive odor as a method of broadcasting alarm to underground workers. In 1918, valeric acid was placed in the intake of the air compressor at one of the mines in Butte, Mont., and the speed with which the odor reached the farthest working points in the mine was highly encouraging. Investigations were then inaugurated by the Bureau of Mines to determine whether this method of warning was practicable and reliable under the many variables encountered in mining practice. Butyl and ethyl mercaptan were finally judged to be the most effective agents, and their use in the compressed-air system was found to be feasible and economically reasonable.

Table II summarizes the comparison of several of the warning agents used in these experiments. The suggested concentrations of warning agents are relative rather than absolute, inasmuch as most mines find it desirable to establish the economic and effective quantities by experimentation. Calibration tests are conducted with observers stationed throughout the mine with synchronized watches and alert odor receptors.

Many different warning procedures were, and still are, in use to assist the

[1] *Soap Sanit. Chemicals*, **17**, 123 (June, 1941).

Table II.—QUANTITIES OF DIFFERENT STENCHES TO USE PER 1,000 CU. FT. OF FREE AIR* PER MINUTE ENTERING MINE†

Warning agent	Quantity, c.c per 1,000 c.f.m.‡	Remarks
Butyl mercaptan......	5	Gives excellent results
Ethyl mercaptan......	8	Boiling point is very low; requires care not to exceed amount indicated; must be kept hermetically sealed until ready for use
Butyric acid..........	12	May escape detection in the odors common to mines
Amyl acetate.........	16	Odor is not disagreeable
Valeric acid..........	40	May escape detection in the odors common to mines; difficult to obtain a sufficiently high concentration because of slow evaporation

* Total of ventilation air and compressed air.
† Adapted from data by Katz, Allison, and Egy, Use of Stenches as a Warning in Mines, *Bur. Mines Tech. Paper* 244, 1920.
‡ The total amount of warning agent to be used, according to this formula, should be injected into the air lines during an interval of one minute.

miners in speedy evacuation of the danger areas. Development of the stench method was the outcome of numerous shortcomings inherent in other kinds of alarm. The compressed-air supply can be interrupted or water can be substituted for air as an indication of trouble; gongs, sirens, or whistles can be installed if care is taken to locate them to the best acoustical advantage; flashing lights are useful in a thoroughly electrified mine; and telephones likewise depend upon extensive use of electrical wiring. The personal-messenger system is slow and sometimes unnecessarily heroic.

Cash and Johnson arrived at the following conclusions as a result of stench warning tests with ethyl mercaptan in the Lake Superior district mines:

All underground metal mines should provide for the use of stench warnings in case of an emergency requiring evacuation of the personnel of the mine. Other existing means of warning underground employees should be continued as supplemental to the stench warning.

Stench tests should be made at each mine during normal operating conditions on each working shift at intervals of not more than a year in order that employees may recognize the odor and retain their familiarity with it and its significance ....

New employees should be promptly familiarized with the odor of the stench in use. Care should be taken to use a diluted odor such as will be encountered in the mine and not the concentrated odor as from smelling an open bottle of the stench ....

Equipment should be installed, and provisions should be made at all metal mines for the prompt and simultaneous injection of stench in the compressed-air system and ventilating currents to give warning to all men in the mine of an emergency requiring immediate evacuation.

The choice of the proper warning agent for mining alarms is a matter of serious concern. It should be sufficiently objectionable that the miners will instinctively seek the open air but should not be nauseating in case some are temporarily trapped. It should be nontoxic in the concentrations required for effective warning and should not be lacrimatory or irritant to the eyes, lest the miners become handicapped in their escape to the surface.

The agent most widely used at present as a mine stench is ethyl mercaptan (C_2H_5SH), which has a very disagreeable odor variously reported as rotting cabbage, garlic, onions, and sewer gas. Less than 100 parts per million in air (0.01 per cent) will give a very strong odor. It is detectable in dilutions as high as 1 part per billion in air and will give adequate warning to con-

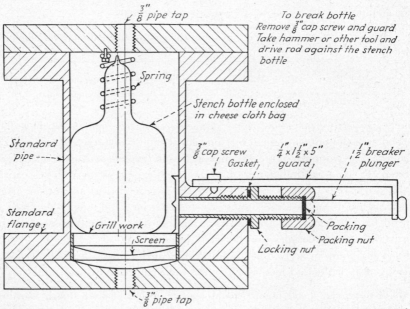

FIG. 3.—Mine warning stench-bottle container and breaker. (U.S. Bureau of Mines.)

scious persons in concentrations of 1 part in 15 million parts of air or 0.01 lb. per million cu. ft. of air.[1] Ethyl mercaptan is usually purchased in hermetically sealed glass or metal containers that may be placed directly into the injecting device (Fig. 3).

A common method of introducing a stench into the compressed-air line makes use of a liquid holder similar to a pressure sight-feed oil cup with pipe connections to the air line above and below the liquid, as illustrated in Fig. 4.

The liquid preferably should drop onto a screen of 12 to 16 mesh placed at an angle inside the air line, which tends to prevent the drops of the chemical from

[1] SAYERS, FIELDNER, YANT, LEITCH, and PEARCE, *Bur. Mines, Rept. Investigation* 3007, 1930.

being deposited on the bottom of the pipe; it also causes the liquid to volatilize readily. The screen should be cleaned after each use.[1]

It is apparent that the amount of compressed air being used at underground points will determine the interval of time between the injection of the stench and its recognition, and therefore the reliability of the odor in warning persons at every possible working face. If compressed-air-driven devices such as drills, pumps, and hoists are not in operation, the stench method of alarm must depend on leaks in the air lines. However, in many mines the air valves, pipe joints, and equipment connections usually do leak sufficiently so that a highly potent warning agent may issue its alarm within a reasonable

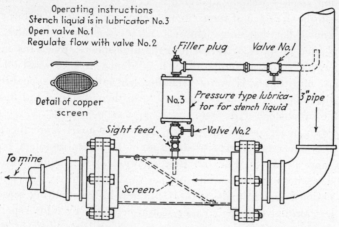

Fig. 4.—Mine warning stench-injector device. (U.S. Bureau of Mines.)

period. In some cases it may even be advantageous to provide minute air vents or bleeders at strategic points in the lines to guarantee that a rapid warning will occur at sections far removed from the mine opening.

While it is often recommended that simultaneous injections of warning agent be made at the air-compressor and ventilating-fan inlets, relatively few mines are equipped to give positive air circulation at all remote points, where the warning is most needed. Furthermore, the general ventilation currents move at necessarily low rates throughout the mine passages in comparison with the potential speed of air movement through compressed-air piping. Application of stench to the ventilation air current is therefore currently regarded as a supplement to the primary dependence on distribution by the compressed-air system.

[1] HARRINGTON, D., and J. H. EAST, JR., *Bur. Mines Information Circ.* 7246, 1943.

Chapter XXI

Odor Repellents and Odor Attractors

FUNDAMENTALLY, there is little that is new in the contemplation of odors to repel enemies or attract friends. No one will question the effectivity of the skunk's weapon of defense. Less known is the fact that some butterflies in the presence of their enemies emit a noxious odor. Equally, it is common knowledge that some animals attract their sexual mates through odors implanted in spoor or thrust into the atmosphere. When the mother of a child hangs a bag of asafetida about her infant's neck to ward off disease, she perhaps unwittingly is merely making her infant less appealing, odorously, so that fondlers are more likely to keep their distance and thus fail to transfer the organisms of disease.

Lately, with much greater frequency, and quite apart from the realm of perfumery, commercial enterprise has sought to capitalize upon both odor repellents and attractors. For the first mentioned, the actual need is well established, such as in the fending of insects, sharks, birds, and animals. It has been claimed that animals, notably bitches, in their rutting seasons may be made less attractive to their eager would-be mates by odor repellents. In the second category falls the rising practice of utilizing pleasant odors for sales appeal. When the restaurateur devises a street sign of a coffeepot and connects the spout of this sign with the discharge of steam from his coffee urns inside, he may as well enlarge his coffee counter. The seller of country-cured hams need only impart to his promotional literature the aroma of broiling ham at its best in order quickly to dispose of his wares. The northern woods hostelries seeking patronage will find a waiting line in front of their registry if the odor of pines is imprinted into the advertising leaflets.

The old-time hunter for "wild bees" and their stored "wild honey" took advantage of the aroma of honey or molasses as an attractive bait to lure the scouting bees, which after loading themselves, disclosed their "bee tree" by the direction of their flight—clearly the use of odor attraction.

Full development of the opportunities for the commercial exploitation of odor appeal and odor repulsion would in itself require a book-sized publication. Such matters somewhat closely approach a realm that carefully has been avoided in the pattern of this present publication. However, since odor repellents are more closely identified with offensive odors, the chief concern

248

of this publication, a limited presentation of odor repellents is introduced, foremostly in relation to insect pests.

It is assumed, and probably rightly so, that odors from chemicals used as repellents constitute the repulsive factor. Since no one fully may determine just what insects and other low-life forms may detect as odors, the possibility exists that properties other than odors of chemicals may serve as repellents. It follows that some effective repellents might be quite odorless, at least within the human odor spectrum. Capacity for the odor repulsion of pests is highly selective. Mere odor offensiveness by human standards is no index. One's admiration for the beauty of butterflies may be curbed by seeing a horde of some types feasting on fresh horse manure. Decomposing flesh, so enormously disturbing to humans, is one of the best baits for the attraction of flies. Daily, floral odors may be noted as highly attractive to citizens of the insect world, while the greater number of practical repellents for insects, such as the time-honored "citronella," possess a fruity or floral odor. Thus, largely on a trial-and-error basis repellents have been recognized.

THE FIELD OF NEED FOR ODOR REPELLENTS

Unfortunately, not all insects are warded off by the same fending agent. With some overlapping, it may be asserted that different agents are required for mosquitoes, flies, gnats, fleas, chiggers, jiggers, mites, and others. In fact, house flies are little responsive to any odor repellent. Whatever effective agents may be disclosed, the chief applications are as follows:

1. The protection of humans for comfort
2. The protection of humans against the transmission of disease
3. The promotion of comfort and protection against disease of livestock and other domestic animals
4. The protection of vegetation against insect invasion
5. The discouragement of insects against entry into their natural breeding places

Lest it may appear that undue emphasis is placed on insect repellents, let it be recorded that, other things being equal, preference is expressed for insecticides over insect repellents.

QUALITIES OF A GOOD INSECT REPELLENT

Disregarding some highly specific uses of insect repellents, and knowing that at the present time repellents are foremostly directed to the well-being of humans, some desirable qualities that should influence the choice of a repellent are as follows:

Effectivity against a wide variety of insects
Usability in several forms, *i.e.*, solution, powder, cream, etc.
Prolonged repellent action
Lack of deterioration on standing

Harmlessness to man and higher animals
Harmlessness to fabrics, coatings, woods, foods, etc.
Serviceability in all kinds of weather
Effectiveness in small volumes
Absence of odors offensive to humans
Inexpensiveness
Ready availability

SUPERIOR INSECT REPELLENTS

For generations citronella, as a mosquito repellent, found its way into scores of proprietary preparations and is still widely popular. Granting to citronella some virtue, as well as to dozens of other essential-oil and petroleum products, it may be asserted that, owing to military needs and investigations related thereto, some other insect repellents have been shown to be at least ten times as efficacious as these older agents. At the present time, chief reliance is placed upon indalone, dimethyl phthalate, Rutgers 612 (2–ethylhexanediol–1,3), phenylcyclohexanol, and other complex chemicals. No one of these substances or mixtures thereof provides a universal repellent. Indalone, which is alpha alpha-dimethyl-alpha'-carbobutoxydihydrogamma-pyrone in 5 per cent alcoholic solution, is credited with being twelve times more effective than citronella as ordinarily furnished.

Ethyl hexanediol is believed by some investigators to possess a wider field than some other repellents for successful application against mosquitoes, chiggers, fleas, gnats, and certain flies.

The foregoing do not preempt the field of insect repellents. Others include pyrethrum (more of an insecticide), essences of thyme and geranium, cinnamic aldehyde, phenyl salicyate, geranyl acetate. All of the foregoing are effective against biting flies. For mosquitoes a new repellent product has been developed representing a mixture of diethylene glycol-monobutyl ether acetate, diethylene glycol-monoethyl ether, ethyl alcohol, corn oil, and perfume. The investigators of the substance just mentioned specify that the familiar citronella in their experience is second in a long series of substances and mixtures examined. For chiggers, dimethyl phthalate, indalone, or Rutgers 612 provided excellent protection, with preference for the first-named. For fleas, the last-named group of substances are accorded favor. Paradichlorobenzene remains the agent of choice for the repellence of household moths. Some of the substances mentioned in this discussion are subject to patent control.

PRACTICAL CONSIDERATION OF THE USE OF REPELLENTS ABOUT THE PERSON

1. Most repellents are more effective and are of longer action when applied to clothing rather than to the skin.

2. Many effective repellents are not designed for application to the person

because of the potentialities of skin irritation. The number includes pyrethrum mixtures, kerosene-containing preparations, cinnamic aldehyde, cresol, thymol, citral, hedeoma, caprylic alcohol.

3. With or without the property of being skin irritants, some repellents may provoke a state of specific sensitivity.

4. Some repellents, such as against fleas, may be applied to bedclothing in preference to the skin.

5. In order to avoid the multiplicity of needed skin protectors, some insect repellents may be incorporated with other preparations such as protectors against excessive sunlight.

6. In the absence of a universal repellent, it may become necessary to utilize a combination of two or more agents.

7. It is unlikely that 100 per cent continuing effectivity may be expected of any repellent.

8. Some repellents applied to personal garments may be effective against some insects as long as thirty days, while others may not be efficacious for more than a few hours. For any specific preparation the maximum effective duration of action should be known.

This minor comment is augmented in presentations found in the citations below, which citations do not appear in the general bibliography.

GINSBURG, J. M.: Outdoor Protection from Mosquitoes, *J. N. Y. Entomol. Soc.*, **52**, 247 (1944).

GRANETT, P.: Studies of Mosquito Repellents, I. Test Procedure and Method of Evaluating Test Data, *J. Econ. Entomol.*, **33**, 563 (1940).

—: Studies of Mosquito Repellents, II. Relative Performance of Certain Chemicals and Commercially Available Mixtures as Mosquito Repellents, *J. Econ. Entomol.*, **33**, 566 (1940).

—: W. RUDOLFS, and G. C. FURNESS: Evaluation of Mosquito Repellents, *Chem. Inds.*, **53**, 850 (1943).

MACNAY, C. G.: Studies on Repellents for Biting Flies, *Can. Entomologist*, **71**, 38 (1939).

MADDEN, A. H., A. W. LINDQUIST, and E. F. KNIPLING: Tests of Repellents against Chiggers, *J. Econ. Entomol.*, **37**, 283 (1944).

Chapter XXII

The Making of an Odor Survey

NO UNIVERSALLY applicable pattern may be laid down for the investigation of odor problems. In the majority, no special techniques are required. A few substantial ones may tax all the ingenuity of skilled investigators. When odors arise from a dead cat killed by a passing automobile, both the source of odors and the remedy are obvious. But otherwise, if the inhabitants in the area along 25 miles of the course of a stream into which pours industrial and sanitary waste are disturbed by odors, the detection of the prime offender may constitute a major engineering enterprise.

For our purposes, let it be assumed that numerous complaints are arising from the citizenry of a residential district near a highly industrialized area. Of the industries potentially involved, there is more than one plant of the same sort of industrial activity. Some of the complaints have been made to the Public Health Department, others to the councilmen of the district chiefly involved. There is no unanimity of opinion as to the source of odor. To a mild extent the community is in an uproar. What steps shall the investigator undertake in alleviating the situation?

Proper steps are likely to arrange themselves in five categories, with some overlapping and with some simultaneity in the quest for information. These are as follows:

1. Investigation of the complaints made
2. Investigation of the physical factors involved
3. Particular investigation of the detected source
4. Determination of remedial measures and their application
5. Appraisal of possible legal procedures

Before developing these four categories, the principles set forth by Lumsden as basic guides in this type of investigation are here introduced.

1. First and foremost and above all else, *work*, and that means hard work and plenty of work.
2. Patient, painstaking, careful and thorough collection of all available facts which may have any bearing on the situation, and due consideration of every possible factor until the inoperative ones can be eliminated beyond reasonable doubt.
3. Broad-mindedness and open-mindedness in obtaining and in studying data, and, in conducting interviews to obtain data; avoidance of any tendency to lead witnesses.

4. Maintenance of a reasonably clear perspective, and refrainment from superficial surmises, from hasty half-baked conclusions and from fixed opinions or efforts to prove something which may not be so, or to marshal facts so that they may tend to support unduly a "hunch" or a preconceived hypothesis or theory before all the salient returns are in.

5. Assemblage of the data so that they will make a clear-cut, readable picture with first things first and with the foremost facts sufficiently but not unduly emphasized.

6. Common sense and honesty in the interpretation of the findings so that the facts will compel a reasonable conclusion and not be twisted, distorted, or obfuscated so as to be made to appear to support a conclusion perhaps desired but false.[1]

INVESTIGATION OF THE COMPLAINT MADE

At the outset it should be realized that emotional elements may color the situation and that exaggeration is usual. Any substantial inquiry should not be limited to any small group, such as the residents in one block. The inquiry should include numerous persons who have not made complaints. Those persons who claim that odors are present should make statements as to the constancy or intermittency of odors; the hours of the day that odors are chiefly present; the direction of the wind at the time of odor presence; the character of the odor—that is, "putrid, burnt, chemical, oily," etc., opinions as to the source of odor, if possible the precise cause; the period over which odors have been noticed—that is, days, weeks, months, etc., variations in intensities of odors, and multiplicity of odors.

From this phase of the investigation it is likely to develop that many persons have detected no offensive odors, that more than one possible source is stigmatized; that the odor is either continuous or intermittent, that the odor disturbance occurs at a fixed time, and that the level of odor intensity is or is not given to surges; but there is likely to be no consensus in the description of the odor itself. By this time the investigator is likely to have reached a conclusion as to the actuality of one or more significant odors and the extent of the area involved—that is, how far the odors travel.

INVESTIGATION OF THE PHYSICAL FACTORS INVOLVED

Within the domain of this caption, the investigator should study the terrain and note the season of the year; the temperature; the variations in wind direction; the presence of streams (with particular reference to pollution); the extent and state of vegetation; the nature of industrial activities and their distances from involved areas; the presence of dumps, burning waste piles, and kennels; the number of smokestacks; and the nature of highway, rail, and water traffic—for example, the passage of barges loaded with garbage, the truck haulage of dead animals, etc. As a part of this activity the inves-

---

[1] LUMSDEN, L. L., Epidemiological Principles, *Southern Med. J.*, **29**, 303 (1936).

tigator should seek personal experience with the odors involved, should form his own appraisal, and, if odors have not been personally encountered, should make himself readily available for calls from complainants alleging that odors are then and there present.

By this time the investigator, in the presence of a genuine odor situation, should be so oriented as to suspect one or more sources. It is common experience that more than one odor will have been recognized, but, of several, one is likely to dominate the situation. The investigator is likely to lay aside such odors as those from the smoke of passing trains. In the presence of clear-cut odors, wind direction will tend to eliminate some possible points of origin. It is manifest that, if a definite odor is present, all those suspected points downwind usually may be eliminated, although rarely it comes about that some odors may so cling to vegetation as later to be moved in any wind direction. As a result of this phase of the inquiry significance may be attached to definite types of industries or other potential offenders. Thus, if the odor be that of putrescent material, more concern will be directed to slaughterhouses, tanneries, rendering plants, fertilizer mills, stockyards, sludge banks, open sewers, food factories, canneries, etc. On the other hand, if the chief odor is "chemical" in nature, other types of operations are likely to be placed in the group of suspects. This lay term of "chemical" odor is intended to embrace such items as chlorine, sulfur dioxide, hydrogen sulfide, and other sulfur compounds. It will be found that those persons making complaints seldom are able precisely to recognize an exact chemical although the investigator may. In this situation chief concern naturally is to be directed to those plants making or using chemicals, such as paper mills, pharmaceutical manufacturers, oil refineries, and on a much lower level, such workplaces as foundries (Fig. 1).

Activity thus far should direct the investigator to limit his chief concern to one or a few operations, industrial or other—that is, for example, to one or a few refineries, rendering plants, open sewers, or dump piles. Thus narrowed, further activity should be directed to the few probable sources and eventually to the precise site of the odor creation. For our purposes let it be assumed that the offender proved to be a small abattoir operating under unsanitary conditions with uncommendable disposal of its wastes—the offensive odors there present are identified as identical with that complained of in the residential areas.

PARTICULAR INVESTIGATION OF THE DETECTED SOURCE

The choice of the example cited is made at random and is without antipathy for abattoirs. Some other example might reflect less desirable conditions, some better. Further examination should be extended to

1. The work processes involved
2. The duration of these operations
3. The methods for the disposal of solid wastes
4. The methods for disposal of liquid wastes
5. The methods for the control of gaseous and vaporous wastes
6. The determination of the exact practices leading to odors
7. Examination of the methods and maintenance of odor-controlling installations
8. Appraisal of the magnitude of the odor problem

Manifestly, the nature of the examination of the particular activity must be suited to the immediate situation. In the example selected, the approach

Fig. 1.—In some odor surveys portable comparison units may be required for odor analysis in the field. (*Florida Chemical Research, Inc.*)

focuses on waste material. In many other circumstances the inquiry will take dissimilar turns. In some, chemical analysis may be required.

THE DETERMINATION OF REMEDIAL MEASURES AND THEIR APPLICATION

The most difficult phase of the investigation is likely to arise in connection with the decision as to the remedy. Methods of abatement must be practical and economic and should be based upon an unbiased consideration for the public and for those persons responsible for the odor creation. Commonly, decisions must be made as to (1) emergency relief and (2) long-range control. The ways and means of odor elimination are set forth in another portion of this book and need not here be repeated. It is the function of the investigator to make suitable choice from these many methods and to seek for application. It is rarely sufficient merely to charge the odor producers with responsibility for the matter, leaving methods to their initiative. Technical guidance is in order. Subsequent decisions and directives are related to the following:

1. Decision as to methods of emergency abatement
2. Instruction as to emergency abatement
3. Decision as to long-range abatement procedure
4. Instruction as to long-range abatement procedure
5. The setting of time limits for the procurement of results
6. In the absence of cooperation, the institution of legal measures

INQUIRY AS TO EXISTING LEGAL PROVISIONS

The abatement of odors, like the abatement of other nuisances, should be accomplished with the least display of authority. Most odor creators gladly will accept practical, friendly, ameliorative guidance. The ostentatious waving of legal demands naturally engenders the desire to inquire into the sometimes equally available legal defenses. No less, the investigator as part of his equipment should be armed with precise knowledge of legal instruments available to him should the need arise through recalcitrancy. Better data are provided through that chapter concerned with legal aspects, but the investigator should be familiar with the extent of rights as to legal entry of premises, general local ordinances applicable to the situation, specific ordinances or regulations governing the situation, state laws or other legal provisions that may be invoked, related legal measures such as may indirectly provide relief (such as for wildlife conservation through antistream-pollution laws), and the common-law rights of a citizenry or an individual.

Throughout any odor investigation, careful and extensive records should be kept. While litigation is always undesirable, it is not always inescapable. The absence of exact and unprejudiced records often hampers the application of necessary legal controls.

While the investigation of offensive odors may be tedious and irksome, long drawn out, and attended by hostility, faithful application of painstaking methods almost unfailingly will lead to the detection of odor sources and eventually to means for their eradication should abatement be just and warranted.

Chapter XXIII

The Legal Aspects of Odor Nuisances

IN THE thinking of many persons, no one has greater right to toss an offensive odor through the window of a citizen than he has to toss the dead cat from which the odor emanated. Actually the legal situations may widely differ. For the second act ordinarily there is no justifiable defense. For the first, "the permitting of an offensive odor to disperse," there may be many and sometimes justifiable defenses. Such matters enter the realm of nuisances, private or public, of which odors are but one variety. Many villages, cities, counties, states, and their counterparts in other countries, have been clothed with some legal measures devised for the protection of the citizenry against nuisances at times, as to both prevention and abatement. At once it may be noted that political units such as cities have been, more often than any other agency, the violators of their own laws and regulations through the maintenance of open sewers, uncollected garbage, faulty sewage or garbage disposal, haulage of neglected garbage, etc. More than one city that provides laws against the transportation of dead animals by private agency offends equally or more so by its own methods of garbage haulage.

WHAT IS A NUISANCE?

For at least a hundred years, the courts, high and low, of many lands have provided legal definition of nuisances and have labeled them as torts or as misdemeanors under different circumstances. With specific direction to odors, some of these definitions become futile and introduce a laudable defense by setting forth such language as "odors injurious or detrimental to health." Since no odor, per se, is detrimental to health, these regulations may fail in their inception. Some judicial definitions now follow.

DEFINITION OF NUISANCES

The most popular definition of a nuisance is that attributed to Judge Jeremiah Smith—"a nuisance is whatever the court decides is a nuisance." Many other are more delineative, and a few are here introduced as typical.

Webster's Dictionary definition: "An offensive, annoying, unpleasant or obnoxious thing or practice, a cause or source of annoyance, especially a continuing or repeating invasion or disturbance of another's rights. But a sin-

257

gle act may be a nuisance. A nuisance affecting the public or a community in general is a public nuisance; one affecting some particular person or persons, a private nuisance; one both affecting the public and doing special individual damage, a mixed nuisance."

Washington State Board of Health definition: "A public or common nuisance shall be considered as that which is set up, maintained or continued, as to be injurious to the health, or an obstruction to the use of property by interfering with the repose, safety or life of any considerable number of persons."

Blackstone in Commentaries 5, 216: "Whatsoever unlawfully annoys or does damage to another." "Anything that worketh hurt, inconvenience or damage." In Commentaries 3, 166: "Offenses against the public order or economical regimen of the state, being either the doing of a thing to the annoyance of the king's subjects or the neglecting to do a thing which the common good requires."

Pollack: "The wrong done to a man by unlawfully disturbing him in the enjoyment of his property, or, in some cases, in the exercise of a common right." "All conditions that give rise to offense to the senses."

Common definition: "Nuisance may be defined as the use of one's property in such a way as to injure the rights of others and to inflict damages."

Utah's statutory definition (1889, 45 Sec. 1) : "Whatever is dangerous to human life, and whatever renders soil, air, water, or food impure or unwholesome, are declared to be nuisances."

Nuisances are commonly subdivided as private, public, or mixed nuisances. Various other terms appear, such as "continuing nuisances," "nuisance per se," "nuisance per accidens," "nuisance at common law" and "nuisance by legislation."

TYPICAL NUISANCES (IN GENERAL)

From the very definition it is impossible to contemplate any preemptive list of nuisances. At any time divers new acts, states, or things may be designated as nuisances. The following list embraces some of the common nuisances that have attracted attention in court or otherwise throughout or at some period during recent centuries. Inclusion on this list in no wise records the belief that any or all of the circumstances implied necessarily constitute nuisances.

> The improper maintenance, haulage, or disposal of garbage, ashes, or swill
> The condition of cesspool, privy, vault, sink drain, or plumbing
> The condition of public or private dumps
> The disposal of dead animals
> The method of haulage of dead animals, offal, hides and skins, or garbage
> The maintenance of piggeries, stables, or stockyards

Odors
Smoke
Dust
Toxic or irritating chemicals
Fume
Steam
Tanneries
Rendering plants
Fertilizer plants
Slaughterhouses
Glue factories
Soap works
Oil refineries
Fisheries
Flesh markets
Vegetable markets
Breweries and distilleries
Gasworks
Smelters
Mines
Canneries
Dehydration plants
Ice manufacture
Defective cellars
Congestion in tenements and rooming houses
Excavation
Weed growth
Obnoxious flowers
Unsanitary condition of railroad coaches, streetcars, and busses
Industrial wastes
Improper use of salt on streets and highways in icy weather
Spitting in public places
Veterinary hospitals
Maintenance or disposal of manure
Maintenance of stagnant water and marshes
Brothels
Conditions connected with the illegal sale of intoxicants
Offenses against decency

TYPICAL AND ATYPICAL ODOR NUISANCE SITUATIONS

While any or all of the industries below mentioned may be operated without offense to the point of incrimination as involving a nuisance, the greater number of court actions have been directed against such industries or activities. A few items are appended to reflect casual, bizarre circumstances that rarely have led to court procedure on the allegation of odor nuisance.

The method of storage, transport, or disposal of garbage
The transport of dead animals
The rendering of dead animals

The rendering of abattoir waste
Slaughterhouses
Stockyards
Stables
Piggeries
Dairies
Fisheries
Veterinary hospitals
Zoos and circuses
Fertilizer plants
Glue factories
Tanneries
Smelters
Petroleum plants
Burning gasworks
Industrial wastes
Gob piles of mines
Burning dumps
Certain chemical works
Food dehydration
Suture preparation
Tallowmaking
Candlemaking
Public transportation
Pesthouses
Toilets
Privies
Cesspools
Vaults

Atypical circumstances may be noted in the following:

A dead whale or other large marine animal may be washed up by the tide onto private property. In this grievously odorous circumstance, whose is the duty to remove the large offender? This occurrence is actual but not frequent along seaboard areas.

A stray horse or other animal invades the premises other than that of the owner and there dies. Whose is the responsibility to abate the odor nuisance?

In any public or private auditorium, in the midst of discord, a noisome stink bomb may be liberated. Does this act constitute the committing of an odor nuisance or is it otherwise criminal?

Certain sects and peculiar individuals of certain families, eschewing embalming, may maintain a human corpse to the point of odor offense. Within whose domain is the control?

Some persons with overdeveloped zoophilic affection may harbor in tenements, apartments, or separate residences unusual numbers of pets, to the nasal distress of the zoophobic. At what numbers may this state of affairs be expected to have legal disapproval?

The driver of a truck laden with odorous decomposing garbage loses control and the entire load is deposited in the residence of a dweller along the street. May the highly outraged dweller expect to recover for other than property and personal damage?

This type of odor problem arises through endless variations to vex attorneys and public-health officials and to tax the wisdom of courts and juries.

THE PREVENTION OF ODOR NUISANCES THROUGH ANTICIPATION

In many states existing laws relative to nuisances may not be applied until the nuisance actually exists. Expensive structures and installations may be contemplated for an offensive trade under circumstances leading to the assumption that operations will eventuate in an odor or other nuisance. Until operations begin and the nuisance is proved, many otherwise effective laws are powerless. A splendid example may be cited in the Lakes Island case (New York City). In this instance plans were made for the construction of a garbage reduction plant with a daily capacity of about 2,000 tons. An odor nuisance was anticipated, and vigorous protests were made by the residents of the vicinity and others near to the transportation routes of such garbage. The State Health Commissioner conducted a lengthy and expensive series of hearings prior to the erection and operation of the plant. The conclusion reached was to the end that a nuisance was in prospect, but until such nuisance demonstrably existed the state laws would permit of no action. These same residents, or a portion of them, instituted grand jury action on a large scale; but again it was established that the content of the law afforded no anticipatory relief. The plant was constructed, operations were begun, and the nuisance was proved. Then only was it possible for the Health Commission of the City of New York to conduct adequate hearing, which quickly eventuated in the decision that the nuisance was actual and unwarranted. Further conduct of this business was then forbidden. Bankruptcy of the company followed.

Without invading the controversy as to whether this plant might have been operated without offense, it becomes apparent that the final results might have been anicipated and that the heavy expenses of construction and litigation might have been avoided under the existence of anticipatory regulatory measures. It may be manifest that such difficulties might be obviated through other types of control such as legally effective zoning and city planning.

HISTORICAL BACKGROUND

In the Roman Empire about 300 A.D. slaughtering was carried out by "lanii" or "canufices," who were slaves and by edict were not allowed to live within the limits of the city.

In 1338 in England a decree was promulgated to the butchers of Oxford forbidding them to slaughter within that city "because several persons of note had died from the effects of foul odors."

In medieval towns, by regulation, separate and somewhat isolated streets were designated for various trades, all of which were regarded as offensive. Thus there were established "Butchers Row," "Tanners Lane," etc. The most offensive trades might not be plied within the walls of the city but were operated in designated districts beyond the walls.

In 1692 the Massachusetts Bay Colony, through its General Assembly, in its first year of activity empowered the selectmen of towns to designate the location of slaughterhouses, tallowmakers, and tanneries.

In Pennsylvania the original charters of Philadelphia, Bristol, Chester, and Lancaster extended to municipalities authority to abate nuisances.

The province of South Carolina in 1698 designated two commissioners for the control of offensive privies, slaughterhouses, and swineries but specified that such offensive states were related to the comfort of the inhabitants rather than to their health. In 1704 South Carolina promulgated regulations related to the health of the people with specific reference to garbage disposal, slaughterhouses, and maintenance of livestock in the city, forbidding the boiling of naval stores within the city and giving as the reason "the air is greatly infected and many maladies and other intolerable diseases daily happen."

About the year 1805[1] the Minister of Interior of France, having consulted an institute with reference to the significance of odors, was furnished the following recommendations:

The result, then, of our report is, 1st, That establishments for the making of catgut, dunghills, steeping of hemp, and, in general, all those in which a great mass of animal or vegetable matter is heaped up to rot or putrefy, are prejudicial to health, and that they ought to be carried on at a distance from cities, and every other habitation. 2ndly, That buildings from which disagreeable smells are emitted by the action of fire, as in the making of acids, of Prussian blue, and sal ammoniac, form a dangerous neighborhood only from want of due precaution; and that the care of administration ought to center in an enlightened and active superintendence, having for its objects the perfection of the processes employed, the management of the fire, and the maintenance of cleanliness. 3rdly, That it would become a good and wise administration to enact regulations for prohibiting in future, without previous authority, the establishment of manufactures in towns, or near dwelling-houses, the vicinity of which is necessarily dangerous or inconvenient. In this class may be comprehended the manufactories of poudrette, tan-pits, starch-manufactories, founderies, melting-houses for tallow, slaughter-houses, rag warehouses, manufactories of Prussian blue, varnish, glue, sal ammoniac, potteries, etc.

Such are the conclusions we have the honour to submit to the Class.

These conclusions have been approved of by the Institute, and transmitted to Government, with an invitation to adopt them as the basis of its decisions.

[1] GUYTON-MORVEAU and CHAPTAL, *Edinburgh Med. and Surg. J.*, **2**, 295 (1806).

Shortly thereafter various other political bodies devised enactments of similar nature, the greater number of which were directed to the control of offensive trades.

LEGAL RESPONSIBILITIES OF POLITICAL UNITS

No doubt may be entertained that political units at various levels are well empowered to institute legal procedures in the control of nuisances. More often than not authority to this end is vested by law or custom in the public-health officer (under any title). To some extent this choice is predicated upon the now outmoded assumption that odors are detrimental to health. Since the chief detriment of odors appears to be damage to or debasement of value of property, the public-health officer often finds this responsibility to be irksome and scarcely within his domain and to require the exercise of routine inspection and police power far beyond the domain of public-health maintenance at its best. Since always there is likely to be a shortage of funds and personnel for a full complement of public-health work in any community, nuisances may be extended only limited consideration in a general health program. In large cities wherein the municipal activities are broken down into many subdivisions odor control is frequently diverted to the particular agency concerned, such as the sewage-disposal department, the water-works department, etc.

Chosen almost at random for citation purposes are a number of laws applicable to nuisances in general but embracing odors. From many other sources may be located the nuisance laws of any individual state or city. *Lawton v. Steele* (1894), 152 U. S. 136, 14 S. Ct. 400, 38 L. Ed. 338:

Speaking of police power of the state, U. S. Supreme Court stated that it "is universally conceded . . . to justify the destruction or abatement, by summary proceedings of whatever may be regarded as a public nuisance."

One state may sue another or sue a corporation or individual in another state in welfare of its citizens (usually citizen of one state may not sue the other state in these cases), *e.g.*, *Georgia v. Tennessee Copper Co.* (1907), 206 U. S. 230, 27 S. Ct. 618, 51 L. Ed. 1038. U. S. Supreme Court issued injunction to restrain a manufacturing plant in one state from discharging noxious fumes to detriment of health of people of another state.

Michigan Law, 1943 Revision:

Powers of Villages

Section 1596

Council of any village shall have power to prevent and remove or abate all nuisances dangerous to life or health within the village; and may require any person, corporation or company causing such nuisance to remove or abate . . ,

Section 1597

Cellars, vaults . . . etc. shall be considered nuisances if offensive.

Section 1598

Abatement measures shall be at private expense; village may collect expenses.

Section 1599

Council of any village may assign places by ordinance for the location of offensive trades; it may forbid their exercise in certain localities; it may change or revoke such assignments.

Powers of Cities

Section 1945

City shall have power to prevent injury or annoyance from anything dangerous, offensive, or unhealthy; to prevent and abate nuisances and punish those neglecting or refusing to abate such nuisances. Specifically it shall have power to compel the owner or occupant of any grocery, tallow chandler shop, soap or candy factory, butcher shop or stall, slaughter house, stable, barn, privy, sewer or other offensive, nauseous, or unwholesome place or house, to cleanse, remove, or abate the same whenever the council shall deem it necessary for the health, comfort or convenience of the inhabitants.

Act 328, P. A. 1931
Section 534

Any person or his agent in charge of any slaughter house, yard or pen within one mile of any city or park or 30 rods of highway or street car line, who shall dispose of offal, heads, horns, hides or other portions of any dead animals in such manner as to be a nuisance shall be guilty of a misdemeanor.

Section 6523–48

Any person injured, either in his comfort or the enjoyment of his estate, by any such nuisance, may have an action on the case for the damages sustained thereby, in which action the defendants may plead the general issue, and give any special matter in evidence.

Duties and Rights of Board of Health

Chapter 35, R. S. 1846
Section 6482

Board of Health of township shall examine into all nuisances that may be injurious to health; may destroy, remove or prevent nuisances.

Section 6483

Board of Health may order to remove source of nuisance; penalty for failure not to exceed $100.00.

Section 6484

Removal by the Board shall be at private expense.

Note: In suit by property owner to restrain court order for removal or abatement, "a court of equity in determining whether it will destroy defendant's business, will consider whether the thing complained of is noxious or only disagreeable and also whether the complainant voluntarily put himself into the disagreeable neighborhood." *Balentine v. Webb* (84/38, 48).

Private Nuisances

Chapter 20, Judicature Act of 1915
Section 14493

In actions on cases for a private nuisance, when the plaintiff prevails, he shall, in addition to the usual judgment for damages and costs, also have judgment that the nuisance be abated and removed unless the judge shall certify in the minutes of such trial that abatement thereof is unnecessary.

Section 14494

Abatement if ordered to be at expense of defendant.

Section 14495

Court may order stay of warrant on application of the defendant (not over 6 months).

Washington State Law, 1941 Revision:

Section 6094

Powers and Duties of Health Officers

The county health officer . . . shall have authority to order the abatement or removal of any nuisance detrimental to the public health . . . .

Rules and Regulations of State Board of Health; State of Washington.

Book V. Sanitation, Olympia, State Printing Plant, December 15, 1936

Section 18 (re offensive trades)

No person, partnership, firm or corporation maintaining slaughter house, rendering works, depository of dead animals, glue works, tannery, wool washing establishments, paper mill, by-product coke oven, glue works, oil refinery, dairy, creamery, cheese factory, milk station or similar establishment; or engaged in manufacture of gas, chemicals, explosives, fertilizers or similar products; or in business of soap making, fish oil extraction, bone boiling or similar occupation; shall allow any noxious exhalation, odors or gases that are deleterious or detrimental to public health to accumulate.

BRIEF ABSTRACTS FROM OUTSTANDING LEGAL CASES INVOLVING ODORS

Brief excerpts are here introduced, some of general import and some directed to specific issues.

108 U. S. 317, 334:

There are many lawful and necessary occupations which, by the odors they engender, or the noise they create, are nuisances when carried on in the heart of a city, such as the slaughtering of cattle, the training of tallow, the burning of lime, and the like. Their presence near one's dwelling-house would often render it unfit for habitation. It is a wise police regulation, essential to the health and comfort of the inhabitants of a city, that they should be carried on outside of its limits. Slaughter-houses, lime-kilns, and tallow furnaces, are, therefore, generally removed from the occupied parts of a city, or located beyond its limits. No permission given to conduct such an occupation within the limits of a city would exempt the parties from liability for damages occasioned to others, however carefully they might conduct their business.

Municipalities responsible for Nuisances. *Bowman v. Humphrey*, 132 Iowa 234, 109 N. W. 714, 6 L. R. A., N. S. 1111:

Nuisance is a condition, not an act or failure to act on part of person responsible for the condition. If the wrongful condition exists, and the city charged therewith is responsible for its existence, it is liable on the resulting damages, though it has used the highest degree of care to prevent or minimize them.

Nuisance Liability of Cities, *ibid.*, 11: 322, Aug. 1940:

Generally speaking, municipalities (are) not liable for damages resulting from governmental functions, but higher courts consistently hold them liable for legal nuisances even in performances of governmental functions. They have been held liable for depreciation of land values ("taking property without due compensation"), *e.g.*, *Bowie Sewerage v. Chandler*, 138 S. W. (2nd) 285, Ft. Worth, Texas, reported April 30, 1940. Sewage dumped by municipal works into creek "emits highly offensive and unhealthful odor"; Court rules that the depreciation of rental value was the proper measure of the damage.

Reasonableness of use of property, as construed by court; Supreme Court of Massachusetts, 1932:

The defendant (Beacon Oil Co., Everett, Mass.) is engaged in a lawful business in the conduct of which it is found that odors necessarily will escape into the air; but it also appears that the defendant has adopted the most approved methods and devices to control and confine such odors at an expense of many thousands of dollars; it also is further found that such odors would not be unbearable or injurious to the health of normal persons . . . .
Whether there is a nuisance in a certain locality depends upon the attendant circumstances, including the character of the neighborhood, the acts complained of and their effect upon the comfort or health of people in general. The district where the defendant's plant is situated has for many years been increasingly devoted to manufacturing purposes; some of the plants were located there many years ago, and from some of them odors are thrown off at times which are offensive and disagreeable, but as those discharged by the defendant are not injurious to the lives or health of normal persons, it cannot be held that a nuisance exists.
It is a matter of common knowledge that in thickly settled manufacturing communities the atmosphere is inevitably impregnated with disagreeable odors and impurities. This is one of the annoyances and inconveniences which everyone in such a neighborhood must endure. Mere discomfort caused by such conditions without injury to life or health cannot be ruled as a matter of law to constitute a nuisance. Each case must depend upon its own facts and no rule can be formulated which will be applicable to all cases.

Article 9-A of the General Corporation Laws, New York State, provides in Section 200:

That any domestic or foreign corporation which shall so conduct its business without the State by the emission or discharge of dust, smoke, gas, steam, or offensive, noisome or noxious odors or fumes, so as to unreasonably injure or endanger the health or safety in this State (New York) of any considerable number of the people of this State, shall be deemed guilty of a nuisance, and the charter of such corporation if incorporated, or formed by or under any law of this State shall be deemed forfeited in the manner prescribed in this Section, or its certificate of authority to do business in this State (New York) if incorporated or formed under the laws of any other State shall be declared revoked and annulled in the manner prescribed in this Section and in either case shall not be revived except as prescribed in the next Section.

A nuisance continued is a "fresh nuisance" every day of its duration. *Conestee Mille v. City of Greenville* (1931), 160 S. C. 10, 158 S. E. 113, 75 A. L. R. 519.

Discomfort not Sufficient to Justify Damages; *State v. Smith* (1906), 42 Wash. 237, 84 P. 851, 114 A. S. R. 114, 5 L. R. A. (N. S.) 674, 7 Ann. Cas. 577. Gases, exhalations and odors from plumbing not basis for justifiable damages as requested since not a cause of disease even though they may cause discomfort.

A more nearly adequate presentation of the legal aspects of odors may be found in publications by the American Society of Civil Engineers.[1]

PRACTICAL APPRAISAL (NONLEGAL) OF PLAINTIFF'S APPROACHES TO LEGAL ODOR CONTROL

In the commonest type of legal action seeking odor elimination some division of a municipality or state brings action on complaint of one or more citizens under existing ordinances or laws. Assuming that there may be merit in the complaints, a poor showing is still likely to develop owing to the methods utilized in the prosecution. Without legal capacity, the authors here introduce some items of observed weakness.

1. Almost without exception the true facts are exaggerated almost to the point of comedy. Neighborhood witnesses extravagantly claim damage to household contents, damage to garments, destruction of paint and wallpaper, and tarnishing of silver; hens no longer lay; mild-mannered dogs become vicious; automobiles refuse to run. Even the most credulous of juries is unlikely to be favorably impressed.

2. Complainants are prone to attribute to odors actual diseases that palpably could not have derived from odors. An epidemic of measles may on occasion be laid at the door of odors as the cause through the testimony of a well-meaning lay witness duly sworn.

3. Denial of the existence of other odors in a community when in fact numerous odors are known to arise quickly engenders some plausibility of unwarranted persecution. Community organization that functions in "gang-

---

[1] Detection and Elimination of Odors, a Symposium, reprinted from *Transactions*, **89**, 339 (1926), and Odors and Their Travel Habits by Louis L. Tribus, M. Am. Soc. C. E., reprinted from *Transactions*, **85**, 378 (1922).

ing up" on one defendant to the exclusion of other known equal offenders represents just so much valid testimony on behalf of the opposing side.

4. Most regulatory acts require that the violation be fixed as for a specific date. Complainants, believing that the offense is substantially continual, may by common consent agree upon a certain date. On more than one occasion it has been possible for the defense to establish in full fact that on that date, and possibly for several days antedating, the plant was not in operation whatever, or to introduce the undisputable official weather report revealing that the wind direction throughout the violation date was just opposite to that necessary for the transport of odorous materials to the area of complaint.

5. In a competitive world one organization within the same industry as another may systematically go about the abetting of ill will against a competitor without full disclosures of evil intent. The citizens may be induced to direct their ire to a single unit of industry to the exclusion of others. This sharp practice seeking to put a competitor "out of business" readily comes to light and jeopardizes the efforts of more substantial residents to eradicate the full measure of evils that may attend community life.

6. In the hearings on nuisance evil in courtrooms charged with hysteria, exaggeration, and disaffection, better qualified official witnesses for the plaintiff too often lose their objectivity and lack of bias and become engulfed in a program of testimony illy befitting their public or professional status. On one occasion an essentially skilled professional witness testified to the presence of a highly toxic odorous gas in quantities so great that, were his statements true, he would not have survived sufficiently long to have set up his testing aparatus. It became easy indeed for the defense to establish that any such concentration of gas specified as present by the engineer would have been fatal after one minute of exposure.

Odors, when present, may in truth be discomforting and annoying; but any hysterical effort to elevate their importance to that of a scourge of the plague is vulnerable in the courtroom and defeat is the preponderant outcome.

THE DEFENSES AVAILABLE TO THE DEFENDANT

In any litigation there may arise elements concerned with the laws themselves, the jurisdiction of the court, the propriety of the complaint as drawn, etc. To no degree does the comment shortly to follow seek to invade such legal aspects. On the other hand, the engineer or public-health worker investigating an alleged odor difficulty may bring to light disclosures useful to the defendant. The authors, with some experience from observation in court or from actual investigative participation, record some observations helpful to the defendant.

1. The location of the offending source as primarily occupied by industry rather than by residences.

2. The location of the offending source in an isolated area prior to the invasion for residential purposes.

3. The continuation of operation through identical processes over long periods of time, such as twenty or thirty years.

4. The introduction of the best available methods for odor control.

5. The continuing maintenance of protective devices in a manner best suited to the elimination of odors.

6. The inevitability of temporary periods of odor production due to unanticipatable failure of machinery.

7. The uncontrollable malaction of unexpected, unusual weather conditions, such as extreme heat.

8. The inherent production of some odors characteristic of the operations involved.

9. The lack of sufficient man power in periods of labor shortage or in periods of stress for the suitable maintenance of protective mechanism and practices.

10. The essentiality of the product during unusual periods such as warfare.

11. The proximity of other plants with similar operations or other plants producing offensive odors against which no complaints have been made.

12. The contributory influence of other nuisances, such as noise, as unrecognized factors in the total state of discomfort.

13. The well-established fact that odors do not cause diseases or ill-health.

14. The fact that the odors against which complaint has been made are disturbing to only a small percentage of individuals equally exposed.

15. In some instances the economic security of fair numbers of persons employed in industries threatened with closure on account of nuisances would be jeopardized, and possibly unjustly so, through such action.

REMEDIES AT LAW AVAILABLE AGAINST NUISANCES

1. Suit at law for damages (private action)
2. Suit in equity to enjoin or abate
3. By injunction (temporary or permanent)
4. Summary abatement in certain issues
5. Revocation of license to operate
6. Failure to renew periodic license
7. Indirect legal relief (particularly in case of odors) through the invocation of other measures primarily enacted for little related purposes, such as laws for conservation of fish and other wildlife, for control of industrial wastes in relation to potability of water, laws vesting police power in humane societies, land drainage laws, etc.

As a rule a private suit by an individual or small group in connection with a public nuisance will not be accorded court sanction unless some unique aspect of damage may be demonstrated.

Throughout the total body of judicial opinions relative to odors there appears wide lack of unanimity. With intent of maintaining utter impartiality, two widely divergent court opinions are here introduced to indicate this lack of agreement under different circumstances.

Opinion by Judge Vincent M. Brennan, Jan. 20, 1942. *City of Melvindale v. Darling and Company:*

The court will find the defendant, Darling & Company (operating a rendering plant), not guilty. This being a criminal case, there is, I take it, no necessity for a formal opinion. The verdict of not guilty is a final determination of the matter, of course, and it disposes of the issues presented to this court for determination. However, the court, I think, might well informally state some of the considerations which have brought me to this decision.

This case is brought under an ordinance of the City of Melvindale enacted in 1936, in which it is set forth, in Section 2, as follows:

"A nuisance is hereby declared to be all those now such at common law, or any ill smelling place, building, or other thing which is so offensive, for any reason, as to annoy the public, or which is so offensive from any cause as to depreciate and make less in value any property belonging to any person, individual, firm or corporation, et cetera."

The People have offered some testimony to show that there is, at times, an objectionable odor which emanates from the rendering plant operated by Darling and Company. The court, however, finds that the plant does not constitute a nuisance as defined in the ordinance, and that, furthermore, the People have failed to establish beyond a reasonable doubt that it is an ill smelling place, as contemplated by the ordinance.

It is fundamental, of course, that an ordinance, under the law of the State of Michigan, must be reasonable. If an ordinance is unreasonable, it is void.

It is a matter of common knowledge that in any industrial community there are certain features with reference to noise, dust, smoke and odor which are not always pleasant, but it is elementary that people who live in a large city must put up with certain unpleasant and, at times, uncomfortable features.

It is a matter of common knowledge and of course the court will take judicial notice of the fact that Detroit has grown from a city of 205,876 at, I believe, the time of the 1890 census, to a community now comprising, with outlying environs, in the neighborhood of two million people.

It appears that the plant in question was first installed in 1894. At that time, of course, the location was not a residential one. The plant was built a considerable distance from the city limits of Detroit. Melvindale, of course, was not yet in existence. The Ford Motor Company had not been dreamed of, and most of these other establishments which have been referred to in the testimony were non-existent.

It would be a peculiar law which would provide that when a business is established in good faith, and people later,—some time later,—move to the neighborhood of that plant, they could by their presence there, plus the enactment of an ordinance, outlaw what hitherto had been a perfectly legal enterprise.

The court does not say that, under no circumstances, could a nuisance be abated if it were so violent as to require some action, but the court does hold that, under the facts of this case, considering all of the elements involved, a verdict of guilty would be wholly unjustified. In the first place, the People have failed to establish that this neighborhood, primarily, is a residential neighborhood. It is my finding that primarily it is an industrial neighborhood, and that the people who live there, built or bought or rented their homes with a view to the existing conditions, moved there with their eyes open, having in mind the drawbacks as well as the advantages of living in that particular locality. Therefore the complaining witness, and others associated with him, cannot properly be heard to complain, if the condition today is no worse than it was at the time they moved there. As a matter of fact, the court finds that the condition is much better today than it was in the earlier years, and that the Darling Company, since it took over the plant some ten or twelve years ago, has installed modern machinery which tends greatly to decrease the odors complained of.

Secondly, the court finds that the People have failed to show that there was any unnecessary odor emanating from the plant, or that the plant was improperly equipped and operated.

Third, the court finds that the People have wholly failed to establish that any odors were injurious to the health of the people in the community; and, finally, the court holds that the People have failed to show that there was any offensive odor particularly on May 2, 1941, the date which is the basis of this complaint.

In reaching my conclusions I have considered the case of *Wreford v. The People*, 14 Michigan, page 41; *People v. Windsor Ferry Company*, 187 Michigan 177; *People v. Wabash Railroad*, 197 Michigan 403, and *Waier v. Peerless Oil Company*, 265 Michigan 398, as well as *McMorrow v. Cleveland-Cliffs Iron Company*, 253 Michigan 65.

We have in the instant case the testimony of Mr. Motter, which has not been contradicted, that all reasonable and practical devices have been installed in this plant to reduce the odor to a minimum. That is corroborated by the testimony of several witnesses called by the defendants, who testified positively that the odor is much less than it was some years ago.

In the Detroit, Belle Isle, and Windsor Ferry Company case (supra), it was held that where there is testimony of practical experts that no device existed that would prevent the emission of smoke from the boilers of ferry boats, the court is required to hold an ordinance invalid and unreasonable which requires that no smoke should issue from such boat. In other words, the law, of course, may not require the impossible or the unreasonable of an enterprise such as is involved in this case, particularly having in mind the entire history of this plant, the fact that the community grew up about it, and all of the other elements involved.

In making this holding, the court has in mind the objections which have been raised, and, in a sense, it sympathizes with the complaining witness and with others who find it necessary or desirable to live near this plant; but as I said at the outset, this is merely one example of things which arise every day in modern metropolitan life.

We had another example some years ago of some very fine residential streets which were ruined for all practical purposes by the installation of street car lines on them. Streets which, up to that time, had been very quiet, became noisy, and, in a sense, unsightly; but the Supreme Court of our State held that was one of the accidents which attaches to life in a large city; that we cannot expect conditions to remain the same forever, and that we must take the bad with the good.

In our case, as I said earlier, we have not even the situation such as I referred to in the street car case. In our case, the plant was there first, and the residences came later. We have the case of one witness for the People who testified that she sold her house and bought another house after having lived in that neighborhood for several years. That is some proof, of course, that the situation is not intolerable. Some people, on the other hand, are more sensitive than others. We find that is true in every walk of life. Some judges, for instance, are more bothered by noise and disturbances than others. But we have to take the general average in a case of this kind, and we have to apply the testimony to the case considering all of its elements, and all of the surrounding circumstances. I find that while there are some people, such as the complaining witness and some of the other witnesses, who have had occasion, at times, to complain, there certainly is not enough testimony in this case to warrant a verdict of guilty, and, therefore, this court, somewhat informally, has outlined the reasons why a verdict of not guilty has been rendered.

Opinion of Unnamed Court cited by W. H. Dittoe in his monograph, How to Control Nuisances from Offensive Trades:

It is no defense to an indictment for maintaining such a nuisance, that the business, trade, or occupation which occasions it is a useful one, or that it is really a public benefit, contributing largely to the enhancement of the wealth, prosperity, or commercial importance of the community, or that it furnishes, on the whole, a convenience to the public which more than counterbalances the detriment it occasions. For if it is in reality a nuisance or operates as such on the public, no measure of necessity, usefulness, or public benefit will afford a justification for maintaining it. Nor is it any defense to show that the business is carried on in the most prudent and careful manner possible; that the most approved appliances known to science have been adopted to prevent injury. The question of care is not an element in this class of wrong; it is merely a question of results, and the fact that injurious results proceed from the business, under such circumstances, would have a tendency to show the business a nuisance, per se, rather than to operate as an excuse or defense, and the Courts would feel compelled to say that, under such circumstances, the business is intolerable, except when so far removed from residences and places of business as to be beyond the power of visiting its ill results on individuals or the public.

BIBLIOGRAPHY

Explanatory Notes

Little effort has been made to organize the bibliographic material in relation to the chapters of the text. Since many publications are general or embrace more than one aspect of olfaction, the arrangement by chapter categories is not wholly successful.

Books and larger brochures are indicated by an asterisk (*).

Some items missing from the bibliography but mentioned within the text are cited as part of the text. Appearance of names of authors within the text without citation indicates the presence of due citation within the bibliography but not necessarily in connection with the very chapter containing the authors' names, since some are mentioned in many chapters.

It has been quite impossible to gain access to original publications in hundreds of instances. This required dependence upon the method and accuracy of citation in other compilations and publications. Testing of a sizable sample revealed some errors.

This bibliography is not presented as exhaustive. The number of items might have been readily doubled. For no single chapter or topic is the compilation complete, although some are more nearly exhaustive than others.

While the scope of this publication does not include such items as perfumery, cosmetics, etc., some bibliographic inclusions have been made in order that this bibliography may possess reference data beyond the book's contents.

A. Anatomy of the Olfactory System

a. Invertebrates Other Than Insects

ABRAHAM, A., and A. WOLSKY: Olfactory Organs in Crustacea, *Z. wiss. Biol., Abt. A, Morphol. Ökol. Tiere*, **17**, 441 (1930).

BELLONCI, G.: Sui lobi olfattorii del Nephrops norvegicus, *Mem. reale accad. sci. ist. Bologna, classe sci. fis.*, 4s, **1**, 429.

CHADIMA, J.: Über die von Leydig als Geruchsorgan bezeichneten Bildungen bei den Arthropoden, *Mitt. nat. Ver. Steuermark* (1873).

DAHL, F.: Das Gehör- und Geruchsorgan der Spinnen, *Arch. mikroskop. Anat. Entwicklungsmech.*, **24**, 1 (1885).

GICKLHORN, J., and R. KELLER: Structure, Function and Innervation of Olfactory Rods in Olfactory Organs of Crustacean, *Z. wiss. Zoöl.*, **127**, 244 (1926).

GRIFFITHS, A. B.: On the Olfactory Organ of Helix, *Proc. Roy. Soc. Edinburgh*, **19**, 198 (1891).

HANSTROM, B.: The Olfactory Centers in Crustaceans, *J. Comp. Neurol.*, **37**, 221 (1924–1925).

JATTA, G.: La vera origine del nervo olfattivo nei cefalopodi, *Boll. soc. nat. Napoli*, **1**, 92 (1887).

JOHANSSON, G.: Olfactory Homologies in Limulus, *Acta zool.* (Stockholm), **14**, 1 (1933).

KRAEPELIN, K.: The Organ of Smell in Arthropods, *Am. Naturalist*, **20**, 889, 973 (1886).

LANGDON, F. E.: The Sense Organs of the Lumbricus Agricola, *J. Morphol.*, **11**, 225 (1895).

LEKNOFF: Fossettes olfactives des cephalopodes, *Bull. soc. naturalistes Moscou*, 2s, **43**, (1869).

LEYDIG, F.: Structure des organes olfactifs des invertèbres, *Arch. Anat. Physiol.* (1861).

MARCUS, K.: Über Geruchsorgane bei decapoden Krebsen aus der Gruppe der Galatheiden, *Z. wiss. Zoöl.*, **97**, 511 (1910–1911).

MOQUIN-TANDON, A.: Mémoire sur l'organe de l'odorat chez les gasteropodes terrestres et fluviatiles, *Ann. sci. nat. Zool.*, 3s, **15**, 151 (1851).

PIERON, H.: Le Sens Chimique des Limnées. *Compt. rend. assoc. franc. pour l'avance des sci.*, 3ᵐᵉ session, 1908, 603 (1909).

QUATREFAGES, A. DE: Mémoire sur la famille des Nemertiens, *Ann. sci. nat.*, 3s, **6**, 173 (1846).

SPENGEL, J. W.: Die Geruchsorgane und das Nervensystem der Mollusken, *Z. wiss. Zoöl.*, **35**, 333 (1881).

WRIGHT, R.R.: Comparison of the So-called Olfactory Organs of Cambarus pellucidus with Those of Cambarus propinquus, *Am. Naturalist*, **18**, 272 (1884).

ZERNOFF: Über das Geruchsorgan der Cephalopoden, *Bull. soc. naturalistes de Moscou*, 2s, **42**, (1869).

b. Insects

BAKER, A. C.: Sensory Structures in the Aphididae, *Can. Entomologist*, **49**, 378 (1917).

BAUNACKE, W.: Statische Sinnesorgane bei den Nepiden, *Zool. Jahrb. Anat.*, **34**, 179 (1912).

BIERBRODT, E.: Der Larvenkopf von Panorpa communis L. und seine Verwandlung, *Zool. Jahrb. Anat.*, **68**, 49 (1942).

BURMEISTER, H.: Beobachtungen über den feineren Bau des Fühlerfächers der Lamellicornier als ein mutmassliches Geruchswerkzeug, *D'Alton u. Burmeister Z.*, **1**, (1848).

FRINGS, H.: The Loci of Olfactory End-organs in Honey-bee Apis Mellifera Linn, *J. Exp. Zool.*, **97**, 123 (1944).

———:The Loci of Olfactory End-organs in the Blowfly, *J. Exp. Zool.*, **88**, 65 (1941).

HAUSER, G.: Physikalische und histologische. Untersuchungen über den Geruchsorgan der Insekten, *Z. wiss. Zoöl.*, **34**, 367 (1880).

———: Organs of Smell in Insects, *Nature*, **23**, 440 (1881).

JOSEPH, G.: Über Sitz und Bau der Geruchsorgane bei den Insekten, *Ver. deut. Naturf. Ärzte*, 174 (1877).

KUESTER: Die Fühlhörner sind Riechorgane der Insekten, *Isis*, **9**, 647 (1844).

LEYDIG, F.: Über Geruchs- und Hörorgane der Krebse und Insekten, *Arch. Anat. Physiol.*, 265 (1860).

McINDOO, N. E.: The Olfactory Organs of Diptera, *J. Comp. Neurol.*, **29**, 457 (1918).

———: The Olfactory Organs of Lepidoptera, *J. Morphol.*, **29**, 33 (1917).

———: The Olfactory Organs of a Coleopterous Larva, *J. Morphol.*, **31**, 113 (1918–1919).

MARSHALL, J.: Location of Olfactory Organs in Insects, *Trans. Roy. Entomol. Soc. London*, **83**, 49 (1935).

MOCQUERYS, E.: Note sur l'organe de l'odorat chez les insectes, *Ann. soc. ent. France*, 3s (1857).

Olfactory Structures in Insects, *Nature*, **95**, 399 (1915).

Olfactory Nerve of Insects, *Sci. American Supp.*, **76**, 315 (1913).

SERGI, G.: Richerche su alcuni organi de senso nelle antenne delle formiche, *Riv. filos. sci.*, **9**, 479 (1890).

SMITH, K. M.: Comparative Study of Certain Sense Organs in the Antennae and Palpi of Diptera, *Proc. Zool. Soc. London*, 31 (1919).

SNODGRASS, R. E.: The Morphology of Insect Organs and the Sensory Nervous System, *Smithsonian Inst. Pub.*, Misc. Collections, **77** (8), 1 (1926).

TREVIRANUS: Über das Säugen und das Geruchorgan der Insekten, *Ann. Wetterau ges.*, **1** (1809).

VOGEL, R.: Beitrag zur Kenntnis des Baues und der Wirkungsweise der Duftschuppen bei Pieriden, *Zool. Anz.*, **36**, 69 (1910).

———: Über die Innervierung und die Sinnesorgane des Schmetterlingsflügels, *Zool. Anz.*, **36**, 193 (1910).

———: Über die Innervierung der Schmetterlingsflügel und den Bau und die Verbreitung der Sinnesorgane auf denselben, *Z. wiss. Zoöl.*, **98** (1911).

———: Zur Kenntnis des feineren Baues der Geruchsorgane der Wespen und Bienen, *Z. wiss. Zoöl.*, **120**, 281 (1923).

VON FRISCH, K.: Über den Geruchsinn der Biene und seine blütenbiologische Bedeutung, *Zool. Jahrb. Anat.*, **37**, 1 (1919).

c. Vertebrates Other Than Humans

ALCOCK, N.: Histology of the Nasal Mucous Membrane of the Pig, *Anat. Record*, **4**, 123 (1910).

ALLEN, H.: On a Revision of the Ethmoid Bone in the Mammalia with Special Reference to the Description of This Bone and the Sense of Smelling in the Cheiroptera, *Bull. Mus. Comp. Zool., Harvard Coll.*, **10** (1882).

ANTHONY, R. L. F., and G. M. ILIESCO: Development of Turbinals in Nose Cavity of Carnivores, *Proc. Zool. Soc. London*, 989 (1926).

ANTON, W.: Beitrag zur Morphologie des Jacobsonschen Organs und der Nasenhöhle der Cryptobranchiaten, *Morphol. Jahrb.*, **38**, 448 (1908).

ARNOLD, G. A.: The Anterior Cranial Nerves of Pipa Americana, *Bull. Essex Inst.*, **25**, 10 (1893–1894).

ASAI, T.: Untersuchungen über die Struktur der Riechorgane bei Mustelus laevis (glatter Hai, Selachier), *Anat. Hefte*, **49**, 441 (1913).

AYERS, H.: On the Structure and Development of the Nasal Rays in Condylura Cristata, *Biol. Zentr.*, **4**, 356 (1884).

BAGLIONI, S.: Zur Kenntnis der Leistungen einiger Sinnesorgane (Gesichtssinn, Tastsinn u. Geruchssinn) und des Zentralnervensystems der Cephalopoden und Fische, *Z. Biol.*, **43**, 255 (1910).

BALLOWITZ, E.: Die Riechzellen des Fluszauges (Petromyzon fluviatilis), *Arch. mikroskop. Anat.*, **65**, 78 (1904).

———: Über den Bau des Geruchsorgans des Cyclostoma, *Sitzber. Berlin, Akad Wiss.*, 671 (1904).

BALOGH, C.: Über das Jacobsonsche Organ des Schafes, *Sitzber. Akad. Wiss. Wien.*, **42**, 449 (1860).

BANCROFT, I. R.: The Nasal Organs of Pipa Americana, *Bull. Essex Inst.*, **27** (1895).

BAUSENHARDT, D.: Nose Development in Amphibia of Choanal Processes and Passages, *Zool. Anz.*, **128**, 24 (1939).

BAWDEN, H. H.: The Nose and Jacobson's Organ, with Special Reference to Amphibia, *J. Comp. Neurol.*, **5**, 117 (1894).

BEARD, J.: The Nose and Jacobson's Organ, *Zool. Jahrb. Anat.*, **3**, 753 (1889).

———: The Nose and Jacobson's Organ, *Ber. Morphol. Stud.*, **1** (Jena, 1889).

BECCARI, N.: Il Lobo paraolfattorio nei mammiferi, *Arch. ital. anat. embriol.*, **9**, 171 (1910).

BEDFORD, E. A.: The Early History of the Olfactory Nerve in Swine, *J. Comp. Neurol.*, **19**, 390 (1904).

BELLAIRS, A.: Observations on Jacobson's Organ and Its Innervation in Vipera Berus, *J. Anat.*, **76**, 168 (1942).

BELLONCI, G.: Intorno all'apparato olfattivo e olfattivo-ottico del cerebello dei Teleostei, *Riv. Accad. Lincei*, 3s, **4** (1885).

BERLINER, K.: Entwicklung des Geruchsorgans beo Selachiern, *Arch. mikroskop. Anat.*, **60**, 386 (1902).

BERTAU, M.: Development of Olfactory Organs in Crocodile, *Z. Anat. Entwicklungsgeschichte*, **104**, 168 (1935).

BIANCHI, L.: Olfactory Nerves: Relation of Olfactory Ganglion to Olfactory and Terminal Nerves in Guinea-pig, *Arch. ital. anat. embriol.*, **29**, 187 (1931).

BLAUE, J.: Über den Bau der Nasenschleimhaut bei Amphibien und Fischen, *Zool. Anz.*, 657 (1882).

———: Untersuchungen über den Bau der Nasenschleimhaut bei Fischen und Amphibien, namentlich über Endknospen als Endapparate des Nervus olfactorius, *Arch. Anat. Physiol.*, 231 (1884).

BLEICHER, M., and E. LEGAIT: Nose Cavity and Accessory Air Spaces, Relations and Homologies in Birds, *Compt. rend. assoc. anat.*, **27**, 43 (1932).

BLIER, Z.: Nasal Mucosa: Nerve Supply, *Am. J. Physiol.*, **93**, 398 (1930).

BOGROVA, V.: Studio della conformazione e dello sviluppo dell'organo dell'olfatto nella Salamandrina perspicillata, *Arch. ital. anat. embriol.*, **10**, 339 (1911).

BORN, G.: Über die Nasenhöhlen und der Thränennasengang der Amphibien, *Morphol. Jahrb.*, **2**, 577 (1876).

———: Das Nasenhöhlen und der Thränennasengang der amnioten Wirbelthieres, *Morphol. Jahrb.*, **5**, 62 (1879).

———: Das Nasenhöhlen und der Thränennasengang der amnioten Wirbeltieres, *Morphol. Jahrb.*, **5**, 401 (1880).

———: Das Nasenhöhlen und der Thränennasengang der amnioten Wirbeltieres, *Morphol. Jahrb.*, **8**, 188 (1883).

BROMAN, I.: Om Jacobsonska organets konstruktion och funktion, *Lands. Univ. Arsskrift*, N.F. Avd. 2, **14**, 1 (1918).

BROMAN, Q.: Das Organ vomeronasale Jacobsonii ein Wassergeruchsorgan, *Anat. Hefte*, **58**, 131 (1920).

BROOKOVER, C.: The Olfactory Nerve, the Nervus Terminalis and the Preoptic Sympathetic System in Amia Calva, *J. Comp. Neurol.*, **20**, 49 (1910).

———: The Development of the Olfactory Nerve and Its Associated Ganglion in Lepidosteus, *J. Comp. Neurol.*, **24**, 113 (1914).

———, and T. S. JACKSON: The Olfactory Nerve and the Nervous Terminalis of Ameiurus, *J. Comp. Neurol.*, **21**, 237 (1911).

BROOM, R.: On the Organ of Jacobson in Monotremata, *J. Anat. Physiol.*, **30**, 70 (1895).

———: On the Organ of Jacobson in an Australian Bat (Miniopterus), *Proc. Linnean Soc. London*, 2s, **10** (1895).

———: Observations on the Organ of Jacobson in the Horse, *Proc. Linnean Soc. London* (1896).

———: A Contribution to the Comparative Anatomy of the Mammalian Organ of Jacobson, *Trans. Roy. Soc. Edinburgh*, **39**, 231 (1896–1897).

———: On the Organ of Jacobson in the Hyrax, *J. Anat. Physiol.*, **32**, N.S. **12**, 709 (1898).

———: On the Organ of Jacobson and Some Other Structures in the Nose of Caenolestes, *Proc. Zool. Soc. London*, 419 (1926).

BRUNER, H. L.: Jacobson's Organ and the Respiratory Mechanism of Amphibian, *Morphol. Jahrb.*, **48**, 157 (1914).

BURCKHARDT, R.: Untersuchungen am Gehirn und Geruchsorgan von Triton und Ichthyophis, *Z. wiss. Zoöl.*, **52**, 388 (1891).

BURR, H. S.: The Effect of the Removal of the Nasal Pits in Amblystoma Embryos., *J. Exp. Zool.*, **20**, 27 (1916).

————: Some Experiments on the Transplantation of the Olfactory Placode in Amblystoma, *J. Comp. Neurol.*, **37**, 455 (1924–1925).

BUSNITZA, T.: Olfactory Organs: Accessory Adjacent Glands in Lampreys, *Compt. rend. soc. biol.*, **106**, 994 (1931).

CHABANAUD, P.: Olfactory Organs: Morphological Relations in Fish, *Compt. rend. soc. biol.*, **185**, 1306 (1927).

————: Migration of Nasal Organ in Flat Fishes, *Compt. rend. soc. biol.*, **202**, 586 (1936).

CHARITON, F.: Beitrag zur Kenntnis der epithelialen Auskleidung des Vestibulum nasi des Menschen und der Säugetiere, *Z. Ohrenheilk.*, **49**, 143 (1905).

CHIARUGI, G.: Sur le Développement du nerf olfactif chez la Lacerta muralis, *Arch. ital. biol.*, **18**, 303 (1893).

————: Intorno all sviluppo dell nervo olfactivo nei mammiferi, *Monit. Zool. ital.*, **5** (1894).

CHRISTENSEN, K.: Components of the Nerves to the Nasal Mucosa in Cats, *Anat. Record*, **55** (4 supp.), 11 (1933).

CHRISTIO-LINDE, A.: On the Cartilago Palatina and the Organ of Jacobson in Some Mammals, *Morphol. Jahrb.*, **48**, 343 (1914).

CISOFF, A.: Beitrage zur Frage nach der Endigungweise der Geruchsnerven beim Frosch, *Arb. naturforsch. ges. zu Kasan*, **8** (1879).

COHN, F.: Zur Entwicklungsgeschichte des Geruchsorganes des Hühnchens, *Arch. mikroskop. Anat. Entwicklungsmech.*, **61**, 133 (1902).

COLASANTI, G.: Untersuchungen über die Durchschneidung des Nervus olfactorius bei Fröschen, *Arch. Anat. u. Physiol.*, 469 (1875).

COOPER, R. S.: Olfactory Organs: Development in Rana, *J. Exp. Zool.*, **93**, 415 (1943).

COUPIN, F.: Nasal Fossae: Anatomy in Aard-vark, *Arch. Mus. Hist. Nat.*, **1**, 151 (1926).

CROSBY, E. C., and T. HUMPHREY: Comparative Study of Olfactory Bulbs in Vertebrates, *Papers Mich. Acad. Sci.*, **24**, 95 (1938–1939).

———— and ————: Olfactory Formations in Mammals, Birds, and Reptiles, *J. Comp. Neurol.*, **71**, 121 (1939).

DIEULAFE, L.: Morphology and Embryology of the Nasal Fossae of Vertebrates, *Ann. Otol., Rhinol. & Laryngol.*, **15**, 1 (1906).

DISSE, J.: Über Epithelknospen in der Regio olfactoria der Säuger, *Anat. Hefte*, Abt. 1, **6**, 21 (1896).

————: Riechschleimhaut und Riechnerv bei den Wirbeltieren, *Ergeb. Anat. Entwicklungsgeschichte*, **10**, 487 (1901).

————: Riechschleimhaut und Riechnerv bei den Wirbeltieren, *Ergeb. Anat. Entwicklungsgeschichte*, **11**, 407 (1902).

DOGIEL, A. S.: Über den Bau des Geruchsorgane bei Fischen und Amphibien, *Biol. Zentr.*, **5** (1886).

————: Über den Bau des Geruchsorgane bei Ganoiden, Knochen-Fischen und Amphibien, *Arch. mikroskop. Anat. Entwicklungsmech.*, **29**, 74 (1887).

DONALDSON, H. H., and H. SHINKISHI: Age and Sex Differences in Olfactory Bulbs in Weight and Water Content of Two Races of Rat, *J. Comp. Neurol.*, **53**, 263 (1931).

DU TOIT, A. E.: The Nasal Region of the Chondrocranium of Elephantulus, *S. African J. Med. Sci.*, **7** (Biol. Supp.), 33 (1942).

DUVAL, M., and P. GARNAULT: L'organe de Jacobson des chiroptères, *Compt. rend. soc. biol.*. 10s, **2**, 478 (1895).

ECKART, H · Das Geruchsorgan einiger ceylonischer Eidechsen, *Jena. Z. Naturw.*, **58**, 271 (1922)

*Ecker, A.: "Lehre von Integument und von den Sinnesorganen. Die Anatomie des Frosches," F. Vierweg & Sohn, Braunschweig, 1864.

Exner, S.: Untersuchungen über die Riechschleimhaut des Frosches, *Sitzber. Akad. Wiss. Wien*, **63**, 44 (1871).

———: Weitere Studien über die Struktur der Riechschleimhaut bei Wirbeltieren, *Sitzber. Akad. Wiss. Wien*, 3 Abt., **65**, 7 (1872).

Felisch, G.: Beitrag zur Histologie der Schleimhäute in den Lufthöhlen des Pferdekopfes, *Arch. wiss. u. prakt. Tierheilk.*, **4** (1878).

Fischer, E.: Beiträge zur Kenntnis der Nasenhöhle und des Thränennasenganges der Amphisbaeniden, *Arch. mikroskop. Anat. Entwicklungsmech.*, **55**, 441 (1900).

Fish, P. A.: The Partial Occlusion of the Olfactory Lobe in the Canidae, *Am. Monthly Microscop. J.*, **22**, 49 (1891).

Fleissig, J.: Zur Anatomie der Nasenhöhle von Cryptobranchus japonicus, *Anat. Anz.*, **35**, 48 (1909).

Foettinger, A.: Recherches sur la structure de l'épiderme des Cyclostomes, *Bull. acad. roy. méd. Belg.*, 2s, **41**, 6 (1876).

Frets, G. P.: Beiträge zur vergleichenden Anatomie und Ontogenie der Nase der Primaten, *Morphol. Jahrb.*, **44**, 409 (1912).

———: Beiträge zur vergleichenden Anatomie und Embryologie der Nase der Primaten, *Morphol. Jahrb.*, **45**, 557 (1912–1913).

Fullarton, M. H.: Development of Olfactory Organs in Lungsfish, *Proc. Roy. Soc. Edinburgh*, **53**, 1 (1932–1933).

Ganin, M.: Jacobsonsche Organ der Vögel, *Zool. Anz.*, **13**, 285 (1890).

Garnault, P.: L'organe de Jacobson, *Comp. rend. soc. biol.*, 10s, **2**, 322 (1895).

Gaupp, E.: Anatomische untersuchungen über die Nervenversorgung der Mund- und Nasenhöhlendrüsen der Wirbelthiere, *Morphol. Jahrb.*, **14**, 436 (1888).

———: Über die angeblichen Nasenmuskeln des Frosches, *Anat. Anz.*, **12**, 23 (1896).

Gawrilenko, A.: Die Entwickelung des Geruchsorgan bei Salmo salar, *Anat. Anz.*, **36**, 411 (1910).

Gellhorn, E., I. G. Spiesman, and A. Weil: Olfactory Nerve Section as Affecting Central Nervous System, *Proc. Soc. Exp. Biol. Med.*, **36**, 643 (1937).

Genschow, J.: Nose Turbinals, Structure in Sirenians, *Z. wiss. Biol.*, *Abt. A, Morphol. Ökol. Tiere*, **28**, 402 (1934).

Geoffrey-St. Hilaire, E.: Mémoires sur la structure et les usages de l'appareil olfactif dans les poissons, *Ann. sci. nat.* (1825).

Gherardi, F.: Nose Mucosa, Vascularization, *Monit. zool. ital.* (Supp.), **48**, 118 (1938).

Grassi, Battista, and Castrouovo Grassi: Beitrag zur Kenntniss des Geruchsorgans des Hundes, *Arch. mikroskop. Anat. Entwicklungsmech.*, **34**, 385 (1889).

Grimm, O.: Über das Geruchsorgan der Störe, *Vorläuf. Mitt.*, *Göttinger Nachrichten*, 537 (1872).

———: Über die Endigung der Nervenfasern in dem Geruchsorgane bei Stören, *Arb. St. Petersburger ges Naturforsch.*, **4**, 114 (1873).

Groth, W.: Origin of Olfactory Cell Neuroblasts and Their Primary Development Up to Formation of Olfactory Nerve in Rabbit, *Z. mikroskop. anat. Forsch.*, **43**, 207 (1938).

Habu, Y.: Nose Development and Dermatophysics in Cattle, *Bull. Imp. Zootech. Exp. Sta. Chiba-Shi, Japan*, **31**, 1 (1935).

Helling, H.: Olfactory Organs of Anura, *Z. Anat. Entwicklungsgeschichte*, **108**, 587 (1938).

Herrick, C. J.: The Cerebrum and Olfactories of the Oppossum, Didelphys Virginiana, *J. Comp. Neurol.*, **2** (February, 1892).

————: On the Morphological and Physiological Classification of the Cutaneous Sense Organs of Fishes, *Am. Naturalist*, **37**, 313 (1903).

————: The Connection of the Vomero-nasal Nerve Accessory Olfactory Bulb and Amygdala in Amphibia, *J. Comp. Neurol.*, **33**, 213 (1921).

————: Olfactory Bulbs, *J. Comp. Neurol.*, **53**, 55 (1931).

HERZFIELD, P.: Über das Jacobsonsche Organ des Menschen und der Säugethiere, *Zool. Jahrb. Anat.*, **3**, 551 (1888).

HIGGINS, G. M.: The Nasal Organ in Amphibia, *Biol. Men. Univ. of Ill.*, **5**, 1 (1920).

HILDING, A.: Changes in Nose Epithelium Following Surgical Interference with Ventilation in Dog and Cat, *Arch. Otolaryngol.*, **16**, 9 (1932).

HOFER, B.: Studien über die Hautsinnesorgane der Fische, *Ber. bayer biol. Versuchsstation, München*, **1**, 115 (1907).

HOFFMANN, C. K.: On Jacobson's Organ in Reptilia, *Bronn Thierreich*, **6**.

HOLM, J. F.: Some Notes on the Early Development of the Olfactory Organ of Torpedo, *Anat. Anz.*, **10**, 206 (1894).

————: The Development of the Olfactory Organ in Teleostei, *Morphol. Jahrb.*, **21**, 621 (1894).

HOLMGREN, N.: Zur Anatomie und Histologie des Vorder- und Zwischenhirns der Knochenfische, *Acta Zool.*, 137 (1920).

HOPKINS, A. E.: Olfactory Receptors in Vertebrates, *J. Comp. Neurol.*, **41**, 253 (1926).

HOPPE, G.: Geruchsorgan von Hatteria punctata, *Z. ges. Anat., Abt.* 1, **102**, 434 (1934).

HOWES, G. B.: On the Probable Existence of a Jacobson's Organ among the Crocodilia, *Proc. Zool. Soc. London*, 148 (1891).

ILIESCO, G. M.: Morphology of Nose in Felidae, *Arch. anat. histol. embryol.*, **5**, 1 (1926).

————: Anatomical Studies of the Nasal Cavities in the Dog, *Arch. anat. histol. embryol.*, **6**, 228 (1926).

INGERSOLL, J. M.: The Nose and Its Accessory Sinuses in the American Bear, *Trans. Am. Laryngol., Rhinol., Otol. Soc.*, **11**, 361 (1906).

JACKEL, O.: Phylogenetic Origin of Nares of Nose, *Palaeontol. Z.*, **9**, 250 (1927).

JACODOWSKI, K. P.: Zur Frage nach der Endigung des Geruchsnerven bei den Knockenfischen, *Anat. Anz.*, **19**, 257 (1901).

JESERICH, M. W.: The Nuclear Pattern and Fiber Connections of Certain Noncortical Areas of the Telencephalon of the Mink, *J. Comp. Neurol.*, **83**, 173 (1945).

JUNG, L., R. TAGAND, and F. CHAVANNE: Nasal Mucosa: Innervation in Dog, *Compt. rend. soc. biol.*, **95**, 835 (1926).

*KANGRO, C.: "Über Entwicklung und Bau der Steno'schen Nasendrüse der Säugethiere," Dorpat, 1884.

————: Nose: Steno's Lateral Glands in Birds and Mammals, *Z. ges. Anat., Abt. I, Z. Anat. Entwicklungsgeschichte*, **85**, 376 (1928).

KATHARINER, L.: Die Nase der im Wasser lebenden Schlangen als Luftweg und Geruchsorgan, *Zool. Jahrb. Anat., Abt. Syst. Biol.*, **13**, 415 (1900).

KAWAGOE, I.: Entwicklungsgeschichte der Geruchsorgane von Megalobatrachus japon, *Folia Anat. Japon.*, **10**, 655 (1932).

KAWAI, I.: Nasal Mucosa: Effect of Extirpation of Superior Cervical Ganglion on Rabbit, *Okayama-Igakkai-Zasshi*, **45**, 2248 (1933).

KELLOGG, R.: Olfactory Organs in Cetacean, *Quart. Rev. Biol.*, **3**, 174 (1928).

KLEIN, E.: The Glands of the Nasal Cavity of the Guinea Pig, *Quart. J. Microscop. Sci.*, **20**, 477 (1880).

————: The Organ of Jacobson in the Rabbit, *Quart. J. Microscop. Sci.*, **21**, 98, 219, 549 (1881).

———: Contributions to the Minute Anatomy of the Nasal Mucous Membrane, and of Jacobson's Organ in the Guinea Pig, *Quart. J. Microscop. Sci.*, **21**, 98 (1881).

———: A Further Contribution to the Minute Anatomy of the Organ of Jacobson in the Guinea Pig, *Quart. J. Microscop. Sci.*, **21**, 219 (1881).

———: The Organ of Jacobson in the Dog, *Quart. J. Microscop. Sci.*, **22**, 299 (1882).

KLINKOWSTROM: Les Lobes olfactifs du Fulmaris glacialis, *Verhandl. biol. Ver. Stockholm*, **3**, 10 (1891).

KÖLLIKER, A.: Über das Geruchsorgan von Amphioxus, *Arch. Anat. u. Physiol.*, 32 (1843).

*———: "Olfactoriusfasern des Ochsen und des Schafes," Würzburg, 1854.

———: Ausbreitung der Nerven in der Geruchsschleimhaut von Plagiostomen, *Sitzber. phys.-med. ges., Würzburg*, **8**, 31 (1856–1857).

———: Beobachtungen über Olfactoriusfasern der Plagiostomen, *Sitzber. phys.-med. ges., Würzburg*, **8** (1858).

———: Über die Entwickelung des Geruchsorganes beim Menschen und beim Hühnchen, *Würzburg. med. Z.*, **1**, 425 (1860).

———: Über den Fornix longus von Forel und die Riechstralung im Gehirne des Kaninchens, *Verhandl. anat. ges., Strasburg* (May 13, 1894).

KOLMER, W.: Intra-epithelial nerve fibers of nose, *Anat. Anz.*, **67**, 148 (1929).

KORMANN, B.: Vergleichende makroskopische Untersuchungen über das Nasenloch und den Nasenvorhof der Haussäugetiere, *Arch. wiss. u. prakt. Tierheith.*, **34**, 390 (1908).

*KRAUSE, E. H. L.: "Die Regio olfactoria des Schafes," Rostock, 1878.

KREINER, G.: Olfactory nerves: topography and myeloarchitectonics of olfactory bulb of white rat, *Z. Anat. Entwicklungsgeschichte*, **102**, 232 (1933).

KUDOO, T.: Development of Olfactory Organs in Giant Salamander, *Tokyo Iji Shinshi*, 2494 (1926).

KUREPINA, M.: Nasal Choanae, Development in Amphibian, *Rev. zool. russe*, **7**, 3 (1927).

———: Development of Olfactory Organs in Amphibians, *Zool. Jahrb., Abt. Anat. Ontog. Tiere*, **54**, 1 (1931).

*KURZ, E. W. L.: "Die Verteilung und Anordnung des Gewebes in der Choanengegend bei Schaf, Hund und Katze," Dresden, 1921.

LAUBMANN, W.: Olfactory Organs: Morphogenesis of Brain of Gymnophiona, *Z. ges. Anat., Abt. I, Z. Anat. Entwicklungsgeschichte*, **84**, 597 (1927).

*LEGAL, E.: "Zur Entwickelungsgeschichte des Thränennasengangs bei Säugethieren," Breslau, 1882.

LEYDIG, F.: Zur Kenntnis der Sinnesorgane der Schlangen, *Arch. mikroskop. Anat. Entwicklungsmech.*, **8**, 317 (1872).

———: Zirbel und Jacobsonsche Organe einiger Reptilien, *Arch. mikroskop. Anat. Entwicklungsmech.*, **50**, 385 (1897).

LOEWENTHAL, N.: Contribution à l'étude du lobe olfactif des reptiles, *J. anat. physiol.*, **30**, 249 (1894).

LUBOSCH, W.: Die Entwickelung und Metamorphose des Geruchsorganes von Petromyzon und seiene Bedeutung für die vergleichende Anatomie des Geruchsorganes, *Z. Naturw.*, **40**, 95 (1905).

LUCAS, A. M.: Nasal Structure in Monkey—Path of Ciliary Current, *Am. J. Anat.*, **50**, 141 (1932).

LUNA, E.: Ricerche sperimentali sulla morfologia dell'organo dell'olfatto negli anfibi, *Arch. ital. anat. embriol.*, **14**, 609 (1915).

MACALLUM, A. B.: The Nasal Region in Eutenia, *Proc. Can. Inst.*, **1**, 390 (1884).

McCotter, R. E.: The Connection of the Vomeronasal Nerves with the Accessory Olfactory Bulb in the Opossum and Other Mammals, *Anat. Record*, **6**, 299 (1912).

———: The Vomero-nasal Apparatus in Chrysemys Punctata and Rana Catesbiana, *Anat. Record*, **13**, 51 (1917).

Madrid-Moreno, J.: Über die morphologische Bedeutung der Endknospen in der Riechschleimhaut der Knochenfische, *Biol. Centr.*, **6**, 589 (1886).

Manfredonia, M.: Localizzazione della zona presuntiva del placode olfattivo negli Discoglossus pictus, *Arch. ital. anat. embriol.*, **40**, 356 (1938).

Marchlewski, J.: Nose: Development and Blood Supply of Conchae, *Bull. intern. acad. polon. sci., Classe sci. math. nat., ser. B, Sci. Nat. (II), Zool.* (1/5), **125** (1933).

Marcus, E.: Nose: Choanae, Germ Layer Derivation, *Zool. Jahrb., Abt. Anat. Ontog. Tiere*, **52**, 405 (1930).

Marples, B. J.: Morphology and Function of Nose Glands in Birds, *Proc. Zool. Soc. London*, **1932**, 829 (1933).

Marshall, A. M.: Notes on the Development of the Olfactory Nerve and Olfactory Organ of Vertebrates, *Proc. Roy. Soc. London*, **28**, 324 (1879).

———: Morphology of the Vertebrate Olfactory Organ, *Quart. J. Microscop. Sci.*, N.S., **19**, 300 (1879).

Martuscelli, G.: L'Organo di Jacobson come organo olfattivo, *Boll. malat. orecchio*, **20**, 265 (1902).

———, and S. Letizia: Sulla fine Struttura dell'organo nell'olfatto sui mammiferi, *Arch. ital. otol.*, **35**, 191 (1924).

Matthes, E.: Olfactory Organs: Two-fold Character in Urodeles, *Z. wiss. Biol., Abt. C, Z. vergl. Physiol.*, **4**, 81 (1926).

May, R. M.: Olfactory Organ: Transplantation, Nerve Center Modification after, Anuran Embryos, *Proc. Nat. Acad. Sci. U. S.*, **13**, 372 (1927).

Meek, A.: On the Occurrence of a Jacobson's Organ with Notes on the Development of the Nasal Cavity in Crocodilus Porosus, *J. Anat. Physiol*, **27** (1893).

———: The Olfactory Organ of the Crocodile and the Homologies of the Ethmoid Region, *Proc. Phil. Soc. Univ. Durham*, **3**, 1 (1908).

Mettler, F. A.: Olfactory Bulbs: Choroid Plexus in Central Canal of Armadillo, *Anat. Record*, **51**, 251 (1931).

Milano, C.: Nasal Mucosa: Importance of Reticuloendothelial System of Mucous Membrane, *Folia med.*, **18**, 667 (1932).

Milligan, W., and J. Cameron: On the Development of Olfactory Nerve in Fishes, Birds, and Mammals, *12 Intern. Med. Congr., London* (August, 1913).

Mueller, J.: Über die Nasendrüse der Schlangen, *Arch. Anat. u. Physiol.*, **14**, 70 (1829).

Ogawa, C.: Dependence of Nasal Duct Formation on Nose, *Folia anat. Japon.*, **6**, 703 (1928).

Okajima, K.: Zur Anatomie des Geruchsorgans von Cryptobranchus, *Anat. Anz.*, **29**, 641 (1906).

O'Leary, J. L.: Olfactory Anatomy of Mouse, *J. Comp. Neurol.*, **67**, 1 (1937).

Operation of Jacobson's Organ in Vertebrates, *Ergeb. Biol.*, **16**, 262 (1939).

Owen, R.: Olfactory and Trigeminal Nerves of the Vulture, Turkey and Goose, *Proc. Zool. Soc. London*, **5**, 34 (1837).

Owsiannikow, P.: Über die feinere Structur der Lobi olfactori der Säugetiere, *Arch. Anat. u. Physiol.*, 469 (1860).

Paschutin, V.: Über den Bau der Schleimhaut der Regio olfactoria des Frosches, *Ber. Verhandl. K. sächs. ges. wiss., Leipzig, math.-phys. Klasse*, **25**, 257 (1873).

PEKAR, J.: Nasal Nerve Endings in Rat's Snout, *Bratislavské Lekárske Listy*, **9**, 190 (1929).

PERESLAWCEWA, S. M.: Über die Structur und die Form des Geruchsorgans bei den Fischen, *Arb. St. Petersburger ges. Naturforsch*, **9**, 39 (1878).

*PEREYASLAWZEFF, S.: "Vorläufige Mitteilungen über die Nase der Fische," Zurich, 1876.

PÉREZ, A. P. R.: Division of Oligodendrocytes in Olfactory Bulb of Cat and Dog, *Arch. neurobiol.*, **13**, 987 (1933).

PETER, K.: Mitteilung zur Entwicklungsgeschichte der Eidechse. I, Das Wachstum des Riechgrübchens, *Arch. mikroskop. Anat. Entwicklungsmech.*, **55**, 585 (1900).

———: Die Entwicklung der Nasenmuscheln bei Mensch und Säugetieren, *Arch. mikroskop. Anat. Entwicklungsmech.*, **79**, 427 (1912).

PINKUS, F.: Über den zwischen Olfactorius- und Opticusursprung des Vorderhirn verlassenden Hirnnerven der Dipnoer und Selachier, *Arch. Physiol.* (Supp.), 447 (1905).

PINUS, A.: Development of Nasal Region in Fetal Elk, *Z. wiss. Biol., Abt. A. Z. Morph. Ökol. Tiere*, **13**, 36 (1928).

POGOJEFF, L.: Über die feinere Struktur des Geruchsorganes des Neunauges, *Arch. mikroskop. Anat.*, **31**, 1 (1888).

PORFIDIA, G.: Nuove recerche istologiche e sperimentali sull'organo di Jacobson dei mammiferi, *Boll. malat. orecchio*, **22**, 1 (1904).

PREOBRASCHENSKY, S.: Beiträge zur Lehre über die Entwicklung des Geruchsorgans beim Hühn, *Mitt. embryol. Inst., Wien*, **5**, (1892).

PUJIULA, J.: Olfactory Neuro-epithelium, in Rat Fetus, *Bol. Soc. iberica cien. nat.*, **26**, 104 (1927).

PUTELLI: Über das Verhalten der Zellen der Riechshleimhaut bei Hühnerembryonen, *Wien. Med. Jahrb.*, 183 (1888).

RAMON Y CAJAL S., Y PEDRO: Estructura dei bulbo olfactorio de las aves, *Gacet. sanit. de Barcelona*, Sept. 10, 1890.

RAUGE, P.: Anatomie macroscopique de l'organe de Jacobson chez le boeuf et chez le mouton, *Arch. intern. laryngol.*, **6**, 206 (1893).

*REIFFSTECK, J. A.: "Dissertatio inauguralis sistens disquisitiones anatomicas de structura organi olfactus mammalium nonnullorum . . .," litteris Ludovici Friedrich Fues, Tubingum (1823).

RETZIUS, G.: Das Riechepithel der Cyclostomen, *Arch. Anat. u. Physiol., Anat., Abt.*, **9** (1880).

———: Die sensiblen Nervenendigungen in der Haut des Petromyzon, *Biol. Untersuch.* N.F., **3**, 37 (1892).

———: Die Riechzellen der Ophidier in der Riechschleimhaut und im Jacobsonschen Organ, *Biol. Untersuch.*, N.F., **6**, 48 (1894).

RICCI, B.: Nasal Mucosa: Histologic Research on Changes Produced by Cervical Sympathectomy on Mucosa in Normal Animals Subjected to Vital Staining, *Boll. malat. orecchio*, **51**, 161 (1933).

ROSE, C.: Über das Jacobsonsche Organ von Wombat und Oppossum, *Anat. Anz.*, **8**, 766 (1893).

ROSE, M.: Summary of Previous Conclusions Dividing Mammalian Cortex, *Bull. intern. acad. polon. sci., Classe sci. math. nat. s. B, Sci. nat. II, Zool.*, 201 (1931).

*ROSENTHAL, F.: "De organo olfactus quorumdam animalium," Jena, 1802.

SCHUCH, K.: Olfactory Organs: Structure, Development, Glands and Adaptation, Urodele, *Zool. Jahrb., Abt. Anat. Ontog.*, **59**, 69 (1934).

SCHÜLLER, H.: Olfactory Organs—Development in Birds, *Z. Anat. Entwicklungsgeschichte*, **109**, 75 (1939).

SCHULTZ, A. H.: The Nasal Cartilages in Higher Primates, *Am. J. Phys. Anthropol.*, **20**, 205 (1935).

SEKI, M.: Increase of Histiocytes in Wall Opposite Nasal Cavity Following Unilateral Obstruction; Experiments on Rats, *Z. Zellforsch. u. mikroskop. Anat.*, **31**, 224 (1941).

————: Vital Staining of Olfactory Epithelium of Mouse with Trypan Blue, *Z. Zellforsch. u. mikroskop. Anat.*, **31**, 218 (1941).

SEYDEL, O.: Über die Nasenhöhle und das Jacobsonsche Organ der Amphibien, *Morphol. Jahrb.*, **23**, 453 (1895).

————: Über Entwickelungsvorgänge an der Nasenhöhle und am Mundhöhlendache von Echidna nebst Beiträgen zur Morphologie des peripheren Geruchsorgans und des Gaumens der Wirbeltiere, *Denkschrift med. naturw. ges. Jena*, **6**, 403 (1900).

SHELDON, R. E.: The Participation of Medullated Fibers in the Innervation of the Olfactory Mucous Membrane of Fishes, *Science*, **27**, 915 (1908).

————: An Analysis of the Olfactory Paths and Centers in Fishes, *Anat. Record*, 108 (1908–1909).

SIMONETTA, B.: Origine e sviluppo del nervo terminale nei mammiferi; sua funzione e suoi rapporti con l'organo di Jacobson, *Z. Anat. Entwickelungsgeschichte*, **97**, 425 (1932).

————: Olfactory Nerves: Research on Origin and Development in Birds, *Arch. ital. anat. embriol.*, **31**, 396 (1933).

SITZEN, A. E.: Size of Nasal Frontal Sinus as Related to Form in Human Races and in Anthropoids, *Anth. Anz.*, **7**, 208 (1931).

SLOTWINSKI, J.: Character of Secretion of Bowman's Olfactory Glands in Mammals, *Compt. rend. soc. biol.*, **108**, 599 (1931).

————: Granulation of Sensorial Epithelium of Olfactory Mucosa in Mammals, *Compt. rend. soc. biol.*, **120**, 459 (1935).

————: Internal Reticular Apparatus (Golgi-Kopsch) in Bowman's Olfactory Glands in Mammals, *Compt. rend. soc. biol.*, **120**, 462 (1935).

SLUITER, C. P.: Das Jacobsonsche Organ von Crocodilus porosus, *Anat. Anz.*, **7**, 540 (1892).

SMITH, C. G.: Olfactory Bulbs and Accessory Bulbs, Volume, Age Changes in Rat, *J. Comp. Neurol.*, **61**, 477 (1935).

SMITH, G. E.: Jacobson's Organ and the Olfactory Bulb in Ornithorhynchus, *Anat. Anz.*, **11**, (1896).

SMITH, L. A.: Relation of Smell Acuity to Nerve Cell in Olfactory Bulbs of Rats, *J. Comp. Neurol.*, **45**, 483 (1928).

SOCHAZEWER, D.: Das Riechorgan der Landpulmonaten, *Z. wiss. Zoöl.*, **34**, 30 (1880).

*SOLGER, B.: "Notiz über die Nebenhöhle des Geruchsorgans von Gasterosteus aculeatus," 1892.

SPADARO, R.: Olfactory Mucosa in Vertebrates, *Arch. ital. otol.*, **37**, 316 (1926).

STREET, S. F.: Nose: Differentiation in Chick Embryo, *J. Exp. Zool.*, **77**, 49 (1937).

STRONG, R. M.: Further Observations on the Olfactory Organs of Birds, *Science*, **37**, 265 (1913).

SYMINGTON, J.: On the Nose, the Organ of Jacobson, and the Dumbbell Shaped Bone in Ornithorhynchus, *Proc. Zool. Soc. London*, 575 (1891).

————: On the Organ of Jacobson in the Kangaroo and Rock Wallaby, *J. Anat. Physiol.*, **26**, 371 (1891–1892).

TELLO, J. F.: Entrance of Olfactory Fibers into Mammillary Body, *Jahrb. Morphol. mikroskop. Anat.*, Abt. II, **36**, 622 (1934).

TORSEGNO, M. E.: Mast Cells in Olfactory Bulb of Newborn Dog, *Trav. lab. recherches biol. univ. Madrid*, **30**, 355 (1935).

TRAHMS, O.: Differences in olfactory organs in races of Pipa, *Z. Anat. Entwicklungs-geschichte,* **105,** 678 (1936).

VALETTE, M.: Olfactory Organs: Vascularity, in Rabbit, Guinea Pig and Rat, *Arch. anat. hist. embryol.,* **13,** 281 (1931).

VAN CAMPENHOUT, E.: Olfactory Cells of Schwann, *Trans. Roy. Soc. Can.,* **27,** 101 (1933).
——: Origin of Olfactory Nerves in Swine, *Arch. anat. mikroskop.,* **32,** 391 (1936).

VAN GEHUCHTEN, A.: Contribution a l'étude de la muqueuse olfactive chez les mammifères, *La Cellule,* **6,** 393 (1890).

—— and I. MARTIN: Le Bulbe olfactif chez quelques mammifères, *La Cellule,* **7,** 203 (1891).

VAN RYSSELBERGE, L.: Organ of Jacobson, *Rec. Inst. Zool. Torley-Rousseau,* **3,** 105 (1931).

VAN WIJHE, J. W.: Über die Kopfsegmente und die Phylogenie des Geruchsorganes der Wirbelthiere, *Zool. Anz.,* **9** (1886).

*VERHOEVEN, M. G. T.: "De organo oboratus per animalium vertebratorum classes," Ludg., 1826.

VILLIERS, C. G. S.: Olfactory Organs: Nasal Capsule in Three Anuran Genera, *S. African J. Sci.,* **27,** 48 (1930).

VIRCHOW, H.: Die Nasenknorpel des Schimpanse, *Z. Ethnol.,* **46,** 478, 673 (1914).

VON BRUNN, A.: Die Endigung der Olfactoriusfasern in Jacobsonsche Organe des Schafes, *Arch. mikroskop. Anat. Entwicklungsmech.,* **39,** 651 (1892).

VON LENHOSSEK, M.: Die Nerven-ursprünge und Endigungen im Jacobsonschen Organ des Kaninchens, *Anat. Anz.,* **7,** 628 (1892).

VON MIHALKOVICS, V.: Nasenhöhle und Jacobsonsches Organ, *Anat. Hefte,* **11,** 1 (1898).

WALDSCHMIDT, J.: Beitrag zur Anatomie des Zentralnervensystems und des Geruchsorgans von Polypter bichir, *Anat. Anz.,* **2,** 308 (1887).

WATENABE, M.: Development of Olfactory Organs in Embryonic to Adult Anuran, *Z. Anat. Entwicklungsgeschichte,* **105,** 519 (1936).

WEISS, R.: Studien an den Bowmanschen Drüsen des Frosches, *Arch. ges. Physiol.,* **130,** 507 (1909).

WIEDERSHEIM, R.: Über rudimentäre Fischnasen, *Anat. Anz.,* **2,** 652 (1887).

WINKLER, C.: On the Olfactory Tract in the Rabbit, *Le Nevraxe,* **14,** 57 (1913).

WOOD-JONES, F.: Olfactory Organs of Diomedea Cauta, *Emu,* **37,** 128 (1937).

WRIGHT, R. R.: On the Nervous System and Sense-Organs of Amiurus, *Proc. Can. Inst.,* **2,** 373 (1884).
——: On the Organ of Jacobson in Ophidia, *Zool. Anz.,* **6,** 144 (1883).

YOFFEY, J. M., and C. K. DRINKER: Nasal Mucosa: Lymphatics in Cat and Monkey, *J. Anat.,* **74,** 45 (1939).

YOUNG, M. W.: Olfactory Nerve: Nuclear Pattern and Fiber Connection of Non-cortical Centers of Telencephalon of Rabbit, *J. Comp. Neurol.,* **65,** 295 (1936).

ZAVADSKY: Circonvolution piriforme et odorat du chien, *Arch. russes sci. biol.,* **15,** 3 (1910).

*ZUCKERKANDL, E: "Das periphere Geruchsorgan der Säugethiere; eine vergleichend-anatomische, Studie," Stuttgart, 1887.

ZWILLING, E.: Development of Olfactory Organs in Anurans, *J. Exp. Zool.,* **84,** 291 (1941).
——: Induction of the Olfactory Placode by the Forebrain in Rana Pipiens, *Proc. Soc. Exp. Biol. Med.,* **31,** 933 (1934).

d. Humans

ALVERDES, K.: Nose Vestibule, Apocrine Glands, Structure and Postnatal Development in Man, *Jahrb. Morphol. mikroskop. Anat.,* Abt. II, **28,** 609 (1932).

ANTON, W.: Beiträge zur Kenntnis des Jacobsonschen Organes bei Erwachsenen, *Z. Heilk.*, **16**, 355 (1895).

———: Über ein transitorisches Faltensystem im Salcus nasalis posterior und im rückwärtigsten Teil des Nasenbodens nebst Beiträgen zur Histologie des weichen Gaumens, *Arch. Laryngol Rhinol.*, **28**, 83 (1913).

BARKER, L. F.: The Sense Areas and Association Centers in the Brain as Described by Flechsig, *J. Nervous Mental Disease*, **24**, 325 (1897).

BASLER, A.: Nose: Form in Chinese, Ancient and Modern, *Z. Morphol. Anthropol.*, **30**, 559 (1932).

BECCARI, N.: Le Strie olfattorie nel Cervello dell'uomo, *Monit. zool. ital.*, **22**, 255 (1911).

BERTELLI, D.: Nomenclature of the Human Nose, *Monit. zool. ital.*, **23**, 313 (1912).

BIGLER, M.: Fetal Nose—histology, *Schweiz. med. Wochschr.*, **64**, 438 (1934).

*BOGUSZEWSKA-JANICKA, H.: "Beiträge zur Histologie der Nasenschleimhaut bei menschlichen Embryonen," Bern, 1910.

BORNSTEIN, W. S.: Cortical Representation of Taste in Man and Monkey; Functional and Anatomic Relations of Taste, Olfaction and Somatic Sensibility, *Yale J. Biol. Med.*, **12**, 719 (1940).

BOVIER-LAPIERRE, E.: De la Vascularité de l'epithélium olfactif, *Comp. rend. soc. biol.*, **6**, 833 (1888).

BRAISLIN, W. C.: Ethnological Characteristics of the Human Nasal Canals, *Science*, **21**, 169 (1893).

BRAUNE, W., and F. E. CLASEN: Die Nebenhöhlen der menschlichen Nase in ihrer Bedeutung fur den Mechanismus des Riechens, *Z. Anat. Entwickelungsgeschichte*, **2**, 1 (1876).

BRIGGS, H. H.: Nose and Human Evolution, *Ann. Otol., Rhinol. & Laryngol.*, **37**, 1110 (1928).

BROOKOVER, C.: Some Points in the Development of the Nose and Olfaction, *Trans. Am. Microscop. Soc.*, **34**, 7 (1915).

BRUBAKER, A. F.: The Innervation of the Nasal Chambers, and Effect upon Olfaction, *Ann. Otol., Rhinol. & Laryngol.*, **25**, 606 (1916).

———: The Vaso-motor and Secretomotor Nerve Mechanism of the Nasal Chambers; a Consideration of the Anatomy and Physiology of the Olfactory Nerve, *Laryngoscope*, **27**, 207 (1917).

CABEZAS, J., H. VACCARO, and A. GONZALES: Nasal and Paranasal Mucosas—Lysozyme, *Rev. Otorinolaring*, **4**, 37 (1944).

CHIGI, C.: Nasal Mucosa: Connective Tissue in Man, *Arch. ital. anat. embryol.*, **29**, 256 (1931).

*COWDREY, E. V. (ed.): "Nasal Mucosa: Cytology. Special Cytology," 2 vols., Paul B. Hoeber, New York, 1928.

*CUNNINGHAM, D. J.: "Textbook of Human Anatomy," 8th ed., Oxford University Press, New York, 1943.

DAVENPORT, C. B.: Nose—Post-natal Development, *Proc. Am. Phil. Soc.*, **80**, 175 (1939).

DEPREE, S. B.: Noses—Olfactory Organs of Man, *Med. Press & Circ.*, N.S. **116**, 95 (1923).

DONALDSON, H. H.: Anatomical Observations on the Brain and Several Sense Organs of the Blind Deaf-mute Laura D. Bridgman, *Am. J. Psychol.*, **3**, 293 (1890); **4**, 248 (1891).

ECKER, A.: Über die Geruchschleimhaut des Menschen, *Z. wiss Zool.*, **8**, 303 (1857).

*EDINGER, L.: "Vorlesungen über den Bau der nervosen Zentralorgane des Menschen und der Tierre Vol I, Das Zentralnervensystem, des Menschen und der Säugetiere," F. C. W. Vogel, Leipzig, 1908, 1911.

FORSTER, H.: Zur Frage nach der Bildung der äusseren Nase beim Menschen. *Arch. Anat. u. Physiol.*, **2**, 163 (1917).

GARBINI, A.: Evoluzione del senso olfattivo nella infanzia. *Arch. Anthropol.*, **26**, 239 (1896).

GEGENBAUR, C.: Über die Nasenmuskeln der Vögel., *Jena. Z. Naturw.*, **7** (1873).

————: Über das Rudiment einer septalen Nasendrüse beim Menschen, *Morphol. Jahrb.*, **11**, 486 (1886).

GHIGI, C.: Relation of Age to Hypertrophy and Hyperplasia of Connective Tissue Fibers in Nose, *Boll. soc. ital. biol. sper.*, **6**, 155 (1931).

GODDALL, T. B.: The Naso-Palatine Apertures, Jacobson's Organ and Stenson's Canal in the Nose, *Vet. J. London*, **68**, 130 (1912).

GOLDSTEIN, K., and W. RIESE: Klinische und anatomische Beobachtungen in einem vierjährigen Riechhirnlosen Kinde, *J. Psychol. u. Neurol.*, **32**, 291 (1926).

GOLLING, J.: Anthropologische Untersuchung über das Nasenskelett des Menschen, *Z. Morphol. Anthropol.*, **17**, 1 (1914).

GRÜNWALD, L.: Der Seitenraum der Nase, dargestellt auf Grund der Entwicklung und der Vergleiche, *Arch. Laryngol. Rhinol.*, **23**, 561 (1920).

*HAECKEL, E.: "Origin and Development of Sense Organs in Evolution of Man," *Evolution of Man*, **2**, 329.

HAIKE, H.: Die Röntgenuntersuchung der Nasennebenhöhlen der Kinder und ihre Ergebnisse für Entwicklungsgeschichte, *Arch. Laryngol. Rhinol.*, **23**, 206 (1910).

HENCKEL, K. O., and J. DALBORGO: Algunas Observaciones sobre el esqueleto de la nariz, *Rev. sudamericana morfol.*, **1**, 63 (1943).

HIS, W.: Die Formentwickelung des menschlichen Vorderhirns; Das primäre Verhalten des Riechnerven. Das Riechganglion und seine Entstehung, *Abhandl. math-phys. Klasse sächs. akad. Wiss (Leipzig)*, **15**, 717 (1889).

HOLLENDER, A. R.: Histopathology of Nasal Mucosa of Older Persons, *Arch. Otolaryngol.*, **40**, 92 (1944).

HOYER: Über die mikroskopischen Verhältnisse der Nasenschleimhaut verschiedener Thiere und des Menschen, *Arch. Anat. u. Physiol.*, **50** (1860).

HUMPHREY, T.: Olfactory and Accessory Olfactory Formations, *J. Comp. Neurol.*, **73**, 431 (1940).

————, and E. C. CROSBY: The Human Olfactory Bulb, *Univ. Mich. Hosp. Bull.*, **4**, 61 (1938).

INGERSOLL, J. M.: The Nose and Naso-pharynx in Infants and Young Children, *Trans. Am. Laryngol. Assoc.*, **31**, 38 (1909).

JACKSON, C. M., and C. E. CONNOR: A Wax Model of the Nasal Cavity and Paranasal Sinuses, *Ann. Otol., Rhinol. & Laryngol.*, **26**, 585 (1917).

JARVIS, D. C.: Nerve Type Indicated by Color of Mucous Membrane, *Arch. Otolaryngol.*, **21**, 131 (1935).

KADANOFF, D.: Nasal Mucosa: Nerve Supply, *Z. wiss. Biol.*, **6**, 337, 342 (1937).

KILLIAN, G.: Zur Anatomie der Nase menschlicher Embryonen, *Arch. Laryngol. Rhinol.*, **2**, 234 (1895).

*KÖLLIKER, A.: "Über des Jacobsonschen Organe des Menschen." Festschrift zur Franz von Rinecker, Engelmann, Leipzig, 1877.

————: Der Lobus olfactorius und die Nervi olfactorii bei jungen menschlichen Embryonen, *Sitzber. phys.-med. ges.*, Würzburg (1882).

*————: "Zur Entwicklung des Auges und Geruchsorganes menschlichen Embryonen." Festschr. d. Schweiz. Univ. Zurich zur Feier ihres 50 jähr. Jubiläums, Stahel, Würzburg, 1883.

KOLMER, W.: Olfactory Organs: Microscopic Anatomy, *Handbuch mikroskop. Anat.*, **2**, 192 (1929).

*KRAFKA, J.: "Human Embryology," Paul B. Hoeber, New York, 1942.

KUBO, I.: Zur Frage des normalen Zustandes der unteren Nasenmuscheln des Menschen, *Arch. Laryngol. Rhinol.*, **19**, 191 (1906–1907).

KYLE, J. J.: Some Observations upon the Cribriform Plate and Olfactory Nerve in Man and Certain Animals, *Laryngoscope*, **21**, 1131 (1911).

LAIRD, D. A.: Length of Your Nose, *Sci. American*, **151**, 30 (1934).

LEBOUCQ, H.: Le Canal naso-palatin chez l'homme, *Arch. biol.*, **2** (1881).

LUSCHKA: Das Epithelium der Riechschleimhaut des Menschen, *Med. Zentr.*, 337 (1864).

MANGAKIS, K.: Ein Fall von Jacobsonschen Organ beim Erwachsenen, *Anat. Anz.*, **21**, 106 (1902).

MARRO, G.: Sur la Division de l'os propre du nez., *Compt. rend. congr. intern., anthropol. crim.*, **6**, 534 (1906).

*MERKEL, F. S.: "Über das Jacobsonschen Organ des Menschen und die Papilla palatina," Festschrift zum fünfzig Jahrigen medizinischen Doktor-Jubiläum des Herrn geheimra A. von Kölliker, J. F. Bergman, Wiesbaden, 1892.

MESOLELLA, V.: Olfaction at Different Ages: Clinical and Histological Study, *Arch. ital. otol.*, **45**, 43 (1934).

MIYAZAKE, H.: Nasal Mucosa: Fine Distribution of Lymph Vessels in Mucosa of Man, *Folia Anat. Japon.*, **11**, 247 (1933).

NAGAHARA, Y.: Experimental Studies on Histologic Changes of Olfactory Organ Following Section of Olfactory Nerve; Finer Structure of the Olfactory Mucous Membrane, *Japan. J. Med. Sci.*, **5**, 165 (1940).

*OBERSTEINER, H.: "Anleitung beim Studium des Baues der nervösen Centralorgane im gesunden und kranken Zustande," 3d ed., Leipzig, 1896.

ONODI, A.: Rindenzentren des Geruches und der Stimmbildung, *Arch. Laryngol. Rhinol.*, **14**, 73 (1903).

PALLESTRINI, E.: Embryology of Nasal Glands, *Arch. ital. otol.*, **37**, 583 (1926).

———: Nasal Glands, Structure and Development in Man, *Arch. ital. anat. embryol.*, **23**, 641 (1926).

PAULSEN, E.: Über die Drüse der Nasenschleimhaut, besonders der Bowmanschen Drüsen, *Arch. mikroskop. Anat.*, **26** (1885).

PAW: Nerve Olfactori Stretched in Hydrocephalus, *Trans. Pathol. Soc. London*, **15**, 2.

PEARSON, A. A.: The Development of Olfactory Nerve in Man, *J. Comp. Neurol.*, **75**, 199 (1941).

———: Olfactory Development in Man; Further Studies, *Ann. Otol. Rhinol. and Laryngol.*, **51**, 317 (1942).

PERRIA, L.: Angioarchitectonics of Olfactory Bulb, Band and Trigone in Human Beings, *Riv. patol. nervosa e mentale*, **56**, 351 (1940).

QUERCY, M. M., and DE LACHAUD: Annular Terminations of Neurological Fibers in Cerebral Cortex, Olfactory Bulb and Epiphysis, *Rev. Neurol.*, **68**, 733 (1937).

READ, E. A.: A Contribution to the Knowledge of the Olfactory Apparatus in Dog, Cat and Man, *Am. J. Anat.*, **8**, 17 (1908–1909).

———: The True Relation of the Olfactory Nerves of Man, Dog, and Cat, *Anat. Record*, **107** (1908–1909).

RETZIUS, G.: Luktloben hos mannishen och de ofriga daggdiwen, *Forh. Svens. Lak-sallsk. sammants.*, 83 (1895).

RICHTER, H.: Development of Ethmoids and Cribriform Portions in Nose of Human Beings, *Arch. Ohren-, Nasen-, u. Kehlkopfheilk.*, **134**, 355 (1933).

ROSE, C.: Über das rudimentäre Jacobsonsche Organ der Krokodile und des Menschen, *Anat. Anz.*, **8**, 458 (1893).

ROSE, M.: Olfactory Center of Cerebral Cortex, *Polska gaz. lek.*, **15**, 565 (1936).

RUGANI, L.: Sulla Distribuzione del tessuto elastio nella mucosa nasale e della cavita accessorie, *Monit. zool. ital.*, **15**, 41 (1904).

SCHAEFFER, J. P.: The Genesis, Development, and Adult Anatomy of the Nasofrontal Region in Man, *Am. J. Anat.*, **20**, 125 (1916).

———: The Mucous Membrane of the Nasal Cavity and the Paranasal Sinuses, Cowdry's "Special Cytology," **2**, 45, Paul B. Hoeber, New York, 1928.

*———: "The Nose, Paranasal Sinuses, Nasolacrimal Passageways, and Olfactory Organ in Man," Blakiston's Son and Co., Philadelphia, 1920.

SCHIFF, J. M.: Der erste Hirnnerv ist der Geruchsnerv, *Moleschott's Untersuchungen zur Naturlehre*, **5** (1858); **6** (1860).

*SCHROETER: "Die Menschliche Nase oder das Geruchsorgan," Leipzig, 1812.

*SCHULTZE, M. S.: "Untersuchen über den Bau der Nasenschleimhaut, namentlich die Structur und Endigungsweise der Geruchsnerven bei dem Menschen und den Wirbelthieren," Halle, 1862.

———: Das Epithelium der Riechschleimhaut des Menschen, *Med. Zentr.*, **25**, 385 (1864).

SCHWALBE: Über die Nasenmuscheln der Säugetiere und des Menschen, *Sitzber. phys-soz. ges Königsberg*, **23** (1882).

SCHWARZ, M.: Structure of Nasal Mucosa, *Z. Hals-, Nasen-, u. Ohrenheilk.*, **40**, 332 (1936).

SEKI, M.: Reticulum Cells in Nasal Mucosa and Their Derivations in Man, *Z. Zellforsch. mikroskop. Anat.*, **31**, 203 (1941).

SEYDEL, O.: Über die Nasenhöhle der höheren Säugethiere und des Menschen, *Morphol. Jahrb.*, **17** (1891).

SLOTWINSKI, J.: Comparative Cytologic Study of Secretion of Bowman's Olfactory Glands in Man, Rodents and Insectivora, *Compt. rend. soc. biol.*, **115**, 1269 (1934).

SMITH: Morphology of the Smell Centre, *Anat. Anz.*, **11**, 49 (1895).

*SOEMMERING, S. T.: "Icones organorum humanorum olfactus," Frankfurt am Main, 1810.

*———: "Abbildungen des menschlichen Organs des Geruches," Frankfurt am Main, 1809.

*SPIEGEL, E. A., and L. SOMMER: "Neurology of the Eye, Nose and Throat," New York, 1944.

SUCHANNEK, H.: Beiträge zur feineren normalen Anatomie des menschlichen Geruchsorgans, *Arch. mikroskop. Anat. Entwicklungsmech.*, **36**, 375 (1890).

———: Beiträge zur Frage von der Specifizität der Zellen in der tierischen und menschlichen Riechschleimhaut, *Anat. Anz.*, **6**, 201 (1891).

———: Differentialdiagnostische Merkmale zur Unterscheidung zwischen normalem und pathologischem menschlichen Riechepithel, *Z. Ohrenheilk.*, **22** (1891).

———: Beiträge zur mikr. Anatomie der menschlichen Nasenhöhle, speziell der Riechschleimhaut, *Z. Ohrenheilk.*, **34**, 93 (1893).

TAKATA, N.: Olfactory Nerve and Organ of Smell, *Arch. Ohren-, Nasen-, u. Kehlkopfheilk*, **121**, 31 (May, 1929).

TOEPLITZ, M.: Five Hundred Examinations of Nose in an Institution for Delinquent Boys, *Med. Record*, **85**, 480 (1914).

TORRIGIANI, C. A.: Valsalvo's Area of Nasal Cavities, Intra-epithelial Capillaries of Man, *Monit. zool. ital.*, **37**, 252 (1926).

———: Sex-limited Symptoms, Inheritance in Nose-Bleed, *Acta Oto-Laryngol.*, **20**, 149 (1934).

TRIMARCHI, A.: Structure of Nose Glands in Vestibule Man and Mammals, *Arch. ital. otol.*, **40**, 556 (1929).

TURNER, A. L., and E. E. REYNOLDS: Nasal Mucosa: Anatomy of Lymphatics, *J. Laryngol. Otol.*, **41**, 717 (1926).

UYEMATSU, S.: A Study of the Cortical Olfactory Center; Based on Two Cases of Unilateral Involvement of the Olfactory Lobe, *Arch. Neurol. Psychiat.*, **6**, 146 (1921).

*VAN ALYEA, O. E.: "Nasal Sinuses, an Anatomic and Clinical Consideration," Balt., 1942.

*VAN DE POLL, H.: "De partibus quae in homine olfactu inseriunt," Ludg., 1735.

VAN GEHUCHTEN, A.: Le Bulbe olfactif de l'homme, *Bibliog. Anat.*, **3** (August, 1895).

VIRCHOW, H.: Die anthropologische Untersuchung der Nase, *Z. Ethnol.*, **44**, 289 (1912).

———: Gips-Abgüsse von der Nase eines Japaners, *Z. Ethnol.*, **45**, 613 (1913).

VOGEL, K.: Nasal Mucosa: Nerve Supply, *Z. Hals-, Nasen-, u. Ohrenheilk.*, **25**, 485 (1930).

VON BRUNN, A.: Über die Ausbreitung der menschlichen Riechschleimhaut, *Naturforsch. ges. zu Rostock* (June 26, 1891).

———: Beiträge zur mikroskopischen Anatomie der menschlichen Nasenhöhle, *Arch. mikroskop. Anat. Entwicklungsmech.*, **39**, 632 (1892).

VON MIHALKOVICS, V.: Anatomie und Entwicklung der Nase und ihrer Nebenhöhlen, *Heymanns Handbuch Laryngol. Rhinol.*, Wien, **3** (1896).

WALLENBERG, A.: Über einige anatomische Grundlagen der Empfindung, *Schriften Naturforsch. ges. zu Danzig*, N.F., **10** (2/3) (1901).

———: Anatomische Beiträge zu Problemen der Empfindung, Wahrnehmung und Beobachtung, *Schriften Naturforsch. ges. zu Danzig*, N.F., **15** (3/4), 17 (1922).

WARD, C. H.: Nasal Characteristics; Human and Comparative, *Trans. Am. Laryngol. Assoc.*, **17**, 200 (1896).

WEISS-FLORENTIN and BRUNNER: Zur postembryonalen Entwicklung der menschlichen Bulbus olfactorius, *Z. Hals-, Nasen-, u. Ohrenheilk.*, **12**, 367 (1925).

WELCKER, H.: Untersuchung der Retinazapfen und des Riechhautepithels bei einem Hingerichteten, *Z. ration. Med.*, **20** (1863).

e. General

AMABILINO, R.: Sulle prime Vie olfattive, *Riv. sper. freniat.*, **29**, 816 (1903).

ANGLADE and ROBERT: Sur Quelques détails de la structure histologique du nerf olfactif, *J. Méd. Bordeaux*, **37**, 73 (1907).

*ARVISET: "Contribution à l'étude du tissu erectile des fosses nasales," Lyon, 1887.

AYERS, H.: Vertebrate Cephalogenesis. Transformation of the Anterior End of the Head Resulting in the Formation of the Nose, *J. Comp. Neurol.*, **30**, 323 (1919).

BABUCHIN: Das Geruchsorgan, *Striker's Handbuch d. Lehre von den Geweben*, **2**, 964 (1872).

*BARTHOLINUS, C.: "De olfactus organo," Hafniae, 1679.

BELLONCI, G.: Sur la Structure et les rapports des lobes olfactifs dans les arthropodes supérieurs et les vertèbres, *Arch. ital. biol.*, **3**, 191 (1883).

BIANCHI, L.: Il Cosi detto ganglio olfattivo e i suoi rapporti d'origine coi nervi olfattivi e terminale, *Arch. ital. anat. embriol.*, **29**, 187 (1931).

———: Olfactory Nerves: Relations in Origin of Terminal Nerve and of Olfactory Nerve, *Boll. soc. ital. biol. sper.*, **6**, 153 (1931) ; **6**, 522 (1931).

BILANCIONI, G.: Felice Fontana's Studies on Anatomy and Physiology of Sense Organs in Second Half of Eighteenth Century, *Archeion*, **12**, 296 (1930).

BONNIER, P.: La Muqueuse nasale et les centres pneumostatiques, *Arch. gén. méd.*, **5**, 197 (1912).

BROCA: Recherches sur les centres olfactifs, *Rev. anthropol.*, 2s, 405 (1879).

BRUNNER, H.: Olfaction: Nerve, *Rev. of Journal Literature for 1942, Laryngoscope*, **53**, 117 (1943).

*CALLEJA: "La Region Olfactoria," Madrid, 1893.

CALOGERO, G.: Olfactory Nerves: Structure of Fibers in Man and in Mammals, *Riv. neurol.*, **3**, 686 (1930).

CARBONIERI: Ein Beitrag zur Lehre der Localisation des Geruchssinnes, *Monatsschr. Ohrenheilk.* (1890).

CHILD, A. L.: Olfactory Nerves, *Popular Sci.*, **17**, 692.

CHRISTMAS, KIRKING, and HOLMFELD: Experimentelle Untersuchungen über den Bau der Geruchsschleimhaut, *Nord. Med. Ark.*, **15** (1883).

CISOFF, A.: Zur Kenntniss der Regio olfactoria, *Med. Zentr.*, 689 (1874).

CLARKE: Über den Bau des Bulbus olfactorius und der Geruchsschleimhaut, *Z. wiss. Zoöl.*, **11** (1860).

CLARKE: Über den feineren Bau des Bulbus olfactorius, *Z. wiss. Zoöl.*, **11**, (1860).

CONIL, C. L.: Des Résultats obtenus par la mèthode de Golgi appliqués à l'étude du bulbe olfactif, *Comp. rend. soc. biol.*, **4**, 179 (1892).

*DELEVAN, D. B.: Articles on Anatomy and Physiology of the Nose, "Reference Handbook of the Medical Sciences," William Wood and Co., New York, 1887.

DEMOOR: Communication préliminaire sur les neurones olfactifs, *Compt. rend. Soc. roy. sci. méd. nat.*, **61**, 16 (1898).

DINOLT, R.: Histology of Human Olfactory Bulb., *Arch. path. Anat. Physiol.*, **302**, 700 (1938).

DISSE, J.: Die erste Entwickelung des Riechnerven, *Anat. Heft*, **9**, 257 (1897).

———: Die Ausbildung der Nasenhöhle nach der Geburt, *Arch. Anat. u. Physiol.*, **29** (1889).

DIXON, W. E.: Nose, Anatomically Considered with Special Reference to Reflexes, *J. Oklahoma Med. Assoc.*, **7**, 320 (1914–1915).

DOGIEL, A.: Über die Drüsen der Regio olfactoria, *Arch. mikroskop. Anat. Entwicklungsmech.*, **26** (1886).

ECKER, A.: Über das Epithelium der Riechschleimhaut und die wahrscheinliche Endigung des Geruchsnerven, *Z. wiss. Zoöl.*, **8**, 303 (1855).

ECKHARD, C.: Über die Endigungsweise des Geruchsnerven, *Beitr. Anat. Physiol.*, **1**, 77 (1855).

EDINGER, L.: Der Lobus parolfactorius, *Anat. Anz.*, **38**, 1 (1911).

———: Vergleichend-entwickelungsgeschichte und anatomische Studien im Bereiche der Hirnanatomie. Riechapparat und Ammonshorn, *Anat. Anz.*, **8** (10), (11), (1892).

*ERICKSEN, F.: "De testura nervi olfactorii ejusque ramorum," Dorpat, 1857.

EXNER, S.: Fortgesetzte Studien über die Endigungsweise der Geruchsnerven, 3 abh., *Sitzber. wiener Akad. Wiss.*, **76** (1877).

FABER, W. M.: Nasal Mucosa and Subarachnoid Space, *Am. J. Anat.*, **62**, 121 (1937).

*FAVILL, J.: "Outline of the Cranial Nerves," Chicago, 1933.

FEDERICI, F.: Nasal Mucosa: Epithelial Fibers, *Monit. zool. ital.*, **40**, 15 (1929).

FENTON, R. A.: Nasal Mucosa: Recent Discoveries, *J. Can. Med. Assoc.*, **32**, 147 (1935).

FÉRÉ, C.: L'Hérédité de l'odeur, *Rev. méd.* (Paris), **12**, 333 (1902).

*FERRIER, D.: "The Croonian Lectures on Cerebral Localization," London, 1890.

*FICK: "Lehrbuch der Anatomie und Physiologie der Sinnesorgane," Lahr, 1864.

FINDLAY, J. W.: A Research into the Histological Structure of the Olfactory Organ, *J. Anat. Physiol.*, **28**, 387 (1893–1894).

FLEISCHER, R.: Beiträge sur Entwickelungsgeschichte des Jacobsonsche Organs und zur Anatomie der Nase, *Sitzber. phys-med. Soc. zu Erlangen*, **12** (1877).

FRANÇOIS-FRANCK: Contribution à l'étude de l'innervation vasodilatatrice de la muqueuse nasale, *Arch. Physiol. norm. pathol.*, 691 (1889).

FRAZER, J. E. S.: Formation of Nasal Cavities (embryology), *J. Anat. Physiol.*, **14**, 347 (1911).

FRETS, P.: Entwickelung des Geruchsorgan, *Morphol. Jahrb.*, **45**, 481 (1913).

——: De Ontwikkeling van den Neus, *Verhandl. Gen. Nat. Genees. Heelk. Amsterdam*, **7**, 335 (1914).

FRIGERIA: Contributo alla localizzazione del senso dell'odorato, *Atti congr. assoc. med. état.* 109 (1887).

*GASTALDI: "Nuove ricerche sopra la terminazione del nervo olfattorio," Torino, 1856.

*GERBER, P. H.: "Etwas über Nasen und Geruchsorgan," Hamburg, 1896.

GHIGI, C.: Nasal Mucosa: Connective Tissue, *Arch. ital. anat. embriol.*, **29**, 256 (1931).

*GOLGI: "Sulla fina struttura dei bulbi olfactorii," Reggio Emilia, 1875.

GORSHKOFF, Y.: Les Voies centrales des sensations olfactives, *Nevrol. Vestnik. Kazan*, **10**, 1 (1902).

GRAIN: Nasal Mucosa: Mucosa of Inferior Turbinates, *Rev. méd.*, Paris, **48**, 690 (1931).

*GRATIOLET: "Recherches sur l'organe de Jacobson," Paris, 1845.

HALSCHEK: Sur le centre olfactif, *Wien. klin. Rundschau*, 47 (1909).

HARTLINE, H. K.: Sense Organs, *Ann. Rev. Physiol.*, **4**, 445 (1942).

HARTZ, H. J.: Physiology and Development of the Nose and Accessory Nasal Reflexes with Reference to Function and Importance of Turbinated Bodies, *Ann. Otol., Rhinol. & Laryngol.*, **18**, 709 (1909).

HARVEY, R.: Note on the Organ of Jacobson, *Quart. J. Microscop. Sci.*, **23**, 50 (1882).

*HEIDENHAIN, A.: "Über die acinösen Drüsen der Schleimhaut inbesondere der Nasenschleimhaut," Breslau, 1870.

HEINDL, A., JR.: Functional and Histological Studies of Olfactory Region—Total Extirpation of Larynx, *Monatsschr. Ohrenheilk.*, **66**, 931 (1932).

HENNING, S. E.: Geruchs und Geschmackszentern, *Monatsschr. Psychiat. Neurol.*, 121 (1919).

HERRICK, C. J.: Current Views of the Structure of the Olfactory Organs and Taste Bulbs, *J. Comp. Neurol.*, **3**, 95 (1893).

——: On the Phylogenetic Differentiation of the Organs of Smell and Taste, *J. Comp. Neurol.*, **18**, 159 (1908).

——: Some Remarks on the Olfactory Nerve, *Science*, 817 (June 17, 1898).

HERTZMANN, A. B., and J. B. DILLON: Selective Vascular Reaction Patterns in Nasal Septum, *Am. J. Physiol.*, **127**, 671 (1939).

HERZOG, F.: Cortical Localization of Sense of Smell, *Orvosi Hetilap*, **71**, 1488 (1927).

HILTON, W.: Sense Organs—Olfactory Receptors, *J. Entomol. Zool.*, **35**, 39 (1943).

HIS, W.: Über die Entwickelung des Riechlappens und des Riechganglions und über diejenige des verlängerten Markes, *Verhandl. anat. ges. zu Berlin* (Oct. 10, 1899).

HOCHSTETTER, F.: Über die Bildung der inneren Nasengänge oder primitiven Choanen, *Verhandl. anat. ges. zu München*, **5**, 18 (1891).

*HOFFMANN, C. K.: "Onderzöckingen over den anatomischen Bouw van de Membrana olfactoria en het peripherische Uiteinde van den Nervus olfactorius," Amsterdam, 1867.

*HUYER: "De tulincae mucosae narium structura," Berlin, 1847.

HUBERT, L.: The Involuntary Nervous System of the Nose, and Its Mechanism, *Laryngoscope*, **32**, 493 (1922).

*HUNTER, J.: "Observations and Description of Nerves Which Supply Organs of Smell," London, 1786.

KADANOFF, D.: Nasal Mucosa: Nerves in Epithelium, *Z. Zellforsch. u. mikroskop. Anat.*, **6**, 342 (1927).

KALLIUS, E.: Geruchsorgan, *Bardeleben, Handbuch Anat. Menschen*, **5**, Abt. 1, Teil 2, 115 (1905).

KAMON, K.: Über die Geruchsknospen, *Arch. mikroskop. Anat. Entwicklungsmech.*, **64**, 653 (1904).

KAUFMANN: Über die Bedeutung der Riech- und Epithelzellen der Regio olf, *Med. Jahrb.*, **2**, 79 (1886).

*KEY, A., and G. RETZIUS: "Studien in der Anatomie des Nervensystems u. des Bindegewebes," 1875.

KLASS, M.: Olfactory Striae, *J. Comp. Neurol.*, **47**, 171 (1929).

KOHLRAUSCH: Über das Schwellgewebe an den Muskeln der Nasenschleimhaut, *Müller Arch.* (1853).

KÖLLIKER, A.: Über den feineren Bau des Bulbus olf, *Sitzber. phys.-med. ges. zu Würzburg*, 1 (1892).

——: Über die erste Entwicklung der Nervi olfactorii, *Sitzber. phys.-med. ges. zu Würzburg*, 127 (1890).

KOLLMER, W.: Zur Kenntnis der Riechepithelien, *Anat. Anz.*, **30**, 513 (1907).

LANDAU, E.: La voie sensitive olfactive périphérique, *Confinia Neurol.*, **5**, 225 (1942–1943).

LARROUDE, C.: Mucosa of Nasal Fossa and of Perinasal Sinuses; Preliminary Report, *Lisboa méd.*, **15**, 151 (1938).

LAUNOIS, P. E.: L'Appareil nerveus de l'olfaction, *Ann. mal. oreille*, **21**, 1 (1895).

LEASURE, J. K.: Mucus Sheet on Respiratory Mucous Membrane,—Nasal Mucosa, *Trans. Am. Acad. Ophthalmol.*, **44**, 341 (1939).

LEI, S.: Zur Kenntniss des Olfactorius, *Ber. naturforsch. ges. Freiburg*, **1**, 7 (1873).

LÉVY, S.: Sur les cellules de soutien de la muqueuse olfactive, *Compt. rend. soc. biol.*, **61**, 243 (1906).

LOCATELLI, P.: Olfactory Nerves: Structure, *Boll. soc. méd.-chir. Pavia*, **2**, 43 (1927).

——: Olfactory Nerve Structure, *Arch. ital. anat. embriol.*, **26**, 331 (1929).

——: Olfactory Nerves: Methods of Demonstrating Peripheral Nerve Fibers, *Bull. soc. méd.-chir. Paris*, **47**, 1009 (1933).

LOCY, W. A.: New Facts Regarding the Development of the Olfactory Nerve, *Anat. Anz.*, **16**, 273 (1899).

*LÖWE, L.: "Beiträge zur Anatomie der Nase und Nundhöhle," Berlin, 1878.

LÖWENTHAL: Contribution à l'étude du lobe olfactif, *J. anat. physiol.* (1894).

LUSSANA: Del Centro nervoso olfactivo, studii anatomosperimentali, *Gazz. med. ital.*, 3s, **6**, 21, 29, 37, 85, 161, 169, 177, 437 (1872).

LUSTIG: Sulle Cellule epiteliale nel regione olfattiva, degli embrioni, *Atti. acad. sci. Torino*, **23**, 324 (1887–1889).

*MAHMOUD, S.: "Recherches anatomo-microscopiques sur la muqueuse olfactive," Paris, 1877.

MAIR, R.: Olfactory Bulbs: Topography, *Anat. Anz.*, **67**, 501 (1929).

MANOUELIAN, Y.: Sur le nouveau type de neurone olfactif central, *Compt. rend. soc. biol.*, 10s, **6**, 230 (1898).

——: Contribution à l'étude de bulbe olfactif, *Compt. rend. soc. biol.*, 10s, **5**, 194 (1898).

————: Les Fibres centrifuges du bulbe olfactif et les neurones olfactifs centraux, *Compt. rend. soc. biol.*, 11s, **1**, 530 (1899).

MARINISCO and GOLDSTEIN: Sur l'architectonie de l'écorce de l'hippocampe et son rapport avec l'olfaction, *Encephale*, **1**, 1 (1911).

MARTIN, H. N.: Notes on the Structure of the Olfactory Mucous Membrane, *J. Anat. Physiol.*, **8** (November, 1873).

MARTUSCELLI, G.: Ricerche sperimentale sui bulbe olfattori, *Atti congr. soc. ital. laringol.*, **95** (1899).

*MEYNERT: "Structure du bulbe olfactif," *Stricker Handbuch*, 1872.

NEUBERGER, J.: Über Verhalten der Riechschleimhaut nach Durchschneidung des Nervus olfactorius, *Zentr. Physiol.*, **11**, 489 (1897).

NEWELL and MARTIN: Über die Struktur der Reichschleimhaut, *J. Anat. Physiol.*, **8** (1873).

OBERSTEINER, H.: Ursprung und centrale Verbindungen der Riechnerven, *Biol. Zentr.* **2**, 464 (1882–1883).

*OEHL: "Sul nervo e sul organo olfactorio," Milan, 1858.

Olfactory Nerve Tract, *Sci. American Supp.*, **48**, 19946 (1899).

O'MALLEY, J. F.: Evolution of the nasal cavities and sinuses in relation to function, *J. Laryngol. Otol.*, **39**, 57 (1924).

*ONODI, A.: "Die Nasenhöhle und ihre Nebenhöhlen," Wien, 1893.

ORTIZ-PICON, J. M.: Nasal Mucosa: Chromatophores, Sometimes Wrongly Considered Sympathetic Cells: Rhinal Sympathetic Receptive Apparatus, *Arch. med. cir. espec.*, **33**, 436 (1930).

PAW: Pressure on Nerve Olfactori, *Trans. Path. Soc., London*, **4**, 16.

PEGLER, L. H.: On the Desirability of a More Extended and Discriminative Nomenclature for the Olfactory Nerves, *Trans. Intern. Congr. Med., London*, Sect. 15, 445 (1913).

PETER, K.: Entwicklung d. Geruchsorgane und Jacobsonsche Organ in d. Reihe d. Wirbeltiere, *Handbuch Entwicklungsgeschichte Wirbeltiere*, **2B**, 1 (1902).

————: Entwicklung d. Geruchsorgan, *Ergeb. Anat. Entwicklungsgeschichte*, **20**, 43 (1911).

*PIANA, G. P.: "Contribuzioni alla conoscenza della struttura e della funzione dell'organo di Jacobson," Bolonga, 1880.

POTIQUET: Du Canal de Jacobson, *Rev. laryngol.* (1891).

PREOBRASCHENSKY, S. S.: Zur Kenntniss des Baues der Regio olfactoria, *Wien. klin. Wochschr.*, **6**, 123 (1891).

*RAMON Y CAJAL, S.: "Terminaciones del nervio olfactori en la mucosa nasal," Barcelona, 1889.

————: Neue Darstellung vom histol. Bau des Nervensystem, *Arch. Anat. u. Physiol.* (1893).

————: Origen y terminación de las figras nerviosas olfactorias, *Gacet sanit.* (Dec. 10, 1890).

RANDACIO, F.: On the Relations of the Nucleus Taeniaeformis with the Olfactory Nerve, *Trans. Intern. Med. Congr., 7 sess., London*, 169 (1881).

RANVIER, L.: Lección sobre el órgano del olfato, *Rev. med. Chile*, **10**, 193 (1881–1882).

*RASMUSSEN, A. T.: "The Principal Nervous Pathways," 2 ed. New York, 1941.

RAUGE, P.: Le Canal incisif et l'organe de Jacobson, *Arch. intern. laryngol.* (1894).

*REMY, C.: "La Membrane muqueuse des fosses nasales," Paris, 1878.

RETZIUS, G.: Die Endingungsweise des Riechnerven, *Biol. Unters*, N.S. **3**, 525 (1892).

————: Zur Kenntniss der Nervenendigungen in der Riechschleimhaut, *Biol. Unters*, N.F., **4**, 62 (1892).

RIEGELE, L.: Nasal mucosa: relations of autonomous nerve fibers of nasal mucosa to reticuloendothelial system and their importance for anaphylactic and allergic processes, *Z. Hals-, Nasen-, Ohrenheilk.*, **35**, 554 (1934).

*ROSENTHAL, F.: "Disquisit. anat. de organo olfactio," Gryphiae, 1807.

ROSSI, U.: Alcune considerazioni sul lavoro di J. Disse, *Ann. fac. med. mem. acad. med.-chir. Perugia*, 11, 23 (1899).

RUBASCHKIN, W.: Über die Beziehungen des Nervus trigeminus zur Riechschleimhaut, *Anat. Anz.*, 22, 407 (1903).

RUGANI, L.: Intorno alla minuto struttura della mucosa delle fosse nasali o delle cavita accessorie, *Arch. ital. anat. embriol.*, 5, 100 (1906).

———: Der feinere Bau der Schleimhaut der Nase und ihrer Nebenhöhlen, *Intern. Zentr. Ohrenheilk.*, 2, 413 (1904).

SACCONE, G.: Sulla localizzazione corticale del centro dell' odorato, *Ann. med. nevale*, 8, 261 (1902).

SAEUGER, M.: Über die acustische Wirkung der Nasenhöhlen, *Arch. ges. Physiol.*, 62, 494 (1896).

SAPPEY: Histologie de la muqueuse olfactive, *Gaz. méd. Paris*, 543 (1853).

*SCARPA: "Anatomicae disquisitiones de auditu et olfactu," Mediolani, 1795.

SCHAFFER, J.: Über den feineren Bau und die Entwicklung des Knorpelgewebes und über verwandte Forman der Stutzsubstanz, *Z. wiss. Zoöl.*, 77, 1 (R10).

SCHAEFFER, J. P.: Purpose of Basal Cells in Respiratory Epithelium of Nose, and Their Fate, *Anat. Record*, 52, 75 (1932 Supp., Feb.).

———: The Genesis of Air Cells in the Conchae Nasales, *Anat. Record*, 4, 167 (1910).

*SCHIEFFERDECKER, P.: "Histologie der Schleimhaut der Nase und ihrer Nebenhöhlen," Heymanns Handbuch d. Laryng. u. Rhinol., Wein, 1896.

SCHULTZE: Über die Endigungsweise des Geruchsnerven und der Epithelialgebilde der Nasenschleimhaut, *Monatsber. kgl. Acad. Wiss. zu Berlin*, 504 (1856).

*SCHWENDT: "Die angeborenen Verschlüsse der hinteren Nasenöffnungen," Basel, 1889.

*SIDKY, M.: "Recherches anatomo-microscopiques sur la muqueuse olfactive," Paris, 1877.

*SLEVOGT, J. H.: "De olfactus praestantia," Jena, 1715.

SMITH, G. E.: The Tuberculum Olfactorium, *Anat. Anz.*, 34, 200 (1909).

———: On the Cortical Olfactory Apparatus, *Anat. Anz.*, 11 (1896).

SPADARO, R.: Contributo allo studio del bulbo olfattorio in alcuni mammiferi e vertebrati inferiori, *Arch. ital. otol.*, 36, 617 (1925).

SUCHANNEK, H.: Beiträge zur normalen und pathologischen Histologie der Nasenschleimhaut, *Anat. Anz.*, 7, 55 (1892).

*TENNER: "De organi olfactus differentia," Lipsiae, 1777.

TOURNEUX: Muqueuse olfactive, *Compt. rend. soc. biol.*, 4, 179 (1883).

TROLARD, A.: Notes sur le bulbe et les nerfs olfactifs, *J. Anat. Physiol.*, 38, 555 (1902).

TROLARD, P.: De l'appareil nerveux central de l'olfaction, *Compt. rend. soc. biol.*, 9s, 664 (1889).

———: De l'appareil nerveux de l'olfaction, *Arch. neurol.*, 20, 335 (1890).

VAN CAMPENHOUT, E.: Contribution à l'étude de la formation des nerfs olfactifs, *Trans. Roy. Soc. Can.*, 3s, 27, 101 (1933).

VAN DER STRICHT, O.: Le Neuro-epithelium olfactif et sa membrane limitante interne, *Mem. acad. roy, méd. de belg.*, 20 (1909).

———: Le Neuro-epithelium olfactif et ses parties constituantes superficielles, *Comp. rend. assoc. anat.*, 11, 30 (1909).

VAN VELZEN, T.: Geruchszentrum, *Psychoencephale Studien*, 5, 205 (1927).

VIOLLET, P.: Les Glandes de la muqueuse nasale, *Rev. hebd. laryngol.*, 2, 417 (1910).

VON BRUNN, A.: Die Membrana limitans olfactoria, *Zentr. med. Wiss.*, 709 (1874).

———: Untersuchung über das Riechepithel, *Arch. mikroskop. Anat. Entwicklungsmech.*, 11, 468 (1875).

————: Weitere Untersuchungen über das Riechepithel und sein Verhalten zum Nervus olfactorius, *Arch. mikroskop. Anat. Entwicklungsmech.*, **17**, 141 (1880).

————: Die Nervenendigung im Riechepithel, *Naturforsch. ges. zu Rostock* (July 30, 1891).

*Von Lenhossek, M.: "Beiträge zur Histologie der Nervensystems und der Sinnesorgane. Die Nervenendigungen in der Riechschleimhaut," Wiesbaden, 1894.

Waldemeyer: Über die Riechschleimhaut des Menschen, *Arch. Psychiat. Nervenkrankh*, **15**, 279 (1884).

Walter, G.: Über den feineren Bau des Bulbus olfactorious, *Arch. path. Anat.*, **22**, 241 (1861).

Wiedersheim, R.: Die Stammesentwickelung des Jacobsonschen Organs, *Tagbl. Versamml. deut. Naturforsch. u. Ärzte im Salzburg* (1881).

Wolff, J. B.: Das Riechorgan, *Nova acta Acad. Naturforsch.*, **38** (1875).

Wright, J.: The Organ of Smell, *Laryngoscope*, **34**, 1 (1924).

Zacharias, L. R.: Nose-gonad Relationship, *J. Comp. Neurol.*, **74**, 421 (1941).

*Zuckerkandl, E.: "Normal und pathologische Anatomie der Nasenhöhle," Wien, 1882.

————: Über die morphologische Bedeutung des Siebbien-Labyrinths, *Wien. med. Wochschr.*, 39, 40 (1887).

*————: "Über das Riechcentrum," Stuttgart, 1887.

————: Das Riechbündel des Ammonshornes, *Anat. Anz.*, **3**, 425 (1888).

*————: "Normale und pathologische Anatomie der Nasenhöhle und ihrer pneumatischen Anhänge," **2**, Wien, 1892.

————: Geruchsorgan, *Anat. Hefte*, **5**, 131 (1895).

————: Über die Wechselbeziehung in der Ausbildung des Jacobsonschen Organs und des Riechlappens, *Anat. Hefte*, **41**, 3 (1910).

————: Das Jacobsonsche Organ, *Ergeb. Anat. Entwicklungsgeschichte*, **18**, 801 (1910).

B. Physiology of the Olfactory Sense

a. Invertebrates Other Than Insects

Adams, L. E.: The Sense of Smell in Limax Maximus, *J. Conchol.*, **9**, 24 (1898).

Allen, W. R.: Food and Feeding Habits of Fresh-water Mussels, *Biol. Bull.*, **27**, 127 (1914).

Balss, H.: Über die Chemorezeption bei Garnelen, *Biol. Zentr.*, **33**, 508 (1913).

Bourne, A. G.: Sense of Taste and Smell in Leeches, *Nature*, **36**, 125 (June 9, 1887).

Copeland, M.: The Olfactory Reactions and Organs of the Marine Snails, *J. Exp. Zool.*, **25**, 177 (1918).

*Demoll, R.: "Die Sinnesorgane der Arthropoden," Braunschweig, 1914.

Dubois, R.: Sur le sens de l'olfaction de l'escargot, *Compt. rend. soc. biol.*, **56**, 198 (1904).

Galiano, F.: Sur les réactions chimiotactiques du flagelle "Chelomonas," *Compt. rend. acad. de sci.*, **172** (1921).

Gradenwitz, A.: Sense of Smell in Snails, *Sci. American*, **94**, 371 (May 5, 1906).

Gross, A. O.: The Feeding Habits and Chemical Sense of Nereis Virens, Sars., *J. Exp. Zool.*, **32**, 427 (1921).

Holmes, S., and E. Homuth: The Sense of Smell in the Crayfish, *Biol. Bull.*, **18**, 155 (1910–1911).

Jennings, H. S.: Studies in Reactions to Stimuli in Unicellular Organisms, *J. Physiol.*, **21**, 258 (1897).

*May, K.: "Über das Geruchsvermögen der Krebse," Kiel, 1887.

Perris, E.: Mémoire sur le siège de l'odorat dans les articules, *Ann. sci. nat.*, 3s, **14** (1850).

Pollock, W. H.: On Indications of a Sense of Smell in Actiniae, *J. Linnean Soc. London, Zool.*, **16**, 474 (1883).

POWERS, E. B.: Reactions of Crayfishes to Gradients of Dissolved Carbon Dioxide and Acetic and Hydrochloric Acids, *Biol. Bull.*, **27**, 177 (1914).

PRITCHETT, A. H.: Observations on hearing and smell in spiders, *Am. Naturalist*, **38**, 859 (1904).

PROUHO: Du Sens de l'odorat chez étoiles de mer, *Compt. rend. soc. Biol.*, **111**, 1343 (1890).

ROMANES, G. J.: Smell in Starfish, *Phil. Trans. Roy. Soc., London*, 1881–1883.

SCHARMER, J.: Smell in Lithobius, *Zool. Jahrb. Anat.*, **54**, 459 (1935).

SCHMIDT, H.: Untersuchungen über den chemischen Sinn einiger Polychoeten, *Biol. Zentr.*, **42**, 193 (1922).

SMITH, A. C.: The Influence of Temperature, Odors, Light and Contact on the Movements of Earthworm, *Am. J. Physiol.*, **6**, 459 (1902).

SPIEGEL, A.: Smell in Crangon Vulgaris, *Z. wiss. Biol.*, **6**, 730 (1927).

THORPE, W. H., A. C. CROMBIE, R. HILL, and J. H. DARRAH: The Foodfinding of Wireworms, *Nature*, **155**, 46 (1945).

VAILLANT, L.: Sur le siège de l'olfaction chez la nassa reticulata, *Bull. soc. philom. Paris*, 6s, **10**, 89 (1873).

*WATKINSON, E. B.: "Untersuchungen über die sogenannte Geruchsorgane der Cephalopoden," Zurich, 1908.

WHITMAN, C. O.: Smell in Leeches, *Quart. J. Microscop. sci.* N.S., **26**, 409.

WREDE, W. L.: Smell in Eupagurus, *Tijdschr. Nederl. Dierkund. Vereen*, **1**, 109 (1929).

YUNG, E.: Recherches sur le sens olfactif des gasteropodes terrestres, *Arch. physiol.*, **1**, (1902).

——: Recherches sur le sens olfactif de l'escargot, *Arch. physiol.*, **1** (1903).

b. Insects

ABBOTT, C. E.: Methods of Orientation in Dragon-fly Larvae, *Psyche*, **33**, 124 (1926).

——: Experimental Data on Olfactory Sense of Beetles, Especially Necrophori, *Ann. Entomal. Soc. Am.*, **20**, 207 (1927).

——: Odor Sense in Necrophori, *Ann. Entomol. Soc. Am.*, **20**, 550 (1927).

——: Temperature and Humidity as Affecting Smell in Blowflies, *Psyche*, **39**, 145 (1932).

ADOLPH, E. F.: Egg-laying Reactions in the Pomace Fly, Drosophila, *J. Exp. Zool.*, **31** (1920).

AMBROS, W.: Smell in Nun Moth, *Zentr. ges. Forstwes.*, **66**, 131, 166 (1940).

ANDREAE, E.: Über den graduellen Unterschied der Duft und Farbenanlockung bei einigen verschiedenen Insekten, *Biol. Zentr.*, **23**, 226 (1903).

——: Inwiefern werden Insekten durch Farbe und Duft der Blumen angezogen, *Beih. Bot. Zentr.*, **15**, 427 (1903).

BARROWS, W. M.: The Reaction of the Pomace Fly, Drosophila Ampelophila Leow, to Odorous Substances, *J. Exp. Zool.*, **4**, 515 (1907).

BEESON, C. F. C.: Sense of Smell in Longhorn Beetles, *Nature*, **126**, 12 (July 5, 1930).

BEGG, M., and L. HOGBEN: Localization of Chemoreceptivity in Drosophila, *Nature*, **152**, 535 (1934).

BEQUAERT, J.: Foodplants for Insects, Chosen by Odor—Masaridinae and Gayellinae, *Bull. Brooklyn Entomol. Soc.*, **35**, 37 (1940).

BONNIER, G.: Le "Sens de la direction" chez les abeilles, *Compt. rend. acad. sci.*, **148**, 1019 (1909).

BROMLEY, S. W.: Smell in Dragonfly Ovipositing on Paved Highway, *Bull. Brooklyn Entomol. Soc.*, **23**, 69 (1928).

BROWN, F. W.: Smell in Insects, *Am. Mus. Novitates*, **299**, 1 (1928).

*BRUN, R.: "Die Raumorientierung der Ameisen und das Orientierungsproblem im Allgemeinen," Jena, 1914.

———: Weitere Untersuchungen über die Fernorientierung der Ameisen, *Biol. Zentr.*, **36**, 261 (1916).

———: Die moderne Ameisen Psychologie—ein anthropomorphistischer Irrtum, *Biol. Zentr.*, **37**, 357 (1917).

BUTLER, C. G.: Smell in Choice of Water by Honey Bee, *J. Exp. Biol.*, **17**, 253 (1940).

CECIL, H.: Smell and Hearing in Insects, *Nature*, **17**, 381 (1878).

COMIGNAN, J.: Smell in Scarabaeus Semipunctatus, *Bull. soc. ent. franc.*, **13**, 214 (1928).

COMSTOCK, J. A.: Foodplants for Insects, Chosen by Odor—Euphyia, *Bull. So. Calif. Acad. Sci.*, **38**, 198 (1939–1940).

——— and C. HENNE: Foodplants for Insects, Chosen by Odor—Nemoria, *Bull. So. Calif. Acad. Sci.*, **39**, 78 (1940).

COTTREAU, J.: L'Odorat chez les insectes, *La Nature*, **34** (1905).

CROMBIE, A. C.: Olfactory Conditioning in Rhizopertha dominica fab, *J. Exp. Biol.*, **18**, 62 (1941).

CRUMB, S. E.: Odors Attractive to Ovipositing Mosquitoes, *Entomol. News*, **35**, 242 (1924).

CUMMINGS: Scent Organs in Trichoptera, *Proc. Zool. Soc. London*, 459 (1914).

CUSHING, J. E.: Experiment on Olfactory Conditioning in Drosophila, *Proc. Nat. Acad. Sci. U. S.*, **27**, 496 (1941).

DE SERRES, M.: De l'odorat et des organes qui paraissent en être le siège chez les insectes, *Ann. mus. hist. nat.*, **18** (1811).

DETHIER, V. G.: Smell in Lepidopteran Larvae, *Biol. bull.*, **72**, 7 (1937).

———: Odor as Factor in Choice of Foodplants of Insects, *Am. Naturalist*, **75**, 61 (1941).

DRIESCH, H.: Sur le Siège de l'odorat chez les insectes, *Institut.*, **7**, 294 (1839).

DUBOIS, R.: Sur le rôle d'olfaction dans les phénomènes d'accouplement chez les papillons, *Compt. rend. assoc. franc. pour l'avance des sci.* (1895).

DUMERIL, A.: Dissertation sur l'organe de l'odorat et sur son existence dans les insectes, *Magas. encycl.*, **2**, 424 (1797).

*FABRE, J. H.: "Social Life in the Insect World," London, 1927.

FIELDE, A. M.: The Progressive Odor of Ants, *Biol. Bull.*, **10**, 1 (1905–1906).

———: Sense of Smell in Ants, *Sci. American Supp.*, **60**, 24820 (1905).

FLANDERS, S. E.: Olfaction by Hymenoptera, *J. Econ. Entomol.*, **37**, 711 (1944).

FLÜGGE, C.: Smell Orientation in Drosophila, *Z. wiss. Biol.*, **20**, 463 (1934).

FOREL, A. H.: Recherches biologiques récentes de Miss Adele Fielde sur les fourmis, *Bull. soc. vaud. sci. natur.*, **39**.

———: Die Eigentümlichkeiten des Geruchssinnes bei den Insekten, *Verhandl. 5 intern. zool. Kongr.*, *Berlin*, 806 (1901).

*———: "The Senses of Insects," London, 1908.

*———: "Le Monde social des fourmis du globe," 1921.

GLASER, R. W.: Smell: Function of Antennae in Insects, *Psyche*, **34**, 209 (1927).

GRABER, V.: Organs of Smell in Insects, *Nature*, **32**, 609 (1885).

———: Smell in Roaches, *Am. J. Psychol.*, **1**, 549.

GRASSE, P. P.: La Reconstruction du nid et le travail collectif chez les termites supérieurs, *J. psychol. norm. path.*, **36**, 370 (1939).

HAMPTON, F. A.: Odor of Flowers in Relation to Insect Attraction, *J. Roy. Hort. Soc.*, **54**, 138 (1929).

HARTUNG, E.: Smell Orientation—Calliphora, *Z. vergl. Physiol.*, **22**, 119 (1935).

HARTWELL, R. A.: A Study of the Olfactory Sense of Termites, *Ann. Entomol. Soc. Am.*, **17**, 131 (1924).

HENNE, C.: Foodplants for insects, chosen by odor—Lepidoptera, *Bull. So. Calif. Acad. Sci.*, **39**, 71 (1940).

HENNING, H.: Künstliche Geruchsspuren bei Ameisen, *Naturw. Wochschr.*, N.F., **15**, 52 (1916).

———: Künstliche Geruchsfährte und Reaktions-struktur der Ameise., *Z. Psychol.*, **74**, 161 (1916).

HERTZ, M.: Smell in Cabbage Butterflies, *Biol. Zentr.*, **47**, 569 (1927).

HILL, A.: Sense of Smell in Flies, *Nature*, **80**, 303 (1909).

IMAMURA, S.: Smell in Beetles, *Bull. Imp. Sericult. Exp. Sta., Japan*, **9**, 1 (1936).

INGLE, L.: Apparatus for Testing Chemotropic Responses of Insects, *J. Econ. Entomol.*, **36**, 108 (1943).

Insects Can be Lured by Scents of Female Sex, *Science News Letter*, **40**, 73 (1941).

Insects Lured by Scent, *Science News Letter*, **40**, 15 (1941).

ISRAEL, W.: Geruchsschärfe den Insekten, *Unsere Welt*, **12**, 107 (1923).

KENNEDY, C. H.: Sensitivity of Insects to Odors, *Ann Entomol. Soc. Am.*, **20**, 87 (1927).

KONINCK, H.: Importance of Smell in Bees, *Ann. soc. roy. zool. Belg.*, **59**, 59 (1928–1929).

LEFEBVRE, A.: Note sur le sentiment olfactif des insectes, *Ann. soc. ent. France*, **4** (1838).

LIEBERMANN, A.: Correlation zwischen den antennalen Geruchsorganen und der Biologie der Musciden, *Z. Morphol. Ökol. Tiere*, **5**, 1 (1925).

LOVELL, J. H.: Conspicuous Flowers Rarely Visited by Insects, *J. Animal Behavior*, **4**, 147 (1914).

———: Odors and the Insect Visitors to Flowers, *Am. Bee J.*, **63**, 450 (1923).

———: Relation of the Honeybee to the Odors of Flowers, *Am. Bee J.*, **63**, 501 (1923).

*LUBBOCK, J.: "Ants, Bees, and Wasps," London, 1882.

LUDWIG, N.: Geruchsempfindung und Riechorgane der Honigbiene, *Natur. Offenbarung*, 554 (1899).

McDUNNOUGH, J.: Foodplants for Insects, Chosen by Smell—Pterophorids, *Can. Entomologist*, **71**, 109 (1939).

———: Foodplants for Insects, Chosen for Odor—New Brunswick *Can. Entomologist*, **72**, 130 (1940).

———: Foodplants for Insects, Chosen by Odor—Peronea, *Can. Entomolgist*, **72**, 59 (1940).

McINDOO, N. E.: The Olfactory Sense of the Honeybee, *J. Exp. Zool.*, **16**, 265 (1914).

———: Olfactory Sense of Hymenoptera, *Proc. Acad. Nat. Sci. U. S.*, **66**, 294 (1914).

———: Olfactory Sense of Insects, *Smithsonian Inst. Pub. Misc. Collections*, **43** (1914).

———: The Olfactory Sense of Coleoptera, *Biol. Bull.*, **28**, 407 (1915).

———: The Olfactory Sense of Orthoptera, *J. Comp. Neurol.*, **31**, 405 (1919–1920).

———: The Senses of Insects, *Smithsonian Inst., Ann. Repts.*, 461 (1920).

———: Senses of the Cotton Boll Weevil—an Attempt to Explain How Plants Attract Insects by Smell, *J. Agr. Research*, **33**, 1095 (1926).

———: Communication among Insects, *Smithsonian Inst., Ann. Repts.*, 541 (1928).

———: Responses of Insects to Odors, *J. Econ. Entomol.*, **21**, 903 (1928).

———: Smell in Lepidoptera, *Smithsonian Inst. Pub. Misc. Coll.*, **81** (1929).

———: Smell and Antennae in Blowflies, *J. Agr. Research*, **46**, 607 (1933).

———: Olfactory Organs in Blowfly, *J. Morphol.*, **56**, 445 (1934).

———: Smell in Insects, Compared with Higher Animals, *Proc. Entomol. Soc. Wash.*, **40**, 25 (1938).

MACIUCA, C.: Effect of Smell Stimulation on Phototropism—Pyrrochoris, *Notationes Biol.*, **3**, 11 (1935).

MATSCHIE: Eigentümlichkeit des Geruchssinnes bei den Insekten, *Natur u. Haus*, **10** (1901).

MECKE, E.: Smell in Butterflies, *Intern. Entomol. Z.*, **21**, 86 (1927).

MEISSNER, O.: Die Bedeutung des Geruchssinnes für die Auffindung der Artgenossen bei Rhopalocuren, *Allgem. Z. Entomol.*, **4**, 268 (1908).

MÉNÉGAUX: Une Observation sur le sens olfactif à distance chez les fourmis, *Bull. inst. gén. psych.*, **6**, 302 (1906).

METZGER, F. W., and C. W. MELL: Odors in Plant Extracts (Clarified) in Relation to Their Susceptibility to Attack by Japanese Beetles, *J. Agr. Research*, **49**, 1001 (1934).

MINNICH, D. E.: An Experimental Study of the Tarsal Chemoreceptors of Two Nymphalid Butterflies, *J. Exp. Zool.*, **33**, 173 (1921).

——: The Chemical Sensitivity of the Tarsi of the Red Admiral Butterfly, *J. Exp. Zool.*, **35**, 56 (1922).

——: The Olfactory Sense of the Cabbage Butterfly, *J. Exp. Zool.*, **39**, 339 (1924).

——: The Chemical Senses of Insects, *Quart. Rev. Biol.*, **4**, 100 (1929).

MURRAY, D.: Foodplants for Insects, Chosen for Odor—Phasis, *J. Entomol. Soc., So. Africa*, **2**, 1 (1939).

NAKAZIMA, S.: Regions for Smell in Silk Worm, *Bull. Miyazaki Coll. Agr. Forestry*, **3**, 129 (1931).

NEWMANN, E.: Insects Attracted by the Offensive Smell of a Flower, *Entomol. Mag.*, **2**, 120 (1834).

PAASCH, A.: Von den Sinnesorganen der Insekten in allgemeinen, von Gehör- und Geruchsorganen im besonderen, *Arch. Naturforsch.*, **39**, 248 (1873).

PICK, W.: Sense of Smell in Louse, *Dermat. Wochschr.*, **83**, 1020 (1926).

PIERON, H.: Le Mécanisme de la reconnaissance chez les fourmis; rôle des données olfactives, *Comp. rend. soc. biol.*, **61**, 471 (1906).

——: Exceptions et variations dans le processus olfactif de reconnaissance chez les fourmis, *Comp. rend. soc. biol.*, **61**, 433 (1906).

——: Le rôle de l'olfaction dans la reconnaissance des fourmis, *Comp. rend. acad. sci.*, **143**, 845 (1906).

PLATEAU, F.: Recherches experimentales sur les fleurs entomophiles peu visitées par les insectes rendues attractives au moyen de liquide sucrés odorants, *Mém. acad. sci. Belg.*, **2**, 55 (1910).

POULTON, E. B.: Smell in Male Moths, *Nature*, **123**, 717 (1929).

PYCRAFT, W. P.: Some Mysteries of Scent in Beetles and Moths, *Illustrated London News*, **199**, 380 (1941).

RAU, P., and N. L. RAU: Smell in Moths—Location of Sensory Apparatus, *Trans. Acad. Sci., St. Louis*, **26**, 81 (1929).

REED, M. R.: Smell Reactions of Drosophila, *Physiol. Zoöl.*, **11**, 317 (1938).

RILEY, C. V.: The Sense of Insects, *Nature*, **52**, 209 (1895).

RIVNAY, E.: Smell in Bedbugs, *Parasitology*, **24**, 121 (1932).

ROHLER, E.: Beiträge zur Kenntniss d. Sinnesorgane d. Insekten, *Zool. Jahrb. Anat.*, **22**, 225 (1906).

RÖHER, A.: Smell in Lepidoptera, *Entomol. Anz.*, **6**, 41 (1926).

ROSENTHAL: Über den Geruchsinn der Insekten, *Arch. Physiol.*, **10**, 427 (1811).

RULAND, F.: Beiträge z. Kenntniss d. antennalen Sinnesorgane d. Insekten, *Z. wiss. Zool.*, **46**, 602 (1888).

SALT, G., and J. LAING: Discriminative Ability of a Parasitoid, *Nature,* **135,** 792 (1935).

SCHALLER, A.: Olfactory Organs in Water Beetle, *Z. wiss. Biol.,* Abt. C, **4,** 370 (1926).

SCHLENIG: Über den Geruchssinn der Schmetterlinge, *Allgem. deut. naturh. Ztg.,* **2** (1847).

SOIKA, A. G.: Smell in Ants, Orientation by, *Boll. soc. ent. ital.,* **64,** 20 (1932).

STEINER, G.: Methodische Untersuchungen über die Geruchsorientierung von Fleischfliegen, *Z. Vergl. Physiol.,* **30,** 1 (1942).

SWAIN, R. B.: Foodplants for Insects, Chosen by Odor, *Univ. Colo. Stud.,* Gen. Ser. A, **26,** 117 (1940).

THORPE, W. H.: Smell—Conditioned Response in Nemeritis, *Proc. Roy. Soc. London,* **126B,** 370 (1938).

——: Smell Conditioning in Drosophila, *Proc. Roy. Soc. London,* **127B,** 424 (1939).

—— and H. B. CANDLE: A Study of the Olfactory Responses of Insect Parasites to the Food Plant of Their Host, *Parasitology,* **30,** 523 (1938).

TIMBERGEN, N.: Smell as Behavior Stimulus in Bee Wolf, *Z. Vergl. Physiol.,* **21,** 699 (1935).

TURNER, C. H.: The Homing of Ants; an Experimental Study of Ant Behavior, *J. Comp. Neurol.,* **17,** 367 (1907).

VALENTINE, J. M.: Smell in Tenebrio Molitor (Mealworm Moth), *J. Exp. Zool.,* **58,** 165 (1930).

VAN THIEL, P. H., J. REUTER, and L. BEVERE: Smell Discrimination in Anophelines, *Riv. malariol.,* **18,** 95 (1939).

VERLAINE, L.: Olfaction and Generalization in Wasps, *Bull. ann. soc. entomol. Belg.,* **72,** 311 (1932).

VON BUTTEL-REEPEN, H.: Der Geruchssinn der Bienen, *Bienenw. Zentr.,* **196** (1907); **3,** 35 (1909).

VON FRISCH, K.: Über den Geruchssinn der Biene und seine Bedeutung für den Blümenbesuch, *Verhandl. zool.-bot. ges., Wien,* **65** (1915).

——: Zur alten Frage nach d. Sitz d. Geruchsinnes bei Insekten, *Verhandl. zool.-bot. ges. Wien,* **69,** 17 (1919).

——: Über d. Sitz des Geruchsinnes bei Insekten, *Zool. Jahrb. Anat.,* **38,** 449 (1921).

——: Language of Bees, *Sci. Progress,* **32,** 29 (July, 1937).

——: Versuche über die Lenkung des Bienenfluges durch Duftstoffe, *Naturwissenschaften,* **31,** 445 (1943).

——: Weitere Versuche über die Lenkung des Bienenfluges durch Duftstoffe, *Biol. Zentr.,* **64,** 237 (1944).

WACKER, F.: Beiträge zur Kenntniss der antennalen Sinnesorgane der Hymenopteren, *Z. Morphol. Ökol. Tiere,* **4,** 739 (1925).

WARNKE: Experimentelle Untersuchungen über d. Geruchssinn v. Geotrupes silvaticus panz u. Geotrupes vernalis Lin, *Z. wiss. Biol.,* Abt. C, **14,** 121 (1931).

WASMANN, E.: Die Bedeutung des Geruchssinnes bei Raupenwespen für die Auffindung der Brutröhre, *Allgem. Z. Entomol.,* N.S., **4,** 190 (1908).

*WIGGLESWORTH, V. B.: "The Principles of Insect Physiology," London, 1939.

WOJTUSIAK, R. J.: Smell in Maintaining Aggregations of Pieris Brassicae Larvae, *Bull. intern. acad. polon. sci. Classe sci. math. nat.,* Ser. B, *Sci. Nat.* (11) Zool. (9/10) 631 (1930).

WOLFF, O. J. B.: Das Riechorgan der Biene, *Nova acta Leopold-Carol. Akad. Naturforsch.,* **38** (1875).

ZANDER, E.: Das Geruchsvermögen der Biene, *Biol. Zentr.,* **33,** 711 (1913).

c. Vertebrates Other Than Humans

ADRIAN, E. D., and C. LUDWIG: Mode of Action of Olfactory Organs in Fish, *J. Physiol.*, **94**, 441 (1938).

ADRIAN, E. D.: Olfactory Reactions in the Brain of the Hedgehog, *J. Physiol.*, **100**, 459 (1942).

ALLEN, G.: Sight and Smell in Vertebrates, *Mind*, **6**, 453 (1881).

ALLEN, W. F.: Nasal Irritation by Vapors—Effect on Respiration and Blood Pressure, *Am. J. Physiol.*, **87**, 319 (1928).

———: Nasal Irritation by Vapors—Effect on Respiration and Blood Pressure, *Am. J. Physiol.*, **88**, 117 (1929).

———: Comparative Study of the Olfactory and Trigeminal Reflexes Elicited by Various Vapors in Different Mammals, *J. Wash. Acad. Sci.*, **26**, 466 (1936).

———: Olfactory Organs and Respiratory Reflexes—Level of Anesthesia for Dogs and Rabbits, *Am. J. Physiol.*, **115**, 579 (1936).

———: Conditioned Olfactory Reflexes in Dogs, *Am. J. Physiol.*, **118**, 532 (1937).

———: Studies on the Olfactory System Based on the Effects of Brain Lesions on Conditioned Reflexes in Dogs, *Am. J. Physiol.*, **126**, 419 (1939).

———: Effect of Ablating the Pyriform Amygdaloid Area and Hippocampi on Positive and Negative Olfactory Conditioned Reflexes and on Conditioned Olfactory Differentiation, *Am. J. Physiol.*, **132**, 81 (1941).

———: Distribution of Cortical Potentials Resulting from Insufflation of Vapors into the Nostrils and from Stimulation of the Olfactory Bulbs and the Pyriform Lobe, *Am. J. Physiol.*, **139**, 553 (1943).

BAGLIONI, S.: Zur Physiologie des Geruchsinnes und des Tastsinnes der Seetierel Versuche an Octopus und einigen Fischen, *Zentr. Physiol.*, **22**, 719 (1908).

BANUS, M. G., H. H. CORMAN, and G. POPKIN: Sensitivity of Nose and Respiratory Center to Hydrogen Ion Concentration, *Am. J. Physiol.*, **142**, 121 (1944).

BATESON, W.: The Sense Organs and Perceptions of Fishes, with Remarks on the Supply of Bait, *J. Marine Assoc. London*, N.S., **1**, 225 (1890).

BAUMANN, F.: Smell Reflexes in Snakes and Food Habits, *Rev. suisse zool.*, **34**, 173 (1927).

———: Delicacy of Discrimination of Smell in Vipers, *Rev. suisse zool.*, **35**, 233 (1928).

BAYER, H.: Narkotische Wirkung von Riechstoffen und ihr Einfluss auf die motorischen Nerven des Frosches, *Arch. Anat. Physiol.* (supp.), 203 (1902).

BELLOWS, R. T., and W. P. WAGENEN: Olfactory Nerve—Effect on Water Intake of Dog, *Am. J. Physiol.*, **126**, 13 (1939).

BENHAM, W. B.: Olfactory Sense in Apteryx, *Nature*, **74**, 222 (1906).

BINET, A., and J. PASSY: Contribution à l'étude de l'olfaction chez le chien, *Comp. rend. assoc. Franc. pour l'avance des sci.*, 24me session, **1**, 292; **2**, 659 (1895–1896).

BOGERT, L. M.: Sensory Cues Used by Rattlesnakes in Their Recognition of Ophidian Enemies, *Ann. N. Y. Acad. Sci.*, **41**, 329 (1941).

BOLING, L. R.: Regeneration of Mucosa, *Arch. Otolaryngol.*, **22**, 689 (1935).

BORGHESON, E.: Effects on Nasal Mucosa of Experimental Castration, *Valsalva*, **7**, 625 (1931).

BOYD, E. M., M. I. MACLACHLAN, and W. F. PERRY: Experimental Ammonia and Gas Poisoning in Rabbits and Cats, *J. Ind. Hyg. Toxicol.*, **26**, 29 (1944).

BOZZELLI: De alcune moderne ricerche sull'odorato del cane del punto di vista fisiologico e psicologico, *Clin. vet.*, **44**, 380 (1921).

BREDER, C. M, and P. RASQUIN: Chemical Sensory Reactions in Mexican Blind Characins, *Zoologica*, **28**, 169 (1943).

BROWN, C. W., and E. E. GHISELLI: Smell Discrimination after Subcortical Lesions, *J. Comp. Psychol.*, **26**, 109 (1938).

BULL, H. O.: Role of Smell in Purposive Movements of Fish, *Dove Marine Lab. Rept.*, **39** (1929).

———: Role of Smell in Purposive Movements of Fish, *J. Marine Biol. Assoc.*, **16**, 615 (1930).

BUYTENDIJK: L'Odorat du Chien, *Arch. néerland. physiol.*, **4**, 434 (1920–1921).

CAHALANE, V. H.: Smell Evaluated as Factor in Finding Food of Western Fox Squirrel, *J. Wildlife Management*, **6**, 338 (1942).

Can Birds Smell? *Literary Digest*, **74**, 70 (Sept. 23, 1922).

CERLETTI, U.: Die Mastzellen als regelmässiger Befund im Bulbus olfactorius des normalen Hundes, *Folia neuro-biol.*, **5**, 718 (1911).

———: Nuovo reperto nel bulbo olfattorio dei cani, *Atti del 14 congr. della soc. freniat. ital.*, 132 (1911).

CIURLO, L.: Olfactory Stimuli as Affecting Respiratory Reflex, *Arch. ital. otol.*, **44**, 109 (1933).

———: Effect on Blood Pressure of Odors, *Arch. ital. otol.*, **44**, 321 (1933).

COLE, L. W.: Reactions of Frogs to Chlorides of Ammonium, Potassium, Sodium, and Lithium, *J. Comp. Neurol.*, **20**, 601 (1910).

COPELAND, M.: The Olfactory Reactions of the Spotted Newt, *J. Animal Behavior*, **3**, 260 (1913).

———: The Olfactory Reactions of the Puffer or Swellfish, *J. Exp. Zool.*, **12**, 363 (1912–1913).

CRAIGIE, E. H.: Smell and Migration in Salmon, *Trans. Roy. Soc. Can.*, **20**, 215 (1926).

———: Vascular Supply of Archicortex of Rat; Smell Sense of Albino Rat at Birth, *J. Comp. Neurol.*, **52**, 353 (1931).

DE MAND, G. W.: The Effects of Olfactory Cues on the Maze Learning of White Rats, *Trans. Kans. Acad. Sci.*, **43**, 337 (1940).

DETWILER, S. R.: Behavior in Amblystoma Larvae Lacking Forebrain, Eyes and Nasal Placodes, *Proc. Soc. Exp. Biol. Med.*, **56**, 195 (1944).

———: Results of Unilateral and Bilateral Extirpation of Forebrain of Amblystoma, *J. Exp. Zool.*, **100**, 103 (1945).

DICE, L. R.: Smell in Squirrels, *J. Mammalogy*, **8**, 55 (1927).

DIETZ, A. A.: pH of Nasal Mucosa of Some Laboratory Animals, *Proc. Soc. Exp. Biol. Med.*, **57**, 339 (1944).

*DIXON, R. M.: The Sense of Snakes, *Verhandl. 5 intern. zool. Kongr.*, Berlin, 1901.

DMITRIEV, V. D.: Effect of Conditioned Reflexes on the Variability of Motor Chronaxie during Excitation of the Olfactory Receptor in the Dog, *Bull. biol. méd. exp. U.R.S.S.*, **11**, 186 (1941).

*DUMERIL, A.: "Mémoire sur l'odorat des poissons," *Magas. encycl.*, **5** (1807).

FLORESCO, N.: Naso-palpebral Reflex, *Bull. fac. Stünte Cernauti*, **7**, 115 (1933–1934).

FRENCH, R. L.: A Method of Studying Olfactory Discrimination in the White Rat, *Psychol. Bull.*, **36**, 643 (1939).

———: Smell Sensitivity—Demonstration in Rat, *J. Comp. Psychol.*, **29**, 307 (1940).

FRUHWALD, V.: Die Folgen des einseitigen Nasenerschlusses auf die Riechschleimhaut und auf den Bulbus und Tractus olfactarius, *Arch. Ohren-, Nasen-, u. Kehlkopfheilk*, **139**, 153 (1935).

*GARTEN, S.: "Beiträge zur Physiologie der marklosen Nerven. Nach Untersuchungen am Riech-nerven des Hechtes," Jena, 1903.

GIOACCHINI, R.: Nasal Mucosa: Action of Some Substances in Rabbit, *Valsalva*, **7**, 765 (1931).

GRUHL, K.: Beiträge zur Physiologie der Cetaceen-nase, Jena., *Z. Naturw.*, **40**, 367 (1911).

GURNEY, J. H.: On the Sense of Smell Possessed by Birds, *Ibis*, **4**, 225 (1922).

GYLEP, F.: Untersuchungen über das Planum nasale der Hauscarnivoren und den Befeuchtungsmodus an demselben, *Anat. Anz.*, **40**, 449 (1912).

HARTRIDGE, H.: Olfaction and Nutrition, *J. Physiol.*, **103**, 34 (1945).

*HEITZENROEDER, C.: "Über das Verhalten des Hundes gegen einige Riechstoffe," München, 1913.

HENNING, H.: Geruchsversuche am Hund, *Z. Biol.*, **70**, 1 (1919).

HOLT, C. M.: Studies on the Olfactory Bulbs in the Albino Rat. I, Effects of a Defective Diet and Exercise; II, Number of Cells in the Bulb, *J. Comp. Neurol.*, **27**, 201 (1917).

HONGO, N.: An Experimental Study on Smelling. (1) Changes in Respiratory Movement Caused by Olfactory Stimulus and Measurement of Smell in Rabbits, *Tohoku Med. J.*, **19** (Supp. 3), 213 (1936).

———: Rise and Fall in the Olfaction in Rabbits, *Tohoku Med. J.*, **19** (Supp. 3), 91, 150 (1936).

HONZIK, C. H.: Use of Smell in Maze Learning of Rat, *J. Comp. Psychol.*, **27**, 149 (1939).

HUGGINS, J. M.: The Sense of Smell in Dogs, *Nature*, **36**, 412 (1887).

HUNNICUTT, L. G.: Effect of $ZnSO_4$ on Olfactory Mucous Membrane in Dogs and Monkeys, *Trans. Pacific Coast Oto.-Ophth. Soc.*, **24**, 72 (1939).

ISAHARA, K.: Smell in Birds, *Z. ges. Anat.*, Abt. I, **98**, 548 (1932).

ITO, M.: Nose Influenced by Vagal Stimulation, *J. Med. Assoc. Formosa*, **39**, 579 (1940).

JOHNSON, H.: A Note on the Supposed Olfactory Hunting Responses of the Dog, *J. Animal Behavior*, **4**, 76 (1914).

JUNG, TAGARD, and F. CHAVANNE: Nasal Mucosa; Histopathology after Incision of Sphenopalatine Block and Superior Cervical Ganglion, with Section of Pneumogastric, *Otorhinolaryngol. intern.*, **12**, 193 (1928).

KEELER, C. E.: Smell Sense as Correlated with Coat Color in Norway Rat, *J. Heredity*, **33**, 371 (1942).

KOBLANCK and H. ROEDER: Tierversuche über Beeinflussung des Sexualsystems durch nasale Eingriffe, *Berlin klin. Wochschr.*, **49**, 1893 (1912).

KRAMER, G.: Smell in Frog, *Zool. Jahrb. Anat.*, **52**, 629 (1933).

KUNYAYEFF, A.: Investigation of Function of Olfaction in Dogs by the Method of Psychoreflexes, *Obsor. psichiat. nevrol. St. Petersburg*, **17**, 215 (1912).

KURE, K., and F. SAKURASAWA: Nasal Mucosa: Secretory Fibers, *Z. wiss. biol.*, Abt. B, **9**, 245 (1929).

LASHLEY, K. S., and R. W. SPERRY: Olfactory Discrimination after Destruction of Anterior Thalamic Nuclei, *Am. J. Physiol.*, **139**, 446 (1943).

LIGGETT, J. R.: Two Methods Used to Determine Sensitivity of Olfactory Organs in White Rat—Vincent's and Yerkes', *Genetic Psychol. Monogr.*, **3**, 1 (1928).

LOCHER, C. J. S.: Smell and Food Perception in Toads, *Z. wiss. Biol.*, Abt. C, **6**, 378 (1927).

LOHNER, L.: Olfactory Efficiency of Police Dogs, *Arch. ges. Physiol.*, **212**, 84 (1926).

LUSTIG, A.: Die Degeneration des Epithels der Riechschleimhaut des Kaninchens nach Zerstörung der Riechlappen desselben, *Sitzber. kgl. Akad. der Wissen. zu Wien*, **89**, 119 (1884).

McKECHNIE, W. E.: Sense of Smell in Birds, *Nature*, **110**, 784 (1922).

———: Soaring Flight and the Olfactory Organs of Birds, *Nature*, **111**, 48 (1923).

MATTHES, E.: Smell in Triton, Change of Medium as Affecting, *Z. wiss. Biol.*, Abt. C, **5**, 83 (1927).

————: Weitere Geruchsdressuren an Meerschweinchen, *Z. wiss. Biol.*, Abt. C, **17**, 464 (1932).

————: Leistungsfähigkeit des Geruchssinnes makrosmatischer Säugetiere, *Forsch. Fortschr.*, **8**, 434 (1932).

MEEK, A.: Sense of Smell in Birds, *Nature*, **110**, 279 (1922).

*MENZEL, E., and R. MENZEL: "Smell in Dog, in Service of Man," Berlin, 1930.

MILAS, N. A.: Area of Olfaction in Steer; Vitamins A and Carotenoids, *J. Am. Chem. Soc.*, **61**, 1929 (1939).

MILSTEIN, T.: Sur la Physiologie de l'organe de Jacobson, *Rev. laryngol.*, **50**, 705 (1929).

MOCCHI, D.: Alterazioni prodotte nella macula lutea e nell' organo di Jacobson del coniglio da distruzione dei bulbi olfattivi, per vedere se quest' organo e in rapporto col senso dell' odorato, *Arch. ital. laryngol.*, **23**, 57 (1903).

MORTIMER, H., *et al.*: Effect of Oestrogenic Hormone Administration upon Nasal Mucous Membrane of Monkey, *Proc. Soc. Exp. Biol. Med.*, **34**, 535 (1936).

————, R. P. WRIGHT, and J. B. COLLIP: Effect of Administration of Estrogenic Hormone in Monkey (Macaca mulatta), *J. Can. Med. Assoc.*, **35**, 503 (1936).

MOST, K., and BRUCKNER: Present-day Hypotheses of the Dog's Nasal Function, *Zentr. Kleintierk, Pelztierk*, **12**, 9 (1936).

MULLER-LIEBENWALDE, J.: Geruchssinn der Wildente und anderer Vögel, *Monatsscher. allgem. deut. Jagschutz-vereins*, 311 (1904).

MURPHY, W. C.: Nasal Mucosa: Anaphylaxis as Affecting in Guinea Pigs, *Arch. Otolaryngol.*, **13**, 842 (1931).

NAGAHARA, Y.: Olfactory Nerve Section-Regeneration, *Trans. Soc. Path. Japon.*, **30**, 648 (1940).

NEMOURS, P. R.: Accessory Sinuses: Comparative Morphology in Reptiles and Birds, *Ann. Otol., Rhinol. & Laryngol.*, **39**, 1086 (1930).

NICOLAI, G. F.: Über die Leitungsgeschwindigkeit im Riechnerven des Hechtes, *Arch. ges. Physiol.*, **85**, 65 (1901).

NICHOLAS, J. S.: Reactions of Amblystoma Tigrinum to Olfactory Stimuli, *J. Exp. Zool.*, **35**, 257 (1922).

NOBLE, G. K.: Functions of Jacobson's Organ in Lizards, *J. Genetic Psychol.*, **43**, 371 (1936).

————: Species and Sex Recognized by Odors: The Snakes, *Bull. Am. Mus. Nat. Hist.*, **73**, 673 (1937).

———— and A. SCHMIDT: Reaction of Snakes to Odor of Prey, *Proc. Am. Phil. Soc.*, **77**, 263 (1937).

NOLTE, W.: Sense of Smell in Ducks, *Zool. Anz.*, **71**, 115 (1927).

OLIVIER, H. D.: Smell in Lions, *J. Bombay Nat. Hist. Soc.*, **33**, 977 (1929).

OLMSTED, J. M. D.: Sense of Smell in Common Catfish, *Am. J. Physiol.*, **46**, 443 (1918).

PAGANO, A.: Smell Acuity: Relation to Amount of Myelin in Olfactory Nerve, *Riv. neurol.*, **6**, 3 (1933).

PARKER, G. H.: Olfactory Reactions in Fish, *J. Exp. Zool.*, **8**, 535 (1910).

————: The Olfactory Reactions of the Common Kill-fish, *J. Exp. Zool.*, **10**, 1 (1911).

————: The Olfactory Sense of Fishes, *Proc. Am. Physiol. Soc.*, **32**, XIX (1911).

————: The Relation of Smell, Taste, and the Common Chemical Sense in Vertebrates, *Hist. Sci.*, **15**, 221 (1912).

————: The Directive Influence of the Sense of Smell in the Dogfish, *Bull. U. S. Bureau Fisheries*, **33**, 61 (1914).

*————: "Smell, Taste and Allied Senses in Vertebrates," Lippincott, Philadelphia, 1922.

—— and R. E. SHELDON: The Sense of Smell in Fishes, *Bull. U. S. Bureau Fisheries*, **32**, 33 (1912).

PIPPING, M.: Smell: Role in Feeding Fish, *Soc. Sci. Fennica Commentat. Biol.*, **2** (4), 1 (1927).

POLIAKOV, K. L.: Conditioned Reflex to Smell in Turtle, *Russ. J. Physiol.*, **13**, 161 (1930).

PUJIULA, J.: Smell and Orientation in New-born Rat, *Bol. soc. iberica cien. nat.*, **26**, 104 (1927).

QUASTLER, H., and H. WEINGARTEN: Regeneration of Olfactory Mucosa in Fish, *Z. wiss. Biol.*, Abt. D, **122**, 763 (1930).

RASPAIL, X.: Sense of Smell in Birds, *Smithsonian Inst. Pubs., Repts.*, 367 (1899).

REESE, A. M.: Food and Chemical Reactions of the Spotted Newt Diemyctilus Viridescens, *J. Animal Behavior*, **2**, 190 (1912).

REID, C.: Blood Sugar after Activation of Nerve Centers of Olfaction, *J. Physiol.*, **102**, 20 (1943).

REPETTI, U.: Smell in Cetacea, *Valsalva*, **3**, 565 (1927).

REYNOLDS, S. R. M., and F. I. FOSTER: Nose Mucosa: Estrogen as Affecting Acetylcholine Content, *Am. J. Physiol.*, **131**, 422 (1940).

RISSER, J.: Olfactory Reactions in Amphibians, *J. Exp. Zool.*, **16**, 617 (1914).

ROMANES, G. J.: Experiments on the Sense of Smell in Dogs, *Nature*, **36**, 273, 317, 412 (1887).

ROSSI, G.: Food Deficiency and Olfaction, *Boll. soc. ital. biol. sper.*, **5**, 584 (1930).

——: Smell: Foods as Excitants, *Lo Sperimentale*, **86**, 75 (1932).

RUDOLPH, K.: Geruchssinn d. Hunde, *Psyche*, **7**, 99 (1923).

RUSSEL, W. J.: The Sense of Smell in Dogs, *Nature*, **36**, 317 (1887).

SAHLSTEDT, A. V.: Beiträge zur Kenntnis des Geruchsmechanismus bei makrosmatischen Säugetieren, *Skand. Arch. Physiol.*, **28**, 1 (1912).

SANDERS, F. K.: Olfaction in Goldfish, *J. Exp. Biol.*, **17**, 416 (1940).

SCHMID: Nasal Function and Psychological Ability of the Dog, *Umschau*, **39**, 457 (1935).

SCHULTZ, W.: Sense of Smell in Triton Larvae, *Z. Morphol. Ökol. Tiere*, **32**, 463 (1937).

Sense of Smell in Birds; a Debated Question, *Nature*, **109**, 783 (1922).

Sense of Smell in Fish, *N. Y. J. Med.*, **110**, 591 (1919).

SHELDON, R. E.: The Reactions of the Dogfish to Chemical Stimuli, *J. Comp. Neurol.*, **19**, 273 (1909).

——: The Sense of Smell in Selachians, *J. Exp. Zool.*, **10**, 51 (1911).

SIGLING, T. D.: Smell: Problem in Bloodhound, *Tijdschr. diergeneesk.*, **55**, 573 (1928).

SNETHLAGE, E.: Smell in Ringed Plover in Brazil, *Bol. mus. nacion., Rio de Janeiro*, **3**, 59 (1927).

SOUDEK, S.: Smell in Birds, *Trans. 19th Intern. Congr. Zool., Budapest*, **1**, 755 (1927).

STONE, C. P.: A Simple Method for Developing Olfactory Discrimination in Rats, *J. Genetic Psychol.*, **58**, 419 (1941).

STRONG, R. M.: On the Olfactory Organs and the Sense of Smell in Birds, *J. Morphol.*, **22**, 619 (1911).

SULZE, W.: Über die elektrische Reaktion des Nervus olfactorius des Hechtes auf Doppel-reizung, *Arch. ges. Physiol.*, **127**, 57 (1909).

SUND, C.: Die Entwicklung des Geruchsorgans bei Spinax niger, *Zool. Jahrb. Anat.*, **22**, 157 (1905).

SWANN, H. G.: Smell Discrimination as Affected by Ablation of Olfactory Bulbs of Rat, *J. Comp. Psychol.*, **15**, 229 (1933).

——: Brain Function in Smell, *J. Physiol.*, **111**, 257 (1935).

TULIN, I. F.: Function of Olfactory Organs as Factor for the Realization of Normal Development of the Sexual System and Libido in Rats, *Bull. biol. med. exp. U.R.S.S.*, **12**, 59 (1941).

VAN DEN BERGHE, L.: Smell: Olfactory Currents in Teleosts, *Bull. acad. roy. Belg., Classe sci.*, **15**, 278 (1929).

VINCENT, S. B.: The White Rat and the Maze Problem. II, The Introduction of an Olfactory Control, *J. Animal Behavior*, **5**, 140 (1915).

VON BOETTICHER, H.: Nasal Structure and Evolution in Birds: Turbinares, *Senckenbergiana*, **12**, 91 (1930).

VON SCHILLER, P.: Reaction of Minnows to Odor, *Z. wiss. Biol.*, Abt. C, **19**, 304 (1933).

WAGNER, H. O.: Olfactory Responses in Birds, *J. Ornithol.*, **87**, 1 (1939).

WALTER, W. G.: Experiments on Sense of Smell in Birds, *Arch. néerland. physiol.*, **28**, 1 (1943).

WALTERS, J. H.: Sight and Smell in Dogs, *Nature*, **7**, 361 (1873).

WILDE, W. S.: The Role of Jacobson's Organ in the Feeding Reaction of the Common Garter Snake, *J. Exp. Zool.*, **77**, 445 (1938).

WILLIAMS, C. B.: The Sense of Smell in Birds, *Nature*, **110**, 149 (1922).

WILLIAMSON, H. C.: Smell and Migration in Salmon, *Contrib. Can. Biol. Fisheries*, **3**, 267 (1927).

WINSLOW, C. E. A., and D. GREENBERG: The Effect of the Respiration of Putrid Gases upon the Growth of Guinea Pigs, *Proc. Soc. Exp. Biol. Med.*, **15**, 123 (1918).

WUNDER, W.: Smell: Role in Feeding Fish, *Z. wiss. Biol.*, Abt. C, **6**, 67 (1927).

ZAHN, W.: Olfactory Sense of Certain Birds, *Z. vergl. Physiol.*, **19**, 785 (1933).

d. Humans

ALLEN, W. F.: Nasal Irritation by Vapors: Effect on Respiration and Blood Pressure, *Am. J. Physiol.*, **88**, 620 (1929).

——— and M. SCHWARTZ: Stimulation of Olfaction: Effect on Sensibility of Organs of Vision, *J. Gen. Physiol.*, **24**, 105 (1940).

ARONSOHN, E.: Die electrische Geruchsempfindung; neue Beweise, *Zentr. med. Wiss.*, **26**, 370 (1888).

AUTENRIETH: Bemerkung über einen Versuch von Galen den Geruchsinn betrefend, *Arch. ges. Physiol.*, **9**, 377 (1809).

BAILEY, E. H. S., and L. NICHOLS: L'Odorat chez les femmes, *Rev. sci.*, **39**, 188 (1887).

BANISTER, H., and O. L. ZANGWILL: Experimentally Induced Olfactory Paramnesias, *Brit. J. Psychol.*, **32**, 155 (1941).

BILANCIONI, G.: La fisiologie dell' istinto dell olfatto in Lorenzo Magalotti, *Riv. storia sci. med. nat.*, **15**, 129 (1924).

———: State of Mucous Membrane of Nose in Man and Woman of Different Ages, *Arch. ital. laringol.*, **50**, 7 (1931).

BISHOP, J.: Observations on the Physiology of the Nerves of Sensation, Illustrated by a Case of Paralysis of the Fifth Pair, *Proc. Roy. Soc., London*, **3**, 205 (1833).

BLAKESLEE, A. F.: Unlike Reactions of Different Individuals to Fragrance in Verbena Flowers, *Science*, N.S., **48**, 298 (1918).

———: Differences between People in Taste and Smell Reactions, *Eugenical News*, **18**, 63 (May–June, 1933).

BOMBELLI, U.: Nasal Mucosa: Relation to Genital Functions in Female, *Riv. oto-neuro-oftal.*, **8**, 230 (1931).

BOMPIANI, R.: A proposito de correlazioni naso-genitali nella donna importanza del fattore endocrino constituzionale, *Clin. ostet.*, **27**, 249 (1925).

BORGHESAN, E.: Nasal Mucosa: Changes in Ovarian Insufficiency, *Valsalva*, **7**, 729 (1931).

BUCHNER: Geruchswahrnehmungen bei Kindern, *Münch. med. Wochschr.*, **78**, 760 (1931).

BULL, N.: The Olfaction Drive in Dislike, *J. Psychol.*, **17**, 3 (1944).

COBB, F. C., and E. V. NAGLE: Bacteriology of the Normal Nose, *Trans. Am. Laryngol. Assoc.*, **73** (1909).

COLENSO, W.: Smell in Maoris, *Living Age*, **196**, 448 (1893).

*COMBE, A.: "Influence des parfums et des odeurs sur les nevropathes et les hysteriques," Paris, 1905.

COMEL, G.: Reaction to Snuff: Clinical and Experimental Study, *Boll. malat. orecchio*, **54**, 98 (1936).

COOLIDGE, E. L.: Baby's Special Senses, *Pictorial Rev.*, **35**, 42 (February, 1934).

DADISET, H. J.: The Nose and the Generative Organ in Human Beings, *Trans. Grant Coll. Med. Soc.*, 51 (1899).

*DARWIN, C.: "The Descent of Man and Selection in Relation to Sex," 2d ed., D. Appleton & Co., New York, 1896.

DAVALOS, R. C.: Psychoneurophysiologic Perception of Fetus and New-born Infant, *Rev. med. cubana*, **53**, 206 (1942).

DE CERQUEIRA FALCAO, E.: Nasal Mucosa: Criticism of Asuero's Book Entitled "Ahora hablo yo," *Semana med.*, **2**, 508 (1930).

DELLA CIOPPA, D.: Variations of Pneumographic Curves and Reflexogenic Zones of Nasal Mucosa in Tracheotomized Patients, *Arch. ital. laringol.*, **55**, 97 (1940).

DISHER, D. R.: The Reaction of New-born Infants to Chemical Stimuli Administered Nasally, *Ohio Univ. Studies*, **12**, 1 (1934).

ELSBERG, C. A.: Newer Aspects of Olfactory Physiology and Their Diagnostic Applications, *Arch. Neurol. Psychiat.*, **37**, 223 (1937).

———: Olfaction as Physiochemical Process and Its Mathematical Expression, *Trans. Am. Neurol. Assoc.*, **64**, 36 (1938).

FALTA, M.: Über die Beziehung der Nase zu den weiblichen Genitalien, *Monatsschr. Ohrenheilk.*, **39**, 506 (1905).

FÉRÉ, G.: Étude expérimentale de l'influence, des excitations agréables et des excitations desagréables sur le travail, *L'Ann. psychol.*, **7**, 82 (1901).

*FAUCONNEY, J.: "La volupté et les parfums; rapport des odeurs avec le sens genital, le parfum naturel de la femme," Paris, 1903.

GEYS, K.: Smell Stimulation in Beer Drinking, *Wochschr. Brau*, **47**, 193 (1930).

GRAZZI, V.: Sulla fisio-pathologia dei nervi olfattivi, *Atti. congr. soc. ital. laringol.*, **4**, 9 (1899).

GRIESBACH, H.: Vergleichende Untersuchungen über die Sinnesscharje Blinder und Sehender, *Arch. ges. Physiol.*, **74**, 577; **75**, 365, 523 (1899).

GRIJNS, G.: Messungen der Riechschärfe bei Europäern und Javanen, *Arch. Physiol.*, 509 (1906).

GRISOGANI, N.: Odors: Effect on Parotid Secretion, *Atti accad. Lincei*, **1**, 602 (1925).

HAGEMANN, J. A.: The Correlation Between Olfactory and Genital Functions in the Human Female, *Med. Record*, **88**, 1091 (1915).

*HAGEN, A.: "Die sexuelle Osphresiologie," Charlottenburg, 1901.

HAMPTON, F. A.: Sense of Smell in Everyday Life, *Nineteenth Cent.*, **106**, 513 (1929),

HANSEN, R., and L. GLASS: Geruchssinn in der Schwangerschaft, *Klin. Wochschr.*, **15**, 891 (1936).

HEERMANN, G.: Über die Lehre von den Beziehungen der oberen Luftwege zu der weiblichen Genitalsphäre, *Samml. Zwangl. Abh. Gebiete der Nasen-, Ohren-, Mund- u. Halskrankh.,* **8**, 1 (1904).

HEETDERKS, D. R.: Nasal Mucosa: Reaction of Normal Nasal Mucous Membrane, *Am. J. Sci.,* **174**, 231 (1927).

Helen Keller's Indian-keen Sense of Smell, *Literary Digest,* **99**, 66 (1928).

HANNING, H.: Psychol. Studien am Geruchssinn, *Handbuch biol. Arbeitsmeth.,* **6A**, 741 (1926).

HENSSGE, E.: Steigerung d. Geruchsempfindlichheit in d. Schwangerschaft, *Psychol. Med.,* **4**, 206 (1930).

HESSE, W.: Physiologic and Clinical Aspect of Sense of Smell, *Semana Med.,* **1**, 258 (1929).

HILL, L.: Nasal Passages: Congestion by Heat Rays, *Brit. Med. J.,* **1**, 1096 (1933).

———: Infra-red Light as Affecting Nasal Mucosa, *Quart. J. Exp. Physiol.,* **23**, 35 (1933).

———: Nasal Mucosa Influenced by Infra-red Rays from Dull and Bright Sources, *Am. J. Hyg.,* **22**, 183 (1935).

———: Measurement of Nose: Airways and Nose-opening Rays, *J. Hyg.,* **36**, 1 (1936).

HOLMES, T. H., H. GOODELL, and N. G. WOLFF: Emotions and Nasal Function, *J. Nervous Mental Disease,* **101**, 597 (1945).

*JOAL: "Des odeurs et de leur influence sur la voix," Paris, 1894.

KUHN, W.: Schärfe. d. Geruchssinnes i. früheren Jahrhundert, *Deut. praxis,* 332 (1907).

LAGOMARSINO, A. S.: Certain Regions of Nasal Mucosa as Point of Departure and Diffusion of Reflexes, *Semana med.,* **2**, 1656 (1931); 581 (1932).

LAIRD, D. A.: What Can You Do with Your Nose?, *Sci. Monthly,* **41**, 126 (1935).

LIERLE, D. M., and L. B. EVERS: Effects of Certain Drugs upon Ciliary Activity of Nasal Mucous Membrane, *Laryngoscope,* **54**, 176 (1944).

LILL, C.: Untersuchung d. Geruchssinnes bei einzelnen Gruppen von Bediensteten d. Wiener städt. Gewerbe, *Z. österr. Ver. Gas- u. Wasserfach.,* 161 (1935).

*LUCIANI, L.: "Human Physiology," **4**, London, 1917.

MACKENZIE, J. N.: The Physiological and Pathological Relations between the Nose and the Sexual Apparatus of Man, *Bull. Johns Hopkins Hosp.,* **9**, 10 (1898).

*MAHNER, P.: "Psycho-physiologische Versuche über die Unterscheidungsfähigkeit im Gebiete des inneren und äuszeren Tastsinnes, des Geschmacks-und Geruchssinnes an taubstummen, blinden, normal-sinnigen, schwachsinnigen, und taub-stumm-blinden Kindern," Leipzig, 1909.

MALAN, D. J.: Réactions respiratoires et circulatoires aux stimulations olfactives, *Arch. intern. laryngol.,* **31**, 666 (1925).

MENZEL, R.: Die Bedeutung der Gesetze über Schwellenwert und Reizsummation bei der Špürarbeit des Hundes, *J. Psychol. u. Neurol.,* **38**, 258 (1929).

MOLINÉRY: Nasal Mucosa: Acapuncture (Ancient Chinese Procedure), *Paris med.* (annexe), **1**, 10 (Feb. 7, 1931).

MONTI, P. C., and F. V. GREGORINI: Nasal Mucosa: Temperature in Normal Women, *Arch. ital. otol.,* **51**, 389 (1939).

MULLER, A.: Der menschliche Geruchssinn als Schutzeinrichtung für d. Organismus, *Mitt. Naturforsch. ges.,* **19**, 6 (1933).

OPITZ: Über die Theorie der nasalen Dysmenorrhée, *Verhandl. deut. ges. Gynakol.,* **10**, 633 (1903).

OPPIKOFER: Untersuchung der Nase sur Zeit der Menses, der Schwangerschaft und der Geburt, *Verhandl. deut. otol. ges.,* 206 (1907).

OTTOLENGHI, S.: L'olfatto nei criminali, *Giorn. real accad. med. Torino,* 3s, **36**, 427 (1888).

————: L'olfatto nella donna, *Rev. quind. psicol.*, **2**, 122 (1898).

PARKER, G. H., and E. M. STABLER: Taste and Smell, *Am. J. Physiol.*, **32**, 230 (1913).

PARKINSON, S. N.: Determination of Hydrogen-ion Concentration within Nose, *Arch. Otolaryngol.*, **41**, 68 (1945).

PROETZ, A. W.: Nasal Mucosa: Cilia as Influenced by Temperature in Man and Rabbits, *Arch. Otolaryngol.*, **19**, 607 (1934).

————— and M. PFLINGSTEN: Nasal Mucosa: Tissue Culture of Ciliated Epithelium, *Arch. Otolaryngol.*, **29**, 252 (1939).

PUTILOFF: Sur l'importance du sense de l'odorat chez l'homme, *Russk. med. St. Petersburg*, **16**, 105 (1891).

RIVERS, W. H. R.: Observations on the Senses of Todas, *Brit. J. Psychol.*, **1**, 321 (1905).

SALTZMANN, M.: Absorptive Capacity of Mucous Membrane, *Arch. Otolaryngol.*, **40**, 44 (July, 1944).

SCHUTZ, E.: Scientific Opinions of the Nose, *Chaut.*, **24**, 594 (1897).

SEN, H.: Alternate Erectility of the Nasal Mucous Membrane, *Lancet*, **2**, 564 (1901).

SCONINA, K.: Beiträge zur Möglichkeit einer Lokalisierung des Geruch, *Zool. Anz.*, **122**, 194 (1938).

SHENKIN, H. A., and F. H. LEWEY: Olfaction: Brain Localization, *J. Nervous Mental Disease*, **100**, 352 (1944).

*STARLING, E.: "Principles of Human Physiology," 3d ed., London, 1920.

STIRNIMANN, F.: Smell in New-born Infants, *Jahrb. f. Kinderheilk.*, **146**, 211 (1936).

————: Senses of New-born, *Rev. franc. pédiat.*, **12**, 455 (1936).

STRAUB, W. J.: Frequency of Allergy in Orthodontic Patients as an Influencing Agent in Growth of Face, and an Important Factor in Nasal Growth, *J. Am. Dental Assoc.*, **31**, 334 (1944).

TORREY, J. C., and M. K. REESE: Initial Aerobic Flora of New-born Infants, *Am. J. Diseases Children*, **69**, 208 (1945).

*TROLAND, L. T.: "The Principles of Psychophysiology," I, D. Van Nostrand Co., New York, 1929; II, 1930.

VALENTIN: The Delicacy of the Sense of Smell, *Am. Naturalist*, **20**, 826 (1886).

VASCHIDE, N.: Recherches expérimentales sur l'olfaction des veillards, *Compt. rend. acad. sci.*, **137**, 627 (1903).

————: L'État de la sensibilité olfactive dans la veillesse, *Bull. laryngol.*, **7**, 323 (1904).

What Your Nose Knows, *Popular Mechanics*, **71**, 217 (February, 1939).

Why We Like Sweet Smells, *Literary Digest*, **93**, 25 (June 18, 1927).

WOLFF, O.: Geruchssinn als Wacht der Genüsse, *Ärztl. Ratgeber.*, 315 (1904).

ZACHARIAS, P.: Über Nasenuntersuchungen an Schwangeren, Gebärenden und Wöchnerinnen, *Med Klin.*, **111**, 57 (1907).

ZWAARDEMAKER, H.: Die Schluckathembewegung des Menschen, *Arch. Physiol.*, 57 (1904).

————: Die absolute Luftdurchgangigkeit der Nasenhölen, *Z. Laryngol.*, **1**, 625 (1908).

e. General

AGEEVA-MAYKOVA, O. G.: Role of Trigmenial Component in Olfactory Activity, *Vopr. Neyrokhir*, **5**, 50 (1941).

ALCHESIEFF, N.: Die Grundformen der Gefühle, *Wundt's psychol. Stud.*, **3**, 235 (1907).

ALLEN, W. F.: Nasal Irritation by Vapors: Effect on Respiration and Blood Pressure. *Am. J. Physiol.*, **81**, 558 (1929).

————: Conditioned Reflexes in Smell, *Am. J. Physiol.*, **121**, 657 (1938).

———: Effect of Ablating Frontal Lobes, Hippocampi and Occipito-parieto-temporal Lobes on Positive and Negative Olfactory Conditioned Reflexes, *Am. J. Physiol.*, **128**, 754 (1940).

———: Olfaction Reflexes, Conditioned, Temporal Lobe Lesions as Affecting, *Am. J. Physiol.*, **132**, 81 (1941).

ALTHAUS, J.: On Certain Points in the Physiology and Pathology of the Fifth Pair of Cranial Nerves, *Med. Chir. Trans.*, **52**, 27 (1869).

———: Zur Phys. und Path. d. Trigeminus, *Arch. klin. Med.*, **7**, 573 (1870).

———: Physiology and Pathology of the Olfactory Nerve, *Lancet*, **1**, 771, 813 (1881).

ALEKSEEVSKII, E. V.: Analysis of Olfaction, *Trudy Leningrad. Khim.-Tekhnol. Inst.*, **10**, 116 (1941).

AMBROSOLI, C.: Ricerche sperimentali su l'organ nervoso olfattivo, *Gazz. med. ital.*, 3s, **6**, 213, 221, 229 (1855) ; 4s, **1**, 53 (1856).

ANTON, W.: Über Störungen der psychischen Funktionen bei einseitiger Behinderung der Nasenatmung, *Prag. med. Wochschr.*, **33**, 301 (1908).

ARONSOHN, E.: Die elektrische Geruchsempfindung, *Arch. Physiol.*, 460 (1884).

———: Beiträge zur Physiologie des Geruchs, *Arch. Anat. u. Physiol.*, 163 (1884).

———: Experimentelle Untersuchungen zur Physiologie des Geruchs, *Arch. Anat. u. Physiol.*, 321 (1886).

ASCHENBRANDT: Über den Einfluss der Nerven auf die Sekretion der Nasenschleimhaut, *Monatsschr. Ohrenheilk.*, **3** (1885).

*———: "Die Bedeutung der Nase für die Atmung," Würzburg, 1886.

BACKMAN, E. L.: Experimental Investigations on the Physiology of the Sense of Smell, *Upsala Läkarefören. Förh., Stockholm*, N. F. **21**, 317 (1916–1917).

———: Einige Ermüdungserscheimungen innerhalb der Gebiete des Geruchs—und Geschmackssinnes, *Hygeia*, **79**, 886 (1917).

BAGLIONI, S.: Die chemischen Sinne, *Winterstein Handbuch vergl Physiol.*, **4**, 538 (1913).

BAGOLSLOVSKY, A. I.: Effect of Acoustic and Olfactory Stimuli upon Optic Chronaxie, *Bull. biol. med. exp. U.R.S.S.*, **8**, 387 (1939).

BAKER, A. F.: The Significance of Smell, *Sci. J. Roy. Coll. Sci., London*, **5**, 84 (1935).

BARNETT, I. F.: Nasal Mucosa—Effects of Aqueous Solutions on Ciliated Epithelium, *Ill. Med. J.*, **64**, 562 (1933).

BAUDREXEL, A.: Mechanismus unser Geruch's und Geschmacksempfindungen, *Deut. Essigind.*, 96 (1915).

BAYER, H.: Athemreflex auf Olfactoriusreiz, *Arch. Physiol.*, 261 (1901).

BECKER, B. M.: Testing Respiration and Olfaction through Nose, *Laryngoscope*, **53**, 55 (1943).

BEDNER, M., and O. LANGFELDER: Sensation and Odor Substance, *Monatsschr. Ohrenheilk.*, **63**, 1292 (1929).

BEEBE-CENTER, J. G.: Variability of Affective Judgments upon Odors, *J. Exp. Psychol.*, **14**, 91 (1931).

BENCIOLINI, F.: Nasal Mucosa: Cellular Secretions in Pituitary Gland; Experiments on Nasal Mucosa in Man and Animals, *Valsalva*, **6**, 786 (1930).

BENEDICT, A. L.: Education of the Sense of Smell, *Med. News*, **73**, 225 (1898).

BENTLEY, L. L., and G. G. BANKER: Education of the Nose, *Ladies' Home J.*, **26**, 42 (September, 1909).

BERTHELOT: Sur les limites de sensibilité des odeurs et des émanations, *Compt. rend. acad. sci.*, **138**, 1249 (1904).

*BERTHEMOT, J.: "Quelle est la valour semeiologique des changements survenus dans l'olfaction?" Paris, 1840.

*Bevermann, W.: "Zur toxischen Beeinflussung des Geruchssinnes," Würzburg, 1898.

Beyer, H.: Nasales Schmecken, *Z. Psychol. u. Physiol.*, **35**, 260 (1904).

*Bianchi, L.: "The Mechanism of the Brain and the Function of the Frontal Lobes," London, 1922.

*Bidder: "Neue Beobachtungen über die Bewegungen d. weichen Gaumens und über d. Geruchssinn," *Dorpat*, 1838.

Bijtel and Van Iterson: Recherches sur le reflexe psychogalvanique, en particulier comme réaction aux excitations olfactives, *Arch. néerland. physiol.*, **10**, 447 (1925).

Binz, A.: Physiological Consideration of Odors, *Deut. Parfüm.-Ztg.*, **4**, 108 (1918).

Birch, C. G.: A Study of Certain Methods of Distracting the Attention: Distraction by Odors, *Am. J. Psychol.*, **9**, 45 (1897–1898).

Bleyer, J. M.: A Memoir of the Odoriferous Sense, *Homeop. Eye, Ear and Throat J.*, **2**, 146, 192, 216, 256 (1896).

Bloch, E.: Über die Erwärmung der Luft auf dem Wege durch die Nasenhöhle, *Z. Ohrenheilk.*, **18**, 215 (1888).

———: Der Geruchssinn in der Vita sexualis, *Anthropophyteia*, **2**, 445 (1905).

———: Geruchssinn in der Vita sexualis, *Anthropophyteia*, **4**, 245 (1907).

———: Geruchssinn in der Vita sexualis, *Anthropophyteia*, **6**, 219 (1909).

———: Sexualität und Geruch, *Prometheus*, 1200 (1913).

———, F. S. Krauss, and Felder: Geruchssinn in der Vita sexualis, *Anthropophyteia*, **6**, 210 (1909).

———, ——— and Waldheim: Der Geruchssinn in der Vita sexualis, *Anthropophyteia*, **7**, 289 (1911).

Bogoslovsky, A. I.: Effect of Olfactory Stimuli upon Optic Chronaxie, *Bull. biol. et méd. exp. U.R.S.S.*, **8**, 387 (1939).

*Bohn: "L'Évolution du pigment," Paris, 1901.

Bolger, E. M., and E. B. Titchener: Some Experiments on the Associative Power of Smells, *Am. J. Psychol.*, **18**, 326 (1907).

Boring, E. G.: Psychology of Perception; Importance in War Effort, *Am. J. Psychol.*, **55**, 423 (1942).

Bornstein, W.: Geruchssinn, *Deut. Z. Nervenheilk.*, **104B**, 55, 173 (1928).

Bosworth, F. H.: Physiology and Neurology of the Nose, *Med. News*, **53**, 117 (1888).

Botey, R.: Disquisiciones sobre higiene olfactoria y gustativo, *Arch. latino-am. rhinol. laringol.*, **16**, 5 (1905).

Bournot, K.: Olfaction Problems, *Z. ges. Naturw.*, **5**, 196 (1939).

Braeuning, H.: Zur Kenntniss der Wirkung chemischer Reize, *Arch. ges. Physiol.*, **102**, 163 (1904).

Brewer, W. H.: The Sense of Smell in Animals, *Nature*, **7**, 360 (1873).

Broca, P.: Fonctions des divers centres olfactifs, *Rev. d'anthropol.*, 2s, 439 (1879).

Bruhl, N.: Geruchs-organ und Geruchsempfindungen, *Natur. Offenbarung*, 661 (1904).

Bryant, W. S.: Experiment to Prove That the Cilia of Human Nose Waft Toward the Anterior Nares, *Am. J. Physiol.*, **33**, 430 (1914).

Buccola, G.: Le recente esperienze sul tempo delle sensazione olfattive, *Osservatore*, **19**, 145 (1883).

Buchalow: Ein Beitrag zur Mikrochemie der Geruchsorgane, *St. Petersb. med. Zeitschr.*, **2**, 294, 336 (1885).

Bull, C. G., and G. H. Bailey: Effect on Nasal Passages of Instillations of Brilliant Green, *Proc. Soc. Exp. Biol. Med.*, **24**, 183 (1926).

Cabanès. De l'influence des sens sur les fonctions genitales; le nez dans ses relations avec l'appareil sexuel, *Gaz. gynécol.*, **12**, 209, 225, 241 (1897).

———: Les Odeurs; leur influence sur les voies digestives, *J. Santé*, **21**, 363 (1904).

CALLIGARIS, G.: Stimulation of Hyperesthetic Lines as Affecting Smell, *Riv. oto-neuro-oftalmol.*, **5**, 485 (1929).

*CARNOT: "Recherches sur le mécanisme de la pigmentation," Paris, 1896.

CHAMPY, C., and N. KRITCH: Correlative Effect of Castration on Odoriferous Glands and Olfactory Apparatus, *Compt. rend. soc. biol.*, **100**, 185 (1929).

CHAUVEAU, C.: Nos Notions sur l'appareil olfactif au cours de ces dernières années, *Arch. intern. laryngol. otol. rhinol.*, **17**, 3 (1904).

CHILOW, K. L.: Ablation of Olfactory Bulbs, Effect on Reflex Nasal, *Beitr. Anat. Ohr-, Nase- u. Hals.*, **28**, 124 (1930).

*CHRISTMANN, K.: "Über die Lokalisation von Geruchsempfindungen," Bayreuth, 1936.

CICARDO, V. H.: Release of Potassium by Excited Nasal Mucosa, *Pub. centro invest. tisiol.*, **7**, 279 (1943).

CIURLO, L.: Olfactory Functioning in New-born, *Valsalva*, **10**, 22 (1934).

———: Hemodynamic Action of Olfactory Stimuli, *Arch. ital. otol.*, **44**, 321 (1933).

CLARKE, H.: Perception in Lower Animals, *Nature*, **7**, 384 (Mar. 20, 1873).

Comparison of Sense of Smell and Sense of Taste, *Hygeia*, **17**, 281 (1939).

*CONTAL, M.: "Contribution à l'étude du réflexe nasofacio-oculaire," Lyon, 1926.

COX, C. N.: The Relation of the Nose and the Reproductive Organs, *Brooklyn Med. J.*, **16**, 332 (1902).

CRANCH, C. P.: Plea for Smell, *Putnam's*, **13**, 315 (1869).

CROZIER, W. J.: Regarding the Existence of the "Common Chemical Sense" in Vertebrates, *J. Comp. Neurol.*, **26**, 1 (1916).

CUTTER, E.: The Action of Odors, Pleasant and Unpleasant, upon Blood Flow, *J. Am. Med. Assoc.*, **30**, 366 (1898).

*CYON, E.: "Techniques des expériences sur le nerf olfactif," Giessen, 1877.

DALY, C. D., and R. SENIOR-WHITE: Psychic Reaction to Olfactory Stimuli, *Brit. J. Med. Psychol.*, **10**, 70 (May, 1930).

DANA, C. L.: The Olfactory Nerve, Its Quantitative and Qualitative Tests and Its Physiological Importance; Its Inter-Cranial Course and Diseases, *N. Y. Med. J.*, **1**, 253 (1889).

DANZIGER: Über die Luftbewegung in der Nase während des Athmens, *Monatsschr. Ohrenheilk.*, 331 (1896).

DAVIS, H.: Special Senses Other Than Vision, *Ann. Rev. Physiol.*, **5**, 357 (1943).

DEARBORN, G. V., and F. N. SPINDLER: Involuntary Motor Reaction and Unpleasant Stimuli, *Psychol. Rev.*, **4**, 453 (1897).

*DEBROU, T.: "Peut-on percevoir des odeurs qui arrivent dans le nez par l'ouverture posterieure des fosses nasales?" Paris, 1841.

Decadent Sense, *Sci. American Supp.*, **74**, 55 (1912).

DE JONC, H. G., and G. G. P. SAUBERT: Stimulation of Organs of Olfaction, *Proc. Acad. Sci., Amst.*, **40**, 302 (1937).

DERCUM, F.: The Sensory Organs; Suggestions with a View to Generalization, *Am. Naturalist*, **12**, 581 (1878).

DERHAM, A. P.: The First Sense in Memory and Medicine, *Med. J. Australia*, **1**, 234 (1925).

DeSILVA, H. R., and B. L. GOLUB: Influence of Smell on Reaction Time, *J. Gen. Psychol.*, **16**, 279 (1937).

DIXON, W. E.: Nose, with Special Reference to Reflexes, *Southwest J. Med. Surg.*, **22**, 561 (1914).

DMITRIEV, V. D.: Change in Motor Chronaxie under Influence of Stimulation of Olfactory Receptor and Development of Conditioned Reflexes on Basis of This Change, *Bull. biol. et méd. exp. U.R.S.S.*, **8**, 430 (1939).

DOFLEIN, J.: Geruchssinn der Wassertiere, *Biol. Zentr.*, **31**, 706 (1911).

DUBOIS, R.: Sur la Physiologie comparée de l'olfaction, *Compt. rend. acad. sci.*, **111**, 66 (1890).

DUMERIL, A. H.: Von der Natur und physiologischen Wirking der Gerüche, *Frorieps neue Not.*, **25**, 58 (1843).

*———: "Des odeurs, de leur nature et de leur action physiologique," Paris, 1843.

ECHOLS, D. H., H. J. RICHTER, and M. M. PEET: Effect of $ZnSO_4$ on Sense of Smell, *Bull. Univ. Mich. Hosp.*, **3**, 32 (1937).

EHRENSVÄRD, G.: General Relationship between Molecular Structure and Physiological Action with Special Reference to Odoriferous Substances, *Acta Physiol. Scand.*, **3** (Supp. 9), 1 (1942).

ELSBERG, C. A.: Olfactory Fatigue, *Bull. Neurol. Inst. N.Y.*, **4**, 479 (1935).

———: The Summation of Olfactory Impulses from the Two Olfactory Membranes and Its Physiological Significance, *Bull. Neurol. Inst. N.Y.*, **4**, 544 (1936).

———: Monorhinal, Birhinal, and Bisynchronorhinal Smell, *Bull. Neurol. Inst. N.Y.*, **4**, 496 (1935).

———: Role of Cerebral Cortex in Smell, *Bull. Neurol. Inst. N.Y.*, **6**, 118 (1937).

———: Smell: Cerebral Activity Including Conscious Sensation as Physiochemical Process with Evidence to Indicate That Many Processes Can Be Expressed in Simple Mathematical Relationships, *Bull. Neurol. Inst. N.Y.*, **7**, 212 (1938).

———, E. D. BREWER, and I. LEVY: Sense of Smell; Relation between Olfactory Coefficients and Boiling Points of Odorous Substances, *Bull. Neurol. Inst. N.Y.*, **4**, 26 (1935).

———, ———, and ———: Relative Importance of Volume Pressure of Impulse for Sensation of Smell, and Nature of Olfactory Process, *Bull. Neurol. Inst. N.Y.*, **4**, 264 (1935).

———, ———, and ———: Sense of Smell; Trigeminal Effects of Odorous Substances, *Bull. Neurol. Inst. N.Y.*, **4**, 270 (1935).

———, ———, and ———: Sense of Smell; New Principle for Classification of Odors Based upon Their Olfactory Coefficients, *Bull. Neurol. Inst. N.Y.*, **4**, 20 (1935).

———, and H. SPOTNITZ: Are Vision and Olfaction Governed by the Same Law?, *Bull. Neurol. Inst. N.Y.*, **6**, 421 (1937).

———, and ———: Smell Stimulation and Refractory Period, *J. Neurophysiol.*, **2**, 227 (1939).

———, ———, and E. I. STRONGIN: Effect of Stimulation by Odorous Substances upon Amount of Secretion of Parotid Glands, *J. Exp. Psychol.*, **27**, 58 (1940).

ERDMANN, E.: Über den Geruchssinn und die wichtigsten Riechstoffe, *Z. angew. Chemie* (5), 103; (11), 270; (14), 345; (33), 813 (1900).

*ESCHRICHT, D. F.: "De functiones nervorum faciei et olfactus organi," Hafniae, 1825.

———: De functionibus primi et quniti paris nervorum in olfactoris organo propriis, *J. physiol.*, **6**, 350 (1826).

FABRICANT, N. D.: Relation of the pH of Nasal Secretions in Situ to the Activity of Lysozyme, *Arch. Otolaryngol.*, **41**, 53 (1945).

FABRONI, M.: Impossibility of Affecting Gastric Secretions by Smelling Odoriferous, Non-alimentary Substances, *Valsalva*, **6**, 175 (1930).

FAUVELLE. Des Relations Entre les Organes du toucher et de l'odorat, *Bull. soc. anthropol. Paris*, 3s, **9**, 274 (1886).

FELDERMAN, L.: Relationship of Gustatory to Olfactory Systems, *Ann. Otol., Rhinol. & Laryngol.*, **44**, 685 (1935).

*FÉRÉ, C.: "Sensation et mouvement," Paris, 1900.

————: Recherches expérimentales sur la fatigue par les excitations de l'odorat, *N. iconog. de la Salpêtrière*, **14**, 327 (1901).

FINCK, H. P.: Nasal Mucosa: Tissue Changes, *Trans. Laryngol., Rhinol. & Otol. Soc.*, **33**, 63 (1927).

FISCHER, E., and F. PENZOLDT: Über die Empfindlichkeit des Geruchssinnes, *Sitzber. phys.-med. Soc. Erlangen*, **18**, 7 (1886).

FLAU: L'Influence des odeurs sur la voix, *Gas. gynécol.*, **10**, 113 (1895).

FOERSTER, R.: The Nature of the Sense of Smell, *Wochschr. Brau.*, **28**, 356.

*FORSTER, P.: "The Recognition and Localization of Odorous Substances Presented Simultaneously to the Right and Left Sense Fields," Bad Wilduengen, 1935.

FOX, C. A., W. A. McKINLEY, and H. W. MAGOUN: An Oscillographic Study of Olfactory System of Cats, *J. Neurophysiol.*, **7**, 1 (1944).

FRANK, J. D.: Affective Value vs. Nature of Odors in Relation to Reproduction, *Am. J. Psychol.*, **43**, 479 (1931).

FRANKE, G.: Experimentelle Untersuchungen über Luftdruck, Luftbewegung und Luftwechsel in der Nase und ihren Nebenhöhlen, *Arch Laryngol., Rhinol.*, **1**, 230 (1893).

FREUND, L.: Effect of Light on Functioning of Auditory and Olfactory Organs, *Strahlentherapie*, **34**, 110 (1929).

FROHLICH, R.: Über einige Modificationen des Geruchssinnes, *Sitzber. Akad. Wiss. Wien, Math-Naturw. Klasse*, **6**, 322 (1851).

*GALOPIN, A.: "Le Parfum de la femme et le sens olfactif dans l'amour. Étude psychophysiologique," Paris, 1886.

GARIN, R. F., *et al.*: Stomach Secretion Induced by Smell, *Lyon Med.*, **143**, 409 (1929).

GIANUZZI, J.: Recherches physiologiques sur les nerfs de l'olfaction, *Compt. rend. soc. biol.*, 3s, **5**, 97 (1863).

GLAZE, J. A.: Sensitivity to Odors and Other Phenomena during a Fast, *Am. J. Psychol.*, **40**, 569 (1928).

GOETSCH, W.: Neuere Untersuchungen dem Geruchs und Geschmacksvermögen, *Natur.*, **16**, 155 (1925).

GOLDSTEIN, M. A.: Further Investigation of Special Sense Organs, *Laryngoscope*, **38**, 633 (1928).

GORDON, K.: The Recollection of Pleasant and Unpleasant Odors, *J. Exp. Psychol.*, **8**, 225 (1925).

*GOUREWITSCH, A.: "Über die Beziehung des Nervus olfactorius zu den Athembewegungen," Bern, 1883.

HAEDICKE, J.: Significance of Sensory Organs; Energy of Human Organism, *Psychiat.-neurol. Wochschr.*, **44**, 57 (1942).

*HALBRON, P.: "Contribution à l'étude de certaines interréactions neurvégétives de l'oeil et du nez," Paris, 1936.

HALLIDAY, J. L.: Reconsideration of Sense of Smell, *Glasgow Med. J.*, **105**, 182 (1926).

HANSTRÖM, B.: Experimente und Reflexionen über Geruch, Geschmack und die allg. chem. Sinn, *Z. wiss. Biol.*, Abt. C, **4**, 528 (1926).

HASAMA, B.: Über die elektrischen Begleiterscheinungen an der Riechsphäre bei der Geruchsempfindung, *Arch. ges. Physiol.*, **234**, 748 (1935).

HAUG: Über die Beeinflussung gewisser subjectiver Ohrerscheinungen durch Behandlung der genitalen Sphäre der Nase, *Monatsschr. Ohrenheilk.*, **37**, 96 (1903).

HEINZ, H.: Geruchssinn der Tiere, bei d. Insekten, und seine forstl. Bedeutung, *Forst Jagdzeutung*, 333 (1937).

HENNING, H.: Physiologie und Psychologie des Geruchs, *Ergebn. physiol.*, **17**, 572 (1919).

————: Assoziationsgesctz und Geruchsgedächtnis, *Z. Psychol. Physiol. Sinnesorgane*, **89**, 38 (1922).

HENRY, C.: Influence de l'odeur sur les mouvements respiratoires et sur l'effort musculaire, *Compt. rend. soc. biol.*, **43**, 443 (1891).

HENSCHEN, S. E.: Über die Geruchs- und Geschmackszentren, *Monatsschr. Psychiat.*, **45**, 121 (1919).

HERRICK, C. J.: Functions of the Olfactory Parts of the Cerebral Cortex, *Proc. Nat. Acad. Sci.*, **19**, 7 (1933).

HESSE, A.: Physiologie und Klinik. des Geruchssinnes, *Lit. Welt.*, **3**, 307 (1932).

HEYMANN, R.: Über die Beziehungen der Nase und den weiblichen Geschlechtsorganen, *Zentr. Gynäkol.*, **25**, 1319 (1901).

*HEYNINX, A.: "Essai d'olfactique physiologique," Bruxelles, 1919.

HEYNINX, M.: Physiology of Olfaction, *Rev, otoneuro-ophthalmol.*, **11**, 10 (1933).

HEYWOOD, A., and N. VORTRIEDE: Some Experiments on the Associative Power of Smells, *Am. J. Psychol.*, **16**, 537 (1905).

HILBERT, R.: Über Geruchsempfindungen, welche durch den innerlichen Gebrauch gewisser chemischer körper erregt werden, *Memorabilien, Heidbr.*, N.F., **11**, 3 (1891–1892).

HILEY, J. S.: On the Odoriferous Plants and Their Effects on the Animal Economy, *Lancet*, **1**, 736 (1841–1842).

HILGARD, T. C.: Experimental Observations on Taste and Smell, *Proc. Am. Assoc. Adv. Sci.*, **8**, 248 (1854).

HILL, A.: Abstracts of Three Lectures on the Brain—Mechanism of Sight and Smell, *Brit. Med. J.*, **1**, 436, 485, 538 (1886).

HIROSE, S.: Olfactory Perception Produced by Electric Stimulation, *Japan. J. Med. Sci.*, **3**, *Biophysics*, **6**, 76 (1940).

HOBBS, A. G.: Another Case of Priapism from Nasal Reflex, *Gaillard's South. Med.*, **84**, 187 (1906).

HOFMANN, F. B.: Der Geruchssinn beim Menschen, *Handbuch normalen pathol. Physiol.*, **11**, 253 (1926).

HOWARD, W. L.: The Nose and the Sexual Apparatus, *Maryland Med. J.*, **38**, 335 (1898).

JANORSKI, J., and S. IWANICKI: Relationship of Various Nasal Phenomena to Female Genitals, *Gaz. lek., Warzawa*, 2s, **22**, 429, 456 (1902).

JANSEN, H.: Nasal Mucosa: Surface Temperature and Water Evaporation, *Beitr. Anat. Ohr-, Nase-, u. Hals.*, **25**, 145 (1927).

JUHASZ, A.: Über eine neue Eigenschaft. d. Geruchsempfindungen, *Ber. 9 Kongr. exp. Psychol.*, 178 (1925).

Imitative Odors, *Chambers's J.*, **73**, 389 (1896).

KAHN, H.: Subjective Sensations of Smell and Their Significance, *Ill. Med. J.*, **14**, 326 (1908).

KALISCHER, O.: Weitere Mitteilungen über die Ergebnisse der Dressur als physiologische Untersuchungsmethode auf dem Gebiete des Gehörs-, Geruchs- und Farbensinnes, *Arch. Anat. u. Physiol., Physiol. Abt.*, 303 (1909).

KEKCHEEV, K.: Mechanism of Sensitivity Changes of Sense Organs, *Nature*, **150**, 491 (1942).

KENNETH, J. H.: Mental Reactions to Smell Stimuli, *Psychol. Rev.*, **30**, 77 (1923).

————: Some Experiments on Mental Reactions to Odours, *Perfumery Essent. Oil Record*, 85 (1924).

————: Odours and Visual Imagery, *Nature*, **119**, 818 (1927).

————: Fluctuations in Affective Reactions to the Odour of Caraway Oil, *Nature*, **120**, 366 (1927).

KILLIAN, G.: Zur Sensibilitätsprüfung der Nasenschleimhaut, *Deut. med. Wochschr.*, **37**, 410 (1911).

*KIRWAN, H. A.: "De l'odorat et de l'influence des odeurs sur l'écomonie animale," Paris, 1808.

KOMURO, K.: On Smelling during Complete Exhaustion, for a Given Odour, *Proc. Koninkl. Akad. Wetenschap. Amsterdam, sect. sci.*, **24**, 1442 (1922).

*KOROLCHUK, A. I.: "Relation of Animal Organism to Aromatic Oxyketones," Yuryev, 1894.

KRAUSS, F. S.: Geruchssinn im menschlichen Liebesleben, *Liebeslehre*, 239 (1928).

KRAVKOV, S. V.: Dependence of Irradiation of Light in Eye on Accessory Visual, Auditory and Smell Stimuli, *Arch. Ophthalmol.*, **129**, 440 (1933).

————: Critical Frequency of Flicker and Indirect Stimuli, *Compt. rend. acad. sci. U.R.S.S.*, **22**, 64 (1939).

————: On Some Correlations of Different Receptors in Color Vision, *Comp. rend. acad. sci. U.R.S.S.*, **22**, 67 (1939).

————: Influence of Odors on Color Vision, *Acta ophthalmol.*, **17**, 426 (1939).

KREMER, H. J.: On the Absorption of Odoriferous Substances and Odorous Narcotics by the Cells of the Sense Organs and the Brain, *Nederland. Tijdschr. Geneesk.*, **1**, 1800 (1917).

KÜMMEL, F.: Physiologie des Geruchs, *Natur und Haus*, **7** (1908).

LATIS: Rapports entre la sphère génitale et la muqueuse du nez et importance de la rhinococaïnisation, *Mèd. orient.*, **10**, 519 (1906).

LEASURE, J. K.: Secretions of Mucous Membrane of Nose, *Trans. Indiana Acad. Ophthalmol. Otolaryngol.*, **18**, 13 (1934).

LENK, E.: Geruchssinn und Erotik bei Tieren, *Aufklarung*, **1**, 309 (1931).

LINDENOV, H.: Mechanism of Perception of Odor, *Hospitalstid.*, **76**, 734 (1933).

LOTMAR, N.: Beziehungen zwischen Geruchssinn und Geschlechtstrieb, *Geschlecht. Ges.*, 99 (1910).

LOVELL, J. H.: Relation of the Sense of Smell to the Odors of Flowers, *Am. Bee J.*, **63**, 335 (1923).

LOW, W. S., and I. D. CHEPMELL: Functions of the Nose, *Lancet*, **1**, 278 (1914).

*LUBBOCK, J.: "Senses of Animals," London, 1899.

LUGLI, G.: Metabolism of Organs of Olfaction, *Arch. ital. med. sper.*, **4**, 697 (1939).

MAGENDIE, F.: Le Nerf olfactif est-il l'organe de l'odorat?, *J. physiol. exp. pathol.*, **4**, 169 (1824).

MAGITOT, A., and A. DUBOIS: Nasal Mucosa: Modification of Mariotte's Spot by Excitation, *Bull. soc. d'ophthalmo, Paris*, 85 (Feb., 1934).

MAGNOTTI, T.: Importance of Sense of Smell in Development and Functions of Genital Organs, *Boll. mal. orecchio*, **54**, 281 (1936).

MALHERBE: Sur les propriétés olfactives de la muqueuse palatine, *J. connaissances méd.*, 487 (Sept., 1852).

*MARKOVITCH, K.: "Des relations entre l'appareil nasal et la sphère genitale de la femme," Paris, 1923.

MARQUARDT, M.: Problems of "Physiologic" Sense Perception, *J. Nervous Mental Disease*, **95**, 46 (1942).

MARTINCLADERIN, A.: Physiology of Olfaction, *Siglo med.*, **69**, 365, 395 (1923).

MILES, G. M.: Influence of Olfaction on Digestion, *J. Am. Med. Assoc.*, **53**, 1271 (1909).

MINK, P. J.: De Neus als Reflex-organ, *Geneesk. Bl. Klin. en Lab.*, *prakt.*, **15**, 21 (1909).

MIRA, E.: Psychology of Sensoperceptive Function, *Arch. neurobiol.*, **14**, 803 (1934).

MITSUHASHI, H.: Fats and Pigments in Nasal Mucosa, *Arch. path. Anat. Physiol.*, **261**, 1 (1927).

MITTERMAIER, R., and A. MARCHIONINI: pH Measurements in Nasal Mucosa, *Z. Hals-, Nasen- u. Ohrenheilk.*, **20**, 253 (1928).

MOLDENHAUER, W.: Über die einfache Reactionszeit einer Geruchsempfindung, *Wundts philos. Stud.*, **1**, 606, 614 (1883).

MONNIER, M.: Die Bedeutung der Sinnesfunktionen für die Beziehungen zwischen Individuum und Umwelt, *Schweiz. med. Wochschr.*, **73**, 351 (1943).

MORIMURA, S.: Studies on Olfactory Sense, *Tohoku J. Exp. Med.*, **22**, 417 (1934).

MORRILL, A. D.: The Innervation of the Olfactory Epithelium, *J. Comp. Neurol.*, **8**, 180 (1898).

MORTIMER, H.: Genito-nasal and Genito-aural Relationships—Nasal Mucosa, *Laryngoscope*, **50**, 349 (1940).

———, R. P. WRIGHT, and J. B. COLLIP: Estrogenic Hormones as Effecting Nose Mucosa, *J. Can. Med. Assoc.*, **35**, 615 (1936).

MÜNSTERBERG, H.: Physiologische Begründung der Gefühle, *Intern. Kongr. Psychol.*, London (1892).

*NAGEL, W. A.: "Vergleichend Physiologische und anatomische Untersuchungen über den Geruchs- und Geschmackssinn und ihre Organ, mit einleitenden Betrachtungen aus der allgemeinen vergleichenden Sinnesphysiologie," Stuttgart, 1894.

———: Geruchssinn, *Handbuch Physiol. Mensch.*, **3**, 589 (1905).

———: Einige Bemerkungen über nasales Schmecken, *Z. Psychol.*, **35**, 268 (1904).

———: Über Mischerüche und die Komponentengliederung des Geruchssinnes, *Z. Psychol. Physiol. Sinnesorg.*, **15**, 82 (1897).

Nasal mucosa: Sympathicotherapy; Answers to Questionnaire, *Vie méd.*, **15**, 897 (1934).

NEGUS, V. E.: Epiglottis Function in Smell, *J. Anat.*, **62**, 1 (1927).

NENCKI, M.: Sur le sort des oxycétones aromatiques dans l'organisme animal, *Arch. sci. biol.*, St. Petersburg, **111**, 120 (1894).

NICCOLINI, P.: Biological Reactions from Odors, *Arch. ital. sci. pharmacol.*, **4**, 77 (1935).

———: Smell-action of Thiocyanate, *Arch. ital. sci. pharmacol.*, **7**, 297 (1938).

———: Effect on Thiocyanante Concentration in Nasal Mucous of Irritant and Non-irritant, *Boll. soc. ital. biol. sper.*, **10**, 429 (1935).

———: Physiocopharmacology. Study of Olfaction, *Arch. ital. sci. pharmacol.*, **9**, 41 (1940).

NILES, G. M.: The Influence of the Olfactories on Digestion, *Southern Med. Surg.*, **86**, 58 (1924).

OGLE, W.: Cases Illustrating the Physiology and Pathology of Sense of Smell, *Brit. Med. J.*, **1**, 166 (1870).

Olfatto e sesso, *Policlinico*, **41**, 945 (1934).

OLMSTED, J. M. D.: Physiology of Sense Organs; Recent Advances, *Calif. Western Med.*, **41**, 20 (1934).

———: Special Senses, *Ann. Rev. Physiol.*, **1**, 447 (1939).

———: Special Senses, *Ann. Rev. Physiol.*, **2**, 287 (1940).

PANYREK, D.: The Question of the Relation of the Nose to the Genital Sphere, *Lék. rozhledy*, Praha, **11**, 296 (1903).

PARKINSON, S. N.: Determinations of Nasal pH; Discussion and Criticism, *Arch. Otolaryngol.*, **41**, 68 (1945).

PASSY, J.: Sur la perception des odeurs, *Compt. rend. soc. biol.*, **4**, 239 (1892).

————: Revue générale sur les sensations olfactives, *Ann. psychol.*, **2**, 363 (1895).

PATRICK, G. T. W.: On the Confusion of Tastes and Odors, *Psychol. Rev.*, 160 (March, 1899).

PAULSEN, E.: Experimentelle Untersuchungen über die Strömung der Luft in der Nasenhöhle. *Sitzber. Wien. Akad. Wiss., math-nat. Klasse*, Abt. 3, **85**, 352 (1882).

PEARLMAN, S. J.: Jacobson's Organ: Function (re Smell), *Ann. Otol., Rhinol., & Laryngol.*, **43**, 739 (1934).

PENZOLDT, F., and E. FISCHER: A report of a Study of Sensitiveness of Smell, *Liebig's Ann.*, **231**, 131.

PETO, E.: Development of Smell Feeling, *Brit. J. Med. Psychol.*, **15**, 314 (1936).

*PICHT, F.: "De gustus et olfactus nexu, praesertim argumentis pathologie et experiments illustrato," Berolini, 1829.

PODOLSKY, E.: Olfactory Perceptions and Sexual Emotion, *Urol. and Cutaneous Rev.*, **29**, 203 (1925).

PONZO, M.: Reflexes of Gustation and Smell, *Arch. ital. biol.*, **77**, 93 (1926).

————: Ripercussione respiratorie di stati d'animo provocati da rappresentazione olfattive, *Arch. ital. psicol.*, **4**, 110 (1924).

PRADINES, M.: Objectivity of Odors, *J. psychol. norm. path.*, **26**, 16 (1929).

PREVOST, J. L.: Note relatif aux fonctions des nerfs de la première paire, *Arch. sci.*, **22** (1869).

PROETZ, A. W.: Fractional Fatigue of the Olfactory Apparatus, *Arch. Otolaryngol.*, **1**, 638 (1925).

*————: "Essays on the Applied Physiology of the Nose," St. Louis, 1941.

*RANSON, S. W.: "The Anatomy of the Nervous System, from the Standpoint of Development and Function," 7th ed, rev., Philadelphia, 1943.

REKO, B.: Wechselbeziehungen zwischen Nase und Geschlechtsapparat, *Med. Monatsschr.*, **16**, 93 (1905).

REUTER, C.: Beiträge zur Untersuchung des Geruchssinnes, *Z. klin. med.*, **22**, 114 (1891).

ROBERTSON, G. A.: Functions of the Olfactory Organ, *Am. Pract. and News*, **44**, 574 (1910).

ROLLETT, A.: Beiträge zur Physiologie des Geruchs, des Geschmacks, der Hautsinne und der Sinne im allgemeinen, *Arch. ges. Physiol.*, **74**, 383 (1899).

ROSE, J. E., and C. N. WOOLSEY: Potential Changes in the Olfactory Brain Produced by Electrical Stimulation of the Olfactory Bulb, *Fed. Proc. Am. Soc. Exp. Biol.*, **2**, 42 (1943).

ROSEDALE, R. S.: Nasogenital Relationship, *Arch. Otolaryngol.*, **42**, 235 (1945).

SAKHAROFF, N. A.: Chemical Process Under-lying the Action of the Organ of Olfaction in Smelling, *Protok. zasaid. Kaykazsk. med. Obsh.*, **37**, 496 (1900–1901).

*SAVELYEFF, N. A.: "Physiology of olfactory nerve; historical and experimental investigations," Moskva, 1892.

————: Physiology of Smell; Historical and Experimental Research, *Trudy fiziol. lab. imp. Moskov. Univ.*, **4**, 121 (1893).

SAXL, E.: Experimentelle Hilfsmittel z. Erforschung der Geruchsempfindung, *Z. wiss. Biol.*, Abt. C., **10**, 227 (1929).

SCHIEFFERDECKER, P.: Der Weg des Luftstromes in der Nase, *Deut. med. Wochschr.*, **29**, 147 (1903).

————: Die Bedeutung des Duftes für das Geschlechts und Liebesleben des Menschen und der Tiere, *Z. Sexualw.*, **10**, 137 (1923).

SCHMIDT, H.: Enstehung dem Geruchsempfindungen, *Prometheus*, **25**, 1295 (1914).

SCHNECKENBERG, E.: Physiologic Experiments with Ozonized Air, *Gesundh.- Ing.*, **35**, 965 (1912).

SCHULTZE, E.: Die sexuelle Bedeutung des Geruchssinns, *Z. Sexualw.*, **5**, 343 (1918).

SCHUSTER, W.: Geruch und Gesicht bei Mensch und Tier, *Der zool. Garten*, 85 (1905).

SERCER, A.: Nasal Mucosa: Reflex Influence of Stimulation on Tension in Lung on Same Side, *Acta Oto-Laryngol.*, **14**, 82 (1930).

SHIELDS, T. E.: The Effect of Olfactory Sensations upon the Blood-supply to the Brain, *Johns Hopkins Univ. Circ.*, **14**, 71 (1895).

SHIROTA, G.: Nasal Mucosa: Changes after Conchotomy; Experimental Study, *Mitt. med. Akad. Kioto*, **6**, 1466 (1932).

SINEXON, J.: Nasal Conditions Dependent upon the Generative Organs, *Med. News*, **86**, 825 (1905).

SMITH, W.: Note on a Reflex Action of the Olfactory Nerves upon the Nerves of the Palate and Stomach, *Med. Chron.*, **5**, 463 (1886–1887).

SPENCE, G., and J. P. GUILFORD: Affective Value of Combinations of Odors, *Am. J. Psychol.*, **45**, 495 (1933).

SPOTNITZ, H., and C. A. ELSBERG: The Relative Refractory Period of Olfaction and of Vision, *Bull. Neurol. Inst. N.Y.*, **7**, 78 (1938).

*STASINSKI, J.: "Beiträge zur Physiologie des Geruchssinnes," Posen, 1894.

STERNBERG, W.: Unterscheidungsfähigkeit im Gebiete des Geschmacks und Geruchs, *Arch. ges. Physiol.*, **131**, 425 (1910).

———: Geruch und Ekel., *Allgem. med. Central-ztg.*, 194 (1916).

Studying the Sense of Smell, *Harpers Weekly*, **49**, 1949 (1905).

SUÑE Y MOLIST, L.: Disquisiciones sobre hygiene olfactôria y gustativa, *Arch. ital. rhinol, e laringol.*, **16**, 184 (1905).

SUNGERI: La fatica del senso dell'olfatto, *Atti accad. sci. med. Palermo*, 146 (1920).

SWANN, H. G.: Function of the Brain in Olfaction, *J. Comp. Psychol.*, **15**, 229 (1933).

TALBOT, E. S.: Relations of the Nose and the Genitalia, *Medicine*, **10**, 258 (1904).

*TARDIF, E.: "Étude critique des odeurs et des parfums et leur influence sur la sens génésique," Bordeaux, 1898.

*TAUBER, E.: "Das Verhalten der aromatischen Verbindungen im thierischen Organismus," Jena, 1878.

THOMAS, F.: Geruchsempfindung, ein weiteres Beispiel von Assoziation durch eine, als unbewusstes Mitglied., *Z. Psychol. Physiol. Sinnesorgane*, **12**, 60.

TRAUTMANN, G.: Zur Frage der Beziehungen zwischen Nase und Genitalien, *Monatsschr. Ohrenheilk.*, **37**, 129 (1903).

TZKIPURIDAE, L.: Modification of Motor Chronaxie in Connection with Adequate Stimulation of Olfactory Receptor, *Bull. biol. méd. expér.*, *U.R.S.S.*, **7**, 151 (1939).

VALOKHOV, A. A.: Investigation on the Chronaxie of Cutaneous Receptors During Post Natal Development, *Fiziol. Zhur. S.S.S.R.*, **30**, 147 (1941).

VAN DER VELDEN, F.: Zur Physiologie der Geruchsempfindung, *Fortschr. Med.*, **24**, 804 (1906).

VAN ITERSON, C. J. A.: Psycho-galvanic Reflex and the Sense of Smell, *Nederland. Tijdschr. Geneesk.*, **67**, 1985 (1923).

VAN OSDOL, H. A.: Systemic Effect of Nasal Hyperplasia as it Affects Nasal Ganglion, *J. Indiana Med. Assoc.*, **24**, 3 (1931).

VASCHIDE, N.: Recherches expérimentales sur la fatigue olfactive, *J. anat. physiol.*, **38**, 85 (1902).

VEIT, GRABER: Über die Empfindlichkeit einiger Meertiere gegen Riechstoffe, *Biol. Zentr.*, **8**, 473 (1889).

VERESS: Über die Reinung des Riechorgane durch directe Einwirkung riechender Flüssigheiten, *Arch. ges. Physiol.*, **95**, 368 (1903).

VINTSCHGAU, M.: Physiologie des Geruchssinnes, *Hermanns Handbuch Physiol.*, **3**, 225 (1880).

*VON FREY, M.: "Vorlesungen über Physiologie," Berlin, 1904.

VON SKRAMLIK, E.: Über das Verhalten des Geruchssinns bei gleichzeitiger Einwirkung zweier Reize, *Klin. Wochschr.*, **2**, 1250 (1923).

WEISS, S.: Über ein Verfahren, die Geruchsempfindung nach Belieben zu sistiren, *Osterr. Z. Heilk.*, **12**, 249 (1866).

WELLS, F. L.: Reaction times to Affects Accompanying Smell Stimuli, *Am. J. Psychol.*, **41**, 83 (1929).

WENDE, G. W., and F. C. BUSCH: Localized Facial Sweating Following Certain Olfactory Stimuli, *J. Am. Med. Assoc.*, **53**, 207 (1909).

WESTON, W.: Effects of Food Elements upon Special Senses, *Trans. Am. Laryngol. Rhinol., Otol. Soc.*, **34**, 426 (1928).

WIKLER, A., H. WOLFF, and N. GOODELL: Effects of Analgesic Agents on Sensations other than Pain, *J. Pharmacol. Exp. Therap.*, **83**, 294 (1945).

WINSLOW, C. E. A., and L. P. HERRINGTON: Influence of Odors on Appetite, *Am. J. Hyg.*, **23**, 143 (1936).

Wo sitzt der Geruchssinn? *Hygiene-Korrespondenz.*, 4 (1936).

WOLFF, B.: Sexual Osphresiology, *Med. News*, **85**, 955 (1902).

WRIGHT, J.: The Relation of the Biophysical Laws of Osmosis to Nasal Vasomotor Processes, *N. Y. Med. J.*, **94**, 861 (1911).

WUNDT, W. M.: Über die einfache Reactionszeit einer Geruchsempfindung, *Wundts philos. Stud.*, **1**, 556 (1883).

YOUNG, P. T.: Group Experiment upon the Affective Reaction to Odors, *Am. J. Psychol.*, **49**, 277 (1937).

ZWAARDEMAKER, H.: Test-en smaakgewaaresordigen bij het ruiken, *Nederland. Tijdschr. Geneesk.*, **1**, 113 (1899).

———: Bijdrage tot de physiologie van den reuk, *Lancet*, **1**, 1300 (1889).

———: Sur le norme de l'acuité olfactive, *Arch. néerland.*, **25**, 131 (1892).

*———: "Die Physiologie des Geruchs," Leipzig, 1895.

———: Die Physiologie des Geruches, *Verhandl. Ges. deut. naturforsch. Äerzte*, **68**, 420 (1895).

———: Influence des parfums sur le sens génital, *Interméd. biol.*, **1**, 322 (1897–1898).

———: Les Sensations olfactives, leurs combinations et leurs compensations, *L'Année psychol.*, **5**, 203 (1898).

———: Riechend schmecken, *Arch. Anat. u. Physiol., Physiol. Abt.*, 120 (1903).

———: Die Luftbrücke, *Onderzoch. physiol. Lab. Utrecht*, **5**, 421 (1903).

———: Eine bis jetzt unbekannt gebliebêne Eigenschaft des Geruchssinnes, *Arch. Anat. u. Physiol.*, 43 (1904).

———: Vergelijking van neus-en mondaderuhaling, *Nederland. Tijdschr. Geneesk.*, **40**, 314 (1904).

———: "Über Geurverwantschappen," *Koninkl. Akad. Wetenschap. Amsterdam, Versl.*, **16**, 183 (1908).

———: On Physiological Radioactivity, *J. Physiol.*, **53**, 275 (1920).

———: Physiologie der Nase und ihrer Nebenhöhlen, *Handbuch Hals-, Nasen-, Ohrenheilk.*, **1**, 439 (1925).

———: Sur le norme de l'acuité olfactive, *Am. J. Psychol.*, **5**, 98.

———: Contribution à la physiologie de la perception olfactive, *Arch. néerland. physiol.*, **9**, 261 (1924).

C. Pathology and Perversion of Odor Perception

a. Anosmia, parosmia, perversions

ALIKHAN, M.: Anosmia and Epilepsy, *Schweiz. med. Wochschr.*, **50**, 211 (1920).

ALURRALDE, M.: Considerciones fisiopatalogicas sobre un caso de neuritis sensorial (anosmia), *Rev. soc. med. argent.*, **10**, 322 (1902).

*ANHALT, G.: "Über traumatische Riechlähmungen," Leipzig, 1908.

BAHR, F.: Geruchs-Empfindungstörung, *Monatsschr. Unfallheilk.*, **20**, 383 (1914).

———: Störung d. Geruchsempfindung verbunden mit Störung des Geschmacks, *Monatsschr. Unfallheilk.*, **24**, 17 (1918).

*BAUER, J. H.: "Manuductiones ad veram theorem morborum praxinque clinicam specimen xi, de odoratu abolito," Altorfiis Norcorum, 1751.

BAUMGARTEN: Einige Fälle von Störungen des Geruchs und des Geschmacks, *Med.-chir. Presse*, **25**, 193 (1889).

BEDNAR, M.: Anosmia as a Symptom of Influenza, *Med. Klin.*, **26**, 1787 (1930).

BENNETT, O. P.: Loss of Sense of Olfaction, *North Am. Pract.*, **4**, 16 (1892).

BERBERICH, J.: Treatment of Anosmia with Insulin, *Schweiz. med. Wochschr.*, **67**, 226 (1937).

BEYER: Zur Frage der Parosmie, *Z. Psychol. Physiol. Sinnesorgane*, **35**, 50 (1904).

BIASOLI and MASUCCI: Un Caso interessante di anosmia, *Arch. ital. otol.*, **21**, 391 (1910).

*BIBARD, C.: "Contribution à l'étude de troubles de l'odorat," Paris, 1897.

BILANCIONI, G.: Dysosmia- clinical Study, *Riforma med.*, **43**, 1155 (1927).

BLOCH, J., and HECHINGER: Anosmie bei Schlafenlappensbsz, *Arch. Ohrenheilk.*, **76B**, 32 (1908).

BRICE, A. A.: Sense of Smell in Neuroses and Psychoses, *Psychoanal. Quart.*, **1**, 42 (1932).

BROECKAERT: Un Cas d'anosmie tramatique, *Ann. soc. med. Gand.*, **79**, 134 (1900).

BROMBERG, W., and P. SCHILDER: Olfactory Imagination and Olfactory Hallucination of Sense of Smell in Normal and Psychotic Persons, *Arch. Neurol. Psychiat.*, **32**, 467 (1934).

BRÜNNICHE: Stryknim mod anosmia, *Hosp. Tijdschr. Kjobenk.*, 2s, **1**, 372 (1874).

BULLEN, F. ST. J.: Olfactory Hallucinations in the Insane, *J. Mental Sci.*, **45**, 513 (1899).

CAMAUER, A. F.: Hyperosmia—interesting case, *Hosp. argent.*, **5**, 319 (1934).

CARRARI, G.: Vertiginous Syndrome with Anosmia and Dysgensia due to Bilateral Plugs of Ear Wax, *Bull. malat. orecchio*, **52**, 234 (1934).

CASTEX, A.: Anosmie traumatiques, *Bull. laryngol., otol., rhinol.*, **16**, 204 (1913).

CAUSSÉ, R.: Semeiology of Disturbances of Sense of Smell, *Presse méd.*, **41**, 1394 (1933).

*CHARISIUS, C. E.: "De olfactu deficiente," Gryphiswaldiae, 1747.

COLLET: Rapport sur l'anosmie, *Arch. intern. laryngol.*, **12**, 237 (1899).

COLLETT, F. J.: Anosmia: Etiologic and Statistical Study, *J. belge neurol. psychiat.*, **33**, 439 (1933).

CROSLAND, H. R., M. GOODMAN, and A. HOCKETT: Anosmia and Its Effect upon Taste Perceptions, *J. Exp. Psychol.*, **9**, 398 (1926).

CROSLAND, H. R., et al.: Oral Perception in Relation to Anosmia, *J. Exp. Psychol.*, **11**, 161 (1928).

CRUCIANI, J.: Chromic Acid in Therapy of Anosmia of Spasmodic Rhinitis, *Dia med.*, **10**, 447 (1938).

D'ABUNDO: Ansomia ed ipogensia ereditaria, *Soc. fra cultori scienze med.*, Caligiari, 1894.

D'AGUANNO, A.: Un Cas de guérison d'une anosmie remontant à quarante ans, *Boll. malat. orecchio, Ann. mal. oreille laryn.*, **8**, 129 (1890).

Daughter, Grandsons Inherit Smell-blindness, *Sci. Digest*, **18**, 83 (1945).

DAVIDSON, G. M.: Smell Hallucinations, *Psychiat. Quart.*, **12**, 253 (1938).

DUDLEY: Anosmia, *Trans. Am. Laryngol., Rhinol., Otol. Soc.*, **26**, 471 (1920).

DUNDAS, GRANT: Anosmia, *J. Laryngol.* (December, 1888).

DURANTE, G.: The Loss of Smell, *N. Y. Med. J.*, **55**, 634 (1892).

EBERS, J.: Hyperasthesie des Geruchssinnes als forensische Frage; ein Diebes-Riecher, *Urteilforsch. gerichtl. off. Med., Berlin*, **16**, 278 (1859).

FELICI, F.: Guarigione di un caso di anosmia, *Boll. malat. orecchio*, **7**, 133 (1889).

FÉRÉ, C.: Note sur des sensations subjectives d'odorat chez un epileptique, *Compt. rend. soc. biol.*, **3**, 1036.

————, P. BATIQUE, and P. OUVRY: Recherches sur le minimum perceptible de l'olfaction de la gustation chez les épileptiques, *Bull. soc. de biol.*, 2s, **29**, 259 (1892).

FIEBER, F.: Anosmia, *Ärztl. Ber. Krankenh. Wien.*, 321 (1867).

FISHER, B.: Vollständiges Defekt des Olfactorius bei einer 58 jährigen Frau, *Deut. med. Wochschr.*, 1737 (1905).

FLEISSNER, H.: Geruchsstörung bei Schlag, *Z. angew. Chem.*, 1845 (1908).

FORCHHEIMER, L.: Geruchs- und Geschmacksempfindungen nach intravenösen Injektionen von Salvarsan, *Dermatol. Zentr.*, **6** (1916).

FOX: Anosmia, Dryness, and Crustings of the Nose, in a Man Aged Thirty, *Proc. Roy. Soc. Med., Laryngol. Sect.*, **1**, 13 (1907–1908).

FREITAG: Geruchshalluzinationen und Falschriechen, *Unsere Welt.*, 21 (1937).

FRIEDMANN, H.: Ein Fall von Geruchshalluzination bei Tumor cerebri, *Wien. kl:n. Rundschau*, **47**, 787 (1909).

FULD: Störung des Geruchssinnes, *Ärztl. Ratgeber*, 56 (1903).

GATSCHER, S.: Rechtsseitige Anosmie nach Schädeltrauma, *Monatsschr. Ohrenheilk.*, **54**, 167 (1920).

GILLILAND, A. R.: The Taste Sensitivity of an Anosmic Subject, *J. Exp. Psychol.*, **4**, 318 (1921).

GLASER, O.: Hereditary Deficiencies in the Sense of Smell, *Science*, N.S., **48**, 647 (1918).

GOTTSCHALK: Ein Fall von Anosmie nach operativer Entfernung der Eierstöcke, *Deut. med. Wochschr.*, **26** (1891).

GRAVES, R. J.: Total Loss of Sense of Smell, Occasioned by Exposure to a Very Strong and Disagreeable Odour, *Dublin J. Med. Chem. Sci.*, **6**, 69 (1834).

GRAZZI: La Parosmie, ses causes et son traitement, *Boll. malat. orecchio*, **5**, 8 (1887).

GRAZZI, V.: A Cured Case of Parosmia, *Boll. malat orecchio*, **46**, 61 (1928).

HAHN, R.: Un caso di assoluta anosmia in seguito a trauma del capo, *Boll. malat. orecchio*, **20**, 193 (1902).

HAMILTON, B. R.: Case of Loss of Smell, *Am. J. Med. Sci.*, N.S., **61**, 418 (1871).

HARRIMAN, P. L.: Case of Olfactory Hallucination in a Hypochondriacal Prisoner, *J. Abnormal Psychol.*, **29**, 457 (1935).

HARRIS, T.: A Case of Hyperosmia, *Trans. Am. Laryngol., Rhinol., Otol. Soc.*, 367 (1907).

HARTMANN, M.: Hallucinations of Smell, *Arch. Psychiat.*, **94**, 847 (1931).

*HEINEMANN: "Über Anosmie," Göttingen, 1888.

HELLWIG, A.: Eine suggestivo bewirkte Geruchsillusion, *Arch. Krim.-Anthrop. Kriminalist*, **50**, 14 (1912).

HELSMOORTEL, J.: Troubles de l'olfaction et de gout, *J. neurol. psychiat.*, **29**, 298 (1929).

HELSMOORTEL, J., JR., and R. NYSSEN: Anosmia Following Cranial Trauma, *Riv. oto-neuro-ophtalmol.*, **10**, 171 (1935).

————, ————, and R. THIENPONT: Olfactory Disturbances in Cranio-cerebral Trauma, *Riv. oto-neuro-ophtalmol.*, **11**, 489 (1933).

————, ————, and ————: Complete Anosmia and Ageusia following Cranial Trauma, *J. belge neurol. psychiat.*, **34**, 226 (1934).

——, ——, and ——: Anosmia and Ageusia of Traumatic Origin, *Acta psychiat. neurol.*, **11**, 251 (1936).

HEYMANN, R.: Geruchssinn und Störungen, *Gesundheit*, **2**, 732 (1906).

HOFMANN, F. B.: Über Geruchsstörungen nach Katarrhen der Nasenhöhle, *Münch. med. Wochschr.*, **65**, 1370 (1918).

——: Zur Theorie des Geruchssinnes. I. Parosmie-Studien, *Z. Biol.*, **73**, 53 (1921).

*HOFFMAN, K. R.: "Disturbances of Olfaction and Taste in Fractures of the Base of the Skull," Charlottenburg, 1938.

HOLTHAUS, B.: Störungen des Geruchssinnes bei Epileptikern zugleich ein Beitrag zur Frage der klinischen Geruchsprüfung, *Arch. Psychiat. Nervenkrankh.*, **97B**, 238 (1932).

HUTCHINSON, J.: Anosmia, *Am. J. Med. Sci.*, **23**, 146 (1852).

——: On Subjective Aberrations of the Sense of Smell, *Arch. Surg.*, **11**, 302 (1890–1891).

IRIBARNE: Les Troubles de l'odorat, *Rev. psychothérap.*, **38**, 141 (1913–1914).

JACKSON, J. H.: Subjective Sensations of Smell with Epileptiform Attacks, *Ophthalmol. Hosp. Rep., London*, **5**, 304 (1866).

——: Subjective Sensations of Smell with Epileptiform Seizures, *Lancet*, **1**, 376 (1871).

——: Remarks on Loss of Smell and Loss of Taste, *Lancet*, **2**, 622 (1874).

——, and C. E. BEEVOR: A Case of Epilepsy with Olfactory Aura from a Tumour in the Temporo-sphenoidal Lobe, *Brit. Med. J.*, **1**, 414 (1889).

JACOB, E. H.: Report of Case of Anosmia, *Lancet*, **1**, 778 (1882).

JACQUES, P.: Un Cas d'anosmie complète, *Rev. hebd. laryngol.*, **19**, 689 (1899).

——: Anosmie traumatique par plongeon, *Bull. laryngol. otol., rhinol.*, **9**, 1 (1906).

JASTROW, J.: Observations on the Absence of the Sense of Smell, *Am. J. Psychol.*, **4**, 407 (1891–1892).

JEKELS, L.: Psychopathologie der Alltagleben tendenziöse Geruchshalluzinat, *Intern. Z. ärztl. Psychoanalyse*, **3**, 37 (1915).

JOUET, R.: Troubles de l'odorat, *Bull. oto-rhino-laryngol.*, **15**, 190 (1912).

KENNETH, J. H.: Classification of pathosmia, *J. Laryngol. Otol.*, **43**, 410 (1928).

KIESOW, F.: Über Geschmacks- und Geruchsträume, *Atti 5 Congr. intern. psicolog.*, 282 (1906).

KILLIAN, J. A.: Subjektive Kakosmie, *Münch. med. Wochschr.*, 1741 (1904).

KINDLER, W.: Geruchsstörungen nach Schädel-verletzung in Medizin und soziale Bedeutung, *Med. Welt.*, 150 (1936).

KLAMANN: Ein Fall von Anosmie, *Allgem. med. Zentr.-Ztg.*, **56**, 369 (1887).

KNEELAND, S.: Case of an Affection of the Olfactory Nerve, with Total Loss of Smell and Taste, *Extr. Rec. Boston Soc. Med. Improv.*, **1**, 102 (1853).

KOBRAK, E.: Subjektive Kakosmie, *Med. Klin.*, 1835 (1908).

KÖRNER, O.: Die Störungen der Geruchsempfindung, des Gefühls und der Absonderungen in der Nase, *Heymanns Handbuch Laryngol. Rhinol.*, **3**, (1).

KRAUPA-RUNK, M.: Perverse Geruchs- und Geschmacksempfindungen nach Neosalvarsaninjektion, *Münch. med. Wochschr.*, 46 (1916).

KUTZINSKI, A.: Geruchs-halluzinationen, *Med. Klin.*, 394 (1912).

——: Geruchshalluzination nach Hirnverletzunung, *Monatsschr. Psychiat. Neurol.*, **57**, 321 (1925).

LAEMMLE, H.: Disorders of Smell: Clinical Aspects, *Arch. Ohren-, Nasen- u. Kehlkopfheilk.*, **130**, 22 (1931).

LAUTER, A.: Über Anosmie, *Z. Laryngol. Rhinol.*, **9**, 57 (1919–1920).

LEGG, J. W.: A Case of Anosmia following a Blow, *Lancet*, **11**, 659 (1879).

LEIGH, A. D.: Defects of Smell after Head Injury, *Lancet*, **244**, 38 (1943).

LENNHOFF, G.: Subjektive Kakosmie, *Med. Klin.*, 1146 (1908).

LEVINSTEIN, O.: Traumatische Anosmie, *Arch. Laryngol. Rhinol.*, **23B**, 455 (1910)

———: Berufsanosmie der Feuerwehrleute, *Arch. Laryngol. Rhinol.*, 410 (1911).

———: Über hereditäre Anosmie, *Arch. Laryngol. Rhinol.*, **32**, 172 (1919).

LITTLE, T. E.: Congenital Deficiency of Left Olfactory Nerve, *Proc. Path. Soc. Dublin*, N.S., **4**, 88 (1868–1871).

LOCKMANN: Zur Kasuistik der Geruchsanomalien, *Z. Nat. Med.*, **12**, (1861).

LÖHNER, L.: Detection of Simulated Anosmia, *Wien. klin. Wochschr.*, **51**, 1018 (1938).

———: Smell Tests, with Special Reference to Genuine and Simulated Anosmia, *Monatsschr. Ohrenheilk.*, **74**, 479 (1940).

LOTMAR, N.: Eigentümlichkeiten des Geruchssinnes, *Kleinwelt*, **7**, 77 (1915).

McBRIDE, P.: A Case of Anosmia for Diagnosis and Suggestions as to Treatment, *J. Laryngol. London*, **18**, 325 (1903).

———: Clinical Remarks on the Functional Element in Certain Forms of Anosmia, *Brit. Med. J.*, **11**, 945 (1907).

McSHERRY: Loss of Sense of Smell, *Maryland Med. J.*, **4**, 294 (1878–1879).

MAINLAND, R. C.: Absence of Olfactory Sensation, *J. Heredity*, **36**, 143 (1945).

MARCUS, H.: Epilepsie und Geruchsaura, *Z. ges. Neurol.*, **30**, 118 (1915).

MELLO, M., DE: Parosmia and Parageusia after Cerebral Trauma, *Rev. brasil oto-rino-laring.*, **8**, 467 (1940).

MEYER, J.: Traitement de la cacosmie d'origine digestive par la respiration diaphragmatique, *Bull. soc. pédiat. Paris*, **24**, 266 (1926).

MILELLA, M.: Caso di anosmia completa in individuo poi affetto da porpora emorragica, *Ann. med. nav. Roma*, **6**, 432 (1900).

MONTEIRO, A.: Traumatic Anosmia, with Report of Case, *Brasil-med.*, **56**, 561 (1942).

MORSIER, G., DE: Complete Anosmia and Transitory Parosmia after Slight Trauma of Occipital Region, *Rev. oto-neuro-opht.*, **16**, 111 (1938).

*MULLER, M.: "Syringomyelie mit Anosmie," Jena, 1896.

MUNGER, C. E.: Parosmia; with History of a Peculiar Case, *Laryngoscope*, **14**, 384 (1904).

NADOLECZNY, M.: Über Geruchsstörungen, *Münch. med. Wochschr.*, 1676 (1933).

*NIQUE: "Contribution à l'étude des anosmies et en particulier des troubles olfactifs dans les maladies de l'oreille," Lyon, 1897.

NOQUET: Un Cas de parosmie subjective, *Nod. med., Lille*, **4**, 287 (1898).

NOTTA: Recherches sur la perte de l'odorat, *Arch. gen. med.*, **1**, 385 (1870).

NYSSON, R.: Hereditary, Familial, and Congenital Anosmia, *J. belge neurol. psychiat.*, **33**, 422 (1933).

OGLE, W.: Anosmia; or Cases Illustrating the Physiology of the Sense of Smell, *Med. Chir. Trans.*, **53**, 276 (1870).

ONODI, A.: Fälle von Parosmien, *Monatsschr. Ohrenheilk.*, **25**, 69 (1891).

———: Parosmie, *Wien. med. Wochschr.*, **12**, 486 (1898).

———: Anosmie, *J. Otol. Laryngol.*, **13**, 183 (1899).

———: Über Anosmie, *Ärztl. Zentrztg.*, 527 (1900).

———: Intermittentte Zerstörung des Geruchs, *Orvosi hetiszemle* (Budapest), **4**, 391 (1909).

———, and A. ZIRKELBACH: Zur Pathologie d. Anosmie, *Arch. Laryngol. Rhinol.*, 125 (1903).

PARKER, E.: Anosmia from Tobacco Poisoning, *Phila. Med. News* (Sept. 20, 1890).

PARREL, DE: L'Anosmie et son traitement, *Rev. gén. clin. therap.*, **34**, 201 (1920).

PASKIND, H. A.: Parosmia in Tumorous Involvement of Olfactory Bulbs and Nerves, *Arch. Neurol. Psychiat.*, **33**, 835 (1935).

PELTESOHN: Geruchssinn und Unfall, *Ärztl. Sachverstandigen-ztg.*, 284 (1910).

PEREGUD, G. M.: Anosmia in Tumors of Fourth Ventricle, *Russ. oto-laringol.*, **24**, 101 (1931).

PETIT-DUTAILLES, D.: Anosmia in Cerebral Tumors, *Gaz. méd. France*, **43**, 99 (1936).

PLACZEK, S.: Angeborene doppelseitige Anosmie, *Berlin klin. Wochschr.*, **51** (1899).

PLAHNER, S.: Schnellheilung der Geruchshalluzination, *Jahrb. Psychoanalyse*, **3**, 182 (1929).

PONZO, M.: La modelita degli atti dell'annosare come direttivo per scoprire la simulazione e la dissimulazione delle anosmie, *Arch. ital. Otol.*, **33**, 340 (1922).

POTTS, C.: Two Cases of Hallucination of Smell, *Univ. Med. Mag.*, Philadelphia (1891).

PREVOST, J. L.: Atrophie des nerfs olfactifs, fréquente chez le vieillard et correspondant avec la diminution ou la perte du sens de l'odorat, *Gaz. méd. Paris*, 3s, **21**, 597 (1866).

Queer Mistakes of Smell, *Literary Digest*, **114**, 22 (1932).

QUINCKE, H.: Anosmie bei Hirndruck, *Cor.-Bl. schweiz. Ärzte*, **12**, 471 (1882).

QUIX, F. H.: Die Störungen des Geruchssinnes, *Handbuch Neurol.*, Berlin, **1**, (1910).

RADIUS: Einiges über Anosmie, *Beitr. med. chir. Klin. Leipzig*, **111**, 333 (1833–1834).

RAYNAUD, M.: Note sur un état curieux d'anosmie intermittente, *Union méd.* (July 10, 1870).

————: Note sur un cas curieux d'anosmie intermittente, *Bull. mem. soc. med. hopit.*, Paris, 2s, **16**, 168 (1880).

REH, H.: Congenital Fistulas of Lacrimal Sac Combined with Congenital Aural Fistulas and Anosmia, *Klin. Monatsbl. Augenheilk.*, **104**, 55 (1940).

RÉNÉ, A.: Anosmie, *Bull. soc. de biol.*, 439 (1890).

REUTER, C.: Geruchslosigkeit: essentielle Anosmie, *Arch. Laryngol. Rhinol.*, **9B**, 343 (1899).

————: Cocain-hyperosmie, *Onderzoek ged. in h. physiol. Lab. Utrecht. Hoogeschool.*, 5 R, **2**, 46 (1900).

————: Geruchsempfindungsstörungen, *Bibl. ges. med. Wiss.*, **16**, **17**.

RHODES: Anosmie, *N. Y. Med. Record* (July 5, 1890).

RIESE, W.: Bau und Leistungen des Zentralnervensystems eines vierjahrigen riechhirnlosen Kindes, *Deut. Z. Nervenheilk.*, **89**, 37 (1926).

RIVA, A.: Anosmia e consequente agensia da nevrosi dell' olfattoria, *Giorn. internoz. sci. med.*, **1**, 584 (1879).

ROBERTSON, C. A.: Remarkable Nervous Perturbation of Smell, *Boston Med. Surg. J.*, **89**, 280 (1873).

ROTCH, T. M.: A Case of Traumatic Anosmia and Ageusia, with Partial Loss of Hearing and Sight, *Boston Med. Surg. J.*, **99**, 130 (1878).

SAFRANEK, J.: Anosmie, *Berlin klin. Wochschr.*, **48**, 1038 (1911).

SCHAECHTER-NANCY, M.: Olfactory Hallucinations, *Cervello*, **17**, 280 (1938).

SCHALCK, E.: Anosmia, *Med. Record*, **41**, 292 (1892).

SCHIRMAN, A.: A Case of Absolute Loss of Smell and Taste, *Med. Record*, **49**, 372 (1896).

SCHLACHTER, M.: Insulin in Therapy of Anosmia, *Folia oto-laryng. orient.*, **3**, 173 (1936).

SCHLÄGER: Über die im Bereiche des Geruchssinnes auftretenden Illusionen bei Geistesgestörten, *Z. Ges. Ärzte, Wien*, **14**, 259 (1858).

SCHMALFUSS, B.: Erlebnis eines Geruchs, wie Phenylacetaldehyd; nach Niesen oder Anprall d. Stirn, *Z. Psychol. Sinnesorg.*, **63B**, 185 (1932).

SCHMELZER, H.: Einseit. Stauungspupille und Störung des Geruchssinnes, *Klin. Monatsbl. Augenheilk.*, **91**, 479 (1933).

SCHMIDT, H.: Anosmia and Ageusia in Pregnancy, *Klin. Wochschr.*, **4**, 1967 (1925).

SCHÖNFELD: Zur Therapie der Anosmie, *Med. Klin.*, **25**, 1780 (1929).

SCIUTI, M.: Un caso di anosmia traumatica, *Osped. psichiat.*, **3**, 3 (1935).

SEIFERT, O.. Traumatic Anosmia, *Monatsschr. Ohrenheilk. Laryngol.-Rhinol.*, **40**, 650 (1912).

SEYDELL, E. M.: Olfactory Disturbances, *Trans. Sect. Laryng., Otol. Rhinol., Am. Med. Assoc.*, 93 (1932).

SHAFARENKO, M. M.: Absence of Sense of Smell and its Treatment, *Vrachebnoe Delo*, 19, 253 (1936).

SIEBERT, W.: Ein Fall von Hirntumor mit Geruchstäuschungen, *Monatschr. Psychiatr. Neurol.*, 6, 81 (1900).

SPECHT, F.: Smell Disorders, *Handbuch Hals-Nasen-Ohrenheilk.*, 5, 673 (1929).

STERLING, W.: Über traumstische Anosmie zerebralen Ursprungs, *Neurol. Zentr.*, 38, 482 (1919).

———: Traumatische Cerebrale Anosmie, *Neurol. polska*, 6, 329 (1922).

———: Anosmia Due to Intercranial Trauma, *Rev. neurol.*, 2, 135 (1927).

STERNE, A.: Un Cas d'anosmie hystérique, *Compt. rend. soc. méd. Nancy*, 30 (1900–1901).

STREFEL, J.: Anosmie und Enophthalmos Traumaticus, *Deut. med. Wochschr.*, 40, 1959 (1914).

STRICKER, W.: Verlust des Geruches in Folge localer Anästhesirung, *Arch. path. Anat.*, 12, 290 (1867).

SUNE, L.: Anosmie et cacosmie, *Ann. maladies oreille larynx*, 10, (1893).

TARCHETTI, C.: Anosmia and Aphonia after Laryngectomy for Cancer, *Oto-rino-laringol. ital.*, 7, 316 (1937).

THOMSON, H. C.: Anosmia, *Polyclin. London*, 5, 74 (1901).

———: Clinical Lecture on Cerebral Tumour Associated with Subjective Sensation of Smell, *Brit. Med. J.*, 11, 1761 (1907).

TILLEY, H.: Three Cases of Parosmia; Causes and Treatments, *Lancet*, 11, 907 (1895).

TISDALL, F. F., A. BROWN, and R. D. DEFRIES: Persistent Anosmia ZnSO₄ Nasal Spraying, *J. Pediat.*, 13, 60 (1938).

TOULOUSE, E., and N. VASCHIDE: Influences des crises epileptiques sur l'olfaction, *Compt. rend. soc. biol.*, 51, 742 (1899).

TRIVAS: Deux Cas d'anosmie totale consécutive à un traumatisme du crane, *Rev. hebd. laryngol.*, 2, 581 (1905).

TUCKER, B. R.: Report of a Case of Tumor of the Pontocerebellar Angle on the Left Side of the Brain; with Bilateral Loss of Smell and Disturbance of Taste, *Old Dominion J. Med. Surg.*, 13, 327 (1911).

Über Anosmie, *Wochschr. Klin. Therap.*, 1000 (1900).

Über Anosmie, *Wien. med. Presse*, 41, 1469 (1900).

Über Anosmie, *Wien. med. Blätter*, 23, 554 (1900).

URBANTSCHITSCH, E.: Vollständige Anosmie nach Schädelbasisfraktur bei sonst negativem Nerven-, Ohren- und Nasenbefund, *Monatsschr. Ohrenheilk.*, 3, 603 (1918).

VAN HOEVEN: Une Anomalie de l'odorat, *Z. Sinnesphysiol.*, 42.

VAN ITERSON, C. J. A.: Subjective Cacosmia, *Geneesk. Tijdschr.*, 8, 705 (1930).

*VAN VLEUTEN, M.: "Disturbances of Olfaction in Fractures of the Base of the Skull," Charlottenburg, 1938.

VIMONT: À-propos d'un cas d'anosmie traumatique, *Soc. méd. légale* (Feb. 12, 1906).

WEIDENREICH, F.: Über partiellen Riechlappendefekt und Eunuchoidismus beim Menschen, *Z. Morphol.*, 18, 157 (1914).

WHEELER, D.: An Unusual Psychoneurosis of War, Functional Loss of the Sense of Smell, *Bull. Can. Army Med. Corps*, 100 (November, 1918).

WOELK, H. A.: Traumatic Anosmia, *Z. Laryngol. Rhinol.*, 18, 283 (1929).

———: Traumatic Anosmia, *Monatsschr. Unfallheilk.*, 37, 1 (1930).

ZANDER, P.: Verlust des Geruchs-verögens keine Erwerbsbschränkung, *Med. Klin.*, 32, 893 (1915).

ZANZUCCHI, G.: So-called Olfactory Component of Metallic Taste in Relation to Nasal Disturbances, *Arch. ital. otol.*, **48**, 654 (1936).

ZARNIKO, K.: Über Kakosmia subjectiva, *Z. Chrenheilk.*, **27**, 340 (1895).

ZICKGRAAF, G.: Xerose and Anosmie, *Z. Laryngol. Rhinol.*, **3**, 53 (1910).

ZIEGLER, H.: Störungen der Geruchs- und Geschmacksempfindungen, *Monatsschr. Unfall-heilk.*, **26**, 213 (1920).

ZIEM, G.: Zur Lehre von der Anosmie, Parosmie und Ageusie, *Monatsschr. Uhrenheilk.*, **38**, 461 (1904).

ZWAARDEMAKER, H.: Cocain-anosmie, *Fortschr. Med.*, **7**, 481 (1889).

———: Anosmie. Eine klinische Studie, *Berlin Klin.*, **26**, 1 (1890).

———: Eine Empfindung der Geruchslosigkeit, *Arch. Physiol.* (Supp.), 420 (1902).

b. General Pathology (Including Medico-legal)

ADELHEIM, R.: Über die Einteilung der Gase in ihrer Beziehung zur Pathologie, *Frankfurt. f. Pathol.*, **25**, 261 (1921).

AGAR, J. S., and A. CAZORT: Allergy Relations in Nose Pathology, *Southern Med. J.*, **32**, 1063 (1939).

AGNELLO, F.: Nasociliary Syndrome of Nasal Nerve and Trigeminal Neuralgia due to Traumatic Corneal Lesion, *Riv. oto-neuro-oftal.*, **15**, 79 (1938).

ALLEN, I. M.: Spontaneous Olfactory and Gustatory Phenomena with and without Organic Lesions of the Brain, *New Zealand Med. J.*, **43**, 165 (1944).

ANTONA, S.: Trypan Blue Absorption from Nose, *Pathologica*, **21**, 1 (1929).

ARTAULT, S.: Troubles nerveux provoqués par des émanations de laurier-rose, *Compt. rend. soc. biol.*, **104**, 84 (1897).

BAGBY, G. F.: Ozena; its Treatment, *Homeop. Eye, Ear, Throat J.*, **13**, 57 (1907).

*BALLENGER, W. L., and H. C. BALLENGER: "Diseases of the Nose, Throat and Ear, Medical and Surgical," 8th ed., Philadelphia, 1943.

BERARD, P. H.: Observation d'une affection tuberculeuse du cerveau ayant détruit les nerfs olfactifs, *N. physiol. exper. pathol.*, **5**, 17 (1825).

BILLIARD, G.: Les Rhumes des foins, *J. méd. franc.*, **9**, 494 (1920).

BLEYER, J. M.: The Sense of Smell in Relation to Medicolegal Questions, *J. Respir. Org. N. Y.*, **1**, 181 (1889).

BLUMENTHAL, F.: Kritische Studie über den Stand der Lehre von den nasalen Reflex-neurosen, *Med. Klin. Berlin*, **17**, 356 (1721).

BOHL, W.: Nasal Mucosa: Amyloidosis in Horses, *Deut. tierärztl. Wochschr.*, **38**, 321 (1930).

BOWERS, W. C.: Tuberculosis of the Nasal Mucosa, *Laryngoscope*, **30**, 736 (1920).

BRIANT, M.: Une Forme singulière d'aura ou de prodrome épileptique; odeur nauséabonde répandue par le malade, *J. psychol. norm. pathol.*, **20**, 764 (1905).

BRILL, A. A.: The Sense of Smell in the Neuroses and Psychoses, *Psychoanalyt. Quart.*, **1**, 42 (1932).

BROWN, E. A., and P. L. GORTEIN: The Meaning of Asthma, *Psychoanalyt. Rev.*, **31**, 299 (1944).

BRUN, R.: Disorders of Smell and Taste as Signs of Focal Lesion of Temporal Lobe. *J. belge neurol. psychiat.*, **37**, 262 (1937).

BURCHARDT: Die Luftströmung in der Nase unter pathologischen Verhaltnissen, *Arch. Laryngol. Rhinol.*, **17**, 123 (1905).

*BUSCH, H.: "Phantom der normalen Nase des Menschen," München, 1914.

*BUXTON, D. W.: "Anaesthetics, Their Uses and Administration," Philadelphia, 1920.

*CASTEX, M. R.: "Maladies du larynx, du nez et des oreilles," Paris, 1907.

COLLET: Des Troubles olfactifs dans les maladies de l'oreille, *Soc. franc. laryngol.* (May 12, 1898).

*———: "L'Odorat et ses troubles," Paris, 1904.

COMPAIRED: L'Atrophie ozénateuse, *Rev. hebd. laryngol.*, **1**, 615 (1910).

COZZOLINO, V.: Alterazionale dell' odorat, *Gazz. napol. psichiat.* (1881).

DANDY, W. E.: Smell as Influenced by Man's Right Cerebral Hemisphere, *Bull. Johns Hopkins Hosp.*, **53**, 31 (1933).

*DEL CASTILLO, E. B.: "Secreciones internas," 3d ed., Buenos Aires, 1943.

DE MARTINES, E.: Recherches sur les troubles du goût et de l'odorat dans la paralysie générale progressive, *Rev. méd. Suisse Romande*, **20**, 405, 452 (1900).

DENKER: Die Entwicklung der Diagnostik und der Therapie der Eiterungen der Nebenhölen der Nase, *Münch. med. Wochschr.*, **58**, 2584 (1911).

*DESCHAMPS: "Des Maladies des fosses nasales et leur sinus," Paris, 1803.

EAGLETON, W. P.: Intercranial Complications of Nasal Origin, *Laryngoscope*, **30**, 673 (1920).

ERIKSON, S.: Olfaction: Roentgen Diagnosis of Meningiomas, *Acta radiol.*, **22**, 581 (1941).

ESSEVELD, H., and W. KOUWENEAR: Nose Mucus Proteus X Strains from Normals, *Geneesk. Tijdschr. Nederland-Indië*, **80**, 1871 (1940).

FABRICANT, N. D.: Secretions of Nose: Lysozyme Activity and H-ion Concentration of, *Arch. Otolaryngol.*, **41**, 53 (1945).

*———: "Nasal Medication, a Practical Guide," Baltimore, 1942.

FAUST, F. B., and J. M. SIMMONS: Sulfadiazine in Treatment of Nasopharyngitis, *J. Am. Med. Assoc.*, **125**, 552 (1944).

FEINBERG, S. M., and S. FRIEDLANDER: Nasal Congestion from Frequent Use of Privine Hydrochloride, *J. Am. Med. Assoc.*, **128**, 1095 (1945).

FENTON, R. A.: Nasal Mucosa; Immunity, *Ann. Otol., Rhinol., Laryngol.*, **41**, 705 (1932).

FINAMORE, G.: Effetti morbosi prodotti delle emanazione odorifere delle noce, *Compania med., Caserta*, **3**, 21 (1874).

FLEXNER, S.: Modes of Infection in Poliomyelitis, *Contrib. Med. Sci. in honor of Dr. E. Libman*, **1**, 425 (1932).

FOY, R.: L'Imperméabilité fonctionnelle nasale; son traitement par la rééducation, *Rev. hebd. laryngol.*, **11**, 641 (1909).

FRANCO, E. E.: Olfactory Nerve: Unusual Malformation of Left Olfactory Peduncle and End-bud, *Arch. ital. anat. istol. patol.*, **1**, 105 (1930).

FRIDENBERG, P.: Mental Symptoms in Nasal Affections, *Med. Record*, **71**, 1071 (1907).

FURSTENBERG, A. C., E. CROSBY, and B. FARRIOR: Neurologic Lesions which Influence Sense of Smell, *Trans. Am. Laryngol., Rhinol., Otol. Soc.*, **48**, 40 (1942).

GALKIN, W. S.: Olfactory Nerve: Effect on Epileptic Attacks Following Freezing of Occipital Cortex, *Z. ges. exp. Med.*, **81**, 374 (1932).

GAULT: Du Traitement de l'ozène, *Arch. intern. laryngol.*, **26**, 847 (1908).

GEGENBAUR, C.: Ein Fall von mangelhafter Ausbildung der Nasenmuscheln, *Morphol. Jahrb.*, **5**, 191 (1879).

GILLET, P.: Nasal Mucosa: Sympathicotherapy; Excitation of Nasal Mucosa in Diseases of the Nervous System, *Arch. intern. neurol.*, **53**, 1 (1934).

GOLDSWORTHY, N. E., and H. FLOREY: Nose Secretions, Bacterial, Inhibitory and Lytic Powers, *Brit. J. Exp. Path.*, **11**, 192 (1930).

GORONCY, C.: Geruchswahrnehmungen und ihre kriminalistische Bedeutung, *Arch. Kriminol.*, **75B**, 163 (1924).

GOVER, M., and J. B. YANKEY: Defects of Nasal Septum in Low-income Farm Families, *U. S. Pub. Health Repts.*, **60**, 1069 (1945).

GRADENIGO: Sur l'importance de l'examen du sens olfactif comme moyen de diagnostic dans certaines affections nasales et auriculaires, *Comm. acad. roy. med. Turin* (May 5, 1894).

GRAYSON, C. P.: The Nasal Phenomena of Neurasthenia, *Laryngoscope*, **20**, 1114 (1910).

GRUENFELDER, B., and W. LASCH: Peculiar Association of Genital Malformation with Defect of Olfactory Nerves, *Acta Oto-Laryngol. orient*, **1**, 6 (1945).

GUILLAIN, G., and R. MESSIMY: Olfactory Disturbance in Paget's Disease, *Compt. rend. soc. biol.*, **131**, 499 (1939).

HABER, P.: Olfactory Nerves: Mechanism of Centripetal Propagation of Poliomyelitis Virus after Surgical Suppression of Olfactory Bulb, *Compt. rend. soc. biol.*, **120**, 761 (1935).

HAGA, J.: Unilateral Absence of the Olfactory Tract, *Nederland. Tijdschr. Geneesk.*, **11**, 2450 (1915).

HALL, C. R.: On the Rise, Progress and Mysteries of Mesmerism in all Ages and Countries. Effects on the Sense of Smell, *Lancet*, **1**, 281 (1845).

HANDMANN: Serous Cyst of Orbit Springing from Misplaced Nasal Mucosa, *Z. Augenheilk.*, **65**, 321 (1928).

HANSEL, F. K.: Nose: Secretions in Allergy, *J. Allergy*, **10**, 241 (1939).

HARGETT, E. R.: Nasal Mucosa: Deficiency Reaction (of Nasal Mucous Glands of Epithelium), *Ann. Otol., Rhinol., Laryngol.*, **47**, 917 (1938).

HARIES, C. F.: Osmologiae medicae elementa sive odorum exposito physiologico-pathologica-therapeutica, *Opera Min. Acad. Med.*, **1**, 231 (1815).

HARRIS, T. J.: Papilloma of the Nose (Disordered Smell), *Trans. Am. Laryngol., Rhinol., Otol. Soc.*, **13**, 366 (1907).

HARTMANN, A.: Über nasalen Kopfschmerz und nasale Neurasthenie, *Deut. med. Wochschr.*, **33**, 716 (1907).

HARTMANN, W.: Question of Relationship between Sensitivity to Odor of Horses and Horse Serum Hypersensitivity, *Z. Immunitätsforsch. exp. Therap.*, **99**, 257 (1941).

HAYS, H. M.: Headaches and the Nose, *Med. Times, N. Y.*, **48**, 64 (1920).

*HEITSCH, R.: "Der Geruchssinn der Epileptiker," Rostock, (1936).

HELSMOORTEL, J., JR., and H. J. SCHERER: Olfactory Meningioma, *J. belge neurol. psychiat.*, **39**, 647 (1939).

HERZOG, F.: Cortical Centers in Pituitary Tumor Cases and Smell, *Deut. Z. Nervenheilk.*, **102**, 221 (1928).

HORESH, A. J.: Odors—Allergy in Infant Eczema, *J. Allergy*, **14**, 335 (1943).

———: Allergy to Odor of Irish Potato, *J. Allergy*, **15**, 147 (1944).

HOROWITZ, E.: Olfaction Nerve: Agenesia, in Human Brain, *Anat. Anz.*, **81**, 353 (1936).

HUGUENIN: Über Neuritis Olfactoria, *Corr.-Bl. schweiz. Ärzte, Basle*, **12**, 257 (1882).

*HURST, A. F.: "The Psychology of the Special Senses and their Functional Disorders," London, 1921.

ISSAJEW, P. O.: Smell in Agenesia of Olfactory Nerve (human), *Anat. Anz.*, **74**, 398 (1932).

JACOBSON, L. O., and G. F. DICK: Normal and Abnormal Microflora of Nose, *J. Am. Med. Assoc.*, **117**, 2222 (1941).

JUHASZ, A.: Die nasalen Reflexneurosen, *Heymanns Handbuch Laryngol. Rhinol.*, **3**, 653 (1900).

*JULIAN, H.: "Troubles du goût et de l'odorat dans le tabes," Paris, 1900.

KAUFMANN, E.: Über eine typische Form von Schleimhautgeschwulst an der äusseren Nasenwand, *Monatsschr. Ohrenheilk.*, **24**, 1890.

KINDLER, W.: Olfactory Involvement in Herpes Zoster Cephalicus, *Arch. Ohren-, Nasen-, u. Kehlkopfheilk.*, **146**, 358 (1939).

KRÖNIG: Über Dysmenorrhoe und nasale Reflexneurosen, *Verhandl. Ges. Geburts. Leipzig*, 41 (1901).

KÜSTER, E.: Review of Nose in Man and Animals (Bacterial Flora and Conjunctival Flora Compared), *Handbuch pathogen. Mikroskop.*, 3 Aufl., **6**, 355 (1928).

*KUTTNER, A.: "Die nasalen Reflexneurosen und die normalen Nasenreflexe," Berlin, 1904.

*LEDERER, F. L.: "Diseases of the Ear, Nose and Throat," 4 ed., Philadelphia, 1943.

LEICHER: Pathology of Nose, *Z. Hals- Nasen- u. Ohrenheilk.*, **20**, 238 (1928).

LEVINTHAL, W.: Nasal Mucosa: Bacterial Flora, *Zentr. Bakt.*, 1 Abt. Orig., **106**, 195 (1928).

MCAULIFFE, G. W., H. GOODELL, and H. G. WOLFF: Pain. Chap. XIII, Pain from Nasal and Paranasal Structures, *Research Publ. Assoc. Nervous Mental Disease*, **23**, 185 (1943).

*MACDONALD, G.: "Diseases of the Nose," London, 1890.

MACHT, D. I., and M. B. MACHT: Comparison of Effect of Cobra Venom and Opiates on Olfactory Sense, *Am. J. Physiol.*, **129**, 411 (1940).

MACKENZIE, J. N.: On Nasal Cough and the Existence of a Sensitive Reflex Area in the Nose, *Am. J. Med. Sci.*, **86**, 106 (1883).

———: Irritation of the Sexual Apparatus as an Etiological Factor in the Production of Nasal Disease, *Am. J. Med. Sci.*, **87**, 360 (1884).

MCMAHON, B. J.: Nasal Mucosa: Late Changes in Dogs Following Ionization, *Arch. Otolaryngol.*, **22**, 454 (1935).

MARIO: La Patogenese delle turbe olfattive, *Riv. clin. med. Firenze*, **26**, 367 (1925).

MARX, H.: Untersuchungen zur Bacteriologie der Nase, *Z. Ohrenheilk., Wiesbad.*, **72**, 37 (1914).

MEEKER, L. H.: Anomalous Olfactory Lobes in Man, *Laryngoscope*, **39**, 379 (1929).

MERRILL, A. P.: Do Odors Cause Disease? *Am. Practitioner*, **1**, 208 (1870).

MILLS, K. C., G. SHIBLEY, and A. R. DOCHEZ: Nasal Mucosa: Bacterial Flora, *J. Exp. Med.*, **47**, 193 (1928).

MOLLIERE: Note pour servir à la pathologie du nerf olfactif, *Lyon med.*, **8**, 385 (1871).

*MORRISON, W. W.: "Diseases of the Nose, Throat and Ear," Philadelphia, 1938.

NÄCKE, P.: Die Rolle des Geruchssinn im Philtrum, *Arch. krim. Anthropol. Kriminalist.*, **41**, 157 (1911).

NAGAHARA, Y.: Experimental Histopathologic Study of Olfactory Organ after Bisection of Nerve, *Trans. soc. path. jap.*, **29**, 482 (1939).

NATHANSON, G.: Acute CO Poisoning; Path. Changes of Olfactory Organ, *Acta Oto-Laryngol.*, **13**, 409 (1929).

NATIER, M.: Ozène nutrition et respiration, étiologie et pathogénie, *Méd. scolaire, Paris*, **4**, 273 (1911).

NELSON, J. B.: Nasal Mucosa: Behavior of Pox Viruses in Respiratory Tract; Response of Mice to Nasal Instillation of Variola Virus, *J. Exp. Med.*, **70**, 107 (1939).

*NEUMANN, R.: "Über Tuberkulose der Nasenschleimhaut," Breslau, 1902.

NYSSEN, R.: Semeiologic Value of Olfactory Reflexes, *Ann. d'oto-laryngol.*, 920 (August, 1933).

*OBRY, F.: "Quelle est la valeur semeiologique des changements survenus dans l'olfaction?" Paris, 1840.

ONOFRIO, F.: Nasal Mucosa: Hypertrophy, Histopathology, *Arch. ital. otol., rhinol., laringol.*, **37**, 689 (1926).

ORNSTEIN, S.: Nasal Mucosa: Sensitivity of Normal and Pathological, *Beitr. Anat. Physiol. Path. Therap. Ohr. Nase u. Hals.*, **26**, 153 (1927).

PARKER, F. L.: Improvement in Sense of Smell Follows Operation by Drilling Bony Stenosis of Vomer with Contracted Inferior, *Trans. S. C. Med. Assoc.*, 59 (1885).

PEPPER, W.: Nostrils and Their Diseases, *Johnson's Universal Cyclopaedia*, **6**, 230.

POCKELS: Anaesthesia Nervi Olfactorii, *Cor.-Bl. deut. Ges. Psychiat.*, **5**, 41 (1858).

PONZO, M.: Über die Wirkung des Stovains auf die Organe des Geschmacks, der Hautempfindungen, des Geruchs und des Gehörs, . . . *Arch. ges. Psychol.*, **14**, 427 (1909).

*PRESAT: "Observation d'un cas d'absence du nerf olfactif," Paris, 1837.

————: Fall wo die Geruchsnerven fählten, *Schmidts Jahrb.*, **22**, 170 (1838).

RADU, I.: Nasal Mucosa: Centrotherapy (Bonnier Method) in Menstrual Disturbances, *Cluj. med.*, **14**, 562 (1933).

RAKE, G.: Absorption through Nasal Mucosa, *Proc. Soc. Exp. Biol. Med.*, **34**, 369 (1936).

————: Rapid Invasion of Body through Nasal Mucosa, *J. Exp. Med.*, **65**, 303 (1937).

REAMES, H. R.: Nasal Mucosa Pathogenesis and Immunity in Ectromelia Virus Infection of Rat, *J. Infectious Diseases*, **66**, 254 (1940).

*RENSCH, P.: "De morte subita ex nimio violarum odore oborta," Vitembergae, 1762.

REUTER, C.: Neuritis olfactoria, *Arch. Laryngol. Rhinol.*, **9**, 147, 329 (1899).

ROBACK, H. N., and M. W. CONWAY: Agenesis of Olfactory Tracts, *Northwest Med.*, **39**, 264 (1940).

ROBERTSON, E. G.: Olfactory Bulbs in Fatal Cases of Poliomyelitis in Epidemic of 1937, *Med. J. Australia*, **1**, 156 (1940).

SABIN, A. B.: Olfactory Bulbs in Human Poliomyelitis, *Am. J. Diseases Children*, **60**, 1313 (1940).

————, and P. K. OLITSKY: Influence of Pathway of Infection on Pathology of Olfactory Bulbs in Experimental Poliomyelitis, *Proc. Soc. Exp. Biol. Med.*, **35**, 300 (1936).

SAVELIEFF, N.: Untersuchungen des Geruchssinnes zu klinischen Zwecken, *Neurol. Zentr.*, **12**, 340 (1893).

Scent Allergy, *Hygeia*, **21**, 159 (1943).

SCHALL, L. A.: Pathology of Mucous Membrane, *Trans. Am. Laryngol. Assoc.*, **66**, 127 (1944).

*SCHMIDT, W.: "Die Krankheiten der Luftwege," Berlin, 1903.

SCHULTZ, E. W.: Olfactory Nerve Regeneration after Application of $ZnSO_4$ Solution, *Proc. Soc. Exp. Biol. Med.*, **46**, 41 (1941).

SCHWARZ, F.: Sense of Smell in Legal Medicine, *Schweiz. med. Wochschr.*, **21**, 428 (1941).

*SERRES, E.: "Histoire d'une alteration du trijumeau avec troubles de l'odorat," Paris, 1827.

SMITH, C. G.: Pathologic Changes in Olfactory Nasal Mucosa of Albino Rats with "Stunted" Olfactory Bulbs, *Arch. Otolaryngol.*, **25**, 131 (1937).

————: Effect of $ZnSO_4$ on Mucous Membrane of Olfactory Tract, *Can. Med. Assoc. J.*, **39**, 138 (1938).

————: Incidence of Atrophy of the Olfactory Nerves in Man, *Arch. Otolaryngol.*, **34**, 533 (1941).

————: Olfactory Nerve-atrophy in Man, Age Incidence, *J. Comp. Neurol.*, **77**, 589 (1942).

SONNENSCHEIN, R.: Headaches; with Special Reference to those of Nasal Origin, *Ill. Med. J.*, **38**, 315 (1920).

SPIELBERG, W.: Etiology of Deviations of the Nasal Septum; Anatomic Theory, *J. Am. Med. Assoc.*, **75**, 1646 (1920).

SPILLANE, J. D.: Olfactory Alloesthesia, *Brain*, **61**, 393 (1938).

————: Smell in Patients with Brain Tumors, *Brain*, **62**, 213 (1939).

STOCKARD, C. R.: Hereditary Deficiencies in the Sense of Smell, *Science*, **49**, 237 (1919).

STRAUSS: Das Geruchsorgan als gerichts-ärztliche Directive, *Vierteljahrschr. gerichtl. Med.*, **26**, 77 (1897).

SUODI, T.: Discusses of the Sense of Smell Caused by Foreign Bodies, *Dai-Nippon Jibiinkokakai Kaiho* (Tokyo), 336 (1901).

TER HEEGE, F. H.: Nose Irritation by Particles in the Air, *Geneesk. Tijdschr. Nederland.-Indië*, **80**, 2512 (1940).

TOOMEY, J. A.: Experiments in Monkeys Lacking Olfactory Nerve Connections, with Central Nervous System, Produced by Intravenous Injection of Virus, *Am. J. Diseases Children*, **57**, 338 (1939).

TORRIGIANI, C. A.: Nasal Mucosa in Ozena, *Sper. Arch. biol.*, **81**, 41 (1927).

TOULOUSE, E., and N. VASCHIDE: L'Asymétrie sensorielle olfactive, *Compt. rend. soc. biol.*, 11s, **1**, 785 (1899).

————, and ————: Influence de la paralysie générale sur l'olfaction, *Compt. rend. soc. biol.* (Feb. 3, 1900).

————, and ————: Recherches expérimentelles sur la sensibilité olfactive dans la paralyse générale, *Rev. psychiat.*, 2s, **5**, 64 (1902).

TRETROP: Les Infections par voie nasale, *Trans. Intern. Congr. Med. London*, Sect. 14, **2**, 335 (1913).

URBACH, E.: Odors (Osmyls) as Allergenic Agents, *J. Allergy*, **13**, 387 (1942).

URBANTSCHITSCH, V.: Über den Einfluss von Mittelohrentzündungen auf die Geruchsempfindungen, *Monatsschr. Ohrenheilk.*, **44**, 258 (1910).

UYEMATSU, S.: A Study of the Cortical Olfactory Center; Based on Two Cases of Unilateral Involvement of the Olfactory Lobe, *Arch. Neurol. Psychiat.*, **6**, 146 (1921).

VACHER, L.: L'Insuffisance nasale; ses formes; ses causes; ses consequences, *Presse méd.*, **13**, 754 (1905).

VASCHIDE, N.: L'Influence des crises hysteriques sur l'olfaction, *Compt. rend. soc. biol.*, **53**, 538 (1901).

VERNIEUWE, J., and H. J. SCHERER: Tumors of Olfactory Bulb in Recklinghausen's Neurofibromatosis, *Rev. laryngol.*, **61**, 61 (1940).

VON FRANKL-HOCHWART, L.: Die nervösen Erkrankungen des Geruches, *Spec. Pathol. Therap. Nothnagel, Wien*, **11**, Pt. 2, 43 (1897).

*————: "Die nervösen Erkrankungen des Geschmacks und Geruchs," 2d ed., Wien, 1908.

VON MURALT, L.: Zur Kenntnis des Geruchsorgans bei menschlicher Hemicephalie, *Neurol. Zentr.*, **20**, 51 (1901).

WAGNER, C.: Smell, Hygienically and Medico-legally Considered, *Aesculapian, N. Y.*, **1**, 64 (1884).

WARDALE, ALAN: Anesthesia of Anterior Ethmoidal Nerve after Head Injury, *Lancet*, **247**, 752 (1944).

WILSON, G. W.: Smell Repression, Hay Fever Role in Sex, *Psychosom. Med.*, **3**, 51 (1941).

WORMS, G., and BOLOTTÉ: Nasal Insufficiency and Smell, *Arch. Intern. laryngol., otol., rhinol. et broncho-oesophag.*, **7**, 641 (1928).

*ZARNIKO, K.: "Die Krankheiten der Nase und des Nasenrachens," Berlin, 1894.

D. BODY ODORS

a. Human

1. In Health

ADACHI, B.: Geruch der Europäer, *Globus; Illus. Z. Länder Völkerk.*, 14 (1903).

*BERNDT, C.: "De transpiratione insensibili corporis humani," Vitembergae, 1695.

BRIEUDE: Mémoire sur les odeurs de la santé et des maladies, *Hist. Soc. roy. méd., Paris*, **10**, XLV (1789).

BUCKING: Von übelriechenden Ausdampfungen des menschlichen Körpers, *N. Mag. Ärzte*, **4**, 425 (1782).

*CAUFEYNON: "La Volupté et les parfums," Paris, 1903.

*CELLARVIA, J. G.: "De transpiratione insensibli et sudore," Jena, 1728.

CROHN, B. B., and R. DROSD: Odors: Garlic on Breath, Mechanism, *N. Y. J. Dentistry*, **12**, 192 (1942).

CURTISS, P.: Middle-class Smell, *Harpers*, **156**, 649 (1928).

DEHN and HARTMAN: Odor of Urine, *J. Am. Chem. Soc.*, **36**, 2136 (1913).

ELLER, J. J.: Body Odor, *Med. Record*, **154**, 167 (1941).

GOODMAN, H.: Odors of Perspiration, *Hygeia*, **21**, 184 (1943).

GRAVES, R. J.: Odor of Musk Exhaled from the Skin, *Dublin J. Med. Sci.*, **11**, 400 (1837).

HAGGARD, H. W.: Why Other People Smell, *Hygeia*, **19**, 12 (1941).

————, and L. A. GREENBERG: Breath Odors, *J. Am. Med. Assoc.*, **104**, 2160 (1935).

HAUSER, O.: Geruchssinn und Geruch der Menschen, *Sonne*, 35 (1926).

*KOELER, J. T.: "De odore per cutem spirante in statu sano ac morboso," Göttingen, 1794.

LAIRD, D. A.: Man's Individuality in Odor, *J. Abnormal Psychol.*, **29**, 459 (1935).

LÖHNER, L.: Über menschliche Individual- und Regionalgerüche, *Arch. ges. Physiol.*, **202B**, 25 (1924).

NIEMAND: Is Individual Odor Sufficient to Cause a Dog to Recognize His Master? *Leipzig-Gelon Gerhardt*, 61 (1938).

NOEL, H.: Les Odeurs du corps humain, *Echo méd. Cevennes, Nîmes*, **111**, 199 (1902).

L'Odeur des Européens, *J. méd. Brux.*, **9**, 388 (1904).

PREVOST, B.: Sur les émanations des corps odorants, *Ann. chim.* (1797).

————: Divers moyens de rendre sensibles à la vue les émanations des corps odorants, *Ann. chim.*, **21**, 254.

*RIZIUS, J.: "De foetoribus humani corporis viventis cognoscendis et curandis," Basileae, 1700.

SCHMID, P.: Ermittelung der menschlichen und tierischen Individualgeruchs durch den Hund, *Z. vergleich. Physiol.*, **22B**, 524 (1935).

SCHINZ: Über die belebende und heilkräftige Wirkung des animalischen Dunstes, *Schweiz. Z. Nat. Heilk.*, N. F., **1**, 149 (1838–1839).

*YULE, J.: "De halitu cuticulari," Edinburgh, 1785.

2. In Disease (Including Diagnosis by Odor)

AINSWORTH, F. C.: Fetid Perspiration of the Feet, *Med. Record*, **18**, 375 (1880).

ASSMANN, H.: Odor of Breath in Cardiac Decompensation, *Münch. med. Wochschr.*, **74**, 1613 (1927).

BENEDICT, A. L.: Odors, *Med. Rev. of Rev.*, N. Y., **26**, 243 (1920).

BLACK, W. D.: The Diagnosis of Headaches of Nasal Origin, *Southern Med. J.*, **14**, 241 (1897).

BLANCHARD, R.: Encore sur la Chromidrose, *Bull. acad. de méd.* 3s, **61**, 702 (1914).

BOGAN, S.: La Cryoscopie de la sueur de l'homme, *J. physiol. path. gen.*, **6**, 1009 (1904).

Brain Doctor Sniffs at Tumors and Shows Them Up, *News Week*, **6**, 25 (1935).

BRUZZO, F.: Odor of Patient as Pathognomonic Sign of Some Diseases, *Illust. med. ital.*, **12**, 121 (1903).

CLARK, L. P.: Odor of Peculiars, *Med. Surg.*, **1**, 1091 (1917).

CLARKE, W. B.: Odors of Disease, *Homeop. Record*, **16**, 254 (1901).

CLELAND, J. B.: The Sense of Smell as an Aid in Diagnosis, *Lancet*, **2**, 188 (1906).

CMUNT: Sense of Smell in Diagnosing Disease, *Časopis Českoslov. Lékárnictva*, **62**, 740 (1923).

COHEN, S.: Clinical and Diagnostic Significance of the Sense of Smell, *Am. Physician*, **28**, 315 (1923).

COOPER, P. R.: On the Cultivation of Smell and Taste and Their Employment in Practical Medicine, *Clin. J.*, **50**, 459 (1921).

COUGHLIN, R. E.: The Sense of Smell as an Aid in Diagnosis, *N. Y. Med. J.*, **98**, 121 (1913).

CROMPTON, D. W.: On the Use of the Nose or Rather the Sense of Smelling in the Diagnosis of Disease, *Birmingham Med. Rev.*, **2**, 251 (1873); **3**, 23 (1874).

DOUBLE, F. J.: Considérations semeilogiques sur les odeurs, *J. gen. med., chir., pharm.*, **35**, 137 (1809).

EBSTEIN, E.: Der Geruch in der klinischen Diagnostik, *Abhandl. prakt. Med.*, **20**, 141 (1920).

———: History of Diagnosis by Smell, *Deut. med. Wochschr.*, **54**, 1174 (1928).

ENGE: Der Geruchssinn in Medizin und Krankenpflege, *Irrenpflege*, 145 (1937).

FRÄNKEL, B.: Über Geruch aus dem Munde, *Arch. Laryngol. Rhinol.*, **10**, 177 (1899).

GAETA, R.: Formic Acid Body Odor as Constant Sign of Incipient Pulmonary Tuberculosis, *Gazz. osp.*, **48**, 1179 (1927).

GAMBERINI, P.: Di un singolare fetore prorompente da tutto il corpo di un giovane infermo, *Bull. s.c. med. Bologna*, **24**, 5 (1853).

HAMMOND, W. A.: The Odor of the Human Body, as Developed by Certain Affections of the Nervous System, *Trans. Am. Neurol. Assoc.*, **2**, 17 (1877).

HAUFFE, G.: Diagnosis by Smell, *Med. Klin.*, **22**, 1455 (1926).

HILL, E. C.: Diagnosis by the Nose, *N. Y. J. Med.*, **86**, 72 (1907).

HOELSCHER, J. H.: Original Research in One Hundred and Thirteen Cases, Perspiration, Odor, etc., *J. Am. Med. Assoc.*, **32**, 1352 (1899).

HUTTON, T. J.: The Value of Clinical Odors, *N. Y. J. Med.*, **28**, 268 (1878).

ISHAM, A. B.: Odor Mortis—the Death Smell, *Clinic* (Cincinnati), **9**, 109 (1875).

JANOWSKI, T.: Klinische Bedeutung des Geruchs, *Klin. Wochschr.*, **8**, 172 (1929).

JEFFRIES, B. J.: Fetid Perspiration of the Feet, *Boston Med. Surg. J.*, **62**, 397 (1860).

JOAL: Epistaxis due aux odeurs, *Bull. soc. franc. laryngol.*, **382** (1897).

———: Urticaire et odeurs, *Bull. soc. franc. laryngol.* (1899).

———: Vertiges et odeurs, *Rev. hebd. laryngol.*, **1**, 513 (1901).

———: Odeurs et troubles digestifs, *Rev. hebd. laryngol.*, **1**, 513 (1903).

———: Odeurs et troubles cardiaques, *Rev. hebd. laryngol.*, **1**, 481 (1905).

*JOCHEM, B.: "Geruchssinn und Diagnose," Bonn, 1938.

JOHNSON, B. C., T. S. HAMILTON, and H. H. MITCHELL: Perspiration: Pseudopyridoxine, 4-pyridoxic Acid and Vitamin B_6 in, *J. Biol. Chem.*, **158**, 619 (1945).

———, ———, and ———: Perspiration: Choline in Effect of Intake and Temperature on, *J. Biol. Chem.*, **159**, 5 (1945).

———, ———, and ———: Perspiration: Nicotinic Acid, Nicotinamide, Nicotinuric Acid and N^1—Methyl-nicotinamide in, *J. Biol. Chem.*, **159**, 231 (1945).

———, ———, and ———: Folic Acid in Perspiration, *J. Biol. Chem*, **159**, 425 (1945).

JOHNSON, H.: On the Sense of Smell Applied to Medicine, *Brit. Med. J.*, **1**, 38 (1866).

KLIMONT, J.: Chemische Grundlage des Geruches in der klinischen Diagnostik, *Klin. Wochschr.*, **1**, 1281 (1922).

KOCHEL, R.: Beitrag zur kriminalistischen Bedeutung der Geruchs-diagnose, *Deut. Z. ges. gerichtl. Med.* **6**, 1 (1925).

KRASNOGORSKI, N.: Gibt es einen spezifischen Geruch bei Infektions-krankheiten? *Jahrb. Kinderheilk.*, **78** (1913).

LADELL, W. S. S.: Perspiration: Chlorides in, Effect of Desoxycorticosterone Acetate on, *J. Physiol.*, **104**, 13 (1945).

LAEHR: On the Odour of the Insane, *J. Mental. Sci.*, **24**, 132 (1878).

LEGOUX: De l'odeur profuse et fétide des pieds, ou bromidrose, *Gas. méd. de Picardie*, **6**, 52 (1888).

LEIBOWITZ, S.: Distinctive Odors in Patients Receiving Sulfanilamide, *N. Y. J. Med.*, **40**, 363 (1940).

LEWALD, H. A.: Foetor ex ore. Pathogenese und seine Beduetung für die Diagnostik, *Zahntechn. Reform.*, **258** (1932).

LIFSON, N., and V. LORBER: Osmotic Activity of Perspiration, *J. Biol. Chem.*, **158**, 209 (1945).

LOENING, V.: Der Geruchssinn in der Krankenpflege, *Z. Krankenpfl.*, 76 (1921).

LONGWORTH, L. R.: On the Pathology of Ill Odor in Bromidrosis Pedum, *Clinic* (Cincinnati), **9**, 205 (1875).

M'CASSY, J. H.: Odor as a Symptom of Disease, *Cincin. Lancet-Clinic*, N. S., **36**, 659 (1896).

McCLURE, F. J., H. H. MITCHELL, and T. S. HAMILTON: Fluorine in Perspiration, *J. Ind. Hyg. Toxicol.*, **27**, 159 (1945).

MANDL, F.: Geruch und klinische Diagnose, *Deut. med. Wochschr.*, **48**, 1280 (1922).

MAYO, W. J.: Relative Value of Special Senses to Surgeon, *Ann. Surg.*, **86**, 1 (1927).

MEYER-BERNSTADT: Eigengeruch der Menschen, *Medico Med. Wochschr.*, **268**, 284 (1905).

MINERBI, C.: Cura semplice del sudore fetido dei piedi, *Acad. sci. med. nat. Ferrara*, **72**, 113 (1897).

*MONIN, E.: "Les Odeurs du corps humain; causes et traitements," Paris, 1886.

*————: Les Odeurs du corps humain; causes et traitements," Paris, 1903.

MULLER, G.: Geruchsdiagnostik und Syphilis, *Deut. med. Wochschr.*, **49**, 987 (1923).

NIEDERMEYER, A.: Geruchsdiagnostik, *Deut. med. Wochschr.*, **49**, 387 (1923).

NIDERGANG, F.: Les Odeurs d'origine naso-buccale en pratique medicale, *Hôpital, Paris*, **12**, 46 (1924).

QUEKETT, E. J.: Peculiar Odour of the Breath Previous to Death, *Lancet*, **11**, 436 (1845).

RESEDIGER, E.: Geruch und Diagnostik, *Med. Klin.*, **22**, 993 (1926).

RICHTER, H.: Geruchs und Antlitz Diagnostik, *Biochem. Monatsbl.*, **10**, 115 (1933).

*RIZIUS, J.: "De foetoribus humani corporis. Fasc. diss. med. select," Basil, 1710.

ROSENHEIM, T.: Geruchs: Foetor ex ore gastrointestinalen Ursprunges, *Therapie der Gegenwart*, 483 (1902).

RUEDIGER, E.: Smell and Diagnosis, *Med. Klin.*, **22**, 993 (1926).

RUHMANN, W.: Odor of Breath in Cardiac Decompensations. Comparison with Agonal Odor, *Münch. med. Wochschr.*, **74**, 1838 (1927).

*SCHLEICHER, J. T.: "De odorum in diagnosi morborum dignitate," Halse, 1808.

SCHNEIDER: Quelques considérations cliniques et biologiques tirées de l'étude de la sueur chez l'homme, *Pressetherm et climat.*, **65**, 377 (1924).

Smelling Out Diseases, *Literary Digest*, **99**, 24 (1928).

SPERANZA: Caso singulare di un individuo spirante soave odore dall' avanbraccio sinistro, *Ann. univ. med.*, **61**, 225 (1832).

THIN, G.: On Bacterium Foetidum: an Organism Associated with Odor and Profuse Sweating from Soles of Feet, *Proc. Roy. Soc. London*, **30**, 473 (1880).

————: On the Cause of Bad Odour Sometimes Associated with Excessive Sweating of the Feet, *Brit. Med. J.*, **2**, 463 (1880).

THOMAYER, J.: Diagnostic Importance of Smelling, *Časopis Českoslov. Lékárnictva*, **62**, 668 (1923).

TRACY, J. L.: The Sense of Smell in Diagnosis, *Toledo Med. Surg. Reporter*, **4**, 547 (1891).

VAN LICHTENBERGH, B.: Sudor pedum foetidus, *Nederland. mil. geneesk. Arch.*, **6**, 300 (1882).

VIEUSSE: Du la sueur fétide des pieds, *Rev. méd. Toulouse*, **20**, 519 (1906).

VOGEL, W.: Der Geruch als diagnostisches Hilfsmittel, *Biochem. Monatsbl.*, **4**, 69 (1927).

WATSON, W. S.: Impairment or Loss of the Sense of Smell as a Means of Diagnosis, *Ann. Surg.*, **16**, 46 (1891).

WILLCOX, R. L.: Foetid Sweating of the Feet, *Brit. Med. J.*, **2**, 658 (1880).

WYLIE, A.: Foul Breath, Causes and Treatment, *West London Med. J.*, **13**, 77 (1908).

b. *Other Animals, and General*

BARRETT, C. G.: Odour Emitted by the Male of Hepialus Hectus, *Entomol. Monthly Mag.*, **19**, 90 (1882).

BETTEN, H.: Die Stinkdrüsen der Corixiden, *Zool. Jahrb., Abt. Anat. Ontog. Tiere*, **137** (1943).

BOLLINGER, A., and M. H. HARDY: The Sternal Integument of Trichosurus Vulpecula, *J. Proc. Roy. Soc. N.S. Wales*, **78**, 122 (1944).

BORDAS, L.: Produit de sécretion de la glande odorante des Blattes, *Bull. soc. zool. France*, **33**, 31 (1908).

BURGER, A. M.: Animal Odors, *Riechstoffind*, **7**, 125, 152 (1932).

Butterfly Odors, *Literary Digest*, **93**, 24 (1927).

CALKINS, G. H.: Origin of Odors in Specific Organisms, *Repts. Board Health, Mass.*, **24**, 370 (1891–1892).

Caproic Acid Seems Able to Give Previously Used Attractants Even Higher Drawing Power to Beetles Roving in the Neighborhood, *Sci. News Letter*, 375 (1945).

CLARK, A. H.: Scent Organs in Lepidoptera, *Ann. Rept. Board Regents Smithsonian Inst.*, 421 (1926).

COLERIDGE, G.: Animal Attractions and Repulsions, *Contemp. Rev.*, **117**, 539 (1920).

DEEGENER, P.: Das Duftorgan von Hepialus hectus, *Z. wiss. Zoöl.*, **71**, 276 (1902).

DIXEY, F. A.: Scents of Butterflies, *Nature*, **87**, 164 (1911).

EARLEY, W.: Suppression of Scent in Rabbits, *Nature*, **8**, 78 (1873).

EITEL, W.: Geruch des Hautdrüsensekretes von Lacerta pelobates fuscus, *Wochschr. Aquarien—Terrarienk.*, **24**, 28 (1927).

ELTRINGHAM, H.: On the Scent Apparatus of the Male of Amauris Niavius, *Trans. Entomol. Soc. London*, **61**, 399 (1913).

———: Further Observations on the Structure of Scent Organs in Certain Male Danaine Butterflies, *Trans. Entomol. Soc. London*, **62**, 152 (1914).

———: On the Histology of the Scent Organs in the Genus Hydroptila, *Trans. Entomol. Soc. London*, **67**, 420 (1919).

———: Scent Organs in Lepidoptera, *Trans. Entomol. Soc. London*, **74**, 263 (1926).

———: Olfactory Organ in Neuroptera Wing, *Trans. Entomol. Soc. London*, **74**, 267 (1926).

———: On the Scent Organs of Opsiphanes Cassiae Lucullus, *Trans. Entomol. Soc. London*, **77**, 1 (1929).

FREILING, H. H.: Duftorgane der weiblichen Schmetterlinge, *Z. wiss. Zoöl.*, **92**, 210 (1909).

Geruchstoffe bei Tieren, *Naturw.-techn.*, Jahr., **4**, 111 (1924).

GÖZ, H.: Über den Art-und—Individualgeruch bei Fischen, *Z. vergleich Physiol.*, **29**, 1 (1941).

HALL, C.: Peculiar Odour Emitted by Acherontia Atropos, *Entomol.*, **16**, 14 (1883).

HARDY, E.: Animal Perfumes, *Perfumery Essent. Oil Record*, **32**, 227 (1941).

HIRT, O.: Die Dufteinrichtungen der Neotropiden, *Zool. Jahrb.*, **30**, 603 (1910).

*ILLIG, K. G.: "Duftorgane der mänlichen Schmetterlinge," Stuttgart.

JORDON, K.: On the Scent-organs in the Males of Certain American Castniidae, *Novit. Zool.*, **30**, 159 (1923).

KRUGER, P.: Über die Stinkdrüsen der Wasserwanzen, *Z. Naturw.*, **81**, 196 (1909).

MULLER, F.: Die Duftschuppen der Schmetterlinge, *Entomol. Nachr.*, **4**, (1878).

PATTON, W. H.: Scent-glands in the Larva of Limacodes, *Can. Entomol.*, **23**, 42 (1891).

PUTTFARCKEN, H.: Odorous Substances from Animal Sources, *Fette Seifen*, **48**, 196 (1941).

RHOADS, S. N.: The Power Scent in the Turkey Vulture, *Am. Naturalist*, **17**, 829.

ROSSI, G.: Le glandole odorifere dell' Julus communis, *Z. wiss. Zoöl.*, **74**, 64 (1903).

ROTH, L. M.: The Odoriferous Glands of Tribolium Confusum, *Ann. Entomol. Soc. Am.*, **36**, 397 (1943).

SCHAFFER, J.: Odor Producing Organs of the Human Body, *Wien. klin. Wochschr.*, **50**, 790 (1937).

SHUFELT, R. W.: How Skunks Defend Themselves, *Am. Forests & Forest Life*, **28**, 26 (1922).

STORY, H. E.: The External Genitalia and Perfume Gland of Articis Binturong, *J. Mammal.*, **26**, 64 (1945).

*STROHL, J.: "Odors of Animal Origin, Analogies with Poisons," Leipzig, 1926.

SWALE: Odour of Olophrum Piceum, *Entomol. Monthly Mag.*, **5**, 1 (1896).

TEGETMEIER: Pheasants for the Covert and the Aviary: the Suppression of Scent of Pheasants, *Nature*, **8**, 48 (1873).

VAN ALLEN, C.: Suggestions upon Animal Odor, *N. Y. Med. Times*, **5**, 268 (1856).

VIREY, J. J.: Des odeurs que répondent les animaux vivants, *Rec. per. soc. méd. Paris*, **8**, 161 (1800).

VON DALLA TORRE, K.: Die Duftapparate der Schmetterlinge, *Kosmos*, **17** (1885).

VOSSELER, J.: Die Stinkdrüsen der Forficuliden, *Arch. mikroskop. Anat. Entwicklungsmech.*, **36**, 565 (1890).

WEGENER, M.: Scent Organs in Lepidoptera, *Z. Morphol. Ökol. Tiere*, **5**, 155 (1926).

E. CHEMICAL CONSTITUTION AND ODORS

ALQUIER, R.: Odors of Acetals, *Bull. soc. chim.*, **10**, 197 (1943).

ANGELI, A.: Chemical Constitution of Odors, *Atti accad. Lincei*, **11**, 535 (1930).

———: Mechanism of Olfaction, *Gazz. chim. ital.*, **60**, 939 (1931).

———, and A. POLVERINI: Mechanism of Olfaction, *Gazz. chim. ital.*, **61**, 276 (1931).

BACKMAN, E. L.: Note sur la puissance des odeurs et leur solubilité dans l'eau et dans l'huile, *J. physiol. pathol. gén.*, **17**, 1 (1917).

———: The Olfactology of the Methylbenzol Series, *Proc. Koninkl. Akad. Wetenschap. Amsterdam, Sect. Sci.*, **19**, 943 (1917).

BACKER, H. J.: Molecular Form and Odors, *Chem. Weekblad*, **31**, 71 (1934).

BAZZONI, C. B.: Loss of Weight of Musk in Current of Dry Air, *J. Fr. Inst.*, **180**, 463 (1915).

BEAUNIS, H.: Riechstoffe, *Compt. rend. acad. sci.*, **96**, 387 (1883).

BERLINGOZZI, S.: Chemical Constitution of Odors, *Gazz. chim. ital.*, **57**, 264 (1927).

BERT, L., and R. ANNEQUIN: A New Method of Synthesis of Reduction Products of Derivatives of Cinnemaldehyde, *Compt. rend. acad. sci.*, **192**, 1314 (1931).

BIDDER, G. P.: Brownian Movement in Relation to Smell, *Proc. Linnean Soc. London*, **143**, 82 (1930–1931).

BLAS, L.: Attempt to Show Relationship between Chemical Composition and Definite Odors, *Mon. Farm.*, **49**, 135 (1943).

*BOGERT, M. T.: "Synthetic Organic Chemistry in the Study of Odorous Compounds," Columbia University Press, New York, 1927.

———: Chemical Constitution and Musk Odor, *Am. Perfumer*, **24**, 15, 235, 357 (1929).

The Connection between Odor and Constitution in the Benzothiazole Group, *Am. Perfumer*, **32**, 51 (1936).

——, and L. P. CURTIN: Relation between Molecular Structure and Odor in Trisubstituted Benzenes, *J. Am. Chem. Soc.*, **45**, 2161 (1923).

——, and I. GOLDSTEIN: Chemical Constitution of Odors, *Am. Perfumer*, **23**, 524 (1928).

——, and E. H. HAMANN: Beta-phenylethyl Alcohols, Some New Derivatives and the Influence of Structure upon Odor in this Group, *Am. Perfumer*, **25**, 19, 75 (1930).

——, and O. N. JITKOW: The Relation between Structure and Odor in the Case of Certain Derivatives of 2,2,4-trimethyl-3-cyclohexene Aldehyde, *J. Am. Chem. Soc.*, **63**, 1979 (1941).

——, and A. STULL: Odor and Chemical Constitution in the Benzothiazole Group, *Am. Perfumer*, **20**, 453 (1925).

——, and ——: Chemical Constitution of Odors, *Am. Perfumer*, **22**, 63 (1927).

*BOYLE, R.: "Experiments and Observations about Mechanical Production of Odors," London, 1675.

BREWSTER, C. M., and I. J. PUTNAM: Chemical Constitution and Odors of Alkoxybiphenyls, *J. Am. Chem. Soc.*, **61**, 3083 (1939).

BUU-HOI, and P. CAGNIANT: A New Family of Fragrant Compounds, *Compt. rend. acad. sci.*, **214**, 115 (1942).

CAGNIANT, P., and BUU-HOI: Odor and Chemical Constitution in a Series of Substituted a-Tetralones, *Bull. soc. chim.*, **9**, 111 (1942).

——, and ——: Chemical Constitution and Odors of a-Tetralones, *Bull. soc. chim.*, **9**, 841 (1942).

CASTEX, M. R.: Physical Study of Odors, *Bol. acad. nac. med. Buenos Aires*, 722 (November, 1934).

——, and F. VIERHELLER: Optic Propensities (Absorption of Visible Light and of Ultra Violet Rays) of Odorous Substances, *Bol. acad. nac. med. Buenos Aires*, 31 (April, 1938).

——, and ——: Optic Study of Odorous Substances and Their Classification According to Absorption Spectrum, *Prensa méd. argent.*, **27**, 1879 (1940).

——, and ——: Physical Study: Absorption of Light by Natural and Synthetic Substances, *Bol. acad. nac. med. Buenos Aires*, 399 (October, 1941).

——, and ——: Physical Study of Absorption of Light by Natural and Synthetic Aromatic Substances, *Prensa méd. argent.*, **30**, 1957 (1943).

*CAUSSE, H. E.: "Action des aldéhydes sur les phénols polyvents; acétals aromatiques," Paris, 1893.

CHAMULEAN and NOYONS: Odor and Vapor Pressure, *Acta Brevia neerland. physiol. microbiol.*, **2**, 94 (1932).

*CHARABOT, E., J. DUPONT, and L. PILLET: "Les Huiles essentielles et leurs principaux constituànts," Paris, 1899.

CHARPENTIER: Action des sources de rayons N sur différents ordres de sensibilité, notamment sur l'olfaction, et émission de rayons N par les substances odorantes, *Compt. rend. acad. sci.*, **138**, 584 (1904).

Chemical Constitution and Odors, *Seifensieder-Zeitung*, **64**, 639, 689 (1937).

CROCKER, E. C., and L. F. HENDERSON: Vapor Pressures of Odorous Substances, *Am. Perfumer* (October, 1935).

CUCHAKOFF, A. A.: Practical Application of Relation between Smell and Absorption of Odoriferous Substances, *Rev. laryngol.*, **51**, 77 (1930).

CULLINANE, N. M.: Chemistry of Flower Odors, *School of Sci. Rev.*, **22**, 361 (1941).

*CURTIN, L. P.: "Relation between Molecular Structure and Odor in Tri-substituted Benzenes," Columbia University Press, New York, 1923.

DELANGE, R.: Residual Valency and Odor, *Bull. soc. chim.*, **31**, 589 (1922).

————: Relations entre l'odeur des composés organiques et leur constitution chimique, *Rev. Sci.*, **60**, 505 (1922).

————: Relations between Odour and Molecular Structure, *Perfumery Essent. Oil Record*, **13**, 351 (1922).

DE SANCTIS, S.: Applicazione della legge di Weber-Fechner all' olfatto, *Arch. ital. biol.*, **36**, 131 (1901–1902).

DORAN, W.: Odour and Chemical Constitution, *Soc. Chem. Ind.*, **49**, 235 (1930).

DOROUGH, G. L.: Chemical Constitution and Odors of Isomeric Octanols, *J. Am. Chem. Soc.*, **63**, 3100 (1941).

DUBSKY, J. V.: Geruch und chemische Konstitution, *Deut. Parfüm.-Ztg.*, **2**, 297 (1916).

DUBUISSON, M.: L'Olfaction des ions gazeux, *Nat. et Mém. congr. assoc. franc. pour l' avance des sci.*, **43**, 574 (1915).

DURAND, A.: Sur l'olfaction, *Compt. rend. acad. sci.*, **166**, 129 (1918).

————: Correlation entre les phenomena de condensation et d'olfaction, *Compt. rend. acad. sci.*, **166**, 532 (1918).

DURRANS, T. H.: Chemical Constitution of Odors, *Perfumery Essent. Oil Record*, **10**, 104 (1919).

DYSON, G. M.: Chemical Constitution and Odor, *Perfumery Essent. Oil Record*, **17**, 20 (1926) ; **19**, 3, 88, 171, 341 (1928).

————: Survey of the Chemistry of Natural and Synthetic Musk Substances, *Chem. Age*, **24**, 434 (1931).

————: Raman Effect and Concept of Odors, *Perfumery Essent. Oil Record*, **28**, 13 (1937).

Electrical Experiments with Scent-holding Fogs, *Sci. American Supp.*, **82**, 311 (1916).

ELSBERG, C. A.: Sense of Smell: Relation between Olfactory Coefficients and Boiling Points of Odorous Substances, *Bull. Neurol. Inst. N. Y.*, **4**, 26 (1935).

ERB, R. C.: Chemistry of Odors, *Osteopathic Digest*, **1**, 2 (1927).

FAIRBROTHER, T. H.: Chemical Constitution and Odors, *Ind. Chemist*, **2**, 385 (1926).

FISHER, F. E., *et al.*: Aromatization: Catalytic Conversion of Hydrocarbons, *Ind. Eng. Chem.*, **38**, 61 (1946).

GREENSFELDER, B. S., H. H. VOGE, and G. M. GOOD: Aromatic Hydrocarbons, *Ind. Eng. Chem.*, **37**, 1168 (1945).

GRIJNS, G.: Y a-t-il une relation entre le pouvoir absorbant a l'égard de la chaleur rayonnante et le pouvoir odorant des substances?, *Arch. néerland. physiol.*, **3**, 377 (1918).

————: Smell Intensity and Radiant Heat, *Proc. Acad. Sci. Amst.*, **21**, 476 (1919).

HACKH, Q. W. O.: Some Constituents of Essential Oils and Their Structural Relations, *J. Am. Pharm. Assoc.*, **9**, 948 (1920).

HAMANN, E. H.: The Relation between Structure and Odor in Derivaties of b-Phenyl Ethyl Alcohol, Some New b-Phenyl Acrylic Acids, Columbia University (thesis), 1927.

HELLER, H.: Geruchschemie, *Naturw. Wochschr.*, **35B**, 557 (1921).

HENNING, H.: Der Chemismus des Geruches, *Deut. Parfüm. Ztg.*, **3**, 125 (1917).

————: Komponenten Gliederung des Geruchs und chemische Grundlage, *Naturwiss.*, 296 (1917).

————: Beziehung zwischen chemische Konstitution und Geruchssinn, *Handbuch der Kosmet. Chemie*, 385 (1920).

HEROLD: Chemical Constitution of Odor, *Seifensieder Ztg.*, **67**, 426, 460 (1940).

HILL, A.: Vapour-density and Smell, *Nature*, **80**, 427 (1909).

HILL, J. W., and W. CAROTHERS: Odors of Many-membered Cyclic Anhydrides and Esters, *J. Am. Chem. Soc.*, **55**, 5009 (1933).

————, and ————: Chemical Constitution and Odor, *J. Am. Chem. Soc.*, **57**, 925 (1935).

HUNGER, H.: Chemical Constitution and Odors of Ionine, *Seifensieder-Zeitung*, **68**, 431, 441 (1941).

IRWIN, M.: Sensory Stimulation by Unsaturated Alcohols, Polyhydric Alcohols, and Chlorhydrins, *Am. J. Physiol.*, **60**, 270 (1922).

JELLINEK, P.: Analysis by Means of Olfaction, *Riechstoffind*, **5**, 120 (1930).

*JITKOW, O. N.: "The Relationship between Structure and Odor in Di- and Tetrahydrobenzaldehydes, Their Methylated Homologues, and Some of Their Derivatives," N. Y., 1940.

KAUFFMANN, M.: Über eigentümliche Geruchsanomalien einiger chemischer Körper, *Z. Psychol. Physiol. Sinnesorg*, Abt. 2, **42**, 271 (1907).

KENNETH, J. H.: Density and Olfaction, *Nature*, **111**, 151 (1923).

KJELSBERG, F., and A. MÜLLER: Odors of Esters of Butyric and Isobutyric Acid, *Deut. Parfüm.-Ztg.*, **14**, 235 (1928).

KOETSCHET, J., and P. KOETSCHET: Odors of Homovanillins: Detailed Report of Chemical Analysis, *Helv. Chim. Acta*, **13**, 474 (1930).

KREMER, J. H.: Absorption de matières odorantes et de narcotiques odorants par les lipoides, *Arch. néerland. physiol.*, **1**, 715 (1917).

KÜHL, H.: Der Erdgeruch, *Naturw. Umschau chem. Ztg.*, **4**, 102 (1915).

KUNZ-KRAUS, H.: Ozoles as Source of Odors, *Ber. pharm. Gesell.*, **33**, 149 (1923).

LEWINSON, A.: Reviews on Odorous Substances, *Riechstoff Ind. Kosmetik*, **11**, 200, 1047 (1936) ; **12**, 45, 81 (1937).

LOEWE, S.: Zur physikalischen Chemie der Lipoide, *Biochem. Z.*, **42**, 150 (1912).

LORRY: Observations sur les parties volatiles et odorantes, *Hist. mém. soc. roy. med.*, **7**, 306 (1784).

LOSSON, M. M.: Raman Spectra: Aliphatic Alcohols, *J. pharm. chim.*, 9s, **1**, 574 (1940–1941).

MALINOVSKII: Chemical Constitution and Odor, *J. Gen. Chem. (U.S.S.R.)*, **10**, 1918 (1940).

MALLINCKRODT, E., JR.: Reactions of Anesthetic Ethers with Potassium Hydroxide and with Mercury in Test for Foreign Odors, *J. Am. Chem. Soc.*, **49**, 2655 (1927).

MARCHAND, R.: Chemical Constitution of Odors, *Deut. Parfüm.-Ztg.*, **1**, 223, 243, 287 (1915).

MICHAEL, S.: Effect of Ultraviolet Light on Odorous Substances, *Biochem. Z.*, **233**, 470 (1931).

*MICHAELIS, L.: "Bromierung der aromatischen Hydrazine, Amine und Phenole," Berlin, 1893.

MONCRIEFF, R. W.: Chemical Constitution and Odors, *Mfg. Chemist*, **14**, 33, 60, 130, 174, 205, 239 (1943).

MÜLLER, A.: Chemical Constitution and Odors, *Deut. Parfüm.-Ztg.*, **9**, 5 (1923).

———: Chemical Constitution of Odors, *Am. Perfumer*, **32**, 83 (1936).

———: Fluorescence of Odorous Substances, *J. Prakt. Chem.*, **154**, 209 (1940).

———: Discussion of Natural and Synthetic Perfumes Having "Green" and "Leaf" Odors, *Deut. Parfüm.-Ztg.*, **27**, 240 (1941).

NAVES, Y. R., S. SABETAY, and L. PALFREY: Analysis of Natural Perfumes, *Ann. chim. anal. chim. applic.*, **19**, 201, 227 (1937).

NICCOLINI, P.: Smell as Affected by O Content of Odoriferous Substances, *Arch. ital. sci. farmacol.*, **1**, 253 (1932).

———: Chemical Constitution of Odor, *Arch. ital. sci. farmacol.*, **6**, 241 (1937).

Nose in the Chemistry Laboratory, *J. Chem. Education*, **17**, 17 (1940).

NUTTALL, G. C.: Smell of Earth, *Sci. American Supp.*, **46**, 19, 216 (1898).

Odor by Specification, *Mech. Eng.*, **49**, 784 (1927).

PAPACEIT, E.: Chemistry and Physiology of Odors, *Afinidad*, **18**, 322 (1941).

PASSY, J.: Sur l'analyse d'une odeur complexe, *Nature*, **47**, 48 (1892).

———: Sur l'analyse d'une odeur complexe, *Compt. rend. soc. biol.*, 854 (1892).

———: Les Propriétés odorantes des alcools de la série grasse, *Compt. rend. acad. sci.*, **114**, 1140 (1892).

———: Forme périodique du pouvoir odorant dans la série grasse, *Compt. rend. acad. sci.* (May, 1893).

PATTY, F. A., and W. P. YANT: Odors in Methane Series, *U.S. Bur. Mines, Rept. of Invest.*, 2979 (1929).

PERMAN: Vapour Density and Smell, *Nature*, **58**, 369 (1909).

PIRRONE, F.: Odor and Chemical Structure, *Riv. ital. essenze profumi*, **11**, 2 (1929).

POLZAR, C. B.: The Relation between Constitution and Odor of Aromatic Substances, *Rec. soc. chim. russ.*, **1**, 49 (1925).

PRINS, H. J.: Chemical Constitution of Odors, *Perfumery Essent. Oil Record*, **8**, 222 (1917).

RICHARDSON, B. W.: The Physical Action of Odours, *Asclepiad*, **8**, 233 (1891).

ROGER, M., and F. DVOLAITSKAYA: Odors of Heptyl Ethers, *Recherches*, **1**, 13 (1937).

———, and ———: Odor of Heptyl Alcohol, *Mfg. Perfumer*, **2**, 36 (1937).

ROTHSTEIN, I. B.: Chemical Constitution and Odors, *Bull. soc. chim.*, **51**, 691, 838 (1932); **53**, 1106 (1933); **55**, 80, 1936 (1935).

RUPE and MAJEWSKI: Chemical Constitution and Odor, *Ber. Deut. chem. Gesell.*, **33**, 3401 (1900).

RUTHERFORD, R. C.: On the Diffusion of Odors, *Popular Sci. Monthly*, **21**, 84 (1882).

RUZICKA, L.: Die Grundlagen der Geruchschemie, *Chem. Zeitung*, **44**, 93, 129 (1920).

———, G. SALOMON, and K. E. MEYER: Odors of Polymembered Rings, *Helv. chim. acta*, **20**, 109 (1937).

———, SCHINZ, and SEIDEL: Chemical Constitution and Odor, *Helv. chim. acta*, **10**, 695 (1927).

———, and M. STOLL: Chemical Constitution of Odors, *Helv. chim. Acta*, **11**, 1159 (1928).

SABETAY, S.: Reviews on Odorous Substances, *Riechstoff Ind. u. Kosmetik*, **11**, 205 (1936).

———, and L. PALFREY: Odors of Tobacco Blossoms, *Chem. Zentr.* **1**, 685 (1943).

———, and ———: Odors of Tobacco Flowers, *Compt. rend. acad. sci.*, **213**, 805 (1941).

———, and L. TRABAUD: Odors of Tobacco, *Chim. ind.*, **46**, 429 (1941).

SACHS, A. P.: Chemical Constitution of Odors, *Perfumers' J.*, **7**, 12, 28 (1926).

SANDULESCO and S. SABETAY: Pyridine Derivatives and Odor, *Mfg. Perfumer*, **2**, 31 (1937).

SCHÖNBEIN: Untersuchungen über das Wesen des Geruches, welcher sich in Folge gewisser chemischer Wirkungen offenbart, *Froriep's neue Not.*, **14**, 292 (1840).

*SEMMLER, F. W.: "Die atherischen öle nach ihren chemischen Bestandteilen unter Berucksichtigung der geschichtlichen Entwicklung," Leipzig, 1917.

SHORUIGIN, P., and V. KORSHAK: Odors of Ethers of Hydroxy-aldehydes and Their Acetals, *Deut. chem. Ges.*, **68B**, 838 (1935).

SINGH, B. K., and A. B. LAL: Difference in Odour of d,l and d-l Derivatives of Amine— and Bisamino-methylene Camphors, *Nature*, **144**, 910 (1939).

———, and ———: Odor vs. Chemical Structure, Camphor Derivatives, *Proc. Indian Acad. Sci.*, **12A**, 157, 230 (1940).

6423—a Rose; Analytical Smelling, *Time*, **42**, 38 (1943).

SOUTHERDEN, F.: The Bearing of Recent Discoveries on the Physics of Taste and Smell, *Nature*, **67**, 486 (1903).

STEINER, H.: Aromatization: Catalytic Dehydrocyclization of Paraffine, *J. Am. Chem. Soc.*, **67**, 2052 (1945).

STOLL, M., and P. BOLLE: Chemical Constitution and Odors of Lactones, *Halv. chim. acta*, **21**, 1547 (1938).

TAMMAN and OELSEN: Smell and Vapor Pressure, *Z. anorg. allgem. Chem.*, **172**, 407 (1928).

TEMPELAAR, H. C. G.: Over den invloed van licht op reukstoffen, *Onderz. Physiol. Lab. Utrecht*, **14**, 220 (1913).

TEUDT, H.: Origin in molecules of odoriferous substances, *Prometheus*, **30**, 201, 209 (1919).

THOMSSON, E. G.: Chemistry and Mechanics of Olfaction, *Am. Perfumer*, **23**, 71, 161 (1928).

THONE, F.: Rat-repelling Odor: Skunky Smell, *Sci. News Letter*, **40**, 159 (1941).

THORBJÖRNSON, B.: Chemical Composition in Relation to Olfaction, *Tek. Tid. Uppl. C. Kemi.*, **66**, 9 (1936).

TRIBUS, L. L.: Odors and Their Travel Habits, *Proc. Am. Soc. Civil Eng.*, **47**, 125 (1921).

UNGERER, W. G., and R. B. STODDARD: Odour Value Analysis, *Perfumery Essent. Oil Record*, **13**, 41 (1922).

VAN BENSCHOTEN, J.: Odors and Their Travel Habits, *Can. Eng.*, **69**, 13 (1935).

VAN DER VELDEN: Zur Physik der Geruchs-Empfindung, *Fortschr. Med.*, 804 (1906).

VASCHIDE, N.: L'expérience de Weber et l'olfaction en milieu liquide, *Compt. rend. soc. biol.*, 2s, **3**, 165 (1901).

VON BRAUN, J.: Chemical Constitution and Odors, *Schweiz. Apoth-Zeitung.*, **61**, 517 (1911).

———, and E. ANTON: Molecular Asymmetry and Odors, *Ber. deut. chem. Ges.*, **60B**, 2438 (1927).

———, and ———: Chemical Constitution and Odor, *Ber. deut. chem. Ges.*, **62B**, 1489 (1929).

———, ———, and MAY: Chemical Constitution of Odor, *Ber. deut. chem. Ges.*, **70B**, 1250 (1937).

———, and GOSSEL: Chemical Constitution and Odor, *Ber. deut. chem. Ges.*, **57B**, 373 (1924).

———, and W. HAENSEL: Molecular Asymmetry and Odors, *Ber. deut. chem. Ges.*, **59B**, 1999 (1926).

———, and W. KAISER: Chemical Constitution and Odor, *Ber. deut. chem. Ges.*, **56B**, 2268 (1923).

———, and KRÖGER: Geruch und Konstitution, *Ber. deut. chem. Ges.*, **62B**, 2880 (1930).

———, and W. RUDOLPH: Chemical Constitution of Odors, *Ber. deut. chem. Ges.*, **67B**, 1735 (1934).

———, and TEUFFERT: Chemical Constitution and Odor, *Ber. deut. chem. Ges.*, **58B**, 2210 (1925).

WALDSCHMITT, E. T.: Helle und dunkle Gerüche (Chemie des Geruchssinns), *Korable*, 551 (1932).

Wave Length of a Smell, *Literary Digest*, **89**, 24 (1926).

WOERDEMAN, H.: Influence of Temperature of Odoriferous Gas on Olfactory Sensation, *Arch. néerland. physiol.*, **19**, 88 (1934).

———: Water Vapor Effect on Olfaction, *Arch. néerland. physiol.*, **20**, 591 (1935).

WOKER, G.: The Relations between Structure and Smell in Organic Compounds, *J. Phys. Chem.*, **10**, 555 (1906).

YURINO, T.: Odor Propagation through Fluid Media, *Manshu Igaku Zasshi*, **5**, 2 (1926).

ZEEHUIZEN, H.: Über den Zusammenhang bei Riechstoffen zwischen der elektrischen Ladung durch Verstäubung und der Geruchsintensität, *Verhandel. Koninkl. Akad. Wetenschap. Amsterdam, Afdell. Natuurk.*, **28**, 11 (1919).

ZUNTZ, N.: Chemistry and Physiology of Smell, *Z. angew. Chem.*, **23**, 385.

ZWAARDEMAKER, H.: Die Riechkraft von Lösungen differenter Concentration, *Arch. Physiol.*, 415 (1900).

———: De adsorptie van muskongeur tegen vlakten van verschillend materiaal, *Proc. Koninkl. Akad. Wetenschap. Amsterdam, sect. sci.*, **10**, 116, 122 (1907–1908).

———: Herstellung von Mischgerüchen, *Z. biol. Tech. u. Methodik*, 26 (1908).

———: Die Wirkung des ultravioletten Lichtes auf Riechgase, *Monatsshr. Ohrenheilk.*, **46**, 672 (1912).

———: Specific Smell Intensity and the Electrical Phenomenon of Cloudlike Condensed Water Vapours in Chemical Series, *Proc. Koninkl. Akad. Wetenschap. Amsterdam*, **19**, 334 (1916).

———: Electrical Phenomena in Smell Mixtures, *Proc. Acad. Sci. Amsterdam*, **19**, 551 (1916).

———: Le Phénomène de la charge des brouillards de substances odorantes, *Arch. néerland. physiol.*, **1**, 347 (1917).

———: Le Sens de l'adsorption des substances volatiles, *Acta Oto-Laryngol.*, **1**, 54 (1918).

———: Aequiradio-activity, *Am. J. Physiol.*, **45**, 147 (1918).

———: Adsorption of Odors on Solid Surfaces, *Proc. Acad. Sci. Amsterdam*, **23**, 654 (1921).

———: Odeur et chimisme, *Arch néerland. physiol.*, **6**, 336 (1922).

———: Theory of Smell from Standpoint of Modern Views on Molecular Structure, *Nederland. Tijdschr. Geneesk.*, **2**, 1677 (1927).

———: Odor and Ultra-violet Light, *Proc. Acad. Sci. Amsterdam*, **21**, 131 (1918).

———, and F. Hogewind: La Diamagnétisme des substances odorantes, *Arch. néerland. physiol.*, **4**, 224 (1920).

———, and ———: On the Relation between the Electrical Phenomenon in Cloudlike Condensed Odorous Water Vapors and Smell Intensity, *Proc. Koninkl. Akad. Wetenschap. Amsterdam, sect. sci.*, **22**, 175 (1920).

———, and ———: Odorous Spray and Electrical Charge, *Proc. Acad. Sci. Amsterdam*, **22**, 429 (1920).

———, H. R. Knoops, and M. W. Van der Bijl: The Electrical Phenomenon in Cloudlike Condensed Odorous Water Vapours, *Proc. Koninkl. Akad. Wetenschap. Amsterdam*, **19**, 44 (1916).

———, and H. Zeehuisen: Spray Electricity and Odor, *Proc. Koninkl. Akad. Wetenschap. Amsterdam*, **22**, 175 (1919).

F. Classification of Odors

Aronsohn, E.: Versuch einer Nomenklatur der Geruchsqualitätan, *Arch. Laryngol. Rhinol.*, **2**, 42 (1894).

Bienfang, R.: Odor Characterization; (Dimensional), *Chronica Botan.*, **6**, 249 (1941).

Boring, E. G.: New System for the Classification of Odors, *Am. J. Psychol.*, **40**, 345 (1928).

Characterization of Perfumes; Essential Oils Classified into Three Groups, *Riechstoff Ind.*, **6**, 57 (1931).

Cramer, M.: Classification and Detection of Odors, *Protar*, **7**, 127 (1941).

Crocker, E. C.: Nomenclature for Odors. *Ind. Eng. Chem.*, **27**, 1225 (1935).

Findley, A. E.: Studies of Henning's System of Olfactory Qualities, *Am. J. Psychol.*, **35**, 436 (1924).

Gerhardt, O.: Classification and Evaluation of Odors, According to Henning's Prism, *Parfumerie moderne*, **21**, 415 (1928).

Geruchsindex. Abt. 1, Stoffnamen mit Geruchsdefinitiönen, Seifensieder-Zeitung (supp. *Der Parfümeur*), **63–68** (1936–1941); Abt. 2, Geruchsgruppen und Stoffnamen, Seifensieder-Zeitung (supp. *Der Parfümeur*), **68** (1941).

*Greeves, A. F. A.: "An Essay on the Varieties and Distinction of Tastes and Smells," Edinburgh, 1828.

HEATH, B.: Standardization of Odors, *Perfumery Essent. Oil Record*, **28**, 52 (1937).

KENNEL, P.: Essai de classification des odeurs par la méthode des majorités, *Arch psychol.*, **14**, 375 (1915).

KENNETH, J. H.: A Few Odor Preferences and Their Constancy, *J. Exp. Psychol.*, **11**, 56 (1928).

MacDONALD, K.: Experimental Study of Henning's System of Olfactory Qualities, *Am. J. Psychol.*, **33**, 535 (1922).

METZNER, C. A.: Investigation of Odor and Taste, *Wallerstein Lab. Communic.*, **6**, 5 (1943).

LOVELL, J. H.: Classification of Flower Odors, *Am. Bee J.*, **63**, 392 (1923).

NICCOLINI, P. M.: Classification of Elements According to Olfaction, *Boll. soc. ital. biol. sper.*, **9**, 369 (1934).

NIELSEN, A.: Detection and Classification of Odors—Education of Sense of Smell, *Gasschutz u. Luftschutz*, **5**, 214 (1935).

Nomenclature of Smells, *Sci. American Supp.*, **84**, 339 (1917).

OHMA, S.: Classification of Aromatic Odors, *Arch. néerland. physiol.*, **6**, 567 (1922).

PARRY, E. J.: Classification of Odours, *Perfumery Essent. Oil Record*, 129 (May, 1916).

VAN DER WIELEN, P.: Codification of Odors in Pharmacopeia, *Pharm. Weekblad.*, **64**, 550, 594, 636 (1927).

G. ODOR DETECTION, TESTS, AND MEASUREMENTS
(See also under ODOR CONTROL)

ABBENSETH, F., et. al.: Threshold Odor Tests Improve the Water Treatment at Mamaroneck, N. Y., *Water Works Eng.*, **91**, 601 (1938).

ADLER, A., and FINLEY: Elsberg's M.I.O., *Arch. Neurol. Psychiat.*, **40**, 147 (1938).

ANMUELLER, F.: Selection of Odors, *Frontier*, **7**, 6 (1944).

AULD, J. S. M.: Psycho-galvanic Measurement of Smell, *J. Inst. Petroleum Tech.*, **9**, 389 (1923).

BACH, H.: Measurement of Odors, *Gesundh.-Ing.*, **60**, 222 (1937).

BAILEY, E. H. S., and L. M. POWELL: Some Special Tests in Regard to the Delicacy of the Sense of Smell, *Trans. Can. Acad. Sci.*, **9**, 100 (1884).

BANES, B.: Sniff Specialist, *Cornell Countryman*, **36**, 58 (1939).

BAYLIS, J. R.: Procedure for Making Odor and Taste Determinations, *Water Works & Sewerage*, **79**, 425 (1932).

———, and O. GULLANS: An Improved Odor Test on Water, *J. Am. Water Works Assoc.*, **28**, 507 (1936).

BEDNAR, M.: Zu einer neuen Methodik des Geruchs-und Geschmachs-prüfung, *Wien. klin. Wochschr.*, **56**, 1057 (1943).

BLAKESLEE, A. F.: Demonstration of Differences between People in the Sense of Smell, *Sci. Monthly*, **37**, 72 (1933).

———: Dinner Demonstration of Threshold Differences in Taste and Smell, *Science*, N.S., **81**, 504 (1935).

———: Test of the Sense of Smell at the New York Flower Show, *Eugen. News*, **20**, 75 (1935).

BÖRNSTEIN, W.: Methods for Testing Sense of Smell, *Deut. Z. Nervenheilk.*, **104**, 78 (1928).

BUSE, H.: Measurement of Odors, *Z. Wirtschaftsgruppe Zuckeind*, **86**, 564 (1936).

CHAPLET, A.: Olfactometers and Olfactometry, *Parfumerie moderne*, **30**, 3 (1936).

COWLES, M. W.: Instruments and Methods Used in Detecting and Measuring Odors, *Water Works & Sewerage*, **81**, 123 (1934).

———: Odor Control Methods Aided by New Test Technique, *Eng. News*, **114**, 636 (1935).

CROCKER, E. C.: How to Measure Odor and Flavor, *Food Ind.*, **9**, 314 (1937).

The Delicacy of the Sense of Smell, *Med. Record*, **29**, 712 (1886).

DURRANS, T. H.: Factors of Odorous Strength, *Nature*, **111**, 359 (1923).

DUSSIK, K.: Untersuchungen einer neuen Methodik der Geruchs—und Geschmachs-prüfung, *Wien. klin. Wochschr.*, **46**, 745 (1933).

EDMONDSON, J. J.: Odors: Sewage Test, *Surveyor*, **54**, 183 (1918).

ELSBERG, C. A.: Brain Tumors Detected by Scent with Device Keener Than the X-ray, *N. Y. Times* (Nov. 13, 1935).

————: The Localization of Supratentorial Tumors in the Brain, *Ann. Int. Med.*, **10**, 49 (1936).

————: The Sense of Smell. The Odorous Substances to Be Used for Tests of the Olfactory Sense, *Bull. Neurol. Inst. N.Y.*, **4**, 286 (1936).

————: Olfactory Tests, *Med. Physics*, 821 (1944).

————, and E. D. BREWER: A Detail Description of the Technique of Two Olfactory Tests Used for the Localization of Supratentorial Tumors of the Brain, *Bull. Neurol. Inst. N. Y.*, **4**, 501 (1935).

————, I. LEVY, and E. D. BREWER: New Method for Testing Sense of Smell and for Establishment of Olfactory Values of Odorous Substances, *Science*, **83**, 211 (1936).

————, and H. SPOTNITZ: Value of Quantitative Olfactory Disease, *Arch. Neurol. Psychiat.*, **48**, 1 (1942).

————, and J. STEWARD: Quantitative Olfactory Test, *Arch. Neurol. Psychiat.*, **40**, 471 (1938).

EYSENCH, M. D.: Experimental and Statistical Study of Olfactory Preferences, *J. Exp. Psychol.*, **34**, 246 (1944).

FAIR, G. M.: The Determination of Odors and Tastes in Water, *J. New Engl. Water Works Assoc.*, **47**, 248 (1933).

————: Determining Tastes and Odors in Water, *Water Works & Sewerage*, **80**, 360 (1933).

————, and W. F. WELLS: Determining Odors in Water, *Water Works Eng.*, **87**, 1051 (1934).

————, and ————: Meter for Odors, U. S. Patent No. 2,136,844 (1939).

FOURNIE, M.: Olfactoscope for Comparison of Odors, *Perfumery Essent. Oil Record*, **8**, 278 (1917).

GALTON, F.: Arithmetic by Smell, *Psychol. Rev.*, **1**, 61 (1894).

GANT, V. A., and H. D. SHAW: Determination of Concentration of Odors in Air-Conditioned Structure, *Ind. Eng. Chem. Anal. Ed.*, **9**, 16 (1937).

GARBINI, A.: Intorno al minimum percettibile di odore, *Mem. acad. agric., arti, commercio*, **68**, 85 (1892).

GERARDIN, A.: Dosage des odeurs, *Rev. hyg.*, **17**, 597 (1895).

————, and M. NICLOUX: Mesure des Odeurs de l'air, *Compt. rend. acad. sci.*, **122**, 954 (1896).

GOLDZWEIG, L.: Beiträge zur Olfaktometrie, *Arch. Laryngol. Rhinol.*, **6**, 137 (1897).

*————: "Beiträge zur Olfaktometrie," Bern, 1896.

GOOTSCHALK, V. H.: Measuring Odors, *Chem. & Met. Eng.*, **19**, 700 (1918).

GULLANS, O.: Procedure for Making Odor Determinations, *J. Am. Water Works Assoc.*, **25**, 974 (1933).

————: Improved Odor Test on Water, *J. Am. Water Works Assoc.*, **28**, 507 (1936).

GUNDLACH, R. H., and G. KENWAY: Method for the Determination of Olfactory Thresholds in Humans, *J. Exp. Psychol.*, **24**, 192 (1939).

GUNTHER, H.: Olfaktometer, *Med. Klin.*, **9**, 1596 (1913).

HALL, G. L.: Taste and Odor Tests of Paints for Water Tanks, *Eng. News Record*, **106**, 725 (1931).

———: Recent Tests and Odor Tests of Paints for Water Tanks, *Eng. News Record*, **115**, 639 (1935).

HAMBLOCH, H., and J. PUSCHEL: Localization of Sources of Odors, *Z. Psychol. Physiol. Sinnesorg.*, **59**, 151 (1928).

HART, W. B.: Apparatus for Determining Odor in Water, *Ind. Eng. Chem., Anal. Ed.*, **9**, 243 (1937).

HAYNES, L.: Use of Osmoscope with Water, *West Va. Univ., Eng. Sta. Tech. Bull.*, **11**, 15 (1938).

HENRY, C.: Olfactomètre fondé sur la diffusion à travers les membranes flexibles, *Compt. rend. acad. sci.*, **112**, 344 (1891).

———: Recherches nouvelles d'olfactometrie, *Compt. rend. acad. sci.*, **112**, 16, 885 (1891).

*———: "Les Odeurs; demonstrations pratiques avec l'olfactometrie et le pèsevapeur," Paris, 1892.

———: Nouvelles Recherches d'olfactometrie, *Compt. rend. assoc. franc. pour l'avance des sci.*, **20**, 325 (1892).

———: L'Olfactometric et la physique des vapeurs, *Compt. rend. soc. de biol.*, N.S., **4**, 97 (1892).

———: Remarques sur une communication récente de M. J. Passy, concernant les minimums perceptibles de quelques odeurs, *Compt. rend. acad. sci.*, **114**, 8, 437 (1892).

———: Les Odeurs et leur mesure, *Rev. sci.*, **49**, 65 (Jan. 16, 1892).

*HERRMANN, J.: "Gesamterlebnisse bei Gerüchen," Leipzig, 1922.

HESSE, W.: Bestimmung von Geruchsschwellen in Absoluten Werten, *Z. Hals-, Nasen-, u. Ohrenheilk.*, **16B**, 359 (1926).

HIROSE, S.: On Olfactory Sensation, *Z. Otol. Tokyo*, **46**, 618 (1940).

HIRSCH, C.: Klinische Prüfung des Geruchs und Geschmacksinnes, *Münch. med. Wochschr.*, **79**, 1234 (1932).

HOFMANN, K.: Bestimmung von Geruchsschwellen, *Biochem. Z.*, **B156**, 287 (1925).

HOSKINS, W. M., and R. CRAIG: Satisfactory Olfactometer for Insects, *J. Econ. Entomol.*, **27**, 1029 (1934).

HULBERT, R., and D. FEBEN: Studies on Accuracy of the Threshold Odor Values, *J. Am. Water Works Assoc.*, **33**, 1945 (1941).

*HUYER, C.: "De olfactologie van aniline en homologen," Utrecht, 1917.

Instruments Aid Senses of Taste and Smell, *Sci. American*, **152**, 105 (1935).

It's a Stinkometer; New Device Tells When Fish Is Spoiled, *Business Week*, 64 (Mar. 3, 1945).

*JANSSEN, G.: "Die methodik der Geruchsprüfung und ihre praktisch—klinische Bedeutung, Libau," 1930.

JEROME, E. A.: Olfactory Thresholds Measured in Terms of Stimulus Pressure and Volume, *Arch. Psych. N. Y.*, **274**, 44 (1942).

JONES, I. H.: Smell: Precision Instruments, *Laryngoscope*, **49**, 505 (1939).

———: Elsberg Precision Instruments of Sense of Smell, *Trans. Pacific Coast Oto-Ophth. Soc.*, **25**, 197 (1940).

KATZ, S. H., and V. C. ALLISON: Measurement of Odors, *Chem. & Met. Eng.*, **19**, 1747 (1918).

KLEINER, I. S.: Limit of Sensitivity of Olfaction, *J. Am. Inst. Homeopathy*, **18**, 681 (1925).

KOELSCH, H.: Determining Sensitivity to Odor of Gas, *Gas Age*, **67**, 160 (1931).

KOMURO, K.: L'Olfactometrie dans l'air parfumé, *Arch. néerland. physiol.*, **22**, 58 (1921).

———: Minimum Perceptible in an Absolutely Inodorous Space (Camera Inodorata), *Arch. néerland. physiol.*, **6**, 20 (1921).

LANG, O. W., L. FARBER, and F. YEOMAN: Stinkometer for Measurement of Odors, *Food Ind.*, **178**, 116 (1945).

LAUGHLIN, H. F.: The Why and How of the Threshold Test for Water Supplies, *Eng. Contr. Record*, **51**, 11 (1938).

———: Threshold Tests in Odor and Taste Control of Water, *Ohio Conf. Water Purif.*, *20th Ann. Rept.*, 65 (1940).

LEICHER, H.: Sättigungsdrücke und Dampfdichte verschiedener Riechstoffe, *Z. Laryngol., Rhinol., Grenzgebiete*, **18B**, 222 (1929).

LERMOYEZ: L'Olfactometrie clinique, *Presse méd. Paris*, 793 (1905).

Limits of Sensibility of Odors and Emanations, *Sci. American Supp.*, **59**, 24580 (1905).

LUQUE, A. B.: Measuring Odors in Perfumes, *IX Congr. intern. quim. pura aplicada*, **4**, 594 (1934).

McINDOO, N. E.: Olfactometer for Measuring Insect Attraction to Non-flowering Plants, *J. Econ. Entomol.*, **19**, 545 (1926).

———: Olfactory Responses of Blowflies, with and without Antennae, in a Wooden Olfactometer, *J. Agr. Research*, **46**, 607 (1933).

MARMOR: Sur les Limites de la sensiblité olfactive d'après M. Berthelon, *Cosmos*, **50**, 48 (1901).

MASINI, G.: Sulla Misura del tempo di reazione olfattiva, *Atti. Cong. soc. ital. laringol.*, **4**, 94 (1899).

MASUDA, S.: Olfactometric Examination, *Okayama-Iga kai-Zasshi*, **40**, 197 (1928).

Measurement of Odors, *Riechstoff Ind.*, 142, 150, 161 (1927).

MES, L.: Lining an Olfactometer with Mica, *Geneesk., Tijdschr.*, **10**, 972 (1932).

M I O, Minimum Identified Odor, *Time*, **26**, 40 (1935).

MONCRIEFF, R. W.: Detection of Odors, *Am. Perfumer*, **47**, 41 (1945).

NACHTIGALL, G., and E. GRILL: Objective Determination of Odor during Examination of Water, *Arch. Hyg.*, **129**, 196 (1943).

NEVIN, W. M.: A Plea for Olfactories, *Mercersburg Rev.*, **1**, 559.

NICCOLINI, P. M.: Detection of Odors, *Boll. soc. ital. biol. sper.*, **8**, 424 (1933).

Odors Are Judged by Their Wave Lengths, *Nation's Health*, **8**, 113 (1926).

ONODI, A.: Ein Olfactometer für die Praxis, *Arch. Laryngol. Rhinol.*, **14**, 185 (1903).

PARADISE, V. I.: Sipping and Sniffing, *Scribner's*, **70**, 577 (1921).

PARRAVICINI, E. F., and I. LEIR: Ricerche di olfattometria negli ultimi tempi della gravidanza, nel puerperio e nelle epoche calamentiali, *Arch. ostet. ginec.*, **13**, 750 (1906).

PASSY, J.: Notes sur les minimums perceptibles de quelques odeurs, *Compt. rend. soc. de biol.*, N.F. **4**, 84; (7), 137 (1892).

———: Sur les Minimums perceptibles de quelques odeurs, *Compt. rend. soc. de biol.*, **114**, 306, 786 (1892).

PERRYCOSTE, F. H.: Factors of Odorous Strength, *Nature*, **111**, 359 (1923).

*PIESSE, C. H.: "Olfacties and the Physical Senses," London, 1887.

PINI, A.: Sulla Olfattometria, *Gazz. osp. Milano*, **21**, 936 (1900).

POLLAK, A., and T. A. WILLINGHAM: Odorometer, U. S. Patent No. 2,327,060 (1944).

PROETZ, A. W.: A System of Exact Olfactometry, *Ann. Otol., Rhinol., & Laryngol.*, **33**, 746 (1924–1925).

QUIX, F. H.: Olfaktometrische Untersuchungs methode, *Zentr. Ohrenheilk.*, 57 (1904).

REUTER, C.: Demonstration eines speciall zu klinischen Zwecken bestimmten Riechmessers, *Verhandl. Ges. deut. Naturf. Ärzte*, **70**, 311 (1899).

RIDLEY, J. E.: Measurement of Odors of Water, *Sanitarian, London*, **62**, 126 (1944).

RIPLEY, L. B., and G. A. HEPBURN: Olfactometer for Natal fruit fly, *Union S. Africa, Dept. Agr., Entomol. Mem.*, **6**, 19 (1929).

ROCÉN, E.: Localization of "Sweet Smell," *Skand. Arch. Physiol.*, **40**, 129 (1920).

ROSENTHAL, A.: Odor Testing of Oils and Extracts, *Seifensieder-Zeitung*, **55** (*supp. Der Parfümeur*, **2**, 33 (1928).

ROTHE, K. C.: Ein einfaches Glasolfaktometer, *Z. allgem, Physiol.* (1917).

RUBEK, D. D.: Osmoscope, *Paint Ind. Mag.*, **57**, 128 (1942).

RUSS, E. I., and S. S. PALESTRANT: Smell: Sniff Test, *Ind. Arts and Voc. Educ.*, **34**, 465 (1945).

RUTHERFORD, J. T.: Odors: Measuring Concentration in Odorized Natural Gas, *Proc. Am. Petroleum Inst.*, Sect. IV, **21**, 89 (1940).

*SAINT-MAURICE, G.: "De la Méthode de l'eau camphrée pour la mesure de l'odorat," Paris, 1900.

SAXE, E.: Improved Apparatus for Use in Odor Discrimination, *Z. wiss. biol.*, Abt. C, **10**, 227 (1929).

SEEGER, A.: Odor Test in Evaluation of Potable and Industrial Water, *Arch. Wärmewirt.*, **23**, 105 (1942).

SEFFRIN, L.: Über die kleinsten noch wahrnehmbar Geruchsmengen einiger *Riechstoffe beim Hund*, *Z. Biol.*, **47**, 493 (1915).

SEWALL, H.: The Delicacy of the Sense of Smell, *Am. Naturalist*, **20**, 826 (1886).

SHOWALTER, H. A.: Tastes, Odors and Flowers, *Food in Canada*, **5**, 9 (1945).

SIERRA, A. M.: Investigation of Smell by Means of New Clinical Olfactometer, *Acta primera conf. latino am. neurol., psiquiatry, med. leg.*, **1**, 598 (1929).

SMITH, O. K., and WILLIAMS: Detection and Determination of Odorous Substances in Natural Gas, Town Gas, etc., *Gas Age*, **84**, 14 (1939).

SNAPP, O. I., and H. S. SWINGLE: Olfactometer Tests in Conotrachelus Nenuphar, *J. Econ. Entomol.*, **22**, 984 (1929).

SNEESSENS, H.: Olfactometers for Poison Gas, *J. pharm. belg.*, **21**, 977 (1939).

SPAULDING, C.: Quantitative Determination of Odor in Water, *Am. J. Pub. Health*, **21**, 1038 (1931).

———: Some Quantitative Odor Determinations, *J. Am. Water Works Assoc.*, **24**, 1111 (1932).

———: Accuracy and Application of Threshold Odor Tests, *J. Am. Water Works Assoc.*, **34**, 877 (1942).

STAMPE, G., and K. GROSSKOPF: Kits for Testing Olfaction, *Draeger-Hefte*, **201**, 4096 (1939).

STEIN, V.: Recherches sur les fonctions nasales (technique olfactométrique), *Hosp. Tidende, Kobenhagen*, 4R, **8**, 1068, 1091, 1131 (1900).

STERNBERG, W.: Kompendiöser quantitatiber Olfactometer zu klinischen Zwecken, *Deut. med. Wochschr.*, **35**, 1661 (1909).

STEVANI, R.: Un nuovo Olfattometro clinico, *Arch. ital. otol. Torino*, **16**, 301 (1904–1905).

TAKAHASHI, T.: A Newly Devised Olfactometer, *Ryoshoku Kenkyn*, **145**, 531 (1938).

TASMAN, A.: Strength of Odors—Apparatus for Detecting, *Chem. Weekblad.*, **35**, 707 (1938).

THOMAS, H. A., JR.: Calculation of Threshold Odor, *J. Am. Water Works Assoc.*, **35**, 751 (1943).

THOMAS, M. A. R.: Odor: Osmoscope Test in Halitosis, *J. Can. Dental Assoc.*, **7**, 182 (1941).

TITCHENER, E. B.: Apparatus for Experiment on Taste and Smell, *Am. J. Psychol.*, 261 (1900).

TOULOUSE, E.: Mesure de l'odorat par l'eau camphrée, *Compt. rend. soc. biol.*, **1**, 379 (1899).

————, and N. VASCHIDE: Note sur un nouveau moyen de vérifier la loi de Weber-Fechner sur le rapport de la sensation a l'excitation, et sur la vérification de cette loi par la mesure de l'odorat au moyen de solutions decimales, *Compt. rend. soc. biol.* (July 15, 1899).

————, and ————: Mesure de l'odorat chez les enfants, *Comp. rend. soc. biol.*, **1**, 487 (1899).

————, and ————: Mesure de la fatigue olfactive, *Compt. rend. soc. biol.* (Nov. 18, 1899).

————, and ————: Mesure de l'odorat chez l'homme et chez la femme, *Compt. rend. soc. biol.*, **1**, 381 (1899).

————, and ————: Mesure de l'odorat dans l'épilepsie, *Compt. rend. soc. biol.* (July 15, 1899).

————, and ————: Mesure de l'odorat dans l'épilepsie, *Compt. rend. soc. biol.* (July 29, 1899).

————, and ————: Mesure de l'odorat dans le paralysie générale, *Compt. rend. soc. biol.*, **52**, 110 (1900).

Über die Proportionen der Geruchskompensation, *Onderzoek. ged. in physiol. Lab. Utrecht Hoogesch.*, **9**, 309 (1908).

VAN DAM, C.: Un nouvel Olfactomètre, *Arch. néerland. physiol.*, **1**, 660 (1917).

————: Olfactometers—Adsorption of Odorants, *Arch. néerland. physiol.*, **1**, 660 (1917).

————: Adsorption of Substances Used in Olfactometric Tests, *Nederland. Tijdschr. Geneesk.*, **1**, 812 (1917).

VASCHIDE, N.: De l'Olfactometrie, *Bull. laryngol., otol., rhinol.*, **4**, 5 (1901).

————: La Mesure du temps de réaction simple des sensations olfactives, *Arch. ital. biol.*, **36**, 118 (1901–1902).

VAUGHN, J. C.: Laboratory Control at Hammond, Ind., Filtration Plant: Threshold Odor Test, *J. Am. Water Works Assoc.*, **31**, 2137 (1939).

VON HORNBOSTEL, E. M.: "Brightness" of Odors, *Arch. ges. physiol.*, **227**, 517 (1931).

VON SKRAMLIK, E.: Vorrichtung zur Prüfung der Leistungen des Geruchsinnes, *Münch. med. Wochschr.*, **83**, 1564 (1936).

WAGENAAR, M.: Measuring Apparatus for Judging Ability to Detect Odors, *Chem. Weekblad*, **35**, 618 (1938).

WEHRLI, H.: War Gas Testing by Odors, *Protar*, **4**, 10 (1938).

WIETING, J. O. G., and W. M. HOSKINS: Smell in House Flies—Olfactometer, *J. Econ. Entomol.*, **32**, 24 (1939).

WINSOR, A. L., and B. KORCHIN: Device for Obtaining Constant Olfactory Stimulation, *Am. J. Psychol.*, **52**, 114 (1939).

WIRTH, W.: Threshold Values of Odors in Insects, *Biol. Zentr.*, **48**, 567 (1928).

WOODROW, H., and B. KARPMAN: A New Olfactometric Technique and Some Results, *J. Exp. Psychol.*, **2**, 431 (1917).

WOODWORTH, F. K.: Appeal for a Bureau of Standards, *Perfumery Essent. Oil Record*, **13**, 387 (1922).

YOUNG, P. T.: Constancy of Affective Judgment to Odor, *J. Exp. Psychol.*, **6**, 182 (1923).

————: Studies in Affective Psychology; the Scale of Values Method, *Am. J. Psychol.*, **42**, 17 (1930).

ZIGLER, M. J., and A. H. HOLWAY: Smell: Differential Sensitivity to India Rubber, *J. Gen. Psychol.*, **12**, 372 (1935).

ZWAARDEMAKER, H.: Die Bestimmung der Geruchscharfe, *Berlin. klin. Wochschr.*, **25**, 950 (1888).

———: Compensation von Gerüchen mittelst des Doppelriechmessers, *Fortschr. Med.*, **7**, 721 (1889).

———: La mesure des sensations olfactives et l'olfactomètre, *Rev. sci.*, **2**, 810 (1889).

———: L'Olfactomètre double et son emploi dans les recherches physiologiques, *Arch. néerland sci. exp. nat.*, **23**, 445 (1889).

———: Odorimetrie, *Verhandl. X internat. med. Congr.*, **2**, 2 abt., 43 (1890).

———: Over de nor ma der reukscherpte, *Nederland. Tijdschr. Geneesk.*, 2R, **24**, 187 (1890).

———: Zur Metodik der klinischen Olfaktometrie, *Neurol. Zentr.*, **12**, 729 (1893).

———: Ein verbesserter Riechmesser, *Arch. Laryngol. Rhinol.*, **3**, 367 (1895).

———: Riechkraft d. Lösungen verschiedene Konzentration, *Arch. Anat. Physiol. (Phys. supp.)*, 415 (1900).

———: Odorimetrie, *Nederland. Tijdschr. Geneesk.*, **2**, 459 (1902).

———: Odormetrie von procentischen Lösungen und von Systemen im heterogenen Gleichgewicht, *Arch. Physiol.*, 42 (1903).

———: Präzisionsolfaktometrie, *Arch. Laryngol. Rhinol.*, **15**, 171 (1904).

———: Über die Proportionen der Geruchskompensation, *Arch. Physiol.*, Supp. 59 (1907).

———: Eine Methode, um Stoffe in isotonischer Lösung in die Riechspalte zu bringen, *Arch. Laryngol. Rhinol.*, **33**, 433 (1920).

———: Camera Inodorata for Study of Odors, *Perfumery Essent. Oil Record*, **12**, 243 (1921).

———: Olfactometry, *Perfumery Essent. Oil Record*, **12**, 308 (1921).

———: Odorimetry, *Perfumery Essent. Oil Record*, **13**, 5 (1922).

———: Prüfung des Geruchssinnes und der Gerüche, *Handbuch. biol. Arbeitsmeth*, 105 Lief., 455 (1923).

———: Qualitative Geruchsmessung, *Arch. Laryngol.*, **4**, 55 (1896).

H. Odors of Food and Water
(See also under Odor Control)

Akabori, S.: Odors of Soy Sauce, *J. Chem. Soc. Japan*, **57**, 828 (1936).

———, and T. Kaneko: Odors of Soy Sauce, *J. Chem. Soc. Japan*, **58**, 236 (1937).

———, and ———: Odors of Soy Sauce, *Proc. Imp. Acad. Tokyo*, **12**, 131 (1936).

Alvord, Burdick, Russell and Juday: Algae Cause Odors from Monoa Lake at Madison, Wis., *Eng. News-Record*, **85**, 907 (1920).

Arana, F. E.: Odors of Vanilla and Its Development, *Puerto Rico Agr. Exp. Sta. Ann. Rept.*, 2 (1939).

———, and A. G. Kevorkian: Relation of Moisture Content to Quality and Aroma of Vanilla Beans, *J. Agr., Univ. Puerto Rico*, **27**, 105 (1943).

Armstrong, J. G., and W. D. McFarlane: Odors of Linseed Oil Shortening, *Oil and Soap*, **21**, 322 (1944).

Arroyo, R.: Odors of Rum, *Puerto Rico Agr. Exp. Sta. Ann. Rept.*, 42 (1938–1939).

———: Odors of Rum, *Rev. agr., ind., com. Puerto Rico*, **31**, 448 (1939); **32**, 301 (1940); **32**, 593 (1940); **33**, 127 (1941); **33**, 144 (1941).

Aye, D.: Odors of Fungi, *Arch. Pharm.*, **269**, 246 (1931).

Babcock, C. J.: Odors of Milk, *J. Milk Tech.*, **3**, 9 (1940).

Bailey, W. T.: Taste and Odor Problems, *Taste Odor Control J.*, **3**, 8 (1936).

Bakonji, S.: Improvement of Odors of Fungi, German Patent No. 700,537 (1940).

Bartow, E., and R. Warren: Tastes and Odors from Chlorine, *Eng. News-Record*, **89**, 878 (1922).

BENTERUD, O.: Odor Tests on Cream to Improve Butter Quality, *Chem. Centr.* (II), 2215 (1942).

BIDAULT, G., and G. HINARD: Odors in Canned Foods, *Ann. fals.*, **23**, 30 (1930).

BORDAS, F., and TOUPLAIN: De la Rapidité d'absorption des odeurs par le lait, *Compt. rend. acad. sci.*, **142**, 1204 (1906).

BRAIDECH, M. M.: Evaluation of Tastes and Odors in Water Supplies, *Ohio Conf. Water Purif.*, *17th Ann. Rept.*, 1937, 87 (1938).

BRANDT, R. L.: Odors of Coffee, U. S. Patent No. 2,345,378 (1944).

BROEG, W. E.: The Influence of Odor on Palate Acceptance, *Proc. Inst. Food Tech.*, 141 (1944).

BROGE, J. A.: Odors of Herring Oils, *Fette u. Seifen*, **48**, 188 (1941).

BURKE, A. D.: Alamalt in Ice Cream, *Southern Dairy Prod. J.*, **36**, 72 (1944).

BUXTON, L. O.: Improving Odors of Vitamin-bearing Oils, U. S. Patent No. 2,306,776 (1943).

Causes of Tastes and Odors, *Public Works*, **68**, 14 (1937).

CHAPMAN, R. A., and W. D. MCFARLANE: A Soloimetric Method for Estimation of Reducing Groups in Milk Powders, *Can. J. Research*, Sect. B, **23**, 91 (1945).

CLAYDON, T. J., and B. W. HAMMER: Skunk-like Odors in Butter, *J. Bact.*, **37**, 251 (1939).

COLE, W. C., and N. P. TARASSUK: Evaporated Milk as Related to Greenish Discoloration and Off-odor of Coffee, *J. Dairy Sci.*, **28**, 57 (1945).

CROCKER, E. C.: Basic Principles of Flavor Retention in Foods, *Proc. Inst. Food Tech.*, 80 (1944).

———: A Flavorist Views Food Processing, *Food Ind.*, **17**, 247 (1945).

CRUESS, W. V.: Experiments on Garlic and Onion Extracts, *Fruit Products J.*, **23**, 305 (1944).

———: Frozen Pack Fruit Syrups and Concentrates, *Fruit Products J.*, **24**, 36, 61 (1944).

CSISZARY, J., A. BAKOS, and G. TOMKA: Odors of Cheese, *Milchw. Forsch.*, **21**, 236 (1942).

CUNNINGHAM, A.: Odors in Milk Production by Micrococci, *Proc. World's Dairy Congr.*, Copenhagen, Sec. 2, 1 (1931).

———: Bacterial Milk Taint, *J. Dairy Research*, **4**, 197 (1933).

Dairy Research Institute, Pretoria: Odorous Substances in Woods, Absorption by Butter, *Union S. Africa, Dept. Agr., Forestry Sci. Bull.*, **173** (1938).

DALE, J. A. H., D. V. ATHAWALE, and P. N. MATHUR: Odors of Mustard Oils, *J. Sci. Tech.* (India), **1**, 103 (1935).

DAVIS, J. G., L. G. NEWLAND, and P. B. KNUCKEY: The Resazurin and Rapid Resazurin Tests and Their Relation to Other Bacteriological Tests, *Dairy Ind.*, **8**, 23; (2) 71; (3) 115 (1943).

DICE, J. R.: Weed Flavors and Odors in Dairy Products, *North Dakota Agr. Exp. Sta.*, *Bimonthly Bull.*, **6**, 6 (1944).

DIENERT, F.: Odors in Water Examination, *Rev. Hyg.*, **50**, 881 (1928).

DONALDSON, W.: Observations on Chlorination Tastes and Odors, *Eng. Contr.*, **58**, 74 (1922).

DOMBROWSKY, M.: Einige Versuche über den Übergang von Riech-und Farbstoffen in die Milch, *Arch. Hyg.*, **1**, 183 (1904).

DuBois, C. W., and D. K. TRESSLER: Seasonings, Their Effect on Maintenance of Quality in Storage of Frozen Ground Pork and Beef, *Proc. Inst. Food Tech.*, 202 (1943).

EDEL, H.: Odors of Milk, *Milk Dealer*, **29**, 31 (1940).

ELLIKER, P. R.: Effect of Various Bacteria on Diacetyl Content, Odor and Flavor of Butter, *J. Dairy Sci.*, **28**, 93 (1945).

ELLMS, J., and W. C. LAWRENCE: Investigation of Tastes and Odors in the Cleveland Water Supply, *Eng. News Record*, **80**, 1039 (1921).

————, and ————: Causes of Obnoxious Tastes and Odors Sometimes Occurring in the Cleveland Water Supply, *J. Am. Water Works Assoc.*, **9**, 463 (1922).

ESSELEN, W. B., JR.: Methods of Clarification and Blends of Mass. Apples for Apple Juice, *Fruit Products J.*, **24**, 165 (1945).

FINCKE, H.: Odor-producing Substances in Cacao, *Kazett*, **21**, 381 (1932).

————: Odorous Substances of Cacao and Their Effect on Palatability, *Fette u. Seifen*, **46**, 484 (1939).

FINCK, H. T.: The Gastronomic Value of Odors, *Contemp. Rev.*, **1**, 680 (1886).

FINE, M. S., and A. G. OLSEN: Tallowy Odor in Flour, *Ind. Eng. Chem.*, **20**, 652 (1928).

GAEBE, O. F.: Odors of Eggs Stored in Avenized and Unavenized Fillers and Flats, *U. S. Egg Poultry Mag.*, **46**, 346 (1940).

GAMBLE, J. A., and E. KELLY: The Effect of Silage on the Flavor and Odor of Milk, *U. S. Dept. Agr. Bull.*, 1097 (1922).

GARRETT, O. F., R. B. ARNOLD, and G. H. HARTMAN: Formation of Odors in Butter, *J. Dairy Sci.*, **24**, 71 (1941).

GEIGER, E.: Histamine Content of Unprocessed and Canned Fish, *Food Research*, **9**, 293 (1944).

GERHARDT, O.: Odors of Butter, Biacetyl, *Seifensieder-Zeitung*, **58**, 792 (1931).

GISTL, R.: Einiges über Geruchsbildung in Kühlräumen, *Gesundh-Ing.*, 617 (1933).

GÖPP, K.: Effect of Cartox on Odor of Barley, *Wochschr. Brau.*, **57**, 286 (1940).

GRINDLEY, D. N.: Odors of Mimosaceae Seed Oils, *J. Soc. Chem. Ind.*, **64**, 152 (1945).

GRUBER, F.: Odors of Palm Oil, *Chem. Zentr.* (II), 179 (1944).

GUDHEIM, A. R.: Odors of Shortening Packaged in Glass, *Oil and Soap*, **20**, 197 (1943).

GUTHRIE, E. S.: The Causes of Bad Flavors and Odors in Milk, *Milk Dealer*, **33**, 86 (1943).

————: Bad Odors in Milk, *Am. Milk Rev.*, **5**, 338 (1943).

HAAGEN-SMIT, A. J., *et al.*: Chemical Studies of Pineapple. I. The Volatile Flavor and Odor Constituents of Pineapple, *J. Am. Chem. Soc.*, **67**, 1646 (1945).

HALLENBERG, E. A.: Beiträge zur Kenntnis der alkoholartigen Getränke. 1. Untersuchungen uber die Geschmacks- und Geruchsschwelle einiger einatomiger Alkohole, *Skandinav. Arch. Physiol.*, **30**, 75 (1914).

HARTRIDGE, H.: The Importance of Taste and Smell in Nutrition, *J. Physiol.*, **103**, 34 (1945).

HAWTHORNE, J. R.: Odors of Foods, *J. Soc. Chem. Ind.*, **62**, 135 (1943).

HEIMAN, E.: Improving Odors of Beer, U. S. Patent No. 2,316,241 (1943).

HENDERSON, C. R.: Experiences with Algae at Davenport, *J. Am. Water Works Assoc.*, **9**, 622 (1922).

HENNIG, K., and F. VILLFORTH: Odors of Wines, *Vorratspflege u. Lebensmittelforsch.*, **5**, 181 (1942); **5**, 313 (1942).

HERRMAN, J.: Odors and Edibility of Fungi, *Pharm. Zentr.*, **59**, 1, 7, 19 (1918).

HERRMANN, E.: Pilzgerüche, *Pharm. Zen.*, **56**, 555 (1913).

HICKMAN, K. C.: Improvement of Odors in Vitamine Oils, U. S. Patent No. 2,249,524 (1941).

HIERONYMI, E.: Odors of Eggs, *Tierärztl. Runds.*, 483 (1939).

HLYNKA, I., and E. G. HOOD: Keeping Quality of Cheese with Rancid Odor and Unclean Flavor, *Can. Dairy Ice Cream J.*, **23**, 35 (1944).

HOLME, G. E.: Dried Milks, *Milk Plant Monthly*, **34**, 23, 52, 65 (1945).

HOOD, E. G., I. HLYNKA, and C. A. GIBSON: Rancidity in Cheddar Cheese, *Can. Dairy Ice Cream J.*, **20**, 26 (1941).

HOWARD, N. J.: Tastes and Odors in Water, *Can. Engr.*, **68**, 14 (1935).

HUSSONG, R. V., and B. W. HAMMER: Observations on "Fishy" Odors in Butter, *J. Dairy Sci.*, **27**, 45 (1944).

Internationale Nahrungs und Genussmittel A-G: Artificial Coffee Odors, German Patent No. 489,613 (1925).

JOHNSTON, W. R., *et al.*: Preservation of Odors of Fruit Juices, Fruit Flavoring Materials, and Fruit Extracts, U. S. Patent No. 2,315,858 (1943).

KELLER: Boar Odor in Pig Flesh, *Z. Fleisch-Milchhyg.*, **47**, 174 (1937).

KELLOGG, J. L.: Odors of Coffee—Improvement, Evaporation and Staling, U. S. Patent No. 2,288,284 (1943).

KELLY, P. L.: The Effect of Nicotine on Milk Lipase, *J. Dairy Sci.*, **28**, 793 (1945).

KHANDROS, Y.: Odors in Judging Liquors, *Spirto-Vodochnaya Prom.*, **17**, 17 (1940).

KING, W. H., F. F. FLYNN, and J. N. GOWANLOCH: Odors of Oyster-reef Water and Mud, *J. Assoc. Official Agr. Chem.*, **28**, 385 (1945).

KOESTLER and WEGMULLER: Odor in Goat's Milk, *Landw. Jahrb. Schweiz.*, **48**, 842 (1934).

KOMM, E., and G. LEHMANN: Odors of Breads, *Z. Untersuch. Lebensm.*, **78**, 458 (1939).

———, and ———: Odorous Substances in Bread, *Z. Untersuch. Lebensm.*, **79**, 242 (1940).

KREMERS, R. E.: Roasting Beverage Materials, *Food Ind.*, **15**, 74 (1943).

KRETSCHMER, W.: Aromatic Substances Are Responsible for Taste, Which is Independent of Caffein Content of Coffee, *Schweiz. med. Wochschr.*, **70**, 110 (1940).

KRÖNER, W., and H. WEGNER: Odorous Substances in Potatoes, *Naturwissenschaften*, **30**, 586 (1942).

KUHL, H.: Influence of Odor Due to Environment, Bacteria and the Absorption of Odor by Grains Themselves due to the Colloidal Property of Grain, *Mehl u. Brot*, **43**, 353 (1943).

LANG, O. W., *et al.*: Spoilage in Protein Food Prod., Especially Fish, *Ind. Eng. Chem., Anal. Ed.*, **16**, 490 (1944).

LEA, C. H., T. MORAN, and J. A. B. SMITH: The Gas-packing and Storage of Milk Powder, *J. Dairy Research*, **13**, 162 (1943).

LINDNER, E.: Iodoform Odor of Mineral Water Containing Iodine, *Chem. Ztg.*, **60**, 426 (1936).

LINNEBOE, J. B., and E. G. HASTINGS: Odors from Milk from Oidium Lactis Symbiosis in Production, *Zentr. Bakt. Parasitenk.*, Abt. 2, **93**, 278 (1936).

MACDONALD, M. B., and M. JACOB: Inhalation the Chief Factor in Onion. or Garlic Contamination of Milk, *Science*, ns, **68**, 568 (1928).

MCNEAR, R. B.: Water Treatment, *Natl. Butter Cheese J.*, **33**, 18 (1942).

MAIER, F. X.: Odors of Cheese, *Vorratspflege Lebensmittelforsch*, **5**, 209 (1942).

MAKAR'IN, A. M.: Formation of Odors in Butter, *Chem. Zentr.*, **2**, 551 (1939).

MARBLE, D. R., *et al.*: Fishy Odors in Turkey Meat, *Poultry Sci.*, **17**, 49 (1938).

MARCHADIER and GOUJONS: Odor in Burnt Wheat, *Ann. fals.*, **7**, 259 (1914).

MASLING, T.: Odors of Bread, *Mühlenlab.*, **6**, 90 (1936).

MATHIEU, L.: Odors of Wine, *Rev. vit.*, **72**, 327 (1930).

MICKSCH, K.: Odors of Fermented Beverages, *Brennerei-Zeitung*, **46**, 178 (1929).

MONCRIEFF, R. W.: Gustation, *Food Manuf.*, **19**, 203 (1944).

MOORE, A. V.: Odors of Butter and Water Supply, *Natl. Butter Cheese J.*, **31**, 18 (1940).

MORRISON, H. B.: Odors in Dairy Products from Pseudomonas, *J. Dairy Sci.*, **24**, 9 (1941).

MUNIN, F.: Odors of Butter, Keeping Quality, Rancidity, *Fette u. Seifen*, **49**, 297 (1942).

———: Tallowness in Taste and Odor of Milk Fat and Butter, *Fette u. Seifen*, **49**, 449 (1942).

MURPHY and MASON: Odor Absorption by Beer, *Bull. Bur. Bio. Tech.*, **2**, 165 (1927).

NAPRETH, N.: Formation of Odors of Butter, *Milchw. Ztg. Alpen-Sud. Donauraum*, **40**, 649 (1940).

National Oil Products Co.: Improving Odors of Vitamin Preparations, Brit. Patent No. 558,707 (1944).

NEUBAUER, A.: Odors of Berry Juice and Wines, *Obst.- Gemüse-Verwertungsind*, **28**, 373 (1941).

Odors in Cheese, *Trans. Highland and Agr. Soc., Scotland*, **41**, 178.

OMELIANSKI, V. L. Microörganisms Producing Odors, *J. Bact.*, **8**, 393 (1923).

ONGARO, D.: Coffee-like Odors, *Ann. chim. applicata*, **30**, 455 (1940).

OVCHINNIKOV, A. I.: Investigations of Substances Which Cause Aroma in Butter, *Trudy NIMI, Izuchemie Masloobraz. Aromat. Slivochnogo Masla*, **30**, 6 (1939).

PETERSEN, N.: Odors of Butter in Relation to Acetoin-bia-cetyl-butylene Glycol Equil., *Fette Seifen*, **50**, 447 (1943).

PONT, E. G.: Keeping Quality of Tinned Butter, *Australia Counc. Sci. Ind. Research J.*, **18**, 53 (1945).

POST: Odor in Milk, *Pharm. Weekblad.*, **67**, 1309 (1930).

POWER, F. B., and V. K. CHESNUT: Odorous Constituents of Apples: Evidence of Presence of Geraniol, *Am. Chem. Soc. J.*, **44**, 2938 (1922).

RAGA, J. B.: Odors of Coffee, *Afinidad*, **19**, 375 (1942).

RAO, C. N. B. and V. SUBRAMANYAN: Insect-infested Food Grains and Flour Reclaimed, *Science and Culture*, **11**, 136 (1945).

REEVE, R. M.: Odors "Off" of Dehydrated Carrot, *Food Research*, **8**, 137 (1943).

ROWE, K.: Chlorine Tastes and Odors from Pipe Coating, *J. Am. Water Works Assoc.*, **9**, 455 (1922).

SCHNEITER, R.: Effect of Defrosting and Prolonged Storage on Odors of Frozen Eggs, *J. Assoc. Official Agr. Chem.*, **26**, 172 (1943).

SHILLINGLAW, C. A., and M. LEVINE: Vitamin B_1 in Development of Musty and Rubbery Odors in Orange Beverages, *Food Research*, **8**, 453 (1943).

SHUMAN, A. C., and L. W. ELDER, JR.: Odors of Coffee, *Ind. Eng. Chem.*, **35**, 778 (1943).

SMALSHAF, A.: Observations on Tastes and Odors, *J. Southeastern Sect., Am. Water Works Assoc.*, **1**, 38 (1931).

Smell of Sound Meat, *Brit. Med. J.*, **11**, 1018 (1888).

SMOCK, R. M.: O_3 in Control of Box or Musty Odors in Apple Storage Rooms, *N. Y. State Hort. Soc. Proc.*, **86**, 175 (1941).

STADNIK: Odors of Hops, *Brauerei u. Malterie*, **17**, 251 (1927).

STAUBER, M.: Absorption Apparatus for Non-condensable Odorous Substances Liberated in Vacuum Distillation of Fruit Juices, German Patent No. 713,437 (1941).

STAUDINGER, H., and T. REICHSTEIN: Artificial Coffee Odors, U. S. Patent No. 1,696,419 (1929).

STEVENSON, R.: Taste and Odor in Sacramento's Water Supply, *J. Am. Water Works Assoc.*, **19**, 627 (1928).

STREETER, H. W.: Chlorpheno Tastes and Odors in Water Supplies of Ohio River Cities, *Am. J. Pub. Health*, **19**, 929 (1929).

A Study of the Frequency of Tastes and Odors in the Philadelphia Water Supply, *Am. City*, **48**, 53 (1933).

TAKEI, S.: Odorous Substances of Green Tea, *Bull. Inst. Phys. Chem. Research (Tokyo)*, **16**, 773 (1937).

———: Odorous Substances of Tea, *Bull. Inst. Phys. Chem. Research (Tokyo)*, **17**, 871 (1938).

———, and T. IMAKI: Odorous Substances in Raw Sugar, *Bull. Inst. Phys. Chem. Research (Tokyo)*, **15**, 124 (1936).

———, and ———: Odorous Substances of Raw Sugar, *Bull. Inst. Phys. Chem. Research* (*Tokyo*), **15**, 1055 (1936).

Tastes and Odors, *J. Am. Water Works Assoc.*, **9**, 899 (1922).

THALHAMMER, H.: Odors in Spirits, German Patent No. 735,901 (1943).

TIKKA, J.: Formation of Odors in Rye Bread, *Suomen Kemist*, **12A**, 48 (1939).

TOLBERT, N. E., and M. A. AMERINE: Improvement of Odors of Brandy, *Ind. Eng. Chem.*, **35**, 1078 (1943).

TOTH, J.: Odors of Butter and Bread, *Mezögazdasági Kutatások*, **14**, 47 (1941).

TROUT, G. M., and R. E. HORWOOD: Influence of Balbo-rye on Odor of Milk, *Quart. Bull. Mich. Agr. Exp. Sta.*, **27**, 39 (1944).

———, and D. Y. McMILLAN: Experiments to Ascertain Susceptibility of Milk to Surrounding Odors, and to Determine Intensity of Absorbed Odors after Various Exposures, *Tech. Bull. Mich. Agr. Exp. Sta.*, **181**, 1 (1943).

TURRE, G. J.: Algae as a Source of Taste and Odor, *Taste Odor Control J.*, **4**, 1 (1938).

UENO, K.: Determination of Degree of Odor of Scented Tea, *J. Agr. Chem. Soc. Japan*, **15**, 1013 (1939).

VAN BEIJNUM, J.: Odors of Cream and Milk Stored under O, *Chem. Zentr.*, **1**, 3338 (1940).

———, and J. W. PETTE: Odors of Butter Starters, *Verslag. Landbouwk. Onderzoek.* **47**, 101 (1941).

VIRTANEN, A.: Increasing Odors in Butter, *Suomen Kemist*, **14B**, 4 (1941).

VIRTANEN, I.: Formation of Odors of Butter, *Angew. Chem.*, **54**, 491 (1941).

———: Odors of Cream-formation during Souring, *Biochem. Z.*, **307**, 215 (1941).

VOLLHAZE, E., and RAUCHNIG: Changes in the Odors of Butter, *Z. Untersuch. Lebensm.*, **81**, 112 (1941).

VON KOBERT, R.: Wie riecht der Psalliota? *Chem. Ztg.*, **41**, 61 (1917).

WALLS, L. P.: Odorous Substances of Apples, *J. Pomol. Hort. Sci.*, **20**, 59 (1942).

WAYGOOD, W. A.: The Natural Flavours of Foodstuffs, *Chem. & Ind.*, **62**, 59 (1943).

WOLOCHOW, H. R., H. R. THORNTON, and E. G. HOOD: Odor Formation in Milk and Butter by Pseudomonas Putrefaciens, *Sci. Agr.*, **22**, 277 (1942).

WORTMANN, J.: Über den Einfluss der Temperatur auf Geruch und Geschmack der Weine, *Landw. Jahrb.*, 741 (1906).

ZEVERYN, C. C.: Fish Smelling and Tasting of Iodoform, *Fishing Gaz.*, **87**, 223 (1923).

I. INDUSTRIAL ODORS, AND GENERAL

ABBOTT, C. E.: Autumnal Odors, *Lippincott's Mag.*, **66**, 637 (1900).

ABBOTT, S. W.: What Is a Nuisance?, *Boston Med. Surg. J.*, **136**, 309 (1897).

ALLISON, V. C., and S. H. KATZ: Odours for Industrial Uses, Pleasant and Unpleasant, *Engineering*, **107**, 754 (1919).

———, and ———: An Investigation of Stenches and Odors for Industrial Purposes, *J. Ind. Eng. Chem.*, **11**, 336 (1919).

AVIS, H. W.: Reviews on Odorous Substances, *Riechstoff Ind. u. Kosmetik*, **11**, 195 (1936).

BAILEY, T. L.: Odors from Rayon Works, *Chem. Age*, **20**, Dyestuffs Monthly Supp., 47 (1929).

BALLARD: Third Report on Inquiry as to Odor Nuisances Arising from Various Manufacturing and Other Branches of Industry, *Rept. Med. Off. Local Gov. Bd.* 1878, **8** (London, 1879).

BARK, E.: Geruchsfrage bei Druckerzeugung, *Kunststoffe*, 99 (1931).

BAU, R.: Geruchsfrage bei Druckarbeiten, *Mitt Verein Gothisch. Ges. Altertumsforsch*, 150 (1834).

*BELL, J. C.: Report of Manchester and Salford Noxious Vapours Abatement Association on Air Polution (1), Manchester, 1887.

BODE, H. E.: Improvement of Odors of Mercaptan Containing Hydrocarbons, U. S. Patent No. 2,160,116 (1939).

BOGDANO, N. F.: Odors of Paraffin Wax, *Grozenskii Neftyanik,* **6,** 79 (1936.)

*BONNEFOY, P.: "Les mauvaises Odeurs des villes," Paris, 1934.

BOOSER, J. C.: Odors of Insecticides (Household), *Soap,* **16,** *Sanitary Products Sect,* 106 (1940).

BORDAS, F.: Pollution of Air in Cities, *Ann. hyg.,* **10,** 193 (1932).

BORDIER, and NOGIER: Odor from Mercury Vapor Lamp, *Compt. rend. acad. sci.,* **147,** 354 (1908).

BOTTGER, G.: Odor Nuisance due to Sewage, *Gesundh.-Ing.,* **60,** 104, 303 (1937).

BOUDONARD, M. O.: Recherches sur les odeurs de Paris, *Rev. sci.,* **1,** 614 (1912).

BOWDITCH, M., *et al.: Code for Safe Concentration of Certain Common Toxic Substances in Industry, *J. Ind. Hyg. and Toxicol.,* **22,** 251 (1940).

BURKE, J. R.: Your Home and Your Nose, *Am. Home,* **11,** 257 (1919).

CALCOTT, W. S.: Odorization of Refrigerants, U. S. Patent No. 2,283,666 (1942).

CALKINS, E. E.: Smell of Perfume Copy, *Adv. & Selling,* **37,** 34 (1944).

CAPLAN, S.: Cardanyl Benzoate as Russia Leather Odor, U. S. Patent No. 2,284,369 (1942).

CARSON, W. F., JR.: Odors of Thiocyanate Insecticides Improved, U. S. Patent No. 2,339,050 (1944).

CASH, F. E., and E. W. JOHNSON: Odors: Stench Warning Tests, Lake Superior District Mines, *U. S. Bur. Mines, Rept. of Invest.,* 3850, 1945.

*CHOMEL, A.: "An odoramenta salubria?" Paris, 1753.

COLBY, A. L.: Report on Odors from Glucose Factories at Buffalo, *Rept. State Bd. Health N. Y.,* Albany, **4,** 425 (1884).

CONNOR's Carbon Canisters, *Fortune,* **27,** 50 (1943).

COOLHAAS, C.: Effect of Fertilization on Odor of Tobacco, *Proefsta. Vorstenland. Tabak Mededeel,* **66,** 1 (1930).

COX, A. J.: Odorous Substances for Poisons, *Soap Sanit. Chemicals,* **17,** 123 (1941).

DALLA VALLE, J. M., and H. C. DUDLEY: Evaluation of Odor Nuisances in Manufacturing of Kraft Paper, *U. S. Pub. Health Rept.,* **54,** 35 (1939).

DAY, D. E.: Odors in Petroleum Refineries, *Oil Gas J.,* **27,** 114 (1928).

DAYHUFF, W. C.: Odorization of Liquefied Gas, U. S. Patent No. 2,322,617 (1944).

DUDLEY, H. C., and J. M. DALLA VALLE: Odors in Paper (Kraft) Manufacture, *Paper Trade J.,* **108,** 30 (1939).

DUTTON, J. A.: Nuisances, *N. Am. J. Homeop.,* **53,** 62 (1905).

DYSON, G. M.: Odors of Mustard Oils, *Perfumery Essent. Oil Record,* **22,** 278 (1931).

ELLIOTT, R. B.: Odors of Tobacco, U. S. Patent No. 2,264,745 (1942).

Entstehung von Gerüchen in isolierten Kühl und Proviantraumen, *Wärme-u. Kältetech.,* **28,** 189 (1926).

ERDMANN, E.: Über das Verhalten der Geruchsstoffe gegen flüssige Luft, *J. prakt. Chem.,* **61,** 225.

FENNER, G.: Gesundheitschädlichkeit übler Gerüche mit Berücksichtigung klinischen Fragen, *Biol. Heilk.,* 797 (1929).

FICHTER, F.: Avoidance of Annoyance Due to Odors in Gas Collecting, *Helv. chim. acta,* **1,** 430 (1918).

FIEDLER, H.: Improvement of Odors of Shale Oil, German Patent No. 739,270 (1943).

FILDERMAN, J.: Effects of Escaping Water Gas in City, *Bull. mém. soc. méd. Paris,* **16,** 451 (1928).

FINGER, G. C., and F. H. REED: Odors of Fluorides, *Trans. Ill. State Acad. Sci.*, **29**, 89 (1936).

FOUQUET, G.: Odorous Substances as Disinfectants, *Riechstoff Ind. u. Kosmetik*, **11**, 44 (1936).

GAGE, S. D.: Odors and Public Health, *Pub. Health Eng. Abstr.*, **4** (1924).

———: Aerial Nuisances from Refining and Burning of Petroleum Oils, *Am. J. Pub. Health*, **23**, 97 (1933).

———: Determination of Origin, Prevalence and Effect of Obnoxious Odors and Evaluation of an Odor Nuisance, *Proc. Am. Soc. Civil Eng.*, **51**, 820 (1925).

GARDNER, H. A.: Comparison of Odors of Paints (Drying), *Natl. Paint, Varnish, Lacquer Assoc.*, **496**, 388 (1935).

GEORGE, H.: The Poisonous Nuisance Vapours from the Manufactory, *Popular Science Monthly*, **21**, 663 (1882).

GERARDIN, A.: Les Odeurs de Paris, *Rev. hyg.*, **23**, 131 (1901).

GERHARDT, O.: Review on Manufacture of Odorous Substances, *Seifensieder-Zeitung*, **63**, 705 (1936).

*Great Britain: "Noxious vapours commission report of the Royal Commission on noxious vapours," London, 1878.

Great Britain: Act to Consolidate Previous Alkali Acts and Make Further Provisions for Regulating Alkali and Other Works in Which Noxious or Offensive Gases are Evolved, *Vict.*, **44**, **45**, c 37 (1881).

HAAS, P.: Smell Emitted by Seaweeds, *Nature*, **135**, 545 (1935).

HÄGGLUND, E.: Odors in Sulfate Pulp Manufacture, *Pulp & Paper Mag. Can.*, **24**, 1381 (1926).

HALASZ, H. A., and ROVIRA: Odors of Glycol and Glycolaldehyde Derivatives, *Bull. soc. chim.*, **8**, 185 (1941).

HALDANE, J. B. S.: Odors of Carbon Monoxide, *Chem. Products*, **4**, 83 (1941).

HANSEN, F.: Geruch der Druckfarben, *Typograph. Jahrb.* (1927).

HARRINGTON, D., and J. H. EAST, JR.: Stench for Emergency Warnings in Metal Mines, *U. S. Bur. Mines Info. Circ.*, 7246 (1943).

HERMAN, A.: Testing the Odor Contamination Tendencies of Phenol Plastics, *ASTM Bull.* **111**, 33 (1941).

HESSE, A.: Technische Gewinnung und Synthese der natürlichen Riechstoffe, *Ber. deut. pharm. Ges.*, **22**, 121 (1912).

HEYL, G. E.: Odors of Flowers Seed Treatment, U. S. Patent No. 2,168,523 (1939).

HIBBERT, E.: Dyeing Scents, *J. Soc. Dyers Colourists*, **42**, 249 (1926).

History of Efforts of Massachusetts Board of Health about Reforms in Slaughtering—Odors, Drainage, *Mass. Bd. of Health, Rept., Boston*, **3**, 224 (1872).

HOLLICK, A.: Effluvium Noxious Vapours, *Rept. State Bd. Health N. Y.*, **9**, 549 (1889).

HOLTZ, L.: Odorant as Warning in Natural Gas, *Gas Age Record*, **66**, 341 (1930).

HORECZY, J. T.: Improvement by $AlCl_3$ of Hydrocarbon Oils, U. S. Patent No. 2,377,081 (1945).

*HORSFORD, E. N.: "Report on Investigation of Sources of Offensive Odors before State Board of Health," Cambridge, 1873.

ILLINGWORTH, P.: Timbers with Peculiar Odors, *Ind. Educ. Mag.*, **26**, 376 (1925).

JONES, C. B.: Pre-treatment of Lime, *J. & Proc. Inst. Sewage Purif.*, 165 (1943).

JURGES, W., and O. REICHARD: Musty Odors in Cooling Plants, *Gesundh.-Ing.*, **51**, 304 (1928).

KATZ, S. H., V. C. ALLISON, and W. L. EGY: Using Stenches as Mine Warnings, *Sci. American Monthly*, **2**, 241 (1920).

————, ————, ————: Odor as Mine Warning, *U. S. Bur. Mines Tech. Paper*, 244 (1920).

————, and E. J. TALBERT: Odors of Warning Agents for Inflammable and Poisonous Gases, *U. S. Bur. Mines Tech. Paper*, 480 (1930).

KIERMEIER, F.: Determination of Permeability of Packing Materials to Odorous Substances, *Chem. Tech.*, **16**, 204 (1943).

KLASON, P.: Mercaptan in Paper Mills, *Paper Trade J.*, **79**, 30 (1924).

KORSWAGEN, J. H.: Odors in Sewage, *Pharm. Weekblad.*, **64**, 229 (1927).

LAIRD, D. A.: Aromatics to Enhance the Fabrics, *Textile World*, **76**, 1837 (1929).

————: Chemist Adds Invisible Appeal in Finishing Fabrics, *Am. Dyestuff Reptr.*, **18**, 375 (1929).

————: How the Consumer Estimates Quality by Subconscious Sensory Impressions: with Special Reference to the Role of Smell, *J. Applied Psychol.*, **16**, 241 (1932).

LANDT, G. E.: Odorless Resin Products, *Plastic Products*, **10**, 219 (1934).

LAWRENCE, J.: Dyeing Scents or Relationship between Dyeing and the Sense of Smell, *Textile Colorist*, **48**, 816 (1926).

LEWINSON, A.: Review on Manufacture of Odorous Substances, *Riechstoff Ind.*, **10**, 133 (1935).

LOWE, C. B.: Odor as an Aid to the Recognition of Drugs, *Am. J. Pharmacy*, **71**, 416 (1899).

LOWE, H.: Heil und unheile Gerüche, *Jeschuran Monatsschr. Leben Judentum*, 241 (1930).

MACLAURIN, R. D.: Odors from Rendering Offal, *Am. J. Pub. Health*, **17**, 1026 (1929).

MARTINDALE, W. H.: Odour of Oleum Sinapis, *Brit. Med. J.*, **1**, 956 (1915).

MARUSSIG, A.: Geruch und Geräuschbelästigg im Wohnhausbau., *Ber. über Klubs Naturkunde, Brünn* (1912).

MEYER, J.: Odors of Hydrocyanic Acid, *Gasmaske*, **7**, 112 (1935).

MITIKA, J. J., and H. LEVIN: Odors of Gasoline Engine Exhaust Gases, *S. A. E. Journal*, **51**, 12T (1943).

MORRISON, J. A. S.: Odors and Packaging, *Patra Packaging Bull.*, **1**, 28 (1944).

MÜLLER, E.: Klärschlaum as Düngmittel, *Gesundh.-Ing.*, **67**, 99 (1944).

MUNTSCH: Odors of Poison Gas, *Gasschutz u. Luftschutz*, **2**, 2735 (1932).

NÄCKE, P.: Geruch als Warnungssignal, *Arch. Krim.-Anthrop. Kriminalist*, **16**, 473 (1904).

NELSON, K. W., *et al.*: Sensory Response to Certain Industrial Solvent Vapors, *J. Ind. Hyg. Toxicol.*, **25**, 282 (1943).

A New Criminal in the Taste and Odor Field, *Am. City*, **48**, 44 (1933).

NORTHCROFT, G. J. H.: Smells and the Traveler, *Casselli Weekly*, **2**, 53 (1923).

Noxious Vapours, *Lancet*, **2**, 191 (1880) ; **1**, 308, 382 (1881).

Odor of Metals, *Harper's Weekly*, **55**, 21 (1911).

Odor Problem Presents a Challenge to Industrial Chemists, *Sci. American*, **169**, 11 (1943).

Odorgraphia, *Oil, Paint, Drug Reptr.*, **117**, 54 (1930).

Odors Evoke a New Business: Conquest of Smells in Interest of Worker and Customer, *Business Week*, 63 (Nov. 3, 1945).

Odors of Metals, *Sci. American*, **96**, 147 (1907).

Odors of Tobacco—Effect of Fermentation, *Vsesoyuz. Nauch.-Issledovetal. Inst. Tabach. Makhoroch. Prom.*, **142**, 176 (1940).

PETROV, A. A.: Odors of Ethers, *J. Gen. Chem.* (U.S.S.R.), **4**, 1217 (1934).

PFAU, A.: The Aldehydes: Their Odour and Their Uses, *Perfumery Essent. Oil Record*, **13**, 382, 422 (1922).

PICKARD, J., and A. PICKARD: Odor from Quartz, *Arch. Sci. Phys. Nat.*, **25**, 425 (1908).

PIOTROWSKI, W., and J. WINKLER: Odorization of Gases, *Gas J.*, **198**, 208 (1932).

PODOLSKY, E.: Odors as Sales Stimulators, *Management Rev.*, **28**, 320 (1939).

POSTEL-VINAY, P.: Ozone, *Rev. élec.*, **21**, 99 (1927).

RAUB, E.: Odors of Metals, *Mitt. Forsch.-Inst. Probieramts Edelmetalle*, **7**, 51 (1933).

Report on Effluvium Nuisances, *Rept. State Bd. Health N. Y.*, **4**, 229 (1884).

Report of the Physical and Mathematical Class of the Institute upon Question: Are Those Manufactures Which Emit a Disagreeable Smell Prejudicial to Health? *Edinburgh Med. Surg. J.*, **11**, 290 (1806).

RICE, G.: Odors in Woolen Goods, *Textile Colorist*, **52**, 486 (1930).

———: Odors in Dyed Goods, *Textile Colorist*, **59**, 701 (1937).

ROBERTS, W. C.: On Influence of Non-specific Emanations on Public Health, *N. Y. J. Med.*, **13**, 441 (1871).

SABETAY, S.: Progress in the Field of Chemical Aromatics for 1934, *Riechstoff Ind. u. Kosmetik*, **11**, 94 (1936).

———: Review on Manufacture of Odorous Substances, *Riechstoff Ind. u. Kosmetik*, **10**, 1, 19, 34 (1935).

Sales Appeal of Odor, *Literary Digest*, **102**, 30 (1929).

SAVAGE, E. B.: Causes of Offensive Odors from Sewers, *Eng. Contr.*, **52**, 511 (1919).

Scented Paper for Business Use, *Management Methods*, **62**, 213 (1933).

SCHMALFUSS, H.: Biacetyl in Odors of Tobacco Smoke, *Chem. Zentr.*, **11**, 4122 (1939).

SCHWARZ, F.: Odors of Minerals, *Central Min. Geol.*, 660 (1913).

SCHWARZ, L., F. SIEKE, and W. DECKERT: Causes of Presence of Poisonous Gases and Bad Odors in Dwelling Houses, *Arch. Hyg.*, **115**, 351 (1936).

Sell by Smell: New Marketing Slogan, *Forbes*, **34**, 14 (1934).

SHERMAN, E. B.: Redolent World, *New Engl. Mag. N. S.*, **43**, 319 (1910).

SHORUIGIN, P., and V. ISAGULYANTZ: Odors of Reduction Products of Derivatives of Cinnamaldehyde, *J. Russ. Phys.-Chem. Soc.*, **62**, 2033 (1930).

Smelling the Weather, *Literary Digest*, **104**, 29 (1930).

Smells of London, *Brit. Med. J.*, **11**, 608 (1889).

SMITH, R. S., and W. W. WALKER: Surveys of Liquid Wastes from Munitions Manufacture, *U. S. Pub. Health Rept.*, **58**, 1365 (1943).

SPIEGELBERG, O.: Luftsleitung und Abwasserleitung und über Geruchverschlüsse, *Gesundh.-Ing.*, **38**, 398 (1915).

STARNER, H. P.: Odorous Substances for Fires, U. S. Patent No. 2,361,711 (1944).

STILLER, W.: Container for Odorous Substances, German Patent No. 735,947 (1943).

STINNES, M.: Gewerkschaft. Improvement of Odors in Phenols, German Patent No. 514,341 (1927); German Patent No. 515,467 (1927).

STODDARD, R. B.: Perfuming Fly Sprays, *Oil, Paint, Drug Reptr.*, **117**, 66 (1930).

STRACHE, H., and REITMAYER: Imparting Odors to Gas, German Patent No. 172,342 (1904).

STREHLE: Geruch, besonders der Pflanzen, *Gartenwelt*, 313 (1917).

STUDINGER, J., and R. MÜLLER: Odors of Poison Gases, *Chemistry & Industry*, **56**, 225 (1937).

SVEN ELVESTAD, Z. B.: Der Geruch des Weltkrieges, *Frankfurt Ztg.*, **59**, 341 (1914).

Sweet-smelling Print, *Literary Digest*, **109**, 24 (1931).

SZAMATOLSKI, M.: Development of Aromatic Chemical Industry from 1876–1926, *Ind. Eng. Chem.*, **18**, 933 (1926).

TÄNZLER, K. H.: Waste Waters from Fish Meal Factory, *Gesundh.-Ing.*, **65**, 157 (1942).

The Testing of Ambergris, *Perfumery Essent. Oil Record*, **13**, 300 (1922).

THUMMERNICHT: Vom Leersaugen der Geruchverschlüsse, *Haustech. Runds.*, 559 (1935).

Tobacco Smells Increase for Hours after Smoking, *Science News Letter*, **32**, 25 (1937).

TOBLER: Odor of Retting Flax, *Faserforsch.*, **2**, 9.

VACHER, F.: Noxious Vapours, *Sanit. Record*, London, **6**, 363 (1877).

VON FREY, M.: Über den laugigen und metallischen Geruch, *Verhandl. Ges. deut. Natur-forsch. Ärzte,* **75,** 409 (1903).

————: Der laugige Geruch, *Arch. ges. Physiol.,* **136,** 275 (1910).

————: Laugig. und Metall., *Verhandl. Ges. deut. Naturforsch. Ärzte,* **2** (2) 409.

*VAN ZELST, F. T.: "De effluviorum efficacia," Batavia, 1730.

War on Odors: Substitute Products Pose New Problems, *Business Week,* 76 (Mar. 4, 1944).

WERNER, J., and M. T. BOGERT: Odors of Hydroterpenoids from Thujaketone, *J. Org. Chem.,* **3,** 578 (1939).

Werschen-Weissenfelser Braunkohlen-Akt. Ges., German Patent No. 695,474 (1940); German Patent No. 696,532 (1940).

WETMILLER, R. S., and L. E. ENDSLEY: Effect of Diesel Fuel on Odors from Exhaust Valves, *S.A.E. Journal,* **50,** 509T (1942).

When Manufacturer and Perfumer Get Together, *Printers' Ink,* **151,** 25 (1930).

WHITMELL, C. T.: The Smell of Earth, *Nature,* **59,** 55 (1898).

WILBURN, W.: Odors in Dry-cleaning Solvent, *Natl. Cleaner Dyer,* **34,** 12 (1943).

WOOLFENDEN, J. J.: Odor of Sanctity: Improper Drainage of Suds, *Heating and Ventilating,* **41,** 64 (1944).

WRIGHT, R.: Collecting Smoke, *House and Garden,* **51,** 92 (1927).

YOXSIMER, O. H.: Improvement of Odors of Cellulose Acetate Butyrate, U. S. Patent No. 2,372,153 (1945).

J. PERFUMES AND FLORAL ODORS

ALEXANDER, F. W.: Lore of Perfumes, Aromatics, Cosmetics and Soaps; Origins, Uses and Physical Action of Odours, *Med. Press,* **130,** 245, 263 (1930).

Application of Essential Oils and Allied Productions, *Perfumery Essent. Oil Record,* **13,** 103, 146, 185 (1922).

ARNDT, W.: Riechstoffe, *Rohstoffe des Tierreichs,* **11,** 417 (1940).

ARNOLD-FOSTER, W.: Scents of Flowers, *Nation* (London), **33,** 806 (1923).

Art and Science of Perfumery, *J. Soc. Chem. Ind.,* **46,** 740 (1927).

*ASKINSON, G. W.: "Die Fabrikation der ätherischen Öle," 2 ed., Vienna and Leipzig (1887).

*————:, and F. WINTER: "Die Parfümeriefabrikation," 7th ed., Vienna and Leipzig, 1920.

ATKINS, F.: Irritation Index of Perfumes, *Pharm. J.,* **134,** 169 (1935).

————: Perfumes and Skin Irritations, *Perfumery Essent. Oil Record,* **26,** 215 (1935).

Attar of Rose Industry in Bulgaria, *Sci. American Supp.,* **84,** 297 (1917).

BARGELLINI, G.: Odors of Flowers, *Atti* **3** *congr. naz. chim. pura appl.,* 134 (1930).

BEISER, E. T.: Contributions of the Chemist to Perfumery Industry, *Ind. Eng. Chem.,* **7,** 936 (1915).

BIENFANG, R.: Odoriana, *Hobbies,* **49,** 5 (1944).

*BLONDEL, R.: "Les Produits odorantes des Rosiers," Paris, 1889.

BOGERT, M. T.: The Flower and the Organic Chemist; Perfumes, Natural and Synthetic, *J. Ind. Eng. Chem.,* **14,** 359 (1922).

————: Research in Perfume Chemistry, *Oil, Paint, Drug Reptr.,* **107,** 22 (1925).

————: Twenty-five Years' Progress in Aromatic Chemicals, *Am. Perfumer,* **26,** 489 (1931).

————: Recent Progress in the Field of Synthetic Perfumes, *J. Chem. Education,* **8,** 1311 (1931).

————: Perfumes and Progress in Science, *Sci. Monthly,* **36,** 270 (1933).

*BORNEMANN, G.: "Die flüchtigen Öle des Pflanzenreiches," Weimar, 1891.

BOURNOT, K.: Sources of Violet Odors, *Am. Perfumer,* **37,** 38 (1938).

*BRENDEL, F.: "Über die Pflanzengerüche," Erlangen, 1847.

CANDLER, E.: The Smell of Flowers, *Cornhill Mag.,* **47,** 74 (1919).

————: Smell of Flowers, *Living Age*, **302**, 290 (1919).

CARLISLE, N. U.: Fragrance Made to Order, *Am. Mag.*, **132**, 94 (1941).

CARPENTER: L'Arome des chimistes français, *Ann. chim.*, **26**, 232.

CHALEYER, P.: Perfumes in Soaps, *Soap Sanit. Chemicals, Blue Book*, **129**, (1940) ; **131**, (1941).

*CHARABOT, E.: "Les Parfums artificiels," Paris, 1900.

*————: "Les Principes odorants des vegetaux," Paris, 1912.

————, and HERBERT: Influence de la nature du milieu extérieur sur la formation et l'évolution des composés odorants chez la plante, *Compt. rend. acad. sci. Paris*, **136**, 1678 (1903).

CHOKIER, L.: Fards et parfums, *J. med. Bruxelles*, **10**, 254 (1905).

CICCONETTI, E.: Pharmaceutical Aromatization, *Farm. ital.*, **10**, 573 (1942).

*COHN, G.: "Die Riechstoffe," Brunswick, 1904.

*———— and, F. RICHTER: "Die Riechstoffe," 2d ed., Brunswick, 1924.

Collecting the Odors of Flowers, *Bradstreet's*, **57**, 368 (1929).

Coumarin; the Odour of New-mown Hay, *Perfumery Essent. Oil Record*, 394 (1916).

CRAIG, W. N.: Garden of Sweet Odors, *Suburban Life*, **6**, 321 (1908).

CUSHING, C. P.: Rambler on the Fragrance of Travel, *Travel*, **28**, 43 (1917).

*DEBRAY, L.: "Les Parfums," 5th ed., Paris, 1875.

DEVAUX, H.: Measurement of Intensity of Perfumes, *Mfg. Perfumer*, **3**, 331 (1938).

Dollars in Scents, *Literary Digest*, **114**, 39 (1932).

DOPF, K.: Economic Study of Perfumes, *Pharm. Zentr.*, **70**, 182 (1929).

ELA, A.: Anaphrodisiacs in History, Folk-lore and Religion, *Urol. and Cutaneous Rev.*, **24**, 141 (1920).

ELLIS, J. W.: Romance of Perfume, *Chambers J.*, **21**, 635 (1931).

ELLMER, A.: Characterization of Perfumes, *Riechstoff Ind.*, **5**, 156 (1930).

ETTE, C. G.: Odorizer, U. S. Patent No. 636,031 (1899).

F. T. C. on Scent, *Business Week*, 22 (Aug. 16, 1941).

Floral Gas Attack: Sacred African Lily, *Literary Digest*, **109**, 18 (1931).

————: Floral Odors, *Perfumery Essent. Oil Record*, **12**, 139 (1921) ; **13**, 106, 151 (1922).

FLORENTIN, M.: Exotic Woods in Odors, *Deut. Parfüm.-Ztg.*, **25**, 405 (1939).

Flowers Heavenly to Some, Objectionable to Others, *Sci. American*, **153**, 153 (1935).

FOULON, A.: Dangers of Addition of Perfumes to Soap, *Fette u. Seifen*, **48**, 148 (1941).

————: Dangers of Addition of Perfume to Soap, *Wien. pharm. Wochschr.*, **74**, 97 (1941).

FOURCROY: Mémoir sur l'espirit recteur de Boerrhaave, l'arome des chimistes français ou le principe de l'odeur des vegetaux, *Ann. chim.* (1798).

GERHARDT, O.: Odors of Jasminaldehyde, *Chem. Zentr.*, **1**, 1375 (1931).

*GILDEMEISTER, E., and F. R. HOFFMANN: "The Volatile Oils," 2d ed., trans. Kremers, London, 3 vols., 1913–1922.

GILLET, H.: Les Parfums comme antiseptiques, *Méd. hyg.*, **4**, 221 (1906).

GLEASON, S.: Dollars from Smells, *Popular Science*, **134**, 112 (1939).

GLEICHEN-KUSSWURM, A. V.: Wohlgeruch und Mode, *Sammler. Beil. Münch.-Augsburger Abendzeitung*, **14**, 3 (1931).

GRAFE, V.: Natürliche und künstliche Wohlgerüche, *Oesterreich. Rundschau*, **24B**, 441 (1910).

GRANDEL, F.: Importance and Use of Vitamin F in Odors, also Healing Wounds, *Deut. Parfum-Zeitung*, **27**, 166 (1941).

HAMBIDGE, G.: Scents That Make Dollars, *World's Work*, **60**, 32 (1931).

HENK, J. J.: Perfumes in Soaps, *Fette u. Seifen*, **47**, 537 (1940),

HOLDER, W. C. J.: Odors of Orchids, *Riechstoff Ind.*, **6**, 71 (1931).

How the Gladiolus Gets Its Scent, *House Beautiful*, **83**, 72 (1941).

HUNGER, H.: Pine Oil in Making Perfumes, *Seifensieder-Zeitung*, **67**, 377 (1940).

Iris Perfume Industry in France, *Sci. American Supp.*, **84**, 120 (1917).

JACOBS, F.: Perfume in Rubber Industry, *Chim. ind.*, special no. 957 (1934).

JANISTYN, H.: Agents for Deodorization for Cosmetics, *Soap, Perfumery, Cosmetics*, **11**, 894 (1939).

JANNAWAY, S. P.: Disinfectants, Fluids and Sprays Containing Perfumes, *Perfumery Essent. Oil Record*, **30**, 87 (1939).

————: Uses, of Odorous Substances, *Perfumery Essent. Oil Record*, **32**, 46 (1941).

————: Selection of Perfumes, *Perfumery Essent. Oil Record*, **33**, 49 (1942).

————: Review on Perfumes, *Perfumery Essent. Oil Record*, **36**, 56 (1945).

JONES, T. W.: Chemistry and the Sense of Smell, *Discovery*, **7**, 347 (1926).

*KLIMONT, J.: "Die synthetischen und isolierten Aromata," Leipzig, 1899.

KOENNE, A. E.: Perfumes in Depilatories, *Mfg. Perfumer*, **2**, 48 (1937).

LANCHESTER, R.: Smells and Perfumes, *Science from Easy Chair*, **2**, 184.

LANGLAIS, P.: Natural Perfumes, *Am. Perfumer*, **47**, 39 (1945).

LARBALETRIER, A.: L'Odeur de foins, la flouve et la coumarine, *La Nature*, **29** (pt. 2), 154 (1900).

*LE GALLIENNE, R.: "Romance of Perfume," R. Hudnut, New York, 1928.

LOHMEYER, E.: Vom göttlichen Wohlgeruch, *Sitzber. Heidelberger Akad., phil. Klasse* (9), (1919).

LÜDY, F., JR.: Tobacco-smoke-consuming Perfumes, *Schweiz. apoth. Ztg.*, **62**, 397 (1924).

MAGEE, H. W.: Dollars and Scents, *Popular Mechanics*, **68**, 522 (1937).

Manufacture of Synthetic Perfumes, *Sci. American Supp.*, **81**, 272 (1916).

*MARTIN, G.: "Perfumes, Essential Oils and Fruit Essences," London, 1921.

MAURER, E.: Music of Perfumes, *Occult Rev.*, 299 (November, 1926).

MERRIN, A. C.: Reflections on the Perfumer's Art, Classification of Perfumery, Odour Terminology, the Genius, and the Trained Artist-scientist, *Perfumery Essent. Oil Record*, **13**, 409 (1922).

MESNARD, E.: Appareil nouveau pour la mesure de l'intensité des parfums, *Compt. rend. acad. sci.*, **116**, 1461 (1893).

————: Étude critique et expérimentale sur la mesure de l'intensité des parfums des plantes, *Rev. gén. botan.*, **6**, 97 (1894).

*————: "La Mesure de l'intensité des parfums et des plantes," Paris, 1914.

MEYER, M.: Perfume, *Sci. American*, **143**, 118 (1930).

MEYER, E. L.: Accent on Scent, *Readers Digest*, **36**, 77 (1940).

*MIERZINSKI, S.: "Die Riechstoffe und ihre Verwendung," Leipzig, 1894.

MILLON: Mémoire sur la nature des parfums, *Monit. sci.*, **1** (pt. 1), 21 (1857).

MÜLLER, A.: Detection of Perfumes, *J. prakt. Chem.*, **151**, 233 (1938).

————: Fluorescence of Perfumes, *Deut. Parfüm.-Ztg.*, **26**, 37 (1940).

————: Animal Odorous Substances in Flowers and Leaves, *Fette Seifen*, **49**, 290 (1942).

————: Natural Odorous Substances, *Seifensieder-Zeitung*, **69**, 336, 353 (1942).

NARES, Y. R.: Perfumes in Europe from 1940–1945, *Soap, Perfumery, Cosmetics*, **18**, 372 (1945).

Odors of Plants, *Putnam's Mag.*, **9**, 38 (1857).

OLDFIELD, J.: Mystery of Musk, *Discovery*, **17**, 214 (1936).

PAPACEIT, E.: Odors of Perfumes and Individual Variations in Acuteness Thereto, *Afinidad*, **19**, 355, 469 (1942).

PASSY, J.: Natural and Artificial Perfumes, *Popular Science Monthly*, **52**, 86 (1897).

————: Sur la Diffusion des parfumes, *Compt. rend. soc. biol.*, **120**, 513.

Peat Smoke, Leather, New Mown Hay Bought by the Pound for Use in Processing Textiles, *Business Week*, 8 (Dec. 14, 1932).

*PIESSE, S.: "The Art of Perfumery," London, 1862.

*————: "Des Odeurs, des parfums et des cosmétiques," 2d ed. Paris, 1877.

POWER, F. B.: Distribution and Character of Some of the Odorous Principles of Plants, *Ind. Eng. Chem.*, **11**, 344 (1919).

PRATT, J.: Notes on the Unconscious Significance of Perfume, *Int. J. Psycho-Anal.*, **23**, 80 (1942).

PYCRAFT, W. P.: Animals and Perfumes, *Illus. London News*, **183**, 1126 (1933).

*REDGROVE, H. S.: "Scent and All About It," London, 1928.

*RIMMEL, E.: "The Book of Perfumes," London, 1868.

*ROIG Y MESA, J. T.: "Plantas aromáticas o venenosas de Cuba," Havana, Cuba, 1945.

RUEMELE, T.: Perfumes in Soaps, *Chem. Zentr.*, II, 1954 (1940).

RUZICKA, L.: Odor of Musk, *Helv. Chim. Acta*, **9**, 230, 716, 1008 (1926).

————: Natural Perfumes, *Chemistry & Industry*, **51**, 145 (1932).

SAGARIN, E.: Perfumer's Zoo, *Crown*, **34**, 14, 27 (1945).

*————: "The Science and Art of Perfumery," New York, 1946.

*SAWER, J. C.: "Odorographia," London, 1892.

SCHMITT, F.: Perfumes for Food, *Rev. prod. chim.*, **30**, 161, 203, 321 (1927).

SCHWARTZ, L.: Perfumes and Skin Irritations, *U. S. Pub. Health Serv. Bull.*, 215 (1934).

SHADWELL, G. C.: Use of Gas in Perfumery Trade, *Am. Gas Eng. J.*, **111**, 137 (1919).

SHEPHEARD-WALWYN, N. W.: Harmonies of Nature, *Nature Mag.*, **7**, 153 (1926).

THOMAS, W. B.: Musk Mystery, a Suggestion, *Spectator*, **145**, 718 (1930).

THOMPSON, C. J. S.: Mystery and Lure of Perfume, *Lippincott's Mag.*, 247 (1927).

THOMSON, J. A.: Frankincense and Myrrh, *New Statesman*, **7**, 299 (1916).

*TRUMPHIUS, J. H.: "De aromaticorum natura, usu et abusu," Jenae, 1695.

VAN DYKE, *et al.*: Aromatics and Penetrants, *Chem. Industries*, **36**, 58 (1935).

VERSCHOFFELT, E.: Odors of Flowers, *Chem. Weekblad*, **5**, 441 (1908).

VOLZ, O.: Wohlgerüche und Drogen, *Welt u. Technik*, **75**, 449 (1913).

WALKER, R. S.: Natural Perfumes, *Commonweal*, **26**, 565 (1937).

WARREN, H. C.: Odor Mixture, *Am. Naturalist*, **31**, 987 (1897).

WIEDEMANN, E.: Neuer arabischer Parfüm, *Arch. Ges. Med.*, **8**, 83 (1914).

WIMMER, C. P.: Article on Basic Facts of Perfumery, *J. Chem. Education*, **22**, 354 (1945).

WINTER, F.: Characterization of Perfumes, *Pharm. Monatsschr.*, **10**, 36, 74 (1929).

K. ODOR CONTROL

a. Body Deodorants

BAUZA, J.: Deodorization of Perspiration, British Patent No. 368,458 (1930).

DIKESON, T. W.: Agents for Deodorization for Cosmetic Use, British Patent No. 487,855 (1938).

FRANÇOIS, M.: Liquid Deodorant, *J. Pharm. Chim.*, **12**, 220 (1915).

GESCHICKTER, C. F., and M. M. COPELAND: Deodorization of Fungating Wounds in Malignant Disease, *Southern Surgeon*, **7**, 244 (1938).

HARRY, R. G.: Agents for Deodorization for Cosmetic Use, *Mfg. Perfumer*, **4**, 8 (1939).

HAZEN, H. H., and F. BISSE: Deodorants and Depilatories, *Am. J. Nursing*, **32**, 841 (1932).

HEING and SCHAUWECKER: Formoformstreupulver als Schweisswidriges, desodorierendes Mittel, *Deut. med. Wochschr.*, **47**, 713 (1921).

HLAVAC, J.: Desodorisation der Fussschweisse, *Ärztl. Cor.-Bl. Böhmen*, **1**, 224 (1873).

JACKSON, T. A., *et al.*: Experimental and Statistical Analysis of the Effectiveness of Deodorant Creams, *J. Applied Psychol.*, **26**, 308 (1942).

KALISH, J.: Agents for Deodorization-Cosmetic Use, *Drug Cosmetic Ind.*, **46**, 410 (1940).

———: Agents for Deodorization, *Drug Cosmetic Ind.*, **52**, 38 (1943).

KANTOROWITZ: Ein Neues Mittel zur Beseitigung des Schweissgeruchs, *Allgem. med. Zentr.-Zeit., Biol.*, **83**, 13 (1914).

LAMBERT, C. N., and D. W. STICKNEY: New Deodorizing Plaster Bandage, *J. Bone Joint Surg.*, **26**, 836 (1944).

LEVIN, L.: Deodorization of Membranes, German Patent No. 176,690 (1905).

LEWINSON, A.: Odorous Substances as Disinfectants, *Riechstoff Ind.*, **11**, 77 (1936).

MAERCKLEIN, O. C.: Report on Deodorants and Anti-Perspirants, *Assoc. Official Agr. Chem. J.*, **25**, 921 (1942).

Perspiration Deodorant, *Hygeia*, **16**, 368 (1938).

RANDALL, J. W. H., and H. VAN GRUNENBERG: Deodorization of Body Secretions, U. S. Patent No. 2,131,235 (1938).

REDENZ, E.: Urea as Agents for Deodorization, *Münch. med. Wochschr.*, **85**, 1115 (1938).

REDGROVE, H. S.: Reviews on Agents for Deodorization, *Perfumery Essent. Oil Record, Ann. Special*, **15**, 29 (1939).

RICHTER, E.: "Liebecin" Deodorant, *Apoth. Ztg.*, **24**, 816 (1909).

RUEMELE, T.: Deodorization of Perspiration, *Pharm. Zentr.*, **81**, 229 (1940).

SCHMITT AND CO.: Agents for Deodorization after Use of Depilatories, *Hamburg. Chem.-Tech. Ges.*, German Patent No. 712,512 (1941).

SEDDON, H. J., and H. W. FLOREY: Odors: Filter Cloth for Controlling Smell from Plasters, *Lancet*, **1**, 755 (1942).

SMITH and DAVIS: Deodorants—Description of Process, British Patent No. 6,676 (1906).

TAYLOR, W. A.: Cosmetic Creams in Deodorization, U. S. Patent No. 2,294,140 (1943).

THOMPSON, M. R.: Agents for Deodorization for Cosmetic Use, U. S. Patent No. 2,256,505 (1942).

VALLANCE, J. M.: Agents for Deodorization for Cosmetic Use, *Mfg. Perfumer*, **4**, 246 (1939).

WAKELEY, C. P. G.: Description of Milton Dynalysor for Control of Odor—Problems of Colostomy, *Practitioner*, **150**, 159 (1943).

WEBER, F. C.: Deodorization of Skin, U. S. Patent No. 1,813,004 (1931).

WEEKES, C.: Deodorization of the Body, *Drug Cosmetic Ind.*, **32**, 213 (1933).

b. Food and Oil

ABDERHALDEN, E., and W. SCHULTZE: Deodorization of Proteins, German Patent No. 717,510 (1942).

———, and ———: Deodorization of Meat from Marine Mammals, German Patent No. 722,431 (1942).

ABRAMOVICH, S. D.: Deodorization of Distillates Obtained in Heat Treatment of Castor and Linseed Oils, *Khim. Referat. Zhur.*, **7**, 100 (1940).

ANDREW, D. N.: Deodorization of Fish Oils, *Priroda*, **26**, 14 (1937).

ANDREWS, T.: Deodorization of Oils, *Oil Colour Trades J.*, **89**, 367 (1936).

ATWOOD, C. N.: Deodorization of Cream, *Natl. Butter Cheese J.*, **30**, 35 (1939).

BAILEY, A. E.: Steam Deodorization of Edible Fats and Oils, *Ind. Eng. Chem.*, **33**, 404 (1941).

*———: "Industrial Oil and Fat Products," New York, 1945.

———, and R. O. FEUGE: Laboratory Deodorizer for Fats and Oils, *Ind. Eng. Chem., Anal. Ed.*, **15**, 280 (1943).

———, and ———: Deodorization of Fats, *Oil & Soap*, **21**, 286 (1944).

BEACH, R. M., and E. A. ROBINSON: Deodorization of Fat Acids Such as Cod Oil, U. S. Patent No. 2,265,020 (1942).

BLASO, J. G.: Deodorization of Fish Liver Oils, U. S. Patent No. 2,311,633 (1943).

BROOKE, W. L.: Deodorization of Cocoanut Oil, *Phillipine J. Sci.*, **30**, 201 (1926).

BRÜCKE, O.: Deodorization of Fats and Oils, German Patent No. 723,436 (1942) ; No. 744,815 (1943).

BURGESS, C. J.: Deodorization of Air in Food Storage Compartments, U. S. Patent No. 1,999,499 (1935).

BUXTON, L. O.: Odor Removal from Materials Containing Fat-solvent Vitamins, U. S. Patent No. 2,258,671 (1942).

———: Odor Removal of Vitamin-containing Oils, U. S. Patent No. 2,345,097 (1944).

———: Removal of Objectionable Odors in Vitamin-rich Fish-liver Oils, U. S. Patent No. 2,347,462 (1944).

———, and L. T. ROSENBERG: Deodorization of Marine Oils, U. S. Patent No. 2,344,124 (1944).

CARBO-NORIT-UNION VERWALTUNGS-G.M.B.H.: Deodorization of Grain, Flour, etc., British Patent No. 476,412 (1937).

CASAMAJOR, S. F.: Deodorization of Fatty Compounds, French Patent No. 384,492 (1907).

CONQUEST, V.: Deodorization of Oils, *Oil & Soap*, **9**, 114 (1932).

CRIBB, H. H.: Deodorization of Honey, Australian Patent No. 108,134 (1939).

CUKER, K.: Deodorization of Feed and Sugar Beets, German Patent No. 728,908 (1942).

DAVIDSOHN, J., and A. DAVIDSOHN: Deodorization of Fish Oils, *Soap, Perfumery, Cosmetics*, **11**, 901 (1939).

DAVIS, E. M.: Deodorization of Cream and Milk, U. S. Patent No. 2,182,335 (1934).

DEAN, D. K.: Use of Dowtherm, etc., in Systems for Deodorization of Oils, U. S. Patent No. 2,223,407 (1941).

———: Deodorization of Oils, U. S. Patent No. 2,280,896 (1942).

———, and E. H. CHAPIN: Deodorization of Oils, *Oil & Soap*, **15**, 200 (1938).

EKHARD, W.: Deodorization of Animal and Vegetable Materials, British Patent No. 452,682 (1936).

FOSTER-WHEELER CORP.: Deodorization of Oils, British Patent No. 505,810 (1939) ; Patent No. 510,852 (1939).

GANNON, T. A.: Deodorization of Foods during Cooking, U. S. Patent No. 1,681,531 (1928).

GROSS, C. R., and R. M. SMOCK: Deodorization: Studies on Odor Elimination in Apple Storage, *Refrig. Eng.*, **50**, 535 (1945).

GRUENWALD, L. A.: Deodorization of Tung Oil, U. S. Patent No. 2,276,233 (1942).

*HARRIS, J. P. (ED.) : "Industrial Chemical Sales Odors Book: Active Carbon in Deodorization of Oils, Fats and Related Products," New York, 1944.

———, and A. B. McKETCHNIE: Deodorization of Oils, *Oil & Fat Industries*, **4**, 371 (1927).

HELLSING: Deodorization of Mineral Oils, French Patent No. 377,197 (1907).

HEMPTINNE: Deodorization of Train Oil Fatty Acids, Belgian Patent No. 363,078 (1906).

HENNESSY, D. J.: Deodorization of Oils (Marine), U. S. Patent No. 2,321,913 (1943).

HOLCOMB, G.: Deodorization of Cottonseed Oil, *Chem. Eng. News*, **20**, 440 (1942).

HORVATH, E.: Deodorization of Foods, French Patent No. 685,806 (1929).

HUZIMOTO, T.: Deodorization of Fats, Oils and Waxes, Japanese Patent No. 129,040 (1939).

JALMA, M. M., and H. COUTINHS: Deodorization of Gases Evolved in Roasting Vegetable Materials, British Patent No. 505,971 (1939).

JONES, C. R., and E. N. GREER: Deodorization of Flours with Active C, British Patent No. 529,110 (1940).

KININVUETO, R.. Deodorization of Fish Oils, Japanese Patent No. 98,857 (1932).

KOTERA, A.: Deodorization of Foods, U. S. Patent No. 2,146,958 (1939).

LEE, A. P.: Deodorization of Edible Oils, *Oil & Soap*, **14**, 263 (1937).

———: Noncorrosive Metals in Deodorization of Oils, *Proc. Inst. Food Tech.*, 219 (1941).

LEFEVRE, J.: Agents for Deodorization of Solza Oil, *Compt. rend. acad. agr., France*, **26**, 1044 (1940).

LEMON, H. W.: Flavor and Odor Reversion in Hydrogenated Linseed Oil, *Can. J. Research*, Sect. F, **22**, 191 (1944).

McCASHIN, W. L.: Deodorization of Cream, U. S. Patent No. 2,307,227 (1943).

MARKLEY, K. S., and D. F. J. LYNCH: Deodorization of Cottonseed Oil, *Cotton Research Congr., Proc.*, **1**, 211 (1940).

MATSUMOTO, G., and H. MATSUO: Deodorization of Fish Oils, *Repts. Imp. Ind. Research Inst., Osaka, Japan*, **15**, 29 (1934).

MATUMOTO, T.: Deodorization of Sardine Oil, *Repts. Chem. Research Prefect. Inst. Adv. of Learn. Ind., Tokyo*, **3**, 16 (1940).

MEYER, H.: Deodorization of Oils, *Chem. App.*, **21**, 2 (1934).

MILES, H. V.: Correction of Defects of Water Used for Food Manufacture, *Proc. Inst. Food Tech.*, 59 (1944).

MIYASHITA, K., and U. YAMASHITA: Deodorization of Fish, British Patent No. 387,493 (1933).

MOSS, W. W.: Deodorization of Oils, *Trans. Am. Soc. Mech. Engrs.*, **59**, 715 (1937).

MURRAY DEODORIZERS, LTD.: Deodorization of Ice-cream Mixes, British Patent No. 538,755 (1941).

NEAL, R. H.: Deodorization of Alkali-refined Oils Such as Soy-bean, Linseed and Sunflower Oils, U. S. Patent No. 2,351,832 (1944).

NELLENSTEYN, G. D.: Extracting Bad Odors from Vegetables, U. S. Patent No. 431,278 (1890).

NEWTON, R. C., and W. F. BOLLENS: Deodorization of Fats and Oils, U. S. Patent No. 2,124,707 (1938).

Onions and Garlic: Odors Removed by Chloramine, *Time*, **26**, 40 (1935).

PARKER, M. E.: Deodorization of Cream and Milk, U. S. Patent No. 2,207,817 (1940).

PETRYAEV, I.: Deodorization of Fats and Oils, *Masloboĭno-Zhirovaya Prom.*, **16**, 69 (1940).

PHELPS, G. W., and H. C. BLACK: Deodorization: Fatty Material Stabilization, U. S. Patent No. 2,357,543 (1944).

———, and ———: Deodorization of Fats and Oils by Steam, U. S. Patent No. 2,374,234 (1945).

RENNER, H. O.: Inhibiting Development of and Counteracting Undesirable Odors in Fats and Oils, U. S. Patent No. 2,316,621 (1943).

———: Prevention of Odors (Unpleasant) in Fats, Oils and Fat Acids, U. S. Patent No. 2,349,377 (1944).

RIEMENSCHNEIDER, R. W., S. F. HERB, E. M. HAMMAKER, and F. E. LUDDY: Deodorization of Lard; Effect on Stability, *Oil & Soap*, **21**, 307 (1944).

SHORLAND, F. B.: Deodorization of Fats and Oils, *Biochem. J.*, **32**, 792 (1937).

SIMPSON, W. A., and R. R. RUDOLPH: Deodorization of Cold Storage Rooms: Active C, O_3 and Ultraviolet Light, *Western Frozen Foods*, **5**, 9 (1944).

SMITH, W. A.: Deodorization of Hydrocarbon Oils, Canadian Patent No. 421,748 (1944).

STELKENA, W.: Deodorization of Tea and Coffee Preparations, British Patent No. 354,942 (1929).

STEWART, J.: Deodorization of Oils, British Patent No. 476,975 (1937); U. S. Patent No. 2,136,029 (1939); U. S. Patent No. 2,141,941 (1939).

SUDFELDT AND CO.: Deodorization of Fish Oils—Fish Train, French Patent No. 451,127 (1912).

TAMACHI, K., and N. SAKAMOTO: Deodorization of Fish Oils, Japanese Patent No. 101,432 (1933).

TAUSSKY, I.: Deodorization of Shortening, U. S. Patent No. 2,350,082 (1944).

TODD, N. G.: Deodorization of Milk, U. S. Patent No. 1,618,789 (1927).

TOMIYASU, Y.: Odor Removal in Wines, *J. Agr. Chem. Soc., Japan*, **8**, 905 (1932).

TUNOGAE, R., and Y. ENOMOTO: Deodorization of Fats and Oils, Japanese Patent No. 129,647 (1939).

ULLMANN, H. J.: Deodorization of Fats, Oils and Waxes, U. S. Patent No. 2,203,373 (1940).

WALKER, T. B.: Deodorization of Oils or Fats, U. S. Patent No. 1,123,962 (1915).

YAMADA, M.: Deodorization of Saké, *J. Agr. Chem. Soc., Japan*, **15**, 699, 708 (1939).

——, and H. MATIN: Deodorization of Saké, *Bull. Agr. Chem. Soc., Japan*, **14**, 59 (1938).

c. Water

Activated Carbon Removes Taste and Odor from a Water Supply, *Public Works*, **64**, 14 (1933).

ADAMS, C. D.: Chlorination Practice at Four Southern Indiana Towns, *J. Am. Water Works Assoc.*, **36**, 1328 (1944).

ADAMS, R. B.: Odor and Taste Control with Active Carbon for Phenols in Water, *J. Pa. Water Works Operators' Assoc.*, **14**, 59 (1942).

ADLER, R.: Purification and Sterilization of Water by High Chlorination, *Gas-u. Wasserfach*, **72**, 675 (1928).

ALLISON, W. M.: Odor Removal in Water Purification, U. S. Patent No. 2,250,345 (1941).

ALMQUIST, F. O. A.: Taste and Odor Control in Water Purification, *J. New Engl. Water Works Assoc.*, **51**, 41 (1937).

BAILEY, W. T.: Taste and Odor Control at Council Bluffs, Iowa, *J. Am. Water Works Assoc.*, **27**, 458 (1935).

——: Taste and Odor Control in Water, *J. Am. Water Works Assoc.*, **29**, 392 (1937).

BAILLEUL, G.: The Use of Active Carbon for the Purification of Water, *Water and Water Eng.*, **32**, 424 (1930).

BARTOW, E., and R. WARREN: Taste and Odor in Chlorinated Water, *Eng. Contr.*, **54**, 148 (1922).

BAYLIS, J. R.: The Activated Carbons and Their Use in Removing Objectionable Tastes and Odors from Water, *J. Am. Water Works Assoc.*, **21**, 787 (1929).

——: Can Tastes and Odors Be Removed from Highly Polluted Waters? *Water Works Eng.*, **83**, 227, 239 (1930).

——: Development in the Treatment of Highly Polluted Water and in the Elimination of Bad Tastes and Odors, *Proc. 12th Texas Water Works Short School*, 52 (1930).

——: Further Observations on the Use of Activated Carbon in Removing Objectionable Tastes and Odors from Water, *J. Am. Water Works Assoc.*, **22**, 1438 (1930).

——: Further Progress in Taste and Odor Removal, *Proc. Am. Soc. Munic. Eng.*, **37**, 236 (1931).

——: The Use of Charcoal and Activated Carbon in Water Treatment, *Water Works & Sewerage*, **78**, 287, 320, 357 (1931) ; **79**, 14 (1932).

——: Aeration, *Water Works & Sewerage*, **79**, 195, 252 (1932).

——: Taste and Odor Elimination, *J. Am. Water Works Assoc.*, **24**, 635 (1932).

——: Taste and Odor Control in Water Purification, *Bull. Assoc. State Eng. Soc.*, **11**, 23 (1930).

——: Taste and Odor Improvement in Water, *Water Works & Sewerage*, **84**, 310 (1937).

————, *et al.*: Taste and Odor Control in Water Purification, *Am. Pub. Health Assoc. Yearbook* 1932–1933.

————: Taste and Odor Control, *J. Am. Water Works Assoc.*, **26**, 1719 (1934).

BATY, J. B.: Water Treatment Problems. Taste and Odor Elimination by Superchlorination, *Can. Engr.*, **78** (1940).

BEHRMAN, A. S., and S. B. CRANE: Chemical and Mechanical Utilization Activated Carbon in Water Purification, *J. Am. Water Works Assoc.*, **22**, 1399 (1930).

BENGOLEA, D. J., and R. FERRAMOLA: Experiments on Superchlorination of Buenos Aires City Water, *Bol. obras sánit. Nacion. Buenos Aires*, **6**, 20 (1942).

BERNHAGEN, L. O.: Future Problems of Water Works Operators with Regard to Taste, Odor and Palatability, *Proc. 17th Tex. Water Works Short School*, 135 (1935).

BESOZZI, L., and J. C. VAUGHN: Taste and Odor Control in Water, *J. Am. Water Works Assoc.*, **29**, 1603 (1937).

BILLINGS, L. C.: Taste and Odor Control in Water Purification, *Southwest Water Works J.*, **14**, 11 (1932).

————: Tastes and Odors in Water, *Southwest Water Works J.*, **18**, 21 (1936).

————: Taste and Odor Control at Dallas, *J. Am. Water Works Assoc.*, **32**, 613 (1940).

————: Odor and Taste Control in Water Purification, *Southwest Water Works J.*, **22**, 17 (1941).

BLOCHER, J. M.: Purification of Water by Ultra-violet Radiation, *J. Am. Water Works Assoc.*, **21**, 1361 (1929).

BOGREN, G. G.: Active C. and Aeration in Odor and Taste Control in Water Purification, *J. New Engl. Water Works Assoc.*, **56**, 184 (1942).

BOVARD, P. F.: Tastes and Odors in Water, *Western Constr. News*, **9**, 335 (1934).

BRAIDECH, M. M.: American Water Works Association Tentative Method for Determining Odors in Water Supplies and Evaluating Powdered Activated Carbons, *Ohio Conf. Water Purif., 17th Ann. Rept.*, 101 (1938).

BRUERE, S.: The Chemical Sterilization of Water without Chemical Products, *Rev. hyg. pol. sanit.*, **43**, 1247 (1921).

BRUSH, W. W.: Maintaining a Water Purification Standard, *Fire Water Eng.*, **70**, 444 (1921).

————: Prevention of Tastes and Odors Due to Microscopic Organisms, *Eng. Contr.*, **57**, 560 (1922).

BURGER, J., and S. THOMAS: Tastes and Odors in the Delaware River, *J. Am. Water Works Assoc.*, **26**, 120 (1934).

CAIRD, J. M.: Taste and Odor Control in Water Purification, *J. New Engl. Water Works Assoc.*, **49**, 149 (1935).

COHEN, C.: Eliminating Tastes and Odors by Algae in Water, *American City*, **38**, 129 (1928).

CONSOER, A. W., and J. G. NELLIS: Ozone Reduces Water Odors and Tastes, *Eng. News Record*, **127**, 367 (1941).

COWLES, M. W.: Tastes and Odors in Water from Electric Currents, *American City*, **49**, 59 (1934).

COX, C. R.: Laboratory Control—Tastes and Odors, *Water Works Eng.*, **89**, 132; 193 (1936).

————: Taste and Odor Control in Water Purification, *J. Am. Water Works Assoc.*, **28**, 1855 (1936).

CRAM, M. P., and H. D. EVANS: Purification of Water by Adsorption, *J. Ind. Eng. Chem.*, **6**, 166 (1914).

CRAMER, H. C., and F. M. OFFUTT: Taste and Odor Experiences at Two Plants in the Ohio River Basin, *Taste Odor Control J.*, **7**, 1 (1941).

CRANE, H. B.: Recent Development in Odor and Taste Control in Water Treatment, *Proc. 9th Ann. Water Works School, Univ. Kan.,* **3**, 56 (1931).

*DALLYN, F., and R. PARKINSON: Ultraviolet Ray Sterilization of Water, *Ann. Rept. Ontario Bd. Health,* 1914.

DANIELS, F. E.: Tastes and Odors in Water, *Water Works,* **66**, 197 (1927).

De-chlorination Treatment by Activated Charcoal, *Water and Water Eng.,* **32**, 497 (1930).

DELAPORTE, A. V.: Taste and Odor Control in Water Supplies, *J. Am. Water Works Assoc.,* **25**, 677 (1933).

DODD, C. I.: Taste and Odor Control in Water Purification, *J. Am. Water Works Assoc.,* **29**, 322 (1937).

DODD, R.: Taste and Odor Problems at Chester, Pa., *J. Am. Water Works Assoc.,* **26**, 760 (1934).

DUGGER, E. F.: Taste and Odor Control in Water Purification, *Water Works & Sewerage,* **78**, 738 (1931).

————: Removal of Taste and Odors in Filtered Water at Newport News, *Water Works Eng.,* **85**, 1179 (1932).

ECKERT, A.: Activated Carbon Removes Tastes and Odors from Saginaw Water, *American City,* **46**, 90 (1932).

————: The Use of Activated Carbon for the Removal of Tastes and Odors at Saginaw, Mich., *J. Am. Water Works Assoc.,* **25**, 148 (1933).

————: Taste and Odor Control at Hackensack Water Company, N. J., *J. Am. Water Works Assoc.,* **26**, 1730 (1934).

Elimination of Taste and Odor in Drinking Waters, *Water and Water Eng.,* **32**, 225 (1930).

ELLMS, J. W.: Ozone as a Disinfectant in Water Purification, *J. Am. Water Works Assoc.,* **7**, 60 (1920).

Emergency Treatment for Tastes and Odors, *Public Works,* **63**, 47 (1932).

EMERSON, C., and C. BAKER: Effect of Gas Plant Wastes on Taste and Odor of Water, *Proc. Am. Soc. Civil Eng.,* **47** (1921); **48** (1922).

ENSLOW, L. H.: Taste and Odor Control in Water Purification, *Ohio Conf. Water Purif., 13th Ann. Rept.,* 89 (1937).

FLENTJE, M.: Report of Committee on Control of Tastes and Odors, *J. Am. Water Works Assoc.,* **24**, 1738 (1932).

————, et al.: Taste and Odor Control in Water Purification, *J. Am. Water Works Assoc.,* **25**, 1490 (1933).

FORMAN, L.: Eliminating Tastes and Odors from the New Jersey Water Supplies, *N. J. Pub. Health News,* **17**, 35 (1932).

FREDOUX, M. J. P., P. A. A. CHALONO, and J. B. E. COUDERT: Taste and Odor Control in Water Purification, French Patent No. 745,964 (1933).

FREITAG, R.: Disinfection of Water and Odor Control by Chlorination, *Städtereinigung,* **33**, 135 (1941).

FRENCH, A. E.: Successful Taste and Odor Control in El Dorado, Kan., *Public Works,* **71**, 23 (1940).

FULLER, G. W.: The Purification of Water from Standpoints Other than Hygienic, *Intern. Cong. Hyg.,* **15**, 335 (1912).

FURMAN, R. M.: Taste and Odor Control in Water Purification, *Ohio Conf. Water Purif. 9th Ann. Rept.,* 59, 64 (1929).

————: Remedying Taste and Odor Complaints Resulting from the Water of Toledo, *Water Works Eng.,* **85**, 846 (1932).

GALLAHER, W.: Difficulty of Defining and the Removal of Tastes and Odors in Water, *Water Works Eng.,* **86**, 820 (1933).

GERARDY, M. N.: Odor and Taste in Water Purification, *Water Works Eng.*, **94**, 1397 (1941).

GERKINHOFF, T.: Ozone Solves Color, Odor and Taste Problem in Hobart (Ind.) Plant, *American City*, **50**, 47 (1935).

GOOCH, W. T.: Taste and Odor Control in Water Purification, *Proc. 14th Texas Water Works Short School*, 63 (1932).

GRAHAM, R. C.: Activated Charcoal .05 to 2.2 Grains per Gallon Removed Odors from River Water at Brownsville, Texas, *Southwest Water Works J.*, **14**, 12 (1932).

GRUTER, R.: Rendering Water Tasteless and Odorless after Sterilization with a Hypochlorite by Treatment with H_2O_2, U. S. Patent No. 1,078,918 (1913).

GUICHARD, P.: Purification of Potable Water, *Bull. soc. chim.*, 3s, **27**, 941 (1902).

GUILLERD, A.: The Organoleptic Qualities of Water and Correction of Odor and Taste, *Ann. hyg. publ. ind. sociale*, **7**, 446, 510 (1929).

GULLANS, O.: Taste and Odor Control in Water Purification, *Water Works & Sewerage*, **83**, 347 (1936).

————: The Comparison of Odor Elimination Treatments, *J. Am. Water Works Assoc.*, **29**, 60 (1937).

HALE, F. E.: Chloramine Tried by New York City, *Eng. News Record*, **82**, 556 (1919).

————: Taste and Odor in the New York City's Supplies, *J. Am. Water Works Assoc.*, **10**, 829 (1923).

————: Present Status of Aeration, *J. Am. Water Works Assoc.*, **24**, 1401 (1932).

HANSEN, P.: Taste and Odor Control in Water Purification, *J. Am. Water Works Assoc.*, **23**, 1495 (1931).

HARRIS, J. P.: Tastes and Odors: Their Measurement and Control, *Southwest Water Works J.*, **18**, 12 (1936).

————: How to Combat Tastes and Odors during This Dry Spell, *Taste Odor Control J.*, **2** (12), (1936).

————: How to Make Certain That You Can Control Tastes and Odors in Your Plant, *Taste Odor Control J.*, **4**, 1 (1937).

————: Taste and Odor Control in Flooded Areas, *Taste Odor Control J.*, **3** (5)—special issue.

HARRISON, L. B.: Various Methods for the Removal of Tastes and Odors, *Water Works Eng.*, **82**, 1621 (1929).

HASSLER, W. W.: The Desirability of Threshold Odor Control in Water Plants, *Taste Odor Control J.*, **5**, 1 (1939).

————: The History of Taste and Odor Control, *J. Am. Water Works Assoc.*, **33**, 2124 (1941).

————: Bibliography of Odor and Taste Control in Water Purification, *Taste Odor Control J.*, **8** (7), 2; (9) 9; (11) 17; (13) 26; (15) 27 (1942).

HAYNES, L. Methods of Overcoming Phenol Odors and Tastes in Water, *U. S. Pub. Health Eng. Abstr.*, **10**, W, 115 (1930).

————: Experience at Charleston (W. Va.), with Odor and Taste Control, *Proc. 5th Ann. Conf. on Water. Purif.*, *W. Va. Univ. Eng. Exp. Sta.*, *Tech. Bull.*, 35 (1930).

————, and W. GRANT: Reduction of Chemical Odors at Nitro, West Virginia, *J. Am. Water Works Assoc.*, **37**, 1013 (1945).

HELBIG, W. A.: Odor and Taste Control with Activated Carbon, *J. Am. Water Works Assoc.*, **31**, 1931 (1939).

HESS, A. E.: Taste and Odor Control in Water Purification, *Ohio Conf. Water Purif.*, *16th Ann. Rept.*, 73 (1937).

HODGE, W. W.: Tastes and Odors in Water Supplies with Special Reference to Waste Liquors from By-Product Coke Plants, *W. Va. Coll. of Eng.*, *Tech. Bull.*, **1**, 40 (1927).

HOPKINS, E. S.: Latest Practice in Control of Tastes and Odors, *Proc. 5th Ann. Conf. Md.-Del. Water and Sewerage Assoc.*, 87 (1931).

HOUSER, G.: Contol of Tastes and Odors in the Water Supply at Rockport, Mass., *J. New Engl. Water Works Assoc.*, **49**, 156 (1935).

HOWARD, N. J.: Recent Progress in Water Purification, *Contract Record Eng. Rev.*, **38**, 1292 (1924).

————: Taste and Odor Control in Water Purification, *Contract Record Eng. Rev.*, **45**, 501 (1931).

————: Taste and Odor Control in Water Purification; Comprehensive Review of Progress in 1931, *Contract Record Eng. Rev.*, **45**, 1559 (1931).

————: Activated Carbon and Its Value in the Removal of Tastes and Odors from Water Supplies, *Contract Record Eng. Rev.*, **46**, 260 (1932).

————: The Trend of Water Purification and Treatment during the Year 1933, *Eng. Contract Record*, **47**, 1193 (1933).

————: Taste and Odor Control in Water Purification, *J. Pa. Water Works Assoc.*, **7**, 59 (1935).

————: Causes and Control of Tastes and Odors in Public Water Supplies, *Can. Eng.*, **68**, 14 (1935).

————: Taste and Odor Control in Water, *Eng. Record*, **51**, 25 (1938).

————: Odor and Taste Control in Water Purification, *Water Works Eng.*, **93**, 420 (1940).

————: Taste and Odor Treatment, *Taste Odor Control J.*, **6**, 10 (1940).

————: Improved Technique in Taste and Odor Control in Toronto, *Water Works & Sewerage*, **81**, 36 (1943).

————: Odor and Taste Control in Water Purification, *Water and Sewage*, **81** (7), 17, 87 (1943).

HOWSON, L. R.: Taste and Odor Control, *Eng. News Record*, **11**, 786 (1936).

HURST, W. D.: Odor and Taste Control by Break-point Chlorination and $CuSO_4$ in Water Purification, *Eng. Contract Record*, **57**, 8 (1944).

IMHOFF, K., and F. SIERP: Chlorinated Drinking Water: the Use of Activated Charcoal Filters, *Surveyor*, **76**, 225 (1929).

*INDUSTRIAL CHEMICAL SALES: "Taste and Odor Control in Water Purification," New York, 1947.

IRWIN, R. A.: Activated Carbon as a Controlling Agent for Tastes and Odors in Water Supplies, *Eng. Contract Record*, **48**, 268 (1934).

JAENICKE, M.: The Investigation and Evaluation of Active Carbon in Regard to Its Use for Water Purification, *Wasser*, **5**, 83 (1931).

JOHNSON, B. F.: Taste and Odor Control with Activated Carbon, *J. Pa. Water Works Operators' Assoc.*, **4**, 43 (1932).

————: Odor and Taste Control with NH_3Cl and Active Carbon, *J. Pa. Water Works Operators' Assoc.*, **14**, 74 (1942).

JOTTEN, K., *et al.*: The Removal of Troublesome Substances from Drinking Water by Means of Active and Inactive Charcoal, *Gesundh.-Ing.*, **52**, 529 (1929).

KANHAUSER, F., and J. FIEK: Improving the Odor and Taste of Surface Waters, *Plyna Voda*, **16**, 204 (1936).

KERSHAW, N. F.: Control with Carbon of Odors and Tastes from Refinery Wastes in Water Purification, *15th Ann. Conf. Water Purif.*, *West Va. Univ. Tech. Bull.*, **21**, 15 (1941).

KILLAM, S. E.: Measures Adopted to Rid Boston's Spot Pond Reservoir of Disagreeable Tastes and Odors Due to Algae, *Water Works Eng.*, **85**, 1052 (1932).

KLEIN, W., and C. A. BROWN: Removing Color, Tastes and Odors from a Widely Fluctuating Supply, *Water Works Eng.*, **83**, 283, 307 (1930).

KLUMPP, J. B.: Ozone for Water Treatment, *Eng. News Record,* **124,** 158 (1940).

KOENIG, O.: Improvements in Chemical Water Purification and the Use of Active Charcoals and Earths, *Gas u. Wasserfach,* **72,** 1065, 1091 (1929).

KRAUS, R., and B. BARBARA: Sterilization of Drinking Water by Means of Animal Charcoal, *Wien. klin. Wochschr.,* **28,** 810 (1915).

KRUM, H.: Tastes and Odors and Difficulties in Coagulation, *J. Pa. Water Works Operators' Assoc.,* **3,** 19 (1931).

LACKEY, J. B.: Quality and Quantity of Plankton in South End of Lake Michigan in 1942, *J. Am. Water Works Assoc.,* **36,** 669 (1944).

LAUGHLIN, H. F.: Odor and Taste Control in Water Purification, *J. Am. Water Works Assoc.,* **32,** 1191 (1940).

———, J. R. BAYLIS, and N. J. HOWARD: Developments in Taste and Odor Control, *J. Am. Water Works Assoc.,* **32,** 1191 (1940).

LAWRENCE, R. B.: Taste and Odor Control in Water, *Eng. News Record,* **120,** 594 (1938).

LEDOUX, J. W.: Taste and Odor Control in Water Purification, *Water Works Eng.,* **82,** 1531, 1560 (1929).

LLOYD, J. M.: Superchlorination for Taste and Odor Control, *J. Am. Water Works Assoc.,* **31,** 2130 (1939).

LONGLEY, F.: Present status of disinfection of water supplies, *J. Am. Water Works Assoc.,* **2,** 679 (1915).

LUACES, E., and T. STROHM: Activated Carbon in Water Purification, *W. Va. Eng. Exp. Sta., Tech. Bull.,* **4,** 96 (1931).

MACHEN, R. W.: Oil and Odor Removal from Feed Water, *Petroleum Eng.,* **11,** 104 (1940).

MAHLIE, W. S.: Aeration of Water, *J. Am. Water Works Assoc.,* **19,** 692 (1928).

MANGUN, L. B.: Taste and Odor Control in Water Purification, *J. Am. Water Works Assoc.,* **29,** 399 (1937).

MATHESON, D. H.: Experiments on Ontario Water Supplies Which Had Weedy, Fishy, Oily and Woody Odors, *Can. Eng.,* **62,** 84 (1932).

———, *et al.:* Taste and Odor Control in Water Supplies, *J. Am. Water Works Assoc.,* **25,** 680 (1933).

MELLEN, A. F.: Taste and Odor Control at Minneapolis, Minn., *Water Works Eng.,* **87,** 1164 (1934).

MENDELSOHN, I. W.: Water Supply and Purification Developments during 1934, *Water Works & Sewerage,* **82,** 1 (1935).

MILLER, W., and J. KERSLAKE: Color and Odor Removal at Ossining, N. Y., *J. Am. Water Works Assoc.,* **27,** 493 (1935).

MILLS, R. T.: Experience in Taste and Odor Control at Southern Pines, *Taste Odor Control J.,* **2** (4), (1935).

———: Taste and Odor Control in Water Purification, *U. S. Pub. Health Abstr.,* **16,** W, 47 (1936).

MOSES, H. E.: Taste and Odor Control in Water Purification, *J. Am. Water Works Assoc.,* **25,** 1066 (1933).

MURRAY, M. M., and D. C. WILSON: Fluorine in Drinking Water, *Lancet,* **1,** 818 (1943).

New Taste and Odor Control Process: Chlorine Dioxide Treatment, *American City,* **60,** 110 (June, 1945); 117 (September, 1945).

NEWLANDS, J. A.: Taste and Odor Control in Water Purification, *Water Works & Sewerage,* **85,** 625 (1938).

NORCOM, G. D.: Odor Removal from Water, *Eng. News Record,* **110,** 745 (1933).

———, and R. DODD: Activated Carbon for the Removal of Taste and Odor, *J. Am. Water Works Assoc.,* **22,** 1414 (1930).

NORDMAN, C. F.: Experiences with Taste and Odor Control at a Filter Plant, *Water Works Eng.*, **84**, 962 (1931).

O'BRIEN, G. L.: Odor and Taste Control by "Cl Blanket" in Reservoir for Water Purification, *Water Works Eng.*, **96**, 996, 1050 (1943).

POLYAKOV, A. G.: Odor Removal in Water Purification in Army Camps, *Sovet. Zdravookhranenie Turkmenii* **2**, 22 (1942).

POWELL, S. T.: Use of Ozone as a Sterilizing Agent for Water Purification, *J. New Engl. Water Works Assoc.*, **29**, 87 (1915).

PRINDLE, G. B.: Comparative Effectiveness of Taste and Odor Control Treatments, *Eng. Contract Record*, **51**, 14 (1938).

RAAB, F.: Taste and Odor Control in Water Purification, *Water Works Eng.*, **84**, 168 (1931).

————: Algae-produced Odors Reduced by Prechlorination, *J. Am. Water Works Assoc.*, **23**, 430 (1931).

RALSTON, O. C.: Report on Active Carbon for Odor and Taste Control in Water, *U. S. Bur. Mines, Rept. Invest.*, 3473 (1939).

Removal of Tastes and Odors from Filtered Water by an Economical Method of Aeration, *Surveyor*, **72**, 352 (1927).

Report of Committee on Control of Tastes and Odors, *J. Am. Water Works Assoc.*, **24**, 1738 (1932).

Report of Committee on Control of Tastes and Odors in Public Water Supplies, *J. Am. Water Works Assoc.*, **25**, 1490 (1933).

RIKER, R.: Taste and Odor Control in Water Purification, *Public Works*, **68**, 23 (1937).

RODMAN, H.: Taste and Odor Control in Water Purification, U. S. Patent No. 1,933,567 (1934).

ROE, F. C.: Aeration of Water by Air Diffusion, *J. Am. Water Works Assoc.*, **27**, 897 (1935).

ROLLINS, F. L., and A. D. CLAGGETTE: Taste and Odor Trouble at Barberton, and Its Remedy, *Ohio Conf. Water Purif., 13th Ann. Rept.*, 88 (1937).

ROUDINEK, J.: The Purification of Waste Waters with Humin, Clay and Lime, *Z. Zuckerin*, **37**, 128.

RUDOLFS, W.: Developments in Water Treatment, *J. Am. Water Works Assoc.*, **31**, 542 (1939).

RUTH, E.: Elimination of Taste and Odor in the Water Supply of Lancaster, Pa., *J. Am. Water Works Assoc.*, **23**, 373 (1931).

————: Odors and Tastes Caused by Over-loaded Filter Plant, *J. Am. Water Works Assoc.*, **23**, 396 (1931).

SARTORIUS, F., and W. OTTEMEYER: The Removal of Troublesome Substances in Drinking Water, *Gesundh.-Ing.*, **53**, 227 (1930).

SCHINMAN, E. P.: Taste and Odor Removal at South Fallsburg, N. Y., *J. Am. Water Works Assoc.*, **28**, 1998 (1936).

SCHLENKER, E.: Odors: Harmful Waste, Recognition and Elimination from Air and Water, 1920–1930, *Angew. Chem.*, **45**, 397, 432, 445 (1932).

SCHNEIDER, H. J.: Taste and Odor Control at Oshkosh, Wis., *Taste Odor Control J.*, **3** (10), (1937).

SHARE, J. M.: Odor and Taste Control with Active Carbon for Water Purification in Food-processing Plant, *Natl. Carbonator Bottler*, **73**, 84 (1941).

SHINMAN, E. P.: Taste and Odor Control in Water Purification, *J. Am. Water Works Assoc.*, **28**, 1998 (1936).

SIERP, F.: Taste and Odor Control in Water Purification, *Tech. Gemeindeblatt*, **32**, 153, 165 (1929).

————: The Use of Active Charcoal for Purifying Water and Treating Sewage, *Gas u. Wasserfach*, **74**, 764 (1931).

SIGWORTH, E. A.: Summary of Questionnaire for Taste and Odor Control with Powdered Activated Carbon, *Taste Odor Control J.*, **4** (3), (1937).

————: A.B.C. of Taste and Odor Control with Activated Carbon, *Taste Odor Control J.*, **7** (2), (1940).

SMIT, P.: The Use of Active Charcoal in Water Purification, *Genie Civil*, **99**, 570 (1931).

SMITH, M. C.: Review of Status of the Ammonia-chlorine Process, *J. Am. Water Works Assoc.*, **26**, 1623 (1934).

SMOUSE, J. P.: Taste and Odor Problems at St. Joseph, Mo., *J. Am. Water Works Assoc.*, **29**, 401 (1937).

SPALDING, O.: Activated Charcoal as a Deodorant in Water Purification, *J. Am. Water Works Assoc.*, **22**, 646 (1930).

SPALDING, G. R.: Experience with Activated Carbon, *J. Am. Water Works Assoc.*, **24**, 1394 (1932).

SPERRY, W., and L. C. BILLINGS: Tastes and Odors from Chlorination, *Eng. News Record*, **86**, 1041 (1921).

————, and ————: Tastes and Odors from Chlorination, *J. Am. Water Works Assoc.*, **8**, 603 (1921).

SPRINGER, J. F.: Water Purification with Ultra-violet Radiation, *Public Works*, **62** (10), 39; (11) 65 (1931).

Sterilization of Water with Liquid Chlorine and Deodorization by Aeration, *Technica*, **65**, 71 (1923).

STIMMEL, R. M.: Taste and Odor Control in Water Purification, *Am. Ry. Eng. Assoc. Proc.*, **39** (Bull. 400), 188 (1938).

STOVER, F. H.: Elimination of Tastes and Odors from an Army-Post Water Supply, *Public Works*, **76**, 30 (1945).

STUART, F. E.: Taste and Odor Control with Powdered Activated Carbon, *Eng. Contract Record*, **47**, 675 (1933).

————: Taste and Odor Control by Physical Adsorption, *J. Am. Water Works Assoc.*, **25**, 1605 (1933).

————: Taste and Odor Control in Water Purification: Latest Procedures in Use of Activated Carbon, *Public Works*, **65**, 35 (1934).

————: Trend of Modern Taste and Odor Control, *Water Works & Sewerage*, **81**, 327 (1934).

————: Up-to-date Carbon Control of Taste and Odor, *Public Works*, **66**, 27 (1935).

————: The Trend of Modern Taste and Odor Control, *J. Am. Water Works Assoc.*, **27**, 503 (1935).

————: Current Practices in Taste and Odor Control, *Water Works Eng.*, **88**, 940 (1935).

————: Practical Applications of Activated Carbon for Taste and Odor Control, *Proc. 10th Ann. Conf. Water Purif., W. Va. Coll. Eng. Tech. Bull.*, **8**, 8 (1936).

SYNAN, J. F.: Taste and Odor Control with Chlorine Dioxide, *J. Pa. Water Works Operators' Assoc.*, **17**, 55 (1945).

TAYLOR, F. S.: Odor Troubles in the Water of Defiance, *Ohio Conf. on Water Purif., 15th Ann. Rept.*, 50 (1936).

————: Breakpoint Chlorination as Used at Defiance for Odor Control, *Ohio Conf. Water Purif., 20th Ann. Rept.*, 65 (1941).

THOMAS, H. A.: Taste and Odor Control on Lake Michigan, *J. Am. Water Works Assoc.*, **32**, 1183 (1940).

THORNTON, A. C.: Taste and Odor Troubles in Bulawayo Water, with Special Reference to the Use of Activated Carbon, *Inst. Civ. Eng. (London)*, *Selected Eng. Paper* (156), 1 (1935).

THRESH, J., and J. BEALE: Recent Studies Relating to the Purification of Water, *Surveyor*, **68**, 579 (1925).

THUMA, R. A.: St. Paul Eliminates Odors and Taste by Aeration, *J. Am. Water Works Assoc.*, **19**, 631 (1928).

————: Aeration with Compressed Air for Removing Odors, *J. Am. Water Works Assoc.*, **24**, 682 (1932).

THURMAN, R.: Taste and Odor Removal in Water at St. Paul, Minn., *Water Works*, **66**, 124 (1927).

TRICE, M. F.: Chlorination of Deep Well Supply for Taste and Odor Removal, *J. Am. Water Works Assoc.*, **21**, 255 (1929).

TROWBRIDGE, C. E.: Activated Carbon Used in Taste and Odor Control in Water Purification, *Public Works*, **62**, 19 (1931).

————: The Use of Activated Carbon to Remove Tastes and Odors from Water, *Ohio Conf. on Water Purif., 11th Ann. Rept.*, 46 (1932).

————, et al.: Activated Carbon for the Removal of Tastes and Odors from Water, *J. Am. Water Works Assoc.*, **24**, 1492 (1932).

UGLOW, W., and M. BOLTIN: Odor Removal from Water, *Z. Hyg. Infektionskrankh.*, **112**, 655 (1931).

*U. S. PUBLIC HEALTH SERVICE: "Ohio River Pollution Control of Odor, Taste and Epidemiological Studies," *Report of Ohio River Comm.*, Cincinnati, Ohio, 1943.

Use of Activated Carbon for Taste and Odor Removal, *Water Works Eng.*, **85**, 383 (1932).

VEATCH, F. M.: Odor and Taste Control with Activated Carbon, *Eng. News Record*, **124**, 24 (1940).

VEATCH, N. T., JR.: The Function of Aeration in Water Purification, *Proc. 10th Texas Water Works Short School*, 172 (1928).

YAXLEY, R. G.: Taste and Odor Control in Water Purification, *J. New Engl. Water Works Assoc.*, **49**, 152 (1935).

YOUNG, J. E.: Odor Control and Softening for Mg Hardness in Water Purification, *American City*, **55**, 54 (1940).

WAGNER, A.: Odor and Taste in Water Control by Breakpoint Chlorination and $CuSO_4$, *Public Works*, **75**, 19 (1944).

WAGNER, H. F.: Odor and Taste Control in Water Purification, *Can. Eng.*, **80**, 40 (1942).

WARING, F. H.: Tastes and Odors in Water Due to Low Oxygen Content, *Eng. News Record*, **87**, 771 (1921).

————: Tastes and Odors in Public Water Supplies from Decomposing Organic Matter, *J. Am. Water Works Assoc.*, **10**, 75 (1923).

————: Activated Carbon for Removal of Tastes and Odors in Water, *Water Works & Sewerage*, **78**, 329 (1931).

WARREN, R., and E. BARTOW: Taste and Odor in Chlorinated Water, *J. Am. Water Works Assoc.*, **11**, 881 (1924).

WATERMAN, E. L.: Taste and Odor Problems Plague Missouri Valley Operators, *Water Works Eng.*, **89**, 1551 (1936).

WATZL, E.: Superchlorination and Subsequent Dechlorination over Carbon of Water for Municipal Supply, *Ind. Eng. Chem.*, **21**, 156 (1929).

WEIR, P.: The Use of Clay in Coagulation and Taste and Odor Control, *J. Am. Water Works Assoc.*, **30**, 1528 (1938).

WELCH, W. A.: Taste and Odor Control, *Southwest Water Works J.*, **19**, 15 (1937).

————: Milestones in Taste an Odor Control, *J. Am. Water Works Assoc.*, **38**, 57 (1946).

WELLINGTON, M. S.: Controlling Tastes and Odors in Reservoirs of the New Haven Water Co., *J. New Engl. Water Works Assoc.*, **53**, 171 (1939).

WIESNER, H., JR.: Taste and Odor Control with Activated Carbon, *Proc. 8th Ann. Conf. Water Purif., W. Va. Univ. Tech. Bull.*, **6**, 42 (1933).

WILLEY, F. E.: Taste and Odor Control in Water Purification, *J. Am. Water Works Assoc.*, **29**, 406 (1937).

WISELY, W. H.: Odor Control at Treatment Works, *Water Works & Sewerage*, **88**, 323 (1941).

WOLMAN, A., W. DONALDSON, and L. H. ENSLOW: Recent Progress in the Art of Water Treatment, *J. Am. Water Works Assoc.*, **22**, 1161 (1930).

d. Industrial and General (Including Air Conditioning)

AGAR, C. C., *et al.*: Odor Control for Plants Treating Sewage, *Sewage Works J.*, **13**, 1230 (1941).

ALSTEAD, S.: Charcoal Blanket for Deodorizing Discharges, *Lancet*, **1**, 669 (1942).

ANDERSON, E.: Deodorization of Paper Pulp Mill Gases, *Pacific Pulp & Paper Ind.*, **13**, 22 (1939).

*ANDES, L. E.: "Geruchlosmachen," *Leipzig*, 1896.

Aromatics Find Increasing Use for Deodorizing Textiles, *Textile World*, **82**, 1173 (1932).

BACKMEYER, D.: Sludge Problems in Odor and Taste Control, *Sewage Works Eng. and Munic. Sanit.*, **13**, 140 (1942).

BALTES, J.: Agents for Deodorization for Cosmetic Use, *Fette u. Seifen*, **45**, 640 (1938).

BANDT, H. J.: Odors in Streams from Waste Waters from Gas Plants, *Gesundh.-Ing.*, **63**, 19 (1940).

BEHRINGER, H.: Deodorization of Air, British Patent No. 483,076 (1938).

BERGSTROM, H., and K. G. TROBECK: Deodorization of Paper Pulp Sulfate Digester and Diffuser Condensates, *Svensk Papperstidn.*, **48**, 246 (1945).

BOWE, T. F.: Enlarged Sewage Treatment Plant for Small City Stresses Odor Control, *Am. City*, **46**, 66 (1932).

BOYD, D. M., JR.: Deodorization of Petroleum-industry Wastes, *Petroleum Refiner*, **24**, 334 (1945).

BOYER, J.: La Déodorisation des tunnels du Métropolitain par l'ozone, *La Nature*, **53**, 97 (1925).

BRANDLEY, J. M.: Absorbing Noxious Odors, U. S. Patent No. 1,728,656 (1929).

BRIX, I.: Geruchsverschlüsse, *Handwörterb. Kommunalwiss.*, **11**, 346 (1923).

BROWN, E.: Cause of Odors in Home Air Conditioning Installation, *Dom. Eng.*, **148**, 68 (1936).

BROWN, J. R.: Pad for Deodorization, U. S. Patent No. 2,303,073 (1943).

BURTON: Law as Regards Abatement of Noxious Vapours and Nuisances and Protection of Public Health in Scotland, *Sanit. Inquiry: Scotland*, 40 (London, 1842).

CAESAR, F.: Prevention of Typical Hospital Odors: Esthetic Considerations, *Münch. med. Wochschr.*, **79**, 309 (1932).

CAMBIER, M.: Deodorization of Gases, French Patent No. 678,842 (1929).

CARR, K. L.: Odor and Sludge Stability Control in Treatment of Sewage, *Taste Odor Control J.*, **5**, 1 (1939).

CLAYTON, B.: Deodorization of Soap Stock, U. S. Patent No. 2,230,196 (1941).

CLYNE, J. B.: Odorization of Air, U. S. Patent No. 2,124,543 (1938).

COCA, A. F.: Agents for Deodorization, U. S. Patent No. 2,314,125 (1943).

Coconut-shell Carbon Effectively Removes Odors, *Architect. Record,* **82,** 36 (1937).

COLBY, H. S., and R. F. O'MARA: Deodorization of Gases, U. S. Patent No. 2,078,925 (1937).

Condensirung und Verbrennung übelriechender Dämpfe, *Z. Gewerbe-Hyg.,* **7,** 301 (1900).

COOPER, L. S.: Deodorization of Rubber Gas-expanded Products, U. S. Patent No. 2,179,494 (1940).

COTTRELL, F. G.: Deodorization of Gases, British Patent No. 478,215 (1938).

CRAMER, R., and J. A. WILSON: Odors in Sewage-sludge Digestion, *Ind. Eng. Chem.,* **20,** 4 (1928).

CRITES, B. O.: Deodorization of Gases, U. S. Patent No. 2,054,966 (1936).

CUSLOW, L. N.: Use of Cl on Odors at Sewage Works, *Surveyor,* **73,** 1834 (1928).

DAIMLER, K., and C. PLATZ: Sulfonic Acids as Deodorization Agents, German Patent No. 694,062 (1940).

DALLA VALLE, J. M.: Air Sanitation, *Heating and Ventilating,* **41,** 58 (1944).

DAUPHINEE, G. S.: Absorption Apparatus for Deodorization of Air, U. S. Patent No. 2,214,737 (1941).

DECHANT, F. H.: Ozone Goes to Work, *Eng. News Record,* **124,** 516 (1940).

DE G. BEARN, J. L. H.: Deodorization of Rubber, French Patent No. 640,145 (1927).

DEMPSEY, H. J.: Bauxite in Deodorization of Petrolatum, U. S. Patent No. 2,320,223 (1943).

Deodorization of Petroleum, *Deuxième Congr. mondial pétrole,* **2** (Sect. 2, Phys. chim.), 329 (1937).

Disinfectant Agents, Standard Specifications for Deodorization, *Glass Packer,* **16,** 435 (1937).

DITTMAR, H. R.: Odor Removal from Polymeric Bu Methacrylate, U. S. Patent No. 2,265,937 (1942).

DON, J.: Adsorption in Sand Filters, *Eng.,* **3,** 759 (1921).

DRINKER, P.: Control of Odors, *Heating and Ventilating,* **33,** 105 (1936).

DUNLOP RUBBER CO., LTD., and E. W. MADGE: Deodorization of Rubber, British Patent No. 312,443 (1929).

DZERZHGOVSKI, S. K., and N. A. DMITREVSKAYA: Purifying Work of the Puech-Chabal Filters, *Arch. biol. nauk. St. Petersburg,* **18,** 189 (1913–1914).

EARP, J. R.: Odors: Their Sanitary Significance and Their Elimination, *Am. J. Pub. Health,* **13,** 283 (1923).

EDWARDS, H. H.: Unique Method of Elimination of Odors from Industrial Wastes, *Munic. and County Eng.,* **60,** 221 (1921).

Eliminating Odors in Garbage Reduction, *Eng. Record,* **73,** 20 (1916).

Elimination of Odors in Garbage Plant, *Surveyor,* **66,** 343 (1924).

ELLIS, G. H., and R. K. SLADE: Deodorants, British Patent No. 16,558 (1906).

ENGEL, R. A.: Control of Odors in Rubber Goods, *India Rubber World,* **94,** 37 (1936).

ENSLOW, L. H.: Correcting Odor Nuisances at Sewage Treatment Plants, *Am. City,* **38,** 87 (1928).

Experts Testify on Means of Eliminating Odors in Garbage Reduction, *Eng. Record,* **73,** 20 (1916).

FERNANDEZ-COCA, A.: Agents for Deodorization, Canadian Patent No. 407,699 (1942).

FITZGERALD, R. W.: Latest Development in Taste and Odor Control, *Activated Alum. News,* 1 (1940).

FOLEY, M. A.: Odorants in Rubber, *India Rubber World,* **88,** 30 (1933).

FORD, L. A., and D. F. CLAUSEN: Rat Repelling Odor, *Science News Letter,* **40,** 159 (1941).

FOSTER, H. B., JR.: Camp Callan Sewage Treatment Plant, *Calif. Sewage Works J.*, **14**, 31 (1942).

FRANKLIN, M. W.: Air Ozonization, *J. Ind. Eng. Chem.*, **6**, 852 (1914).

FULLER, G. W.: Causes and Remedies of Odors from Sewers, *Munic. J. Public Works*, **47**, 318 (1919).

GEBR. HEYL AND CO.: Deodorants, British Patent No. 23,230 (1909).

Geruchsventilator, *Z. angew. Chem.*, **36**, 232 (1923).

GIBBONS, M.: Elimination of Odors of Industrial Origin, *Ind. Eng. Chem.*, **24**, 977 (1932).

————: Taste and Odor of Industrial Origin, *Taste Odor Control J.*, **2**, 11, (1936).

GOLDSTEIN, A. W.: Agents for Deodorization of Air, U. S. Patent No. 2,228,993 (1941).

GORDON, C. W.: Deodorization of Sewage Sludge Gases, U. S. Patent No. 2,250,864 (1941).

GRADY, R. J.: Agents for Deodorization, U. S. Patent No. 2,317,908 (1943).

GREELEY, S. A.: Elimination of Odors in Garbage Plant, *Proc. Am. Soc. Civil Eng.*, **51**, 832 (1925).

GREEN, F. H.: Prevention and Removal of Smells, *Sci. American Supp.*, **44**, 17, 936 (1897).

GREGORY, W. K.: Air Conditioning in Nature, *Natural History*, **38**, 382 (1936).

GRYNKRAUT, A.: Elimination of Tannery Odors, *Leather Mfr.*, **43**, 138 (1932).

HACKMASTER, G. H.: Odors in Sewage-control by Chlorination, *Eng. News Record*, **99**, 1031 (1927).

HARGRAVE, M. G.: Sweet-scented House: Simple Ways of Eliminating Unpleasant Odours and Ensuring Fresh Atmosphere, *Farmer and Stockholder*, **53**, Farmer's Home Supp., 4 (1939).

HENDERSON, Y., and H. W. HAGGARD: The Elimination of Industrial Organic Odors, *J. Ind. Eng. Chem.*, **14**, 548 (1922).

HENKEL, and CIE: Deodorization of Soaps, Belgian Patent No. 447,475 (1942).

HEUKELEKIAN, H.: Odors: Control in New Brunswick, N. J., Sewage, *Water Works & Sewerage*, **89**, 302 (1942).

HERING, R.: Odors at Refuse Disposal Works Prevented, *Eng. Contr.*, **43**, 81 (1915).

HOLLENBERG, I. R.: Agents for Deodorization-cosmetic Use, *Progressive Perfumery Cosmetics*, 155 (1939).

HOLLIDAY, C. B.: Agents for Deodorization, *Perfumery Essent. Oil Record*, **34**, 196 (1943).

HOUGHTON, F. C., *et al.*: Classroom Odors with Reduced Outside Air Supply, *Heating, Piping, Air Conditioning*, **7**, 247 (1935).

HÜBSCHER, J.: Methods of Purifying Air, *Seifensieder-Zeitung*, **62**, 414 (1935).

I. G. FARBENIND: Deodorization of Rosin (Heat-treated), German Patent No. 740,316 (1943).

IMHOFF, K.: Odor Control in Plants for Sewage Purification, *Gesundh.-Ing.*, **64**, 610 (1941).

In Hot Weather, How Control Odors at Sewage-disposal Plant? *Can. Eng.*, **78**, 23 (1940).

Industry De-smells, *Business Week*, 23 (Aug. 21, 1937).

JANNAWAY, S. P.: Reviews on Agents for Deodorization, *Perfumery Essent. Oil Record*, **30**, 339 (1939).

JOSEPH, E. L.: Contamination: Its Cause and Elimination, *Ice and Cold Storage*, **41**, 77 (1938).

KALISCHER, M.: Recent Trends in Air Conditioning: Ultra Violet Light, Odors and Mood Conditioning, *Eng. Refrig.*, **42**, 7 (1941).

KASS, C. B.: Prevention of Odors in Exhaust Gases, Motor Fuel Blending, U. S. Patent No. 2,324,779 (1944).

KERND'L, A.: Agents for Deodorization, German Patent No. 703,976 (1941).

KIEMSTEDT, H.: Deodorization of Hydrocarbons, German Patent No. 640,204 (1936).

Kimura, R.: Zur Geruchs-Beseitigung durch Lüftigung, *Arch. Hyg.*, **B91**, 183 (1922).

Kipper, H. B.: Deodorization of Hydrocarbons, U. S. Patent No. 2,221,301 (1941).

Kiss, M.: Deodorization of Drugs Containing Essential Oils, *Berl. ungar. pharm. Ges.*, **17**, 137 (1941).

Kisskalt, V.: Deodorisierung, *Zr. Hyg. Infektionskrankh.*, **71B**, 273 (1912).

————: Die Entfernung der Geruchsstoffe durch Ventilation, *Arch. Hyg.*, **71**, 380 (1909).

Kling, W.: Deodorization of Soaps, U. S. Patent No. 2,057,959 (1937).

Kohlen-veredlung u. Schwelwerke Akt. Ges.: Deodorization of Benzines Obtained from Brown Coal, German Patent No. 700,373 (1940).

Kurita, Y.: Agents for Deodorization, Japanese Patent No. 128,990 (1939).

Lab. franc. de chimiotherapie: Deodorization for Amines and Isocyanates, Belgian Patent No. 447,744 (1942).

Laird, D. A.: New Odors for Old, *Ladies' Home J.*, **47**, 128 (May, 1930).

Laughlin, H. F.: How to Determine the Effectiveness of Activated Carbon for the Control of Tastes and Odors, *Eng. Contract Record*, **51**, 31 (1938).

Le Sens de l'adsorption des substances volatiles, *Acta Oto-laryngol.*, **1**, 64 (1918).

Leggett, R. M.: Elimination of Odors from Sewers, U. S. Patent No. 1,341,913 (1920).

Leonhardt, E.: Deodorant, U. S. Patent No. 1,001,964 (1911).

Letheby, H.: On Noxious and Offensive Trades and Manufactures, with Especial Reference to Means of Abating Odor Nuisances Therefrom, *Public Health, London*, **3**, 49 (1875).

Livache: Des Mesures à prendre pour supprimer les odeurs de Paris, *Bull. soc. méd. pub.*, Paris, **17**, 222 (1894).

Lloyd, J. M.: Chlorine in Odor Reductions, *Public Works*, **71**, 46 (1940).

Lord, C. E.: Agents for Deodorization, U. S. Patent No. 2,310,099 (1943).

McClellan, W.: Agents for Deodorization from Tar and Soap Base, British Patent No. 516,195 (1939).

McLean, D. L.: Odor Control at Winnipeg Plant for Treating Sewage, *Eng. Contract Record*, **55**, 32 (1942).

Mahr, H. W., and A. C. Kraft: Investigation on Nature and Elimination of Odor and Dust from a Garbage Reduction Plant, *Ind. Eng. Chem.*, **7**, 778 (1915).

Mantell, C.: Activated Carbon: a Modern Purifying Agent, *Food Ind.*, **2**, 207 (1930).

Masterman, A. T.: Deodorization of Air, British Patent No. 480,176 (1938).

Matthews, F. J.: Odor and Oil Removal from Feed Water, *Eng. and Boiler House Rev.*, **53**, 220 (1939).

Melton, H. E.: Powder Deodorization (for Use in Bandages), U. S. Patent No. 2,144,632 (1939).

Morgan, W. L.: Deodorization of Rubber Adhesives on Wrapping Sheets and Tapes, U. S. Patent No. 2,170,949 (1940).

Morris, G. F.: Deodorization of Cacao Butter, *Gordian*, **46**, 17 (1940).

Moser, H.: Control of Odors in Manufacture of Therapeutic Preparations Containing Garlic, German Patent No. 647,067 (1937).

Mudgett, C. T.: Odor Control for Plants Treating Sewage, *Sewage Works J.*, **13**, 879 (1941).

Munkelt, F. H.: Control of Odors in Air-conditioning System, *Refrig. Eng.*, **33**, 371 (1937).

————: Odor Control in Animal Laboratories, *Heating, Piping, Air Conditioning*, **10**, 289 (1938).

————. Control of Odors, *Architect. Record*, **86**, 70 (1939).

————: Odors, Their Nature, Cause and Control, *Refrig. Eng.*, **51**, 31 (1946).

MUNZ, H.: Agents for Deodorization for Application to Cotton, Wool, Australian Patent No. 109,904 (1940). .

NANN, H.: Metallic Odors and Their Removal, *Mitt. Forsch.-Inst. Probieramts Edelmetalle*, **7**, 55 (1933).

New Odor Dispellers: O.D. 30, *Consumers Research Bull.*, **15**, 20 (1945).

NILOU, K.: Aluminum Chloride Solutions for Deodorization, *Farm. Tid.*, **51**, 785 (1941).

No Home Smells, *Business Week*, 104 (July 22, 1944).

NORCOM, G. D.: Control of Odors Marks Progress in Sterilization, *Eng. News Record*, **110**, 745 (1933).

Odor Removal from Dyes, *Chem. Ind.*, **44**, 523 (1939).

Odors Evoke a New Business, *Business Week*, 63 (Nov. 3, 1945).

ORELUP, J. W., and E. OHLSSON: Agents for Deodorization of Cosmetics, U. S. Patent No. 2,226,177 (1941).

ORFORD, H. E., and E. J. SCHARCH: Odor and Scum Control (Activated Carbon) in Sewage, *Munic. Sanit.*, **9**, 124 (1938).

OSTENBERG, Z.: Odor Absorbing Compositions, Canadian Patent No. 401,098 (1941).

OUCHAKOV, A. A.: Adsorption of Odor Substance in Regard to Sense of Smell, *Acta otolaryngol.*, **14**, 470 (1930).

————: Practical Application of Relation between Smell and Absorption of Oderiferous Substances, *Rev. laryngol.*, **51**, 77 (1930).

PAKHOMOV, E. A.: Deodorization of Synthetic Rubber, Russian Patent No. 46,353 (1936).

PAUTY, E. J.: Deodorization of Petroleum, French Patent No. 836,311 (1939).

PRUTTON, C. F. and J. E. JOHNSON: Deodorization of Hydrocarbon Oils, U. S. Patent No. 2,319,630 (1943).

PUDDEFOOT, L. E.: Deodorization of Chloroprene Polymer, British Patent No. 520,745 (1940).

Raffinerie Tirlemontoise Soc. anon.: Deodorization of Gases, British Patent No. 484,532 (1938).

RASTATUROV, N. S.: Deodorization of Chlorinated Hydrocarbon Condensation Products with Alkali Metal Polysulfides, Russian Patent No. 52,497 (1938).

RAY, A. B.: Removal of Odorous Substances from Air, U. S. Patent No. 2,055,774 (1937).

————, and N. K. CHANEY: Abatement of Industrial Odors by Means of Activated Carbon, *Chem. Met. Eng.*, **28**, 1114 (1923).

————, and ————: Abatement of Industrial Stenches by Means of Activated Carbon, *Trans. Am. Inst. Chem. Eng.*, **15**, 347 (1923).

REGAN, J. M., and M. S. HENDERSON: Charcoal Wool Filter Cloth as Deodorant, *Proc. Staff Meet., Mayo Clinic*, **19**, 268 (1944).

REILLY, F. J.: Household Deodorants, *Soap Sanit. Chemicals*, **20**, 33 (1944).

REISNER: Beseitigung der Geruchsbelästigungen, *Haustechn. Runds.*, 63 (1938).

Remedying Offensive Odors in Sewage, *Eng. News*, **67**, 433 (1912).

RIGGS, W. S., and R. LEHMANN: Agents for Deodorization, from H_2O_2 and Wetting Agents, U. S. Patent No. 2,371,545 (1945).

Rodos—New Rubber De- or Re-odorants, *Rubber Age*, **28**, 306 (1930).

ROEHRICH, V. H.: Deodorization Agents, U. S. Patent No. 2,373,198 (1945).

ROHLAND, P.: The Colloidal Clay Process for Purification of the Waste Waters of Sugar Factories, *Oesterr. ung. Z. Zuckerin*, **44**, 112 (1915).

RUMMEL, K.: Control of Odors in Natural Gas, *Arch. Eisenhüttenw.*, **10**, 541 (1937).

SANBORN, N. H.: Nitrate in Deodorization of Cannery Waste, *Food Ind.*, **13**, 57 (1941).

————: Nitrates in Deodorization of Cannery Waste, *Fruit Products J.*, **20**, 207 (1941).

SCHANTZ, J. M.: Deodorization of Hydrogenated rosin, U. S. Patent No. 2,327,132 (1944).

SCHMEITZNER: Geruchsbeseitigung in Küchenabwassern, *Bauamt. Gemeindebau.,* 156 (1938).

SCHMIDT, A. W.: Deodorization of Diesel Fuels, *Jahrb. brennkrafttech. Ges.,* **20,** 17 (1939).

——, G. SCHOLZ, and F. MOHRY: Odors of Exhaust Gases from Diesel Fuels, *Braunkohle,* **35,** 535 (1936).

SCHUR, M. O.: Deodorization of Paper, U. S. Patent No. 1,905,757 (1933).

SELLERS, W. J.: Deodorization of Wood for Packing Food, Australian Patent No. 113,373 (1941).

SHUGER, L. W.: Masking Odors of Drying Paints and Varnishes, U. S. Patent No. 2,103,830 (1938).

SIMMONS, C. W.: Control of Odors in Gas, *J. West Soc. Eng.,* **36,** 330 (1931).

SKINNER, J. F.: Control of Odors from Sewage Plants, *Surveyor,* **67,** 499 (1925).

SLEIK, H.: Giant Gas Masks to Remove Plant Odors, *Mod. Packaging,* **16,** 88 (1943). 1943).

Soc. anon. pour l'ind. chim. à Bâle: Deodorization of Perishable Material, German Patent No. 534,839 (1926).

Soc. d'études et d'appl. pour le progrès: Deodorization of Gases, French Patent No. 706,750 (1930).

Soc. du gaz de Paris: Deodorization of Gases, French Patent No. 748,097 (1933).

Solvay et Cie: Deodorization of Soap, French Patent No. 829,156 (1938).

SONNENSCHEIN, W.: Deodorization of Carbon Disulfide, U. S. Patent No. 2,328,176 (1944).

SPRINGBORN, W. J.: Elimination of Odors in Garbage Plants, *Public Works,* **52,** 442 (1922).

STEINMETZ, C. P.: Ozone as Deodorant: Results, *J. Am. Med. Assoc.,* **61,** 1007 (1913).

STIEPEL, C.: Deodorization of Train Oil Fatty Acids, German Patent No. 283,216 (1914).

Taste and Odor Control by Activated Carbons, *Public Works,* **65,** 36 (1934).

TESCHNER, G.: Beseitigung Geruchsbelästigung in Natron-sulfat-zellstoff Fabrik, *Kleine Mitt. Mitglied Ver. Wasser-, Boden-, W. Lufthyg.,* **6,** 233 (1931).

30-second Deodorant, *Newsweek,* **20,** 68 (1942).

TRAVERS, J. T.: Deodorization of Air or Other Gases, U. S. Patent No. 1,738,543 (1930).

VAN BENSCHOTEN, J.: Control of Sewage and Industrial Odors, *Eng. Contract Record,* **49,** 728 (1935).

VAN DAM, C.: Adsorption de matières odorantes, *Arch. néerland physiol.,* **1,** 666 (1917).

Ventilation and Atmospheric Pollution, *Am. Pub. Health Assoc. Year Book,* 125 (1941–1942).

WAGNER, C. G., and C. POTTS: Deodorization of Sewage, British Patent No. 335,682 (1929).

WAHL, O.: Deodorization of Induline and Nigrosine Dyes, U. S. Patent No. 2,328,759 (1944).

WALKER, LTD., W. & F., and J. T. FREESTONE: Deodorization of Air in Rooms, British Patent No. 720,440 (1927).

WARRICK, L. F., F. J. McKEE, H. E. WIRTH, and N. H. SANBORN: Methods of Treating Cannery Wastes, *Natl. Canners' Assoc. Lab. Bull.,* **28L,** 1 (1939).

WESTON, R. S.: Detection and Elimination of Odors from Oil Refineries, *Proc. Am. Soc. Civil Eng.,* **51,** 1193 (1925).

WHIGELT, G.: Deodorization of Paints, *Natl. Painters' Mag.,* **5,** 6 (1938).

WHITE, L. J., A. H. BAKER, and C. C. TWORT: Aerial Deodorization and Disinfection, *Nature,* **153,** 141 (1944).

WINSLOW, C. E. A.: Odors in Atmosphere, *Proc. Am. Soc. Civil Eng.,* **51,** 794 (1925).

WIRTH, E.: Deodorant for Heavy Coal-tar Oils, German Patent No. 24,344 (1906),

WITHERIDGE, W. N., and C. P. YAGLOU: Deodorization of Rooms with O_3, *Ice and Refrig.,* **97,** 78 (1939).

WOLPERT: Über die Zerstörung von Gerüchen, insbesondere des Tabakrauches mit Hilfe der Elekricität, *Hyg. Rundschau,* **5**, 589 (1895).

WOODBURY, D. O.: Eliminating Bad Smells, *Collier's,* **113**, 46 (1944).

WOOLDRIDGE, F. V.: Ozone as Deodorant, *Eng. News,* **71**, 778 (1914).

WYLAM, B., and D. RONALD: Deodorization of Gases, British Patent No. 428,606 (1935).

ZAVODOVSKII, A. A.: Deodorization of Rubber (Synthetic), Russian Patent No. 45,061 (1935).

L. THEORIES OF ODOR STIMULATION AND GENERAL TREATMENTS

ACHELLS, J. D.: Geruchsstudien, *Arch. ges. Psychol.,* **71B**, 273 (1929).

ADLER, A.: The Phenomenon of Taste and Smell, *Bull. New Engl. Med. Cent.,* **2**, 237 (1940).

AHLENSTIEL, H.: Untergehender Sinn, *Umschau,* **16**, 496 (1912).

ALIBERT, J. L.: Considérations philosophiques sur les odeurs, et sur leur emploi comme médicament, *Mém. soc. méd. émulat. Paris,* **5**, 44 (1797).

Analyse unserer Geruchsempfindungen, *Naturforscher,* 32 (1924).

Ancestral Memories in Smells, *Literary Digest,* **83**, 70 (1924).

*ATCHLEY, E. G.: "A History of the Use of Incense in Divine Worship," London, 1909.

AYRTON, W. E.: The Physics of Smell, *Nature,* **58**, 450 (1898).

BAEGE, F. P.: Geruch und Geschmack, *Naturw. Umschau Chem. Ztg.,* **18**, 1 (1931).

*BAIN, A.: "The Senses and the Intellect," 3d ed., London, 1868.

*BALLENGER, H. C.: "A Manual of Otology, Rhinology and Laryngology," 2d ed., Philadelphia, 1943.

BAWDEN, H. H.: A Bibliography of the Literature on the Organ and Sense of Smell, *J. Comp. Neurol.,* **11**, 1 (1901).

*BEEBE-CENTER, J. G.: "The Psychology of Pleasantness and Unpleasantness," New York, 1932.

*BERARD, P. H.: "Olfaction," Dict. méd., 2d ed., **22**, 1 (Paris, 1840).

BERGER, R.: Gerüche, *Gesundh.-Ing.,* **40**, 173 (1917).

BERILLON: Psychologie de l'olfaction, *Rev. hypnot.,* **23**, 33, 190 (1909).

*BERNARD, L. "Les Odeurs dans les romans de Zola," Montpelier, 1889.

*BERNSTEIN, J.: "The Five Senses of Man," London, 1876.

BIDDER, F.: Riechen, *Wagner's Handwörterbuch Physiol.,* **2**, 916 (1847).

*BIENFANG, R.: Odor, *Glasser's Med. Physics,* 820 (1944).

*———: "The Subtle Sense," University of Oklahoma Press, Norman, 1946.

BÖCKER, E.: Riechstoffe, *Muspratts chem. Ergänzungsb.,* **3**, 706 (1917).

BOGERT, M. T.: Your Nose Knows, *Sci. Monthly,* **39**, 345 (1934).

*BOYLE, R.: "Essays of the Strange Subtility Determinate Nature Great Efficacy of Effluviums," London, 1673.

BRADBY, G. F.: Noses and They Smell Not, *Living Age,* **282**, 361 (1914).

BRAHN, M.: Experimentelle Beiträge zur Gefühlslehre, *Phil. Stud.,* **18**, 127 (1901).

BREMER, L.: Smell, *Ref. Handbook of the Med. Sci.,* **6**, 487 (1888).

*BUDGETT, H. M.: "Hunting by Scent," New York, 1933.

———: Solving the Mystery of Scent, *Field,* **38**, 170 (1934).

CAMPBELL, W. G.: Odors Review, *Am. Perfumer,* **17**, 437 (1922).

Can a Robot Have a Nose? *Popular Science,* **119**, 70 (1931).

Carpenter Smell, *Todds Cyclopaedia of Anat. Physiol.,* **4**, 698 (1847).

*CLOQUET, H.: "Dissertation sur les odeurs sur les sens et les organes de l'olfaction," Paris, 1815.

———: Odeur, *Dict. sci. méd.,* **37**, 89 (1819).

———: Olfactif, *Dict. sci. méd.*, **37**, 214, 222 (1819).

*———: "Osphresiologie, ou traité des odeurs, du sens et des organes de l'olfaction," Paris, 1821.

COOMBS, E. M.: Odors and Memories, *Lippincott's Mag.*, **37**, 621 (1911).

*CROZIER, W. J.: "Chemoreception," *Handbook of Gen. Exp. Psychol.*, Clark University Press, 1934.

CURTIS, H. H.: Noses, *Am. J. Soc. Science*, **22**, 75 (1887).

CUTORE, G.: Beyond the Limits of Psychosensorial Perceptions; between Waves and Rays, *Riv. san. siciliana*, **24**, 812 (1936).

DAVIS, H.: Symposium on Special Senses in Military Problems, *Federation Proc.*, **2**, 107 (1943).

DE GROOTE, M.: Mechanism of Odors, *Spice Mill*, **46**, 2335, 2350, 2537 (1923).

*DEJEAN: "Traité des odeurs, suite du traité de la distillation," Paris, 1777.

DE JONG, H. G. B., and G. G. P. SAUBERT: Coacervates as Models of Stimulation of Olfaction, *Protoplasma*, **28**, 329 (1937).

*DE MOELLER, C. L.: "De odorum effectibus," Berolini, 1826.

DE SANCTIS, S.: Applicazione della legge di Weber-Feckner al' olfatto, *Arch. ital. di biol.*, **36**, 131 (1901).

DEVARIGNY, H.: Odeurs, *J. débats.*, **36**, 265 (1929).

DILLON, E.: Smell; a Neglected Sense, *Nineteenth Cent.*, **35**, 574 (1894).

DIMMICK, F. L.: Notes on Henning's Smell Theories, *Am. J. Psychol.*, **33**, 423 (1922).

DINOLT, R.: Smell, *Eye, Ear, Nose and Throat Monthly*, **22**, 259 (1943).

DONATH, J.: Über Farbigriechen, *Z. Neurol. Psychol.*, **29**, 112 (1922).

*DUMERIL, A.: "Des Odeurs," Thèse, Faculté des sciences de Paris, 1843.

———: Considérations sommaires sur les odeurs, *Monit. sci.*, **5**, 183 (1863).

DUPONCHAL, A.: Odeurs, *Encyc. mod.*, **22**, 342 (1857).

DURRANS, T. H.: Residual-affinity Theory of Odors, *Perfumery Essent. Oil Record*, **11**, 391 (1920).

DUVALL, E.: Odors, *Lippincott's Mag.*, **61**, 269 (1898).

DYSON, G. M.: Vibration Theory of Odor, *Perfumery Essent. Oil Record*, **19**, 456 (1928).

———: Scientific Basis of Odour, *Chemistry & Industry*, **57**, 647 (1938).

ECKHARDT: Geruch, *Geiträge zur Anat. Physiol.*, **1** (1855).

ECKSTEIN, G.: Sense of Smell, *Harper's*, **184**, 196 (1942).

EHRENSVARD, G., and L. G. SILLEN: Adsorption Potentials and Olfaction, *Nature*, **141**, 788 (1938).

*ELTRINGHAM, H.: "The Senses of Insects," London, 1933.

EVERETT, R.: Odors and the Soul of Man, *Overland*, ns, **57**, 192 (1911).

FARFAN, A. J. T.: Smoke, Gas, and Hunting Scent, *J. Roy. Artillery*, **61**, 382 (1934).

FAUVELLE: Smell and Sight, *Am. J. Psychol.*, **1**, 358 (1888).

FINCK, H. T.: Aesthetic Value of Smell, *Atlantic Monthly*, **46**, 793 (1880).

FISCHER, E., and F. PENZOLDT: Report on Study of Sensitiveness of Smell, *Abst. in Nature*, **36**, 90 (1887).

FISCHER, O.: Gruppenreferat über den Geruchssinn, *Nervenarzt*, **8**, 541 (1935).

FOERSTER, R.: Sense of Smell; Its Limitations and Peculiarities, *Sci. American Supp.*, **73**, 191 (1912).

FOLSOM, N.: The Senses of Smell and Taste, *Boston Med. Surg. J.*, **68**, 231 (1863).

Four Basic Odors, *Rayon*, **25**, 518 (1944).

FRANÇOIS-FRANCK: Olfaction, *Dict. encycl. sci. méd.* (2ser.), **15**, 1 (1881).

FRANK, J. D., and E. J. LUDVIGH: Retroactive Effect of Pleasant and Unpleasant Odors on Learning, *Am. J. Psychol.*, **43**, 102 (1931).

FREITAG: Geruchssinn, *Zahntech. Reform.*, **430** (1934).

FREUDENBERG: Neue Hypothesen über die Natur der physikalischen Bedingungen des Geruches, *Die Übersinnl. Welt.*, **7**, 183 (1900).

FURST, L.: Zur Geruchslehre, *Beilage allgem. Zeitung*, 160.

*FURSTENAU, J. H.: "De oribus," Rintelii, 1732.

GAMBLE, E. A. M.: The Applicability of Weber's Law to Smell, *Amer. J. Psychol.*, **10**, 82 (1898).

GEBLEWICZ, E.: The Psychology of Olfactory Experiences, *Kwart. Psych.*, **7**, 187 (1935).

GEBSATTEL: Versuche; Beschreibung der Geruchswelt, Nach J. Nogué, *Nervenarzt*, **10**, 528 (1937).

Geruch, *Handwörterbuch Naturw.*, **4**, 974 (1913).

Geruch, *Z. Psychol. Physiol. Sinnesorgane*, **74B**, 305 (1916).

Geruch und Geschmack, *Die Irrenpflege*, **5**, 161 (1901).

Geruchswellen, *Giblek* (14), (1901).

*GIESSLER, C. M.: "Wegweiser zu einer Psychologie des Geruches," Hamburg, 1894.

———: Gerüche vom psychogenetischen Standpunkt, *Vierteljahrigesschr. wissenschaft. Philos. Soziol.*, **26**, 49 (1902).

*GODINEAU, H. F.: "Sur l'Odorat," Paris, 1809.

GRÜNWALD, M.: Nature of Olfaction, *Riechstoff-Ind.*, **8**, 44 (1933).

*HACK, F.: "Riechen und Geruchsorgan," Wiesbaden, 1885.

HALD, P. T.: The Nose in Literature, *Lancet*, **1**, 246 (1906).

*HAMPTON, F. A.: "The Scent of Flowers and Leaves, Its Purpose and Relation to Man," London, 1926.

HARRIS, J. W.: On the Associative Power of Odors, *Am. J. Psychol.*, **19**, 557 (1908).

HARTRIDGE, H.: Note on the Sense of Smell, *Proc. Physiol. Soc. London*, **54**, 39 (1920).

HAYCRAFT, J. B.: The Sense of Smell, *Proc. Roy. Soc. Edinburgh*, **14**, 207 (1887).

HAZZARD, F. W.: Descriptive Account of Odors, *J. Exp. Psychol.*, **13**, 297 (1930).

HELLER, H.: Duft und Geruch, *Prometheus*, 418, 426 (1918).

———: Geruch's-theorie von Teudt, *Biol. Zentr.*, **39**, 364 (1919).

———: A Critical Discussion of Teudt's Theory, *Am. Perfumer*, **14**, 365 (1920).

———: Wie entstehen Duft und Geruch?, *Natur*, **11**, 90 (1923).

HENDRICK, E.: Sense of Smell, *Atlantic Monthly*, **111**, 332 (1913).

———: Beyond the Laboratory (Development of Uses of Olfactory Sense), *Harper's Mag.*, **144**, 666 (1922).

HENNING, H.: Geruch, *Z. Psychol. Physiol. Sinnesorgane*, **70**, 161 (1915).

———: Geruch, *Z. Psychol. Physiol. Sinnesorgane*, **75B**, 177; **76B**, 1 (1916).

———: Geruchsspiele in Japan, *Z. angew. Psychol.*, **14**, 322 (1919).

———: Physiologie und Psychologie des Geruches, *Asher und Sprios Ergebn. Physiol.*, **17**, 585 (1919).

———: Psychologische Studien am Geruchssinn, *Abderhaldens Handb. biol. Arbeitsmeth*, **6** (1), (1924).

*———: "Psychologie der chemischen Sinne. Handbuch der normalen und pathologischen Physiologie," Berlin, 1924.

*———: "Der Geruch: ein Handbuch für die Gebiete der Psychologie, Physiologie," 2d ed., Leipzig, 1924.

HENRY, C.: Le Problème de l'odorance, *Rev. sci.*, **49**, 65 (1892).

———: Odors and the Sense of Smell, *Popular Science*, **41**, 682 (1892).

HENSLOW, G.: The Sense of Smell, *Nature*, **34**, 572 (1886).

HESSE, A.: Über den Geruchssinn und die wichtigsten Riechstoffe, *Z. angew. Chemie*, **10**, 240; **11**, 270 (1900).

————:, A. Ellmer, and R. Haarmann: Riechstoffe, *Ullmanns Encyc. tech. Chem.*, **9**, 499 (1921).

Hofmann, F. B.: Zur Theorie des Geruchssinnes, *Sitzber. Ges. Beförder. ges. Naturw.*, **3**, 50 (1918).

————: Theorie des Geruchssinnes, *Z. Biol.*, **73B**, 29 (1921).

————: Theorie des Geruchssinnes, *Z. Biol.*, **75B**, 63 (1923).

Holway, A. A., *et al.*: Psychophysics and Neurophysiology of Olfaction, *J. Gen. Psychol.*, **23**, 65 (1940).

Hudson, W. H.: On the Sense of Smell, *Century*, **104**, 497 (1922).

Jäger, G.: Über die Bedeutung des Geschmackes und Geruchsstoffes, *Z. wiss. Zool.*, **27**, 319 (1876).

Jones, L. E.: Taste and Smell, *Chemistry & Industry*, **60**, 248 (1941).

Keller, H. A.: Smell Is a Fallen Angel, *Century*, **75**, 573 (1908).

*Kenneth, J. H.: "Osmics; the Science of Smell," Edinburgh, 1924.

————: Relation of Language to Physiological Stimuli, *Nature*, **116**, 748 (1925).

————: Odours and the Sense of Smell, *Nature*, **117**, 591 (1926).

————: Note on Forgotten Sixteenth Century Disputation on Smell, *J. Laryngol. Otol.*, **43**, 103 (1928).

Kido, M., and M. Yoshida: On the Common Properties of Olfaction, *Japan J. Psychol.*, 95 (1937).

Kiesow, F.: Sulla Frequenza dei sogni gustativi ed olfattivi, *Arch. ital. de psicol.*, **7**, 226 (1929).

Kinross, M.: Inarticulate Sense, *English Rev.*, **51**, 114 (1930).

Kniep, E. H., *et al.*: Studies in Affective Psychology, *Am. J. Psychol.*, **43**, 406 (1931).

Kodama, S.: Resonance theory of odors, *J. Tokyo Chem. Soc.*, **41**, 975 (1920).

Krancher, O.: Geruchs-oder Gesichtssinn?, *Entomol. Jahrb.*, **13** (1904).

Krause, W.: Geruch und Geschmack, *Jahresber. über Fortschr. Anat. Entwicklungsgeschichte*, **38**, 557 (1903).

Kravkov, S. V.: Odors and Color Vision, *Fiziol. Zhur. S.S.S.R.*, **28**, 313 (1940).

*Krumm-Heller, A.: "Vom Weihrauch zur Osmotherapie," Berlin, 1936.

Laird, D. A.: Normal Odor Effects and Association of Psychoanalytic Significance, *Psychoanalyt. Rev.*, **21**, 194 (1934).

Lamprecht, A.: Vom Wesen des Geruchs, *Gartenlaube*, 749 (1924).

*Lange, M. L.: "De olfactu," Batavia, 1721.

*Langguth, G. A.: "De nonnullis odoratus admirabilibus quaedam commentatus," Wittenbergae, 1762.

*Larguier des Bancels: "Le Goût et l'odorat," Paris, 1912.

————: L'odorat, *Arch. psychol.*, **10**, 1 (1910).

*Lederer, F. L., and A. R. Hollander: Text Book of the Ear, Nose and Throat, Philadelphia, 1942.

*Leideritz, H.: Sympathie und Geruch, Bremervoorde, 1933.

————: Phänomene des Geruchs, *Biol. Heilkunst*, 649, 666 (1933).

Leitch, N.: Science of Smells, *Middlesex Hosp. J.*, 166 (July, 1934).

Levy, L. S., *et al.*: Report of Odorgraphia Committee, *Ind. Eng. Chem. News*, **11**, 114 (1933).

Liégeois: Mémoire sur les mouvements de certains corps organiques à la surface de l'eau et sur les applications qu'on peut en faire à la théorie des odeurs, *Arch. physiol. norm. path.*, **1**, 35 (1868).

McAfee, H.: Sense of Smell, *Nature*, **98**, 57 (1914).

McCartney, W.: The Mystery of Odour, Survey and Suggestion, *Perfumery Essent. Oil Record, Ann.*, special number (1936).

MacCulloch, G.: The Applicability of Weber's Law to Smell, *Am. J. Psychol.*, **10** (1), (1898).

Macdonald, G.: On the Mechanism of the Nose as Regards Taste and Smell, *Brit. Med. J.*, **11**, 1210 (1888).

Macht des Geruches, *Hyg. Korrespond.*, **5H**, (1938).

McIndoo, N. E.: Smell and Taste and Their Applications, *Sci. Monthly*, **25**, 481 (1927).

McKenzie, D.: Riddle of Olfaction, *J. Laryngol. Otol.*, **36**, 288 (1921).

*———: "Aromatics and the Soul; a Study of Smells," London, 1923.

Mackenzie, S.: Smells Are Surer Than Sounds and Sight, *American Magazine*, **104**, 49 (1927).

Magne, H., A. Mayer, and L. Plantefol: Smell: Three Phase Sensation, *J. Psychol.*, **24**, 255 (1927).

Malvezin, P.: Theories of Olfaction, *Ann. chim. anal. chim. appl.*, **4**, 298, 301 (1922).

Martinet, J.: Sur un Phénomène olfactif analogue au phénomène optique de Purkinje, *Rev. gén. sci.*, **44**, 261 (1933).

Mason, A. H.: Odours, Perfumes and Flavours Physiology, Philosophy, History, Sources and Preparations, *Proc. Lit. & Phil. Soc.*, Liverpool, **37**, 195 (1882).

Matthes, E.: Olfacto e gosto no reino animal, *Arq. mus. bocage*, 17 (1938).

Matteotti, L.: Scala naturale degli odori, *Boll. malat. orecchio*, **25**, 49 (1907).

Maybee, G. R.: Perception of Food Odors—Particle and Odor Wave Theories, *Can. Chem. Process Ind.*, **23**, 115 (1939).

Mesnard: À Propos des mélanges des odeurs, *Compt. rend. acad. sci.*, **116**, 1461 (1893).

Metzner, C. A.: Investigation of Odor and Taste, Psychological Principles, *Wallerstein Labs. Comm.*, **6**, 518 (1943).

Michaud, G.: An Olfactory Paradox, *Sci. American*, **103**, 365 (1910).

Michel-Bechet, H.: Olfactory Sense in Works of Baudelaire, *Arch. méd.-chir. de Province*, **25**, 437 (1935).

Missenden, J.: Intensity and Quality of Odors, *Perfumery Essent. Oil Record*, **17**, 62 (1926).

Mitchell, A.: The Sense of Smell, *Nature*, **34**, 521, 572; **35**, 74 (1886).

*Moncrieff, R. W.: "The Chemical Senses," London, 1944.

*Monroe, W. S.: "Experiments Proving the Existence of Olfactory Images in Dreams," *Paper, Intern. Congr. Psych.*, Paris, 1900.

Morgan, T. J.: The Sense of Smell, *Science*, **10**, 240 (1899).

Müller, A.: Dipolar Theory of Olfaction, *Perfumery Essent. Oil Record.*, **27**, 202 (1936).

Munger, C.: Scala naturale degli odori, *Boll. malat. orecchio*, **25**, 49 (1907).

*Munn, N. L.: "An Introduction to Animal Psychology," Boston, 1933.

Myers: Smell, *Cambridge, Anthrop. Exped. Torres Straits*, **2** (pt. 2), 169 (1903).

Mysterious Sense, *Literary Digest*, **89**, 48 (1926).

Mysterious Sense of Smell, *Literary Digest*, **114**, 22 (1932).

Näcke, P.: Vertreibung böser Geister durch üble Gerüche, *Arch. Kriminal-Anthropol.*, **24**, 156 (1906).

Nagel, W.: Geruch und Erinnerung, *Gartenlaube*, **32**, 572 (1905).

New Photos Prove Insect-eating Plant Can Smell, *Popular Science*, **123**, 20 (1933).

Niccolini, P.: Present Status of Author's Research on Smell, *Riv. clin. med.* (*Supp.*), **1**, 154 (1940).

Nichols, E. L., and E. H. S. Bailey: The Sense of Smell, *Nature*, **35**, 74 (1886).

Nickles, J.: Sur la Théorie physique des odeurs et des saveurs, *Mem. acad. Stanislas*, **2**, 356 (1861).

NICOL, H.: The Perception of Odour, *Perfumery Essent. Oil Record*, **17**, 176 (1926).

No Smelling by Radio, *Literary Digest*, **101**, 35 (1929).

NOQUÉ, J.: Essai d'une description du monde olfactif, *J. psychol. norm. Path.*, **33**, 230 (1936).

O'NEILL, J. J.: Sorting Smells by Their Numbers, *Science Digest*, **16**, 87 (1944).

Osmics, *Lancet*, **2**, 1167 (1924).

*OSTERLING: "De olfactu," Batavia, 1731.

Our Chemical Senses, *Sci. American*, **158**, 107 (1938).

PALFRAY, L.: Review on Odorous Substances, *Riechstoff Ind. u. Kosmetik*, **13**, 27 (1938).

————: Review on Odorous Substances, *Riechstoff Ind. u. Kosmetik*, **13**, 50 (1938).

PAPILLON, F.: Les Odeurs d'après les découvertes récentes de la chimie et de la physiologie, *Monit. sci.*, **14**, 296 (1872).

————: Odors and Life, *Popular Science Monthly*, **6**, 142 (1874).

PASSY, J.: Revue général sur les sensations olfactives, *Ann. psychol.*, **2**, 363 (1896).

Photographing Smells, *Popular Science*, **134**, 116 (1939).

Plea for Smell, *Science*, **8**, 520 (1898).

POINSOT, G.: Olfaction, *N. dict. méd. chir. prat.*, **24**, 425 (1877).

POLIMANTI, O.: Le principe de la division du travail et la fonction vicariante dans les organes des sens, *Rev. sci.*, 5s, **11**, 769 (1909).

*POLLARD, H.: "The Mystery of Scent," London, 1937.

PONDER, C.: Sense of Smell, *Living Age*, **329**, 204 (1926).

————: The Sense of Smell, *Discovery*, **7**, 105 (1926).

PORTER, A.: Ever See a Scent? *Collier's*, **115**, 16 (1945).

POWYS, L.: Images and Colors Evoked by the Fifth Sense, *Arts and Decoration*, **19**, 36 (1923).

PRICE, W. A.: Sense of Smell Again, *J. Econ. Entomol.*, **18**, 448 (1925).

Psychology of Smell, *Literary Digest*, **83**, 75 (1924).

PYCRAFT, W. P.: Our Sense of Smell, *Illus. London News*, **170**, 540 (1927).

RADESTOCK, H.: Geruch's Spurenbild, *Kosmos*, 276 (1921).

RAMSEY, W.: Sense of Smell, *Nature*, **26**, 187 (1882).

RAPPORT, V. A.: Seeking a Science of Smell, *J. Home Econ.*, **28**, 460 (1936).

RAYCROFT, J. E.: Character and Special Senses, *Trans. Am. Acad. Ophthalmol.*, **48**, 45 (1943).

*REID, T.: "An Inquiry into the Human Mind on the Principles of Commonsense," 6th ed., Edinburgh, 1810.

RIBOT, T.: Le Goût et l'odorat, *J. psychol.*, **17**, 5 (1920).

RICCITELLI, E.: La teoría sintónica de la visión; nuevos orientaciones en la interpretación del mecanismo de la olfacción, *Rev. soc. argent. otorrinolar.*, **1**, 88 (1925).

ROBINSON, L.: Noses and Minds, *Blackwood's Mag.*, **169**, 796 (1901).

ROGER, G. H., and L. BINET: Smell, *Traité de physiol. norm. path.*, **10**, 982 (1935).

RÖMPPI, H.: Geruchsempfindung, *Schulwarte*, 172 (1933).

ROTHE, K. C.: Geruch und Geschmack, *Lehrerfortbildg.*, 50 (1918).

RUZICKA, L.: Grundlage der Geruchschemie, *Chem. Ztg.*, **44**, 93 (1920).

SACHER, J. F.: Massanalytische Bestimmungen mit Hilfe des Geruchssinnes, *Chem. Ztg.*, **37**, 1222 (1913).

Scent and Memory, *Spectator*, **101**, 52 (1908).

Scent and Memory, *Living Age*, **259**, 437 (1908).

SCHAEFER, H.: Electrical and Chemical Interpretation of Vital Processes, *Klin. Wochschr.*, **20**, 209 (1941).

SCHNEIDER: The Education of the Sense of Smell, *N.Y. Med. Record*, **38**, 452 (1890).

SCONINA, K.: Beitrag zur Möglichkeit einer Lokalisierung des Geruches, *Zool. Anz.*, **122B**, 194 (1938).

SCOTT-MONCRIEFF, R.: Olfaction, *Bull. Vancouver Med. Assoc.*, **15**, 266 (1939).

Secret of the Satisfaction We Derive from Certain Stenches, *Current Opinion*, **55**, 178 (1913).

Seeing with the Nose, *Nation* (London), **33**, 344 (1923).

*SENNERTUS, D.: "De auditu et olfactu," Wittenbergae, 1826.

Sense of Smell, *Spectator*, **93**, 283 (1904).

Sense of Smell in Men and Animals, *Literary Digest*, **103**, 64 (1929).

Sense of Smell Has Not Been Educated in Man, *Hygeia*, **12**, 1045 (1934).

SEYDELL, E. M.: Survey of Fact and Theory in Field of Olfaction, *Ann. Otol., Rhinol., Laryngol.*, **40**, 472 (1931).

SIERRA, A. M.: Psychologist Bergson and His Theory of Perception, *Semana méd.*, **1**, 693 (1941).

SLATER, J. W.: Odors and Their Recognition, *J. Sci.*, **19**, 519 (1882).

SLOSSON, E. E.: Incense as an Aid to Devotion, *Independent*, **52**, 598 (1900).

Smell and Taste, *Encyclopaedia Britannia*, 14th ed., **20**, 819 (1941).

Smellin' Through, *Literary Digest*, **123**, 29 (1937).

SPIER, J.: Geruchsstudien im Felde, *Frankf. Ztg.*, 60 (Feb. 29, 1916).

*STANLEY, R. H.: "Scent and All about It," London, 1928.

STEFANINI, A.: Sulla Teoria della percezione degli odori, *Arch. ital. otol.*, **33**, 144 (1922).

———: Sur la Théorie de la perception des odeurs, *Arch. ital. biol.*, **74**, 8 (1924).

*STERNBERG, W.: "Geschmack und Geruch," Berlin, 1906.

SUTTER, J. J.: Odors, *Ohio State Med. J.*, **18**, 672 (1922).

TEUDT, H.: Erklärung der Geruchserscheinungen, *Deut. Blätt. erzieh. Unterr.*, 716 (1913).

———: Wie Entstehen Geruchsempfindungen, *Prometheus*, **25**, 1282 (1914).

———: Eine neue Geruchstheorie, *Wochschr. Brauerei*, **35**, 92, 99, 107 (1918).

———: Neue Geruchstheorie, *Deut. Essigind.*, **8**, 16 (1919).

———: Theories of Olfaction, *Z. anorg. allgem. Chem.*, **106**, 189 (1919).

———: Theories of Olfaction, *Z. anorg. allgem. Chem.*, **108**, 137 (1919).

———: Erwiderurgen auf Heller's Artikel "Über die Geruchstheorie von Teudt," *Biol. Zentr.*, **40**, 259 (1920).

The Physiological Psychology of Smelling, *J. Am. Med. Assoc.*, **30**, 99 (1898).

TINKER, E. L.: Lafcadio Hearn and the Sense of Smell, *Bookman*, **58**, 519 (1924).

TITCHENER, E. B.: Compensation of Odors, *Am. J. Psychol.*, **27**, 435 (1916).

Training Our Noses, *Literary Digest*, **88**, 78 (1926).

TSCHIRSCH, A.: Smelling Is a Chemical Process Due to Combination of Ionized Odours Substance with the Plasma of Olfactory Cells, *Schweiz. apoth. Ztg.*, **59**, 241 (1921).

———: Eine chemische Theorie des Riechprozesses, *Schweiz. chem. Ztg.*, **60**, 105, 117, 141 (1922).

Über ein abweichendes Geruchssystem, *Onderzoek. ged. in h. physiol. Lab. Utrecht Hoogesch.*, **8**, 394 (1907).

UNGERER, W. G., and R. B. STODDARD: Odor Theory, *Ungerers' Bull.*, **3**, 7 (1922).

VALENTIN, A.: Über die Beschaffenheit der riechbaren Stoffe und die Ursachen des Riechens, *Mitt. naturforsch. Ges.*, 1 hft., 60, (1884).

VAN DER HOEVEN-LEONHARD, J.: Abweichendes Geruchssystem, *Z. Psychol. Physiol. Sinnesorg.*, **42**, 210 (1907).

———: Über ein abweichendes Geruchssystem, *Z. Sinnesphysiol.*, **42**, 210 (1907).

———: Een afwijkend renkstelsil, *Nederland. tijdschr. geneesk.*, **44** (1. Afd.), 497 (1908).

———: Riechschärfen-und Farbensinnabweichungen, *Umschau*, **12**, 368 (1908).

VASCHIDE, N., and VAN MELLE: Une nouvelle Hypothèse sur la nature des conditions physiques de l'odorat, *Compt. rend. acad. sci.*, **129**, 1285 (1899).

*VERYARD, R. G.: "Scent and the Weather," Peschawar, India, 1935.

VOIVENEL, P.: Paradoxes sur l'odorat, *Progrès méd. Paris* (3s), **32**, 453 (1917).

Vom Geruchssinn, *Beibl. gerichtl. Anthrop.*, **11**, 136 (1860).

VON HORNBOSTEL, E. M.: Geruchshelligkeit, *Pflüger's Arch. ges. physiol.*, **227B**, 517 (1931).

VON SKRAMLIK, E.: Olfactory Organs, *Abderhalden Handb. biol. Arbeitsmethod,* Abt. 5, Teil 7, 1677 (1937).

————: Geruch, *Tabulae biol.*, **2**, 289 (1925).

WALBAUM, H.: Über den Geruchssinn und die wichtigsten Riechstoffe, *Z. angew. Chem.*, **17**, 419; **37**, 937 (1900).

WARTENBERG, R.: Qualitätensystem der Geruchsempfindungen, *Ber. 9 Kongr. exp. psychol.*, 234 (1926).

WARUS, S. M.: Associations and Odors, *Lippincott's Mag.*, **41**, 269 (1898).

WATSON, E. R.: Smell, *Biochem. J.*, **16**, 613 (1922).

WATSON, W. S.: On the Therapeutical Influence of Odors, *Med. Press and Circ.*, **20**, 143 (1875).

WEISGERBER, L.: Geruchssinn in unseren Sprachen, *Indogerman. Forschungen*, **46B**, 121 (1928).

*WELLS, H. B.: "The Tonic of Universal Law; Color, Odor, Dictated by Wilbur Stoddard," New York, 1936.

Why Do We Smell? *Sci. American*, **94**, 11 (1905).

WILSON, A. C.: Appeals to Sense of Smell in Literature, *March Lit. Club Papers*, **62**, 149 (1937).

WOLFF, O. J. B.: Die Mechanik des Riechens, *Samml. wiss. Vortäge Virchow Holtzendorff*, **13**, 289 (1878).

WÖLKERLING, W.: Bedeutung und Pflege des Geruchs- und Geschmacksinnes, *Das Rote Kreuz, Korresp. Zentr. Sanitätspflege*, 295 (1902).

ZEISS, M.: Geruch's Materialisation Verstorbener, *Wahres Leben*, **26**, 58 (1925).

Z. Riech- Geschmackstoffe, Rev. intern. aromes, **1** (1), (Feb. 1, 1909); **3** (9), (June, 1911).

ZENNECK: Psychische Seite der Geruchserscheinungen, *Mag. phil. Med. gerichtl. Seelenk.* (2 hft.), 46 (1829).

————: Von ähnlichen Gerüchen, *Buchner's Repertorium Pharm.*, **39**, 215 (1831).

Zur Pflege des Geruchssinns, *Württembergisches Schulwochenbl.*, **85** (1922).

ZWAARDEMAKER, H.: Het mechanisme van het ruihen, *Nederland. tijdschr. geneesk.*, **24**, 321 (1888).

————: Geruch, *Ergeb. Physiol.* 2 abt., 896 (1902).

————: Über die Qualitäten des Geruchssinnes, *Onderzoek ged. physiol. Lab. Utrecht, Hoogesch.*, **7**, 381 (1907).

————: Die vektorielle Darstellung eines Systemes von Geruchskompensationen, *Arch. Physiol.*, 51 (1908).

————: Geruch und Geschmack, *Handbuch physiol. Meth.* **III** (1 abt.), 46 (1910).

*————: "L'Odorat," Paris, 1925.

————: Sense of Smell, *Acta Oto-Laryngol.*, **II**, 3 (1927).

M. LEGAL CASES INVOLVING ODOR

Albert v. *U.S.*, 281 F. 511. That witnesses who testified that certain liquor was whisky were not in express terms shown to be familiar with the taste, smell, and effect of whisky held not to render their testimony incompetent for admission by jury.

Alster v. *Allen*, 42 P. 2d 969, 141 Kan. 661. When offensive odors, fumes, and vapors from creamery station penetrate homes to discomfort of residents, etc., station may be injoined as nuisance.

Anders v. *Met. Life Ins. Co.*, 40 N.E. 2d 738, 314 Ill. App. 196. Insurance—evidence in action on policy—(odor)—result of inhaling carbon monoxide gas.

Anderson v. *State*, 103 So. 305, 20 Ala. App. 505. Witness cannot testify that tub smelled of beer in absence of showing that he knows smell of beer, or knows whether it will leave odor, or for how long.

Andrews v. *Perry*, 216 N.Y.S., 537, 127 Misc. 320. Vapors and odors, to constitute a nuisance, need not be injurious to health, if they interfere with comfortable enjoyment of one's home.

Archey v. *State*, 59 S.W. (2d) 406, 123 Tex. Cr.R. 458. Permitting jury, in prosecution for opening stink bomb in theatre, to smell of container containing offensive substance, though improper, held not reversible error.

Aunt Jemima Mills Co. v. *Lloyd Royal Belge*, 28 F. 2d 398. Odors causing damage in storage of cargo.

Aydlett v. *Carolina By-products Co.*, 2 S.E. 2d 881, 215 N.C. 700. Action to recover damages for injuries to real property by reason of noxious odors from animal by-products factory.

Bainbridge Power Co. v. *Ivey*, 152 S.E. 306, 41 Ga. App. 193. Nuisance created by reservoir over wooded land resulting in mosquitoes and objectionable odors held of permanent character.

Bell v. *State*, 109 So. 900, 21 Ala. App. 550. Testimony as to smell and taste of whisky held admissible where witnesses testified to experience in handling character of liquor involved.

Benton v. *Kernan*, 21 A. 2d, 755, 130 N.J. Eq. 193. Injunction against filling air around a dwelling with noxious or offensive vapors or odors.

Benton v. *Kernan*, 13 A. 2d, 825, 127 N.J. Eq. 434. Odors as nuisance.

Bert v. *City of Alliance*, 32 N.E. 2d 49. City's liability for injuries from inhaling odors caused by sewage.

Billeaudeau v. *Jeansonne*, 149 So. 183 La. App. Farmer residing 250 feet from slaughter-house and storage vat which generated smells which were an intolerable private nuisance held entitled to abate their operation.

Blanke v. *Miranne*, 11 So. 2d 264. Damages for loss of sense of smell.

Burnett v. *State*, 155 N.E. 209, 199 Ind. 49. Officers seeing defendants' truck loaded with tin cans and smelling odor of intoxicating liquor emanating therefrom, were justified in making arrest and searching car without warrant.

Burris v. *State*, 290 S.W. 66, 172 Ark. 609. Opinion based on smell is competent to identify liquor as whisky.

Catagrone v. *U.S.*, 63 F. (2d) 931. Officers holding void search warrant could make search as incident to arrest of person found in residence and arrested when officers detected strong odor of mash coming through doorway.

Champa v. *Washington Compressed Gas Co.*, 262 P. 228, 146 Wash. 190. Gas plant was nuisance because fears of ordinary persons and odors offensive to such persons held proper.

Chandler v. *City of Olney*, 87 S.W. 2d 250, 126 Tex. 230. Owners of farm on creek 4½ miles from city could recover from city which polluted creek by discharge of sewage for discomforts growing out of disagreeable and noxious odors, notwithstanding absence of other damages.

City of Bessemer v. *Chambers*, 8 So. 2d 163, 242 Ala. 666. City's liability for nuisance caused by odors of sewage disposal plant—damages.

City of Edmond v. *Billen*, 42 P. 2d 253. Damages for foul odors emitted from city's adjacent sewage disposal plant.

City of Jasper v. *Lacy*, 112 So. 307, 216 Ala. 26. Damages for injuries from odors from discharge of sewage.

City of Frankfort v. *Ballew*, 151 S.W. 2d 1063, 287 Ky. 141. Common knowledge as to the temporary nature of certain odors.

City of Marlin v. *Criswell*, 293 S.W. 910. Odors from sewage disposal plant held to constitute a nuisance.

City of Miami, Fla., v. *Lithgow*, 12 So. 2d 380. Proof offered for injunction against cremators because of offensive odors.

City of Olney v. *Chandler*, 57 S.W. 2d 323 Modified, Com. App., *Chandler* v. *City of Olney*, 87 S.W. 2d 250, 126 Tex. 230. Mere inconvenience from odors unaccompanied by other injury is not ground for damages.

City of Tyler v. *House*, 64 S.W. 2d 1007. City operating on its premises sewage disposal plant which gives off offensive odors and gases is liable.

City of Wichita Falls v. *Sullivan*, 22 S.W. 2d 982. Discomfort incident to obnoxious odors caused by land being flooded held evidentiary.

Clark v. *Beacon Oil Co.*, 170 N.E. 836, 271 Mass. 27. Hospital record as to odor of alcohol on breath of automobile driver taken to hospital after accident held not erroneous.

Copley v. *State*, 281 S.W. 460, 153 Tenn. 189. Courts may take judicial notice that dogs of some varieties have acuteness of smell which enables them to follow trail upon which they are laid, though crossed by others.

Cross v. *Texas Military College*, 65 S.W. 2d 794. Temporary nuisance caused by offensive odors from slaughtering pen held not recoverable.

Dahl v. *Utah Oil Refining Co.*, 262 P. 269, 71 Utah 1. Evidence of impregnation of atmosphere in thickly settled manufacturing communities with disagreeable odors and impurities.

DeBlois v. *Bowers*, 44 F. 2d 621 D.C. Mass. Operation of steel galvanizing plant emitting obnoxious fumes and odors held to constitute a nuisance.

DeMuro v. *Havranek*, 275 N.Y.S. 186, 153 Misc. 787. Persons living in district not compelled to submit to suffering from dirt, smoke, noisome odors, etc. without compensation.

Dilly v. *State*, 154 N.E. 865, 199 Ind. 158. Liquid that had been in broken bottle could be identified by officers as intoxicating liquor by smell of same.

Donahue v. *U.S.*, 56 F. (2d) 94. Search without warrant of dwelling house held justified where officers, before entering, detected strong odor of whisky and mash and heard still in operation.

Driskill v. *U.S.*, 24 F. 2d 525. Permitting jury to inspect and smell contents of bottles purchased held not in error.

Ebur v. *Alloy Metal Wire Co.*, 155 A. 280, 304 Fla. 177. Smoke, odors, gases, and smudge issuing from plant were "unnecessary and unreasonable" if could be reduced, and constitute a nuisance.

Everson v. *Albert*, 246 N.W. 88, 261 Mich. 182. Eviction of tenant due to odors.

Feder v. *Perry Coal Co.*, 279 Ill. App. 314. Discharge of gases, fumes, and smoke causing noxious odors from a slag pile burning where fire was caused by spontaneous combustion—a nuisance.

Ferrell v. *Commonwealth*, 264 S.W. 1078, 204 Ky. 518. Where driver opened car door when sheriff approached and sheriff could see kegs in rear seat and could smell whisky, sheriff properly arrested occupants of car.

Francisco v. *Dept. of Institutions and Agencies*, 180 A. 843, 13 N.J. Misc. 663. Odors and noises from hospital held not to be cause for nuisance damages.

Galligan v. *U.S.*, 299 F. 172. Testimony by witness familiar with taste and smell of alcoholic liquors that a liquid he drank was whisky, is competent.

Garber v. *Rubel Corp.*, 290 N.Y.S. 633, 160 Misc. 716. Offensive odors as nuisance (ice plant).

General Outdoor Advertising Co. v. *Dept. of Public Works*, 193 N.E. 799, 289 Mass. 149. Common-law nuisance may arise from offensive sights, sounds, or smells.

Gilmore v. *Central Maine Power Co.*, 145 A. 137, 127 Me. 522. Injuries from odors as grounds for compensation under law of eminent domain.

Gorat v. *U.S.*, 61F. (2d) 397 C.C.A. Neb. Agents with three years experience with smell and taste of alcohol held competent to give expert evidence.

Gray v. *City of High Point*, 166 S.E. 911, 203 N.C. 756. Cannot recover for nuisance of occasional odors.

Griffiths v. *Crawford*, 52 P. (2d) 548. Damages for injury causing loss of sense of smell.

Hannon v. *State*, 259 S.W. 1083, 96 Tex. Cr.R. 660. Witness testifying that liquid in certain bottles was homemade whisky called "Shinney" affirming knowledge of its taste and smell was competent to give opinion it was intoxicating without chemical analysis.

Harvey v. *City of Seymour*, 14 S.W. 2d 901 Tex. Civ. App. Exclusion of cotton gins from residential district because of odors.

Hasslinger v. *Village of Hartland*, 290 N.W. 647. Condemnation as not exclusive remedy for odors created by sewage disposal plant.

Heller v. *American Range Corp.*, 234 N.W. 316, 182 Minn. 286. Odors and gases from stove-enameling plant constitute a nuisance.

Higgins v. *Decorah Produce Co.*, 242 N.W. 109, 214 Iowa 276. Owners required to reduce odors to a minimum in operating a poultry and produce plant.

Holman v. *Athens Empire Laundry Co.*, 100 S.E. 207, 149 Ga. 345, 6 A.L.R. 1564. As affecting jurisdiction of equity to restrain nuisances, there is in principle no distinction between cases of smoke, smell, noise or gas.

Hughes v. *State*, 268 S.W. 960, 99 Tex. Cr.R. 244. Testimony of officer, who stated he was acquainted with odor of whisky, that the liquor found had such an odor, and that in his judgment the liquor was whisky, held competent but not conclusive.

Iford v. *Nickel*, 1 S.W. 2d 751. Smells arising from business will not be enjoined as nuisance, unless substantial.

In re Hayward's Will, 256 N.Y.S. 607, 143 Misc. 401. Illuminating gas as a pungent odor immediately discernible to person coming into it from outer air.

Jeakins v. *City of Eldorado*, 53 P. (2d) 798, 143 Kan. 206. City's liability for injuries from odors caused by sewage.

Johnson v. *Drysdale*, 285 N.W. 301. Barns produce penetrating odor and constitute a breeding place for flies.

Johnson v. *State*, 130 So. 777, 222 Ala. 90. Where witness inspects bottle and smells or tastes contents he may state whether in his 'judgment it contains whisky.

K.&L. Oil Co. v. *Oklahoma City*, 14 F. Supp. 492. Judicial notice taken of fact that noxious gases and odors occasioned by drilling oil well.

Kaminski v. *State*, 168 N.E. 612, 91 Ind. App. 160. Officers may identify intoxicating liquor by sense of smell.

Kempinski v. *Tuthill Building Material Co.*, 255 Ill. App. 375. Smoke and odor from operation of factory considered in action as nuisance.

King v. *Ward*, 178 S.E. 577, 207 N.C. 782. Allowing cotton to remain in street for long periods emitting odors that impair comfort of home nearby would be nuisance.

Kuhn v. *Wood*, 36 N.E. 2d 1006. Relief granted to owner of tract from employee causing obnoxious odors amounting to a nuisance by hauling vegetable refuse onto tract.

Kundinger v. *Bagnasco*, 298 N.W. 386, 298 Mich. 15. Evidence of unpleasant odors as nuisance.

Leeth v. *State*, 144 S.E., 133, 38 Ga. App. 353. Evidence of liquor odor from kegs found near defendant's car held wholly circumstantial and insufficient to sustain conviction.

Lewis v. *Lake Charles Stevedores*, 135 So. 630, 17 La. App. 579. Workmen's compensation—causal connection between blow on head and loss of sense of smell.

MacDonald v. *Perry*, 255 P. 494, 32 Ariz. 39. Instructions justifying inference that right to freedom from noxious odors is absolute held erroneous.

McBride v. *U.S.*, 284 F. 416. Agents on premises where there was an unoccupied house smelled fumes from a still, held authorized, without a warrant, to search.

McDuffie v. *State*, 174 So. 801, 27 Ala. App. 403. Opinion evidence of contents of kegs obtained by sense of smell.

McMullen v. *Jennings*, 41 P. 2d 753, 141 Kan. 420. Grain elevator may become nuisance if in operation the air is polluted with dust of foul odor.

McNeill v. *State*, 7 S.W. (2d) 559, 110 Tex. Cr.R. 499. Testimony as to what witness saw, smelled, and heard during raid held not erroneous.

Malacrauis v. *U.S.*, 299 F. 253. Testimony of officer that liquor was being distilled on defendant's premises, due to odor, was competent.

Mathews v. *State*, 106 So. 390, 21 Ala. App. 181. Error to permit witness to testify as to whether contents of receptacle smelled of intoxicating liquor, where witness is not qualified as to sense of smell.

Mattingly v. *Commonwealth*, 251 S.W. 953, 199 Ky. 724. Testimony accepted that white mule, or moonshine, whisky has an odor peculiarly its own.

Mendoza v. *State*, 290 S.W. 1100, 106 Tex. Cr.R. 127. Non-expert witnesses, by tasting and smelling, may testify whether cans contained alcohol.

Mongaup Valley Co. v. *Rockland Light & Power Co.*, 258 N.Y.S. 731, 144 Misc. 718. Landowner granting part of land to power company for reservoir held not entitled to complain of obnoxious odors emanating from reservoir bottom upon withdrawal of water.

More v. *City of San Bernardino*, 5 P. 2d 661, 118, Cal. App. 732. Damages for odors and stenches on account of city's permitting sewage to overflow land.

Mutual Ins. Co. of Richmond, Va. v. *Marshall*, 161 S.E. 61, 157 Va. 427. Carbolic acid has strong pungent odor and produces excruciating pain.

Nat. Container Corp. v. *State* rel *Stockton*, 189 So. 4. Emission of obnoxious odors from wood-pulp mills.

Newton v. *City of Roundup*, 198 P. 441, 60 Mont. 24. Damages to abate nuisance from noxious odors due to negligent operation of septic tank.

Nicoll v. *President & Trustees of Village of Ossining*, 220 N.Y.S. 345, 128 Misc. 848. Village has no right to operate garbage disposal plant in manner so that odors become nuisance.

Nobriga v. *U.S.*, 22 F. (2d) 507. Affidavit that agent saw still in operation in dwelling and smelled fermenting mash held not to authorize issuance of search warrant, in absence of commercial manufacture.

Patterson v. *Commonwealth*, 267 S.W. 160, 206 Ky. 258. Defendant, halted by officers and asked about pronounced odor of whisky replied, "Boys, you have got me," and offered them whisky to turn him loose, arrest without warrant upheld.

People v. *Jones*, 206 N.W. 996, 233 Mich. 514. Testimony of officer that he smelled of bottle and that odor manifested it had recently contained moonshine, was competent, and its weight was for jury.

People v. *Orlando*, 9 N.W. 2d 893, 305 Mich. 686. Search and seizure warranted by odor of stench bomb.

People v. *Reed*, 164 N.E. 847, 333 Ill. 397. Witnesses who testified they were familiar with and recognized odor of dynamite were unable to describe odor, held not to affect value of their testimony.

Pinnington v. *State*, 133 So. 311, 24 Ala. App. 227. Admission of testimony as to smelling whisky on defendant held error, where witness did not qualify as to knowledge of smell of whisky.

Purdy v. *Swift & Co.*, Industrial Indemnity Exchange, Intervenor, 94 P. 2d 389 Cal. App. Permanent loss of sense of smell as result of personal injury.

Quandt Brewing Co. v. *U.S.*, 47 F. (2d) 199. Affidavit for search warrant to search premises occupied by brewery, based on senses of sight, hearing, and smell, held sufficiently to show probable cause.

Roberts v. *State*, 149 So. 356, 25 Ala. App. 477. Body odor admitted as evidence in murder prosecution.

W. F. Robinson & Son v. *Jones*, 72 S.W. (2d) 16, 254 Ky. 637. Testimony of witness that immediately after auto accident he smelled liquor on motorist's breath held admissible.

Rocchia v. *U.S.*, 78 F. (2d) 966 C.C.A. Cal. 1935. Arrest without warrant allowed upon smelling odor of fermenting mash.

Roy v. *Chevrolet Motor Car Co.*, 247 N.W. 774, 262 Mich. 663. Nuisance resulting from smoke, monoxide gas, and noxious odors held denied.

Royalty v. *Strange*, 204 S.W. 870. Owner entitled to injunction abating the nuisance if landowner nearby keeps such a number of hogs in such small pens or feeds them with garbage in such a way as to produce noxious and disagreeable odor.

Salt River Valley Water Users' Assn. v. *Arthur*, 74 P. 2d 582. Conditions causing odor nuisance—decayed vegetable and animal matter.

Sewer & Water Works Improvement Dist. No. 1 v. *McClendon*, 60 S.W. 2d 920, 187 Ark. 510. Damages for 16 acres pasture land rendered dangerous for stock and odors from septic tank injured dwelling.

Sikes v. *State*, 107 So. 800, 21 Ala. App. 220. Evidence that empty vessels smelling of whisky were found on defendant's premises at time of alleged sale is admissible to prove offense.

Singer v. *James*, 100 A. 642, 130 Md. 382. In suit to restrain keeping cattle, horse, hog, and chicken pens and dog kennels close to plaintiff's land, injunction restraining "any foul odors" held too broad.

Smallwood v. *U.S.*, 68 F. (2d) 244. Officers' search of basement of dwelling house held justified as incidental to arrest for offenses committed in "presence of officers" when officers, before entering house, smelled strong odor of whisky mash.

Southwestern Sewer Co. v. *Morris*, 26 S.W. 2d 311. Husband's testimony that he "felt bad" when wife complained of odors from sewage disposal plant held admissible in suit to recover damages.

Spillman v. *State*, 292 S.W. 891, 106 Tex. Cr.R. 455. Evidence of smell of liquor on defendant's breath at time of assault held admissible.

Stankiewoecz v. *State*, 142 N.E. 615, 194 Ind. 246. One who knows smell of whisky may testify a jar of liquor is whisky from having smelled it.

Stanton v. *Sears, Roebuck & Co.*, 38 N.E. 2d 801, 312 Ill. App. 496. Judicial notice that persons become allergic or sensitive to odors.

State v. *Burckhalter*, 151 S.E. 64, 153 S.C. 487. Permitting jury to take liquid into jury room and smell or taste it if they desired held not in error.

State v. *Clark*, 33 S.W. (2d) 890. Proof that liquor found smelled and tasted like moonshine whisky was properly admitted.

State v. *Dalton*, 238 W. (2d) 1. Testimony as to contents of jug as hooch or moonshine through smelling held admissible.

State v. *Eggleston*, 206 N.W. 281, 201 Iowa 1. Testimony that liquor bought from accused smelled and tasted like alcohol held competent.

State v. *Fish*, 143 A. 604, 49 R.I. 397. Testimony of officer familiar with characteristics of beer, that he could tell from smell that men were drinking beer, held admissible.

State v. *Godette*, 125 S.E. 24, 188 N.C. 497. Officer may arrest one for transporting liquor and seize liquor and vehicle when he has absolute personal knowledge "acquired through any of five senses"; knowledge being in this case firm belief.

State v. *Jackson*, 144 A. 193, 101 Vt., 416. Whether near beer and lager beer would produce same breath odor held immaterial; witness having stated merely that he smelled liquor.

State v. *Jackson*, 249 P. 688, 121 Kan. 711. In prosecution for selling intoxicating liquor, permitting members of jury to smell liquor to determine whether it was fit for beverage was not error.

State v. *Jordan*, 285 S.W. 403 Mo. 1926. Jury held properly permitted to inspect sample of liquor by smelling.

State v. *McDaniel*, 237 P. 373, 115 Cr. 187. Officers who, by observation of manner of defendant's walk, flushed face, and by smell of his breath, concluded he was drunk, held authorized to make arrest without warrant and search.

State v. *Miller*, 12 S.W. (2d) 39 Mo. Identification of moonshine by smell accepted as evidence.

State v. *Phillips*, 236 N.W. 104, 212 Iowa 1332. Mere smelling and tasting by jury of liquor involved in prosecution is not prejudicial.

State v. *Rendigs*, 120 N.E. 836, 98 Ohio St. 251. Municipal regulation of noxious odors.

State ex. rel. Renfrow v. *Service Cushion Co.*, 291 S.W. 106, transferred, App. 274 S.W. 491 (Mo. 1927). Offensive odors, deleterious to health, sufficient to authorize finding rubber factory a public nuisance.

State v. *Stough*, 2 S.W. (2d) 767, 318 Mo. 1198 (1928). Experienced lay witnesses may identify hooch, moonshine, and corn whisky by tasting *or* smelling it.

State v. *Williams*, 107 So. 296, 160 La. 435. Evidence acquired by sense of smell is not less valid than that acquired by any of the other senses.

State v. *Work*, 201 N.W. 553 S.D. 1924. Witness may testify that from his sense of smell he is of opinion that certain fruit jars formerly contained whisky.

Steele v. *Rail & River Coal Co.*, 182 N.E. 552, 42 Ohio App. 228. Property owner could not recover for injury from odors and fumes rising from spontaneously combustible coal mine refuse pile, under facts.

Stepney v. *City of Columbia, Miss.*, 127 So. 687, 157 Misc. 193. Odors as evidence in offenses under criminal law.

Stohf v. *Passaic Piece Dye Works*, 153 A. 707, 108 N.J. Eq. 46. Noxious gases and odors from dye works held not sufficient to enjoin operation.

Stoneburner v. *O-Gas-Co. Sales Corp.*, 237 N.Y.S. 339, 135 Misc. 216. Noxious odors affecting comfort of adjoining owner's home gives rise to private nuisance.

Stovern v. *Town of Calmar, Winneshick County*, 216 N.W. 112, 204 Iowa 983. Discomfort from odors caused by pollution of creek is proper element of damage for nuisance.

Sturtevant v. *Ford*, 182 N.E. 560, 280 Mass. 303. Riparian owner's right to damages from upper proprietor because of unpleasant odors, etc.

Sweet v. *Campbell*, 9 N.Y.S. 2d 281. Presence of odors near undertaking establishment (noxious gases and odors).

Thomson v. *Texas Co.*, 143 S.E., 166 Ga. 315. Odors of filling station became a nuisance, but injunction not granted.

Town of Sentinel v. *Riley*, 43 P. 2d 742, 171 Okla. 533. Damage to landowner caused by obnoxious odors and smells due to negligence of city in operation of septic tank and operation of slaughterhouse by others, cause for damage.

U.S. v. *A Certain Distillery*, 24 F. (2) 557. Warrants based merely on affiant's detection of odor of intoxicating liquor emanating from dwelling are insufficient to authorize search of dwelling.

U.S. v. *Fischer*, 38 F. (2d) 830 D.C. Pa. Arrest of defendant smoking opium based on smell held legal.

U.S. v. *Kaplan*, 17 F. Supp. 920. Arrest without warrant by officers who smell cooking or fermenting mash.

U.S. v. *Lee*, 83 F. (2d) 195. Alleged odor of opium through crack of door of dwelling held insufficient to justify arrest without warrant.

U.S. v. *Lotempio*, 58 F. (2d) 358. Affidavit that agents smelled alcohol and heard pumps and motors working, etc., held to show probable cause for search warrant.

U.S. v. *Miller*, 36 F. Supp. 391. Odor of fermenting whisky as sufficient to authorize search warrant.

U.S. v. *Notto*, 61 F. (2d) 781. Agents observing half-barrels in truck, smelling odor of beer had probable cause for arrest and seizure.

U.S. v. *Old Dominion Warehouse*, 10 F. (2d) 736. Agent's affidavit that he saw truck loaded with barrels of intoxicating liquor drive into warehouse and that he smelled liquor held not sufficient on ground it did not show that barrels contained alcoholic beverages.

U.S. v. *Phillips*, 34 F. (2d) 495. Statement that affiant smelled beer mash in process of fermentation was sufficient on which to base search warrant.

U.S. v. *Roma*, 17 F. (2d) 270. Search warrant based on agent's affidavit of detecting odor of alcohol at garage entrance, held not based on probable cause.

U.S. v. *Swan*, 15 F. (2d) 598. Search without warrant induced by smell of mash, held not incidental to subsequent arrest for possessing unregistered still.

U.S. v. *Thiel*, 52 F. (2d) 170 D.C. Mich. Officers detecting odor of beer coming from defendant's premises had right to arrest defendant.

Van Winkle v. *State*, 16 S.W. (2d) 238, 112 Tex. Cr.R. 291. Officers observing liquid and broken glass pouring from auto and detecting odor of whisky had probable cause for arrest and search without warrant.

Varner v. *State*, 166 N.E. 292, 89 Ind. App. 293. Witness familiar therewith may testify liquor was whisky from smell and give opinion whether it was intoxicating.

Waier v. *Peerless Oil Co.*, 251 N.W. 552, 265 Mich. 398. Fact that other plants foul air with odors does not justify introduction of another cause of discomfort.

Walker v. *State*, 137 S.W. 2d 1033, 138 Tex. Cr.R. 660. Harmless error in permitting jurors to smell bottle.

Washington Cleaners & Dyers v. *Albrecht*, 146 A. 233, 157 Md. 389. Odors from noxious gases from cleaning and dyeing company have deleterious effect on residents.

Watson v. *State*, 120 So. 917, 23 Ala. App. 73. Testimony that blanket smelled like whisky held inadmissible, in absence of proof that witnesses knew such smell.

Wereb v. *State*, 154 N.E. 172, 22 Ohio App. 512. Evidence that liquid in bottle was whisky, based on its odor, held sufficient to warrant conviction for unlawful possession of whisky.

Whetstone v. *State*, 98 So. 216, 19 Ala. App. 331. Testimony of smell of an article is admissible as affecting its identity.

Williams v. *Blue Bird Laundry Co.*, 259 P. 484, 85 Cal. App. 388. Operation of laundry constituted nuisance by emitting noises, odors, soot, and grease.

Willis v. *State*, 110 So. 593, 21 Ala. App. 607. Evidence that federal commissioner said he smelled beer on defendant held hearsay but not prejudicial.

Wilson v. *Consolidated Dressed Beef Co.*, 145 A. 81, 295 Pa. 168. Damages for loss of smell.

Wineland ex rel. *Abeln* v. *M. Huber, Inc.*, 275 Ill. App. 264. Injunction warranted to restrain defendants from dumping garbage and refuse on land because of odors from the dump.

Wright v. *Lyons*, 112 N.E. 876, 224 Mass. 167. A petition to restrain defendants from erecting public garage selling and storing gasoline, constituting a nuisance because of noise, odors, etc., is not demurrable as not entitling to equitable relief.

Yeskel Supply Co. v. *U.S.*, 61 F. (2d) 196. Officers smelling hot odor of distilling from building, seeing men working, and hearing can drop, had reasonable cause to believe law was being violated and right to enter building.

INDEX